Ecology
A Systems Approach

Teacher's Guide

ECOLOGY A SYSTEMS APPROACH

TEACHER'S GUIDE

PRASSEDE CALABI

This curriculum was developed by TERC, Inc., Cambridge, Massachusetts. Funded in part by a grant from the National Science Foundation.

KENDALL/HUNT PUBLISHING COMPANY
4050 Westmark Drive Dubuque, Iowa 52002

TERC

PROJECT MANAGEMENT: Nancy Benjamin and Sally Bindari, Books By Design, Inc.
INTERIOR DESIGN: Sally Bindari, Books By Design, Inc.
PAGE LAYOUT: Carol Keller
COPYEDITOR: Nancy Wirtes
COVER DESIGN: Scott Hancock
COVER IMAGES: © 1996 PhotoDisc, Inc.; © E. C. Williams/Visuals Unlimited
SKULL PHOTOS: Scott Hancock and Jamil Simon

CREDITS

User's Guide
Pg. xvii: CALVIN AND HOBBES © Watterson. Reprinted with permission of UNIVERSAL PRESS SYNDICATE. All rights reserved. **Pg. xviii:** CALVIN AND HOBBES © Watterson. Reprinted with permission of UNIVERSAL PRESS SYNDICATE. All rights reserved. **Excerpt:** From ZEN AND THE ART OF MOTORCYCLE MAINTENANCE by Robert M. Pirsig. Copyright © 1974 by Robert M. Pirsig. By permission of William Morrow and Company, Inc. (Pp. 184/bottom–188/top)

Module 2, Unit 1, Chapter 1
Module title page: Martha Cooper/Peter Arnold, Inc.

Module 2, Unit 1, Chapter 2
Pg. 47: CALVIN AND HOBBES © Watterson. Reprinted with permission of UNIVERSAL PRESS SYNDICATE. All rights reserved.

Module 2, Unit 2, Chapter 1
Unit title page: Courtesy of Michael S. Quinton; **Pg. 79–80:** From Leonard B. Radinsky (1987: Figs. 17.1, 17.3[c]). *The Evolution of Vertebrate Design*. Chicago: University of Chicago Press. © University of Chicago Press; **Pp. 81, 82–83:** A. S. Romer (1959: 37). *The Vertebrate Story*. Chicago: University of Chicago Press. © University of Chicago 1959; **Pg. 87:** From Leonard B. Radinsky (1987: Fig. 15.4). *The Evolution of Vertebrate Design*. Chicago: University of Chicago Press. © University of Chicago Press.

Copyrights and acknowledgments continue on page 517, which constitutes an extension of the copyright page.

This book was prepared with the support of National Science Foundation Grant No. ESI-92-52981. However, any opinions, findings, conclusions, and/or recommendations herein are those of the author and do not necessarily reflect the views of the National Science Foundation. Any mention of trade names does not imply endorsement by the National Science Foundation.

ISBN 0-7872-3564-4

Printed in the United States of America

10 9 8 7 6 5 4 3 2

TO JIM

In praise of "imperfection"

since much of the world's richness

and all great science

stems from its exploration.

BTC

CONTENTS

quarter 4

User's Guide to
Ecology: A Systems Approach

Dear Teacher,

Welcome! This curriculum introduces ecology through a systems approach that stresses depth over breadth and that integrates physical and life sciences. Our goal, in a nutshell, is to get your students thinking and to get them doing science through the domain of ecology.

We have designed this User's Guide to help you understand how our text differs from more traditional ones, what to expect as you teach it, and how you can best help your students develop a rich and integrated understanding of some key ecological and scientific principles.

Approach and Goals

How is ***Ecology: A Systems Approach*** different? It does not adopt the typical high-vocabulary, high-memorization approach of many science texts. Rather it allows students to encounter materials that make them think; to do science, not just read about it; and to engage in substantive explorations, not content-free busywork. (And it meets the current National Science Education Standards as set by the National Research Council; see back cover of the book.)

For example, rather than us tell you how and why a same-size mongoose and lizard get and use their energy, you and your students discover how and why, with materials and support from the curriculum. And you build on those discoveries to derive some underlying patterns and principles about energy use, flow, and transfer within and between organisms in an ecosystem. (A mongoose needs more energy to maintain its higher metabolic rate and body temperature; it eats proportionately more food; and that food has more high-energy C–C bonds. The mongoose is high on the trophic pyramid of its ecosystem, eating many species but providing energy for few.)

Traditionally, such material is taught the other way around, that is, starting with principles and then illustrating them with a series of examples. It also usually is taught in a linear progression, starting with abiotic and moving to biotic factors (e.g., latitude and longitude, climate, biomes, organism distributions, and organism interactions).

That approach has three drawbacks. First, although students begin at the "logical" beginning, the smallest or lowest level, that is not the most accessible or generally appealing level. Which would students likely find more immediately appealing: bonds, molecules, mitochondria, and climate—or animals, bony skulls, entire habitats, and fieldwork? Second, traditionally students are not likely to see a whole system until the book or semester is finished. In contrast, each of our Modules illustrates a whole system, and Units within Modules illustrate clusters of concepts, which are analogous to systems by giving closure. Working across levels and with depth over breadth enables students to build level on level, for a rich vertical understanding—in a relatively short period of time—of the principles and concepts they encounter. Finally, because the traditional sequence begins with nonliving things (abiotic factors), it is less dynamic and engages students less than our sequence, in which each Module begins with animals, ecosystems, interactions, and problems of survival.

CONTENTS: HOW THE CURRICULUM IS BUILT CONCEPTUALLY

The curriculum consists of three Modules: **Evolution: A Natural Experiment—The Galapagos Finches**; **Carbon and Energy**; and **Water**, the latter two with multiple units and chapters. Each Module introduces students to key ecological concepts; the second and third Modules focus on the cycling and ecology of molecules that are ecologically important and whose cycles are subject to significant, current human perturbation. The Modules are designed to be used in sequence or separately and together provide a year's worth of material for students who have already taken a general biology course.

The first Module of ***Ecology: A Systems Approach*** deals with evolution by natural selection, since that is a core principle of ecology. In fact, ecology can be considered the expression of natural selection over time. Throughout the curriculum, we explore the lifestyles of many organisms and their interactions with each other and their physical environment. Many such interactions are shaped by evolution, so it is a natural frame within which to place the rest of the curriculum.

The other two Modules build on a basic understanding of carbon compounds and water and, in successive units and chapters, relate those molecules to higher and higher levels of biological complexity. The curriculum is conceived vertically, linking the levels through overarching concepts. (Such integration is part of the curriculum's "systems approach.") **Module 2: Carbon and Energy** and the **Module 3: Water** consider their subjects at five levels:

1. the level of bonds and biochemistry
2. the individual/species level
3. the level of populations
4. the level of ecosystems/communities
5. the global level

The materials are not presented in that order, however, since it is not particularly engaging for an ecology curriculum to begin with bonds. Rather, each Module begins directly with ecological concepts and topics and considers bonds later, when students might want to understand the biochemical bases of their work with individuals, populations, or ecosystems. (Such levels and clustering of concepts also means you can skip around among areas or pick and choose, bypassing some areas altogether.)

The current conversation about science literacy usually stresses a "correct" minimum set of facts. But learning science is much more than learning facts. It means thinking and integrating formal learning (including facts) with phenomena encountered in daily life. It means doing science, understanding mechanism and causality, decomposing things into their component parts, and reintegrating them with a personal understanding. It means empowering students to understand the natural world and how to figure out what they do not understand.

MULTIDISCIPLINARY ASPECTS

In this curriculum, your students will meet subjects they typically encounter in other courses—chemistry, physics, mathematics. They may wonder what these subjects are doing in an ecology textbook. As we explain to them in their "Student Welcome," ecology is an interdisciplinary subject and includes all those subjects and then some. Ecology is about all possible interactions between and among living things and between and among living and nonliving things. So competition between pigeons for food or lions for a mate; coyotes eating mice, geese eating grass, or plants fixing carbon; and effects of climate on plant size and shape are all ecology. We need math to count, measure, weigh, or compare tulips and trees, growth, birth rates, age, size, and averages; we need physics to know how much force a bird's bill or a puma's jaws can exert; we use exponents because sometimes we need to work with very large numbers.

The level of those subjects is basic; this curriculum does not require more than the basic science or math a typical high school sophomore has already been required to take. (The materials have been used and tested by students in grades 9–14.) What will seem novel to some students is that they have to apply simple mathematics or physics to another subject. They soon discover that they know more than they thought they did about the relevant sciences. (If you wish, you may want to team teach one or two topics with a colleague from another science discipline, such as chemistry. We indicate in the **Teacher's Guide** where and when that may be especially appropriate.)

What is the payoff for this degree of integration? Ideally, after using the curriculum, students presented with, say, a tree see a multidimensional scheme they have constructed, including some or all of the following: the tree is a member of a population or species but is individually (genetically) variable; the species exists in a community or ecosystem physically (taking space) and ecologically (interacting with its own and other species—being eaten, photosynthesizing, cycling nutrients, competing); it has an evolutionary history; it is a living thing and must solve all the problems of life (getting and using energy to grow, mate, reproduce, survive).

A more traditional view of the same subject is made up of boxes: the tree box, the photosynthesis box, the competing-for-sunlight box, the water box, the herbivore box. We try to break down the walls of all those boxes to show that everything is connected and cannot be put into boxes, especially in ecological studies.

MATERIALS LAYOUT: A GUIDE

The so-called **Evolution Module** has one Unit, while the **Carbon and Energy Module** and the **Water Module** each has four Units and multiple chapters. In addition, the curriculum includes some frontmatter (including this Guide) and seven formal Techniques. Each Unit has an introductory Unit Overview, a page or more on the progression and concept clusters of the Unit.

The Teacher and Student materials are complementary and overlap as necessary. But neither repeats the other, so it is important that you read both. For example, the first Reading in **Module 1** describes how organisms populated the bare and newly arisen rocky Galapagos Islands. The **Teacher's Guide** to that Reading does not repeat any of the story; instead, it offers suggestions for a class discussion and some further scientific background, both of which assume that you have already completed the Student Reading yourself.

Let's walk through a typical teacher and student chapter, using **Module 2**, **Unit 2**, **Chapter 1**. This is what that particular Table of Contents looks like in the **Teacher's Guide**:

Chapter 10 Bony Skulls: How Animals Acquire Energy

The contents for each chapter includes five brief overview categories (**Introduction**, **Key Concepts**, **Materials and Preparation**, **Suggested Sequence of Sessions**, and **Sessions Guides, by Worksheet**). If you read nothing else when preparing to teach your class, read these five pieces, since they give a succinct summary of the entire chapter.

Now let's look at each section listed in the Table of Contents in greater detail.

Introduction

The Introduction presents the main ideas, focus, and work of the chapter, as well as how it fits with preceding or subsequent material.

Key Concepts

Major concepts raised in the chapter are described, with some context and application.

Materials and Preparation

Here we list items you need to implement the chapter and give instructions or suggestions, if necessary, for logistical matters specific to the chapter.

This section includes **Safety Warnings**, should any work in the chapter be potentially hazardous. Most chapters, however, have no safety warnings, since they depend largely on equipment like pencils, paper, sticking tape, and calculators.

Also in this section are **In Advance**—things you need to prepare before class. If you need to plant beans 1 month before a set of Explorations, we tell you a month in advance. If you need to prepare a way of assigning animal cards for tomorrow's class, we tell you a day or more before. You should not have to ferret out such information; we try to flag it in a clear and timely fashion.

Suggested Sequence of Sessions

This section is the chapter in a nutshell: a blueprint for the work, laid out assignment by assignment, homework and in-class work, discussions, debates, questions and answers, ideas and concepts, the flow of the work, and how it all builds to completion. We are not saying this is the only way the chapter can be used; rather, it has worked this way and we offer the sequence in that spirit. You may want to alter, tailor, add, or delete. Be sure, however, that you keep track if you discard any of the concepts: the chapters are an integrated whole and often refer to each other.

NOTE: The number of likely class sessions, given in parentheses after the section title, is a range (e.g., 6–8). The number of class sessions corresponds to the suggested session sequence, so if you add or delete materials, the number of sessions will vary accordingly. Please also note that we do not always include a class session for discussing the Integration. We suggest that you do so, however, since such discussion likely adds to everyone's understanding of the chapter and helps bring closure.

Session Guides, by Worksheet

Under this category are all the Guides to student materials. We offer ideas, background information, support, and suggestions on how to work with each student worksheet (Case Studies, Explorations, Readings, Integrations). Again, these are not recipes. Your students' responses to the materials and your interests and theirs might take any class session in other directions. But these materials have worked, and you may find them useful. (Infrequently, there is an **Optional Worksheet**, some topic on which you may or may not want to spend time, but which contributes to the general ideas of the chapter. The Worksheet may be more physics than ecology or add depth to something already considered. It is your choice whether to use it.)

Science Background

Ecology is multidisciplinary, so some additional information seems appropriate in a few chapters. You might want to share that information with students directly (photocopy and hand it out) or just incorporate it into class discussions.

References

Sometimes annotated, sometimes not, the Reference list includes literature needed for the chapter (and also noted under Materials and Preparation), additional sources should you or your students want to pursue a topic, and literature specifically cited in the chapter.

Classroom Vignettes

Because this text takes an unusual approach, we thought you might be interested in reading some transcripts of actual classroom discussions of students working with ***Ecology: A Systems Approach***. Their questions, reactions, and comments may help you anticipate your own students' responses.

Appendixes

Occasionally, we include appendixes with information relevant to the chapter material.

Extensions

These "extras" are possible projects that can grow out of the chapter's work in various directions. You and your students will doubtless think of many yourselves; these are starters. Use them as independent projects, additional class material, assessments, or in coordination with other classes (e.g., mathematics, biology, geology, or geography).

Excerpts

Sometimes another author so aptly makes a point that we cannot resist sharing. A few are in the Student Modules. For those that are only in this (your) book, you decide whether and how to share them with your students.

STUDENT TEXT MODULES

The three Student Modules are published as separate books. But all three Modules form an integrated curriculum, and materials pertinent to all three are in this **Teacher's Guide**. A primary objective of the curriculum as a whole is for students to create their own understanding by engaging with and thinking about materials. The Student Modules therefore offer data, ideas, research materials, and support, with little interpretation. Students are encouraged to ask questions and seek answers—with your help—to some of the most important issues in contemporary ecology. Discovering more about the process of scientific inquiry itself is a key goal.

Each Chapter begins with a brief introduction—a preview, question, or observation—to rouse student interest. The introduction usually is followed by a **Case Study**, a tale that brings alive the key idea(s) of the chapter. For example, in the chapter on the properties of water, Insects and Antifreeze: The Moth in Winter poses the question of how insects survive freezing temperatures. Often the Case Studies include questions on which you can build class discussions. In some chapters, the Case Study is a debate or other activity to prepare students for the main work of the chapter.

Explorations center on data. Students manipulate and consider data (which they collect or we provide), such as designing a plant, and otherwise explore materials to answer questions and make predictions about the ideas of the chapter. For example, in the chapter entitled **Abiotic Factors and Plant Distribution**, students read about plant life forms around the world and then make predictions about where most plant biomass is located geographically—and why. In a chapter on thermoregulation, they design a temperature-regulating animal to explore the concepts of endothermy and ectothermy. Usually there are several such Explorations in a chapter, each intended to disembed a different assumption about or aspect of the main ideas.

The short **Readings** expand on the Explorations, elaborating ideas and adding background, different data, and different perspectives. They help tie together concepts and keep the chapter flowing as well as keep major principles alive across chapters. For example, in the chapter **Properties of Water and Its Suitability for Everything**, the Reading entitled Awesome Adaptations introduces students to the adaptations some organisms (camels, cacti, amphibians, and the plant *Lithops*) have for dealing with extremes of water availability.

Integrations serve two primary functions. First, they help students pull together the various strands of the chapter by posing some new question. Second, they provide a performance task that you and the students can use as an assessment tool. Students can assess their own understanding of the work and topics; you can assess their understanding; and the Integrations provide a record, over time, of student progress. For example, we have found that students enjoy periodic opportunities to rethink and apply what they have learned in ***Ecology: A Systems Approach*** by solving a novel problem. In the chapter **Bony Skulls: How Animals Acquire Energy**, we ask students to identify a "mystery tooth" and relate it to animal feeding patterns. What sort of food is the mystery tooth designed to eat?

Physically, both the **Integrations** and the **Integration Guides** are here in the **Teacher's Guide**. That is so you can photocopy the Integrations and distribute them one per student. Because the students write on the photocopies, the integrity of your book and theirs is maintained.

Students can (and should) look back at earlier Integrations, to see how their understanding has deepened over time. Most of the curriculum relies on group work, but to serve as performance tasks and to document student progress, the Integrations should be the work of individual students. Consider having students keep portfolios of all their work to show their changes in understanding over time.

TECHNIQUES

Unlike typical science techniques, the ones in this curriculum have been carefully designed to illustrate the underlying principles. They are not "black box" procedures to be carried out obediently but without understanding. When students burn stuff using the technique of calorimetry, they see that energy is released by combustion as heat, they see that the heat is captured by water, they see that the temperature of the water rises. No black box here.

In addition to the techniques embedded in the body of the text, there are formal Techniques at the end of this book as well as the end of each Student Module. Most Techniques can be used in various places throughout the curriculum, although each is introduced in a particular chapter and context.

SPECIAL NOTE

Although this book includes an Index, the Student Modules do not. So students may ask you to help them locate materials or generally keep them oriented about what is described where—another reason for you to be familiar with the student text as well as with this **Teacher's Guide**. There also is no glossary. We are trying to stay away from vocabulary-based learning in favor of more concept-oriented learning. For terms unfamiliar to students, any general biology text can serve.

PEDAGOGY AND CLASSROOM MANAGEMENT

More than most high school science textbooks, ***Ecology: A Systems Approach*** allows students to do research. They are asked to consider questions, formulate hypotheses, and test those hypotheses using data. This approach has two advantages: it generates student interest, and it presents material in such a way that students do not soon forget it. One student in a field test of this curriculum told us that what he was learning could not possibly be science. When we asked why, he replied, "Science is boring; this is fun!"

The challenge in a curriculum of this type is that you have to be prepared to harness the energy and enthusiasm of your students and feel comfortable with a certain degree of unpredictability. That is an additional reason for you to consult the **Teacher's Guide** before each unit or each class; wherever possible, we attempt to alert you about what may lie ahead.

GROUP WORK

We believe that a science class runs on the same principles as a science lab: doing science, learning science, collaboration, and reflection. We have considered the first two, and reflection runs throughout the curriculum, especially the Integrations. Now, let's focus on collaboration.

Most of the curriculum involves work in small groups, which has several advantages. Often learners do better in a situation of equality and shared responsibility; it is easier to take risks and chance being "wrong" if others participate in the decision. Try to keep group membership at five or fewer individuals, depending on your class size. Three members is ideal, so all members are actively involved.

Group work fosters collaboration rather than competition—thinking together, with each person contributing. It broadens the resource base over what any single person might have, since each member brings different skills, perspectives, and ideas.

Group work (and its supervision) can also be difficult. Culturally, we are competitive. And those same differences that can broaden a group's resources also may lead to friction.

Keep an eye on groups for any extreme—one person dominating, no one engaged, intractable differences among members—and try to help balance things.

DISCUSSIONS

A frequent pattern in the pedagogy of ***Ecology: A Systems Approach*** is to ask students to investigate a topic in their groups (e.g., to build a model water strider out of pipe cleaners and aluminum foil to test water surface tension) and then to have each group report back to the class as a whole. Managing these discussions so students learn from one another is one of the challenges for teachers using this curriculum.

Allowing students so much space for discussion may feel inefficient. And it is certainly true that you might "cover" less material using this approach than with a more standard curriculum. However, the major advantage is that students truly learn. What they explore and discuss, they understand. Moreover, as you will discover, once their curiosity is unleashed, they will (with rare exceptions) become enthusiastic participants. The energy level will be high, students will be excited, and you may need to make decisions about who gets to speak and for how long.

We have two suggestions for enhancing productive discussions. First, keep in mind your goals for the discussion and make sure you touch on all points that seem important to you, but do not expect the discussion necessarily to take up the points in the order you foresee. If, for example, Rachel suddenly has an insight into how lynx and hare populations influence each other during your discussion on predator-prey relations, take advantage of her excitement, even if you had originally planned to discuss the topic at the end of the class period rather than at the beginning. A certain flexibility on your part will reap large rewards in student learning.

At the same time, it is important to students that you periodically review important points (e.g., by listing them on a chalk board or easel flip chart) that have been made and to credit students with their contributions. Comments like "Rachel's good point about hares and lynxes" or "Porter's theory about plant energy capture" give students ownership of ideas and encourage continued participation.

Managing class discussions is hard work, as you doubtless already know. In that sense, this curriculum is demanding—of teachers as well as of students. We think you will soon see that the rewards more than compensate for the hard work. But it is only fair to note that this curriculum does not (and cannot) teach itself. Your facilitations may be less direct than you are used to, in that you guide discussions and explorations rather than presenting conclusions yourself, but it is all the more crucial. We and you want to get students to think. You cannot think for them (just as you cannot eat for them), but without you as facilitator, students will not learn to think about ecology as rapidly or as rigorously, and some may not learn at all. Tips on facilitating discussions are in the **Technique: 21 Questions to Conclusions**, as well as the section Guides throughout the chapters.

BUILDING CONNECTIONS OUTSIDE THE CLASSROOM

Ecology is a science that relates to every place and everybody. That is part of its great appeal, and the curriculum will be more useful with every connection you and your students can make with local ecosystems and current events. Many classrooms have found the following ideas useful.

A scrapbook or bulletin board of environmental readings or clippings from the popular news and scientific press

Newspapers and magazines such as Time, Newsweek, Scientific American, Natural History, and National Geographic frequently carry stories about ecological or environmental issues that the students can read critically and analyze in the light of their study of ecology. Student discussions and research projects can build on these (often controversial) stories. If the items are of interest to their community, there is excellent potential for community involvement.

Student study of a specific organism during the course of the year

A great hindrance to students' learning ecology is their profound ignorance about living things. As a culture, we are divorced from life and physical processes and their interaction. In consequence, few people have any idea of the concept of a life-cycle—that organisms are "born," grow and develop, mate, reproduce, and die. Even fewer people are aware of how organisms go about any of these processes or whether and how other factors (climate, genetics, size and shape, other species, the same species) affect those processes. We recommend that students ground the entire curriculum in a supplemental activity, to run in parallel with the formal curriculum through the school year.

Each student, early in the year, should identify one organism on which he or she wishes to become a specialist and expert. Ideally, the organism should be accessible for observation, but otherwise there need be little constraint on the choice. The creature may be an urban pest or weed, a resident in a zoo or botanical garden, a pet, or a house plant—anything interesting and easily available that the student can observe. Student data on the organism should take two forms: (a) observations, ideas, and concepts prompted by curiosity concerning the organism itself and (b) attempts to relate the ideas and concepts of the curriculum to the organism, to better ground and understand those ideas. When a new topic comes up in class, such as competition or the ratio of surface area to volume, students should relate those issues to their organisms, recording their thoughts and observations. (In **Chapter 3** of **Module 2**, **Unit 2**, each student becomes an animal from either the Serengeti in East Africa or the Northern Hardwoods in the United States. Although these animals may not be available for actual observation, literature research on them is an OK substitute. Some students identify strongly with these animals and use them as reference points anyway—you might want to capitalize on that.)

HAVE FUN!

Does that sound unrealistic? Teachers who have used versions of these materials report that their students are engaged or more engaged; students care about what is happening in class; they do discuss, think, make suggestions. A physics teacher using this approach was shocked to discover that with typical "canned" labs, most of his students did not know why they were doing the labs. Now, for many topics, he begins by putting on the board three columns, labeled "I know," "I think I know," and "I want to know," and fills them in during a class discussion. Enough student suggestions are on topics that he wants the class to consider, and they proceed. But because students are part of the choice and conversation, their ownership motivates them to stay involved. He has replaced about half his canned labs already, with no loss of coverage but with increased student attention and comprehension. He finds the approach so successful that he is slowly replacing all the labs with such student-based work.

Test teachers almost universally have noted that their prep time for using these materials is no more than that for using any new materials—but it is different. One teacher commented that although he had taken chemistry in high school, in college, and for his MAT degree, he found that he did not really understand bonds until he prepared for the chapter clusters on bonds in this curriculum. Because we deliberately try to present a different angle or perspective, one major difference in your preparation is that you also take on this new perspective. Test teachers tended to find it exciting; we hope you do, too.

Please, if you have suggestions or comments, send them to Dr. Prassede Calabi, care of Kendall/Hunt Publishing Company. In case we get to revise the curriculum, your feedback would be invaluable. Thank you.

Here is an example of an Excerpt, such as students will find in their chapters—but this one is intended for you. It nicely illustrates some of our deepest convictions about thinking and teaching (or helping people learn) to think. It describes the experience of the main character of that book with his college students, but we believe it applies equally well to high school teaching. Note especially the sections in bold (our emphasis).

EXCERPT
Zen and the Art of Motorcycle Maintenance, by Robert M. Pirsig

He'd been innovating extensively. He'd been having trouble with students who had nothing to say. At first he thought it was laziness but later it became apparent that it wasn't. They just couldn't think of anything to say.

One of them, a girl with strong-lensed glasses, wanted to write a five-hundred-word essay about the United States. He was used to the sinking feeling that comes from statements like this, and suggested without disparagement that she narrow it down to just Bozeman.

When the paper came due she didn't have it and was quite upset. She had tried and tried but she just couldn't think of anything to say.

He had already discussed her with her previous instructors and they'd confirmed his impressions of her. She was very serious, disciplined and hardworking, but extremely dull. Not a spark of creativity in her anywhere. Her eyes, behind the thick-lensed glasses, were the eyes of a drudge. She wasn't bluffing him, she really couldn't think of anything to say, and was upset by her inability to do as she was told.

It just stumped him. Now *he* couldn't think of anything to say. A silence occurred, and then a peculiar answer: "Narrow it down to the *main street* of Bozeman." It was a stroke of insight.

She nodded dutifully and went out. But just before her next class she came back in *real* distress, tears this time, distress that had obviously been there for a long time. She still couldn't understand why, if she couldn't think of anything about *all* of Bozeman, she should be able to think of something about just one street.

He was furious. "You're not *looking*!" he said. A memory came back of his own dismissal from the University for having *too much* to say. For every fact there is an *infinity* of hypotheses. The more you *look* the more you *see*. She really wasn't looking yet and somehow didn't understand this.

He told her angrily, "Narrow it down to the *front* of *one* building on the main street of Bozeman. The Opera House. Start with the upper left-hand brick."

Her eyes, behind the thick-lensed glasses, opened wide.

She came in the next class with a puzzled look and handed him a five-thousand-word essay on the front of the Opera House on the main street of Bozeman, Montana. "I sat in the hamburger stand across the street," she said, "and started writing about the first brick, and the second brick, and then by the third brick it all started to come and I couldn't stop. They thought I was crazy, and they kept kidding me, but here it all is. I don't understand it."

Neither did he, but on long walks through the streets of town he thought about it and concluded she was evidently stopped with the same kind of blockage that had paralyzed him on his first day of teaching. She was blocked because she was trying to repeat things he had already decided to say. **She couldn't think of anything to write about Bozeman because she couldn't recall anything she had heard worth repeating. She was strangely unaware that she could look and see freshly for herself, as she wrote, without primary regard for what had been said before. The narrowing down to one brick destroyed the blockage because it was so obvious she *had* to do some original and direct seeing.**

He experimented further. In one class he had everyone write all hour about the back of his thumb. Everyone gave him funny looks at the beginning of the hour, but everyone did it, and there wasn't a single complaint about "nothing to say."

In another class he changed the subject from the thumb to a coin, and got a full hour's writing from every student. In other classes it was the same. Some asked, "Do you have to write about both sides?" Once they got into the idea of seeing directly for themselves they also saw there was no limit to the amount they could say. It was a confidence-building assignment too, because what they wrote, even though seemingly trivial,

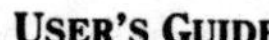

was nevertheless their own thing, not a mimicking of someone else's. Classes where he used that coin exercise were always less balky and more interested.

As a result of his experiments he concluded that imitation was a real evil that had to be broken before real rhetoric teaching could begin. This imitation seemed to be an external compulsion. Little children didn't have it. It seemed to come later on, possibly as a result of school itself.

ACKNOWLEDGMENTS

An effort such as this curriculum reflects input of different kinds and degrees from numerous people. All their contributions are important but are so various they are hard to compare. How does a key phone call of just a few minutes compare with months of development, testing, or evaluation effort? Yet all are essential. Here goes.

First, special thanks to Brian Drayton, project director, for important conceptual, logistical, and development work, especially throughout the first phases of the project. His background complemented my own and lent balance to the total picture. He is co-author and primary developer of specific pieces, as noted, and contributed supporting prose and scientific or pedagogical content throughout.

The writing and preparation of this work has been a project many years in the making. During that time, a number of persons contributed substantially to the text and data compilation contained in *Ecology: A Systems Approach*, some of them persons who have long since left TERC. In particular, the contributions of a former TERC staff member, Dan Perlman, to **Module 2** (the Carbon and Energy module), deserve mention. Dan wrote the original text of portions of many of the chapters in this module, and much of his work survives intact in the final product.

Marsha Pomeroy contributed important work to the Water Module. Our skills were complementary, so between us, we had all the kingdoms and levels. Many thanks for her ideas, research and other efforts, and for being so easy to work with.

Thanks to Janis Burton for contributing expertise to the section on flyways and ducks. William Spitzer, Sylvia Weir, J. Stephen Lowe, and Jane Ceraso helped develop aspects of the whole and contributed to individual pieces—thank you. Thanks also to Tasha Morris, first Administrative Assistant to the project, and to Alison Paddock for balancing this project with a second one and with most of the immediate world.

Thanks to Amy Shulman Weinberg for evaluation and rooting out opacity, and to Deborah Levine for evaluation and assessment.

To Donald Humphrys, Ivo Lindauer, and M. Patricia Morse (at the National Science Foundation) and Alan Vincent (at Kendall/Hunt) for believing in the project.

TEACHERS AND STUDENTS

This text is the better for input from all the teachers and students who used versions of it; to them all—thank you!

Thanks to our local **in-house pilot test students** for their enthusiasm, honesty, and trust in us.

Rachel Bauer, Somerville High School
Marianne Bowers, Somerville High School
Paolo DiFablo, Somerville High School
Peter French, Winchester High School
Antonio Hernandez, Hull High School
Carlos Hernandez, Hull High School
Susanna Hollister, Brookline High School
David Hood, Winchester High School
Eric Hood, Winchester High School
Rachel Megerman, Brookline High School
Sergio Serpa, Somerville High School
Jeff Tahnk, Winchester High School
Dee Wolfe, Hull High School

Our **pilot test teachers** were especially important in testing and helping shape our rough draft materials. Thanks to:

Mark Dewart, Park Tudor School (Indianapolis, IN)
Steve Case and Brad Williamson, Olathe East Senior High School (Olathe, KS)
Peter McLean, St. Andrews School (Middletown, DE)
Susan Oleszko-Szuts, Governor Dummer Academy (Byfield, MA)

Special thanks to our **observation site field test teachers** for their time, energy, and willingness to step into another world with us.

David Chuckran, Bridgewater-Raynham Regional High School (MA)
Charles DeLeo, Weaver High School (Hartford, CT)
Joseph Donager, Hull Environmental High School (MA)
Sarah Fogerty, Lincoln School (RI)
Vicki Goldburgh, Brimmer and May (MA)
Susan Olesko-Szuts, Governor Dummer Academy (MA)
Tad Sudnick, Cambridge Rindge and Latin High School (MA)
Alan Weinstein, Cambridge Rindge and Latin High School (MA)

Special thanks to Sarah Fogerty, Susan Olesko-Szuts, and those who tested both first and second drafts of these materials.

Thanks also to our **other field test teachers and their students** for feedback, good will, and commitment.

Jules Adam, Oak Glen High School (New Cumberland, WV)
Peter Auger, Falmouth High School (Falmouth, MA)
Linda Baker, Davis High School (Davis, CA)
Scott Battaion, West Valley High School (Cottonwood, CA)
Leslie Beaulieu, Shore Country Day School (Beverly, MA)

Donalda Cas, Bridgewater-Raynham Regional High School (Bridgewater, MA)
Debbie Coates, Shore Country Day School (Beverly, MA)
George Collins, Mariemount High School (Cincinnati, OH)
Joseph Donager, Hull Environmental High School (Hull, MA)
David Form, Minuteman Technical High School (Lexington, MA)
Elizabeth Hedgepeth, Mount Arat Junior and Senior High School (Topsham, ME)
Timothy Hoshal, Grand Ledge High School (Grand Ledge, MI)
Thomas Hudson, Garfield High School (Seattle, WA)
Mary Bishop Kennedy, Texas Military Institute (San Antonio, TX)
Phyllis Olson, James Bowie High School (Arlington, TX)
Mary Priestly, Franklin County High School (Winchester, MA)
Melissa Schermer, Souhegan High School (Amherst, MA)
James Sullivan, Hatboro-Horsham High School (Horsham, MA)
Charles Tarleton, Lunenburg High School (Lunenburg, MA)
Lou Verner, Elm Lea Farm (Putney, VT)
Peter Weis, Wachusett Regional High School (Holden, MA)
Michael Vandenberg, Willow Creek High School (Willow Creek, MT)
Christopher Wells, Melbourne High School (Melbourne, FL)

Our **Advisory Board** was especially helpful with comments on pilot materials, and some also in reviewing manuscript—thank you all; and special thanks to S. J. McNaughton.

Steve Case and Brad Williamson, Olathe East Senior High School (Olathe, KS)
Mark Dewart, Park Tudor School (Indianapolis, IN)
Scott Eddleman, Fenway School at Bunker Hill Community College (Charlestown, MA)
Daniel Goroff, Derek Bok Center for Teaching and Learning, Harvard University (Cambridge, MA) and National Research Council (Washington, D.C.)
Robert Harriss, University of New Hampshire Institute for the Study of Earth, Ocean and Space (Durham, NH)
Kelly McConnaughay, Bradley University Biology Department (Peoria, IL)
Peter McLean, St. Andrews School (Middletown, DE)
Samuel J. McNaughton, Biological Research Labs, Syracuse University (Syracuse, NY)
Susan Oleszko-Szuts, Governor Dummer Academy (Falmouth, MA)
Douglas Ryan, U.S. Forest Service (Washington, D.C.)
Alan VanArsdale, Northeast States for Coordinated Air Use Management (Boston, MA)

Many teacher participants in another National Science Foundation–funded project developed by this author (Calabi) also used parts of this curriculum and gave us comments—our warm thanks to them (Teacher Enhancement in Pedagogy through Ecology TE 92-53280).

OTHER GREAT FOLKS

To Books By Design: Nancy Benjamin, Sally Bindari, Carol Keller, and Nancy Wirtes for professionalism, clarity of design, top-quality work, and grace under pressure.

To Sally and Carol especially for appreciating the vertical line, design, and patience.

For his exceptional generosity, our heartfelt thanks to Bill Watterson for permission to leaven the text with his inimitable wit of Calvin and Hobbes.

Warm thanks also to Gwilym S. Jones, Director of the Center for Vertebrate Studies, Northeastern University; Fred Sibley and Paul F. Whitehead, Peabody Museum of Natural History, Yale University; and Jane Winchell, Peabody Essex Museum of Salem, MA, for their generous loan of bony skulls (**Module 2, Unit 2, Chapter 1**), no strings attached.

Thanks to Steven C. Daiber for his drawings (chickadee, hyrax, squirrel) and to M. S. Quinton for his photo (bobcat meets muskrat).

To the indexing party: Kevin Flick, Monica Kearney, Alison Paddock, Kristen Rooney, Paul Rooney, Marsha Pomeroy, Rachel Skiffer, and James Wilkinson.

To Jane Nielson for critical paperwork; to Jim Terrell for a key address; to Patricia Dupree, John Foster, Kevin Flick, Monica Kearney, Barbara Sampson, and Robert Tinker for support at critical moments.

To Rachel Skiffer for her combined skills as typist, bloodhound, and etcetera; Ellen Archer for typing and bibliographic research; Robin Brown for exceptionally careful work on copyright permissions, especially from Tunisia, England, and Outer Mongolia.

For fighting the good fight—and winning the war if not the battle—thanks to Sally Bindari and Scott Hancock.

Special thanks to Scott Hancock for beautiful art, hard work, and easy grace; to Alison Paddock for being there; and to CBB for believing and insisting.

EVOLUTION: A NATURAL EXPERIMENT

THE GALAPAGOS FINCHES

MODULE ONE OVERVIEW

Evolution by natural selection is a core principle of ecology. Thus, it is appropriate to begin our study of ecology with some explorations of evolution.

Using data on finches from the Galapagos Islands, this Module addresses such questions as: What is evolution? Can evolution happen in just a few years? Can we actually see evolution take place? How can such evolution by natural selection be documented? What sorts of data are necessary, and why study these finches?

This Module is both a standalone piece and an overture to the entire curriculum, **Ecology: A Systems Approach**. It focuses on evolution by natural selection, which is one principle of ecology and inseparable from it. (Actually, because of the intertwining of ecology and evolution, one might say that Charles Darwin was the first great ecologist.) Thus, it is appropriate that the first module of the curriculum be some explorations of "evolution in action."

Students model different finches and experience the effects of selection. Some do not survive. They discover that natural selection is about which individuals are able to survive at a given time, in a particular place, and under particular conditions—not about who wants to survive.

Evolution: A Natural Experiment

The Galapagos Finches

Module One Contents

Ecology, Evolution, and Natural Selection

Chapter One

Contents

Introduction

Using data on finches from the Galapagos Islands, this module addresses questions such as what is evolution? Can evolution happen in just a few years? Can we actually see evolution take place? How can such evolution by natural selection be documented? What sorts of data are necessary, and why study these finches?

Together, the three Modules of this curriculum explore many organisms, their lifestyles, and their interactions with each other and their environment. Many of those phenomena have been shaped by natural selection and evolution. So, a sound understanding of the process of natural selection is an essential context in which to place the rest of the curriculum.

Because of ecology's focus on the whole organism, much ecological research is based on field and laboratory observation and experimentation with animals and plants as they go about their lives. Thus, we begin by asking students to simulate foraging birds and thereby enter one of the great stories of ecology as evolution.

KEY CONCEPTS

- Physical factors affect life. They affect both whether an organism can live and how it lives. These factors include gravity, climate, time, latitude, and so on.
- Ecology is primarily the study of organisms and their interactions with physical factors such as their environment and with each other in populations and communities. (Biology, physiology, anatomy, genetics, mathematics, molecular biology, and physics all inform ecology but are secondary to it.)
- Because food (energy) is essential to animal life, the organisms and their environment in a particular place are related as a system, with interlocking networks of interactions.
- Evolution by natural selection is a major aspect of ecology—indeed, ecology has been called "evolution in action."
- Selection refers to the effect in the present of living (other organisms) or nonliving (e.g., temperature, availability of water) factors on the survival of individual organisms. Evolution refers to the effects of selection over generations of individuals.
- Selection can occur from competition within species, between species, or both.

MATERIALS AND PREPARATION

The Explorations require many of the same materials, so although this list is comprehensive, specific materials are listed for each Exploration.

- **Grasping and pinching implements:** several kinds per student group—pliers, tweezers, kitchen tongs, forceps, wire cutters, wrenches, etc.
- **Pliers:** multiple sets of the same size—at least one pair per group. The cheap and standard 6-inch slip-joint type is perfect.
- **Spring scales**, one per student group, calibrated in newtons (at least up to 50 newtons). Most physics and chemistry labs have several spring scales;

they are also available from supply houses for about $5 apiece. Make sure each scale is properly set to zero to start.

- **Seeds of many different kinds.** Start with a 5-pound bag of mixed wild-bird seed; have students and colleagues contribute other seeds to enlarge the range. Include some nuts, such as pecans, hazelnuts, or acorns. Include also some tiny things, such as lettuce and dandelion seed (which are easy to gather in season), thistle seed, or hemp seed (often sold in pet stores).
- **Cardboard or paper cups or bowls** for seed for each group (not glass or ceramic; there may be a lot of pecking, picking, and pounding!)
- **One clock or watch** per group
- **String or twine** to loop around the pliers handles and from which to hang the spring scales. Needs to be able to withstand a force of perhaps 100 newtons (10 kg).
- **Centimeter measure** (for calibrating the pliers)
- A **C clamp** or other mechanism for attaching pliers to tabletop
- **Graph paper** (for Integration)

In Advance

Before Exploration 1, **calibrate pliers** or have students do so in class.

1. Measure the length of the jaws from the fulcrum to the end.
2. Measure the length of the handles from the fulcrum to the ends.
3. Calculate the ratio of handle length to jaw length. For example, on our pliers, the handle length is 12 cm and the jaw length is 4 cm. The ratio between them, then, is 3:1. This ratio tells you how many times to multiply the force you apply to the handles to get the force actually applied to the seed. Referring to our sample pliers: if you apply 10 newtons of force to the handle of the pliers, the seed held in the jaws will experience 30 newtons of force.

Before Exploration 3, make a **list of bill strengths** to assign students. **NOTE:** Make the bill strength assignments such that 85% of the bills have a force below 30 newtons, that is, not sufficiently strong to crack pecans. (Although there are no pecans on the Galapagos Islands, pecans are used to model, or stand in for, the seed species that were still available during the drought of 1977.) Randomly assign a bill strength or force level to each student, either by telling each student her or his force-level number or by letting them pick numbered slips of paper from a bowl.

SUGGESTED SEQUENCE OF SESSIONS (5–8)

Class Session 1

Working in teams of three to five, students explore the idea that food is critical and that not all animals will succeed in feeding themselves. Using different tools (tweezers, pliers, tongs) to model bird bills, students pick or gather seeds for three minutes to find that different bills (tools) differ in their food-getting (seed-picking) abilities (Exploration 1: Finch Bills, Tweezers, and Seed Picking).

Groups pool their data for a class discussion of which "bills" (tools) and seeds are a good match, that is, which allow the bird to eat adequately.

Homework

Class discussion of Case Study: The Galapagos Finches: A Natural Experiment in Evolution.

Class Session 2

Students use different types of pliers to crack the seeds they had been picking up (Exploration 2: Bill Size and Seed "Crackability": Multiple Finch Species). They find variation in how much force it takes to crack different seed types and individual seeds of each type. Also, each "bill" modeled by different pliers differs in its ability to crack seeds. The class discusses these findings.

Class Session 3

Optional Exploration 2a: Finch Bills, Pliers, and Newtons is about calibrating pliers and converting scale readings from newtons to kilograms of force. If you want students better to understand the mechanics and physics of their "bills," definitely use this Exploration.

In Exploration 3: Get Selected: Bill Force and Seed "Crackability," groups model different individuals of one finch species under natural selection. Many finches do not survive.

Homework

Students discover that the difference between survival and death during the drought is 0.5 mm of bill depth (Reading 1: Natural Selection: A Severe Drought).

Class Session 4 (or Homework): Integration

Students calculate effects of selection and survival (Integration: Selection: Numbers, Not Need). Evolution is the outcome of natural selection, survival, and reproductive success, not of an animal's need to change.

Collect the Integration worksheets for your independent reading and comments.

Homework (or Class Reading)

Students read Reading 2: More Selection: A Flood and El Niño.

Class Session 5

In a class discussion, students coalesce their ideas about selection. Selection depends on local conditions, that is, it is relative to local conditions. Selection can also "reverse" itself. For example, birds that survived the drought may not have survived under flood conditions (Reading 2: More Selection: A Flood and El Niño).

SESSION GUIDES, BY WORKSHEET

EXPLORATION 1 GUIDE
Finch Bills, Tweezers, and Seed Picking

Materials

- Several **grasping and pinching instruments** for each group
- A wide range of **seeds and nuts**, enough for at least five to ten trials per kind of seed
- One **watch or clock** per group
- Sturdy **seed container**

Seed Picking

Although chapters typically begin with a Case Study, this one begins immediately with an Exploration to get students right into the topic. Students test various tools (model bird bills) at picking up different sizes and shapes of seeds. They time themselves, so they can draw some conclusions about which tools (bills) are better suited for picking up which seeds. Each group makes its own data recording sheets to keep track of its findings.

Begin with a brief discussion about the whole curriculum, for example, something about the big ideas or key concepts in ecology, and some of the important questions raised in this Module, such as who survives and why. Mostly, you want students to begin "picking seeds"—to get them involved and active and to create in them "the need to know." That is, get them asking questions and trying to solve problems, in this case, about how seed-eating birds use their bills to get food.

You may want to defer full discussion of the students' findings until after they have completed Exploration 2: Bill Size and Seed "Crackability": Multiple Finch Species, since discussions build on one another.

Key Points

Key points are that within the group of birds called finches there is a variety of bills; that even within a single species, the seed gathering ability of each kind of bill differs; and, particularly, that not all bills are equally good at seed picking. It may be a shock to students that animals can literally starve to death—can fail to obtain enough energy (seeds) per unit time to survive.

Note that this Module considers differences within and between species of Galapagos finches. In Exploration 1 and Exploration 2, the tools and the students model different species, with each finch species and its average bill represented by one kind of tool. Exploration 3 focuses on differences within a single species.

Data Management

Keeping track of and organizing data are important skills. While students might perform these tasks in a way that makes sense to them, they should keep in mind that in the scientific community data are shared. That means that others—other students, you, other teachers, and so on—may be interested in seeing their data, perhaps for comparative purposes. Thus, students (and all researchers) should record scientific data and other information in such a way that others can understand it. (Much of the work in this curriculum involves data collection and management. Sometimes the task is simple; sometimes students have tended to want help, which we note in the curriculum.)

Homework

Assign the Reading for homework. Assign the Case Study now if you plan to use it as a homework assignment.

CASE STUDY GUIDE

The Galapagos Finches: A Natural Experiment in Evolution

Students discover how the Galapagos Islands became populated by different species of plants and animals, among them Darwin's finches. They encounter the idea of natural selection and its components: variation within species, heritability of that variation, and differential success at producing babies.

EXPLORATION 2 GUIDE

Bill Size and Seed "Crackability": Multiple Finch Species

Materials

- Several **grasping and pinching instruments** for each group
- A wide range of **seeds and nuts**, enough for at least five to ten trials per kind of seed
- One **spring scale** for each pair of pliers
- **Twine**, tied to the handle of the spring scale and looped around a handle of the pliers (see Figure 10 in student chapter)
- A **C clamp** or some other mechanism, to attach pliers to tabletop
- **Calibrated pliers** (For this Exploration, the pliers need to be calibrated. Either do this beforehand yourself or have your students do it during class. This simple procedure is explained on page 6, under In Advance.)

Safety

> **WARNING**
>
> **It is possible to give yourself a nasty pinch with the pliers "bills." Keep your fingers out from between the mouth and the handles of the pliers.**

Key Points

Exploration 2 continues using tools as models for bird bills. But it examines a different aspect of seeds, namely, crackability or hardness rather than seed handling. Students use several different kinds of pliers to crack the same seed types they picked up before. They find that there is variation in how much force it takes to crack each kind of seed; there is also variation in the amount of force it takes to crack different individuals of the same kind of seeds. Students also see that pliers types differ in their ability to crack seeds.

Data Collection

Once the pliers have been calibrated, students can begin. To compare their data, it is important that the groups get consistent results. Remind students to place the seeds or nuts always in the same location in the pliers jaws, to ensure that consistent force is applied. Moving the seed back toward the fulcrum increases the force, while moving the seed away from the fulcrum decreases the force. The differences can be considerable.

Once again, students make their own data sheets to record their findings. In this case, they need to keep track of which seeds they tried and how much force it took to crack each seed for each kind of tool they used:

SEED TYPE	PLIERS TYPE	NEWTONS OR KILOGRAMS OF FORCE

(To convert between newtons and kilograms of force, use Optional Exploration 2a: Finch Bills, Pliers, and Newtons. Let students read it, or explain the content and demonstrate the calculations.)

Pooling and Analyzing the Data

When most groups have tested at least two types of pliers and a variety of seeds, make a large chart on the board and collect data from each group. Have the students suggest the organization or format of the chart.

Inconsistent Data

Students tend to notice either patterns or inconsistencies in the data, that is, different groups using the same pliers on the same seeds have quite different results. Ask what might account for those inconsistencies, for example:

> Even among the same kind of seeds, there is natural variation in size, toughness, or hardness. That also means that the variation in the plant population (represented by the seeds) interacts with the variation in the predator population (finches or pliers).
>
> There can also be differences in the way people used the tool—where they placed the nuts, how they cracked seeds, or whether they read the scales at eye level.
>
> Perhaps the tools themselves are not uniform, or perhaps there were real errors in how the tools were used or how the numbers were calculated or recorded.

Ask students what they suggest doing about any inconsistencies. First, which kinds of inconsistencies do they see? How severe are they? For instance, if groups' data vary only slightly, consider the concept of an average (the average force to crack an average seed, as measured by an average group). Calculate a few averages and see how much each individual value differs from its average. (If you want, do a statistical comparison between the values and their average, which is explained under Averages.)

If some values are way off the average, let students consider what to do with those data.

(Reexamine the seed-crack setup used by the group whose values are way off average. Have that group check their data recordings and calculations; check whether they misnamed or mislabeled seeds.)

Averages

In this Exploration, we talk a lot about "average" values for seed crackability (in other units, we will use other average values). When we look at data that represent many values of a biological variable, the way we handle the data may tell us a lot, but it may also hide information that is crucial to the biology we are interested in. It is worth spending a few minutes recalling what an "average value" does and does not tell us. If possible, fully discuss the following example with your students.

When people say "average" they usually are referring to the mean. As you recall, the mean is calculated by adding all the values in the data set and then dividing by the number of values. For example, here is a data set of ten annual incomes of people on a city block.

1. $8,500	6. $26,000
2. $15,500	7. $27,000
3. $16,500	8. $35,000
4. $16,500	9. $39,000
5. $25,000	10. $100,000

The sum of these incomes is $309,000. The mean income is $309,000/10 = $30,900.

Now, what does this tell us? Well, if all ten people had to divide up $309,000 so that they all had identical incomes, the even-size pieces would be $30,900. This is informative—if I tell you my town has a per capita income of $10,000, and your town has a per capita income of $20,000, you can conclude that your town has more money coming in per person than mine. But a lot of interesting information is not shown. The next step, therefore, is to take the mean and use it as a point of comparison to look at the individual data and how they relate to the mean and to each other.

So, of the ten incomes in our data set, seven are less than the mean, and three are more than the mean—the mean is not any of the actual values. The three higher values give the impression that most people in the sample make a lot more than is the case. To get some sense of the effect that an unusually high or low value can have, recalculate the mean using all but one of the extremes. For example, if we calculate a mean of nine incomes, leaving aside income 10, we get a mean of $209,000/9 = $23,222—much closer to the majority of actual values. Compare that mean to the most common value—$16,500—and to the median, the value at which there are equal numbers of people above and below. In this case, the median must lie between incomes 5 and 6—take the mean of the two values between which the median lies: ($25,000 + $26,000)/2 = $25,500. The mean value for incomes 1–9 ($23,222) is much closer to the "middle value" ($25,500) than is the mean for incomes 1–10 ($30,900).

Thus, the mean gives us an initial feel for the values that the variable can take. Because the actual values that make up the mean can vary widely, however, there are many other ways of analyzing data that may help us understand more about the situation we are measuring. In the case of the incomes, we can say that one person earns a lot more than all the rest; that almost all the people earn less than $40,000; and that a majority actually earn below the mean income. This is not a particularly wealthy group, even though the mean income seems like a solid middle-class amount.

In the same way, when we look at "average seed crackability" we may be seeing a number calculated from seeds with wide-ranging hardnesses. It is only when we look at the actual data that we can see the likelihood of finding a seed of a particular hardness. The average is a good way to start a comparison of one set of seeds with another, but the analysis does not end there!

Overall patterns in the class discussion of data

Ask students to consider the following questions:

What patterns or trends do you see?
Did all pliers do equally well picking up and cracking seeds?
What are the implications of what happened here for birds?
Do birds ever have a mismatch between their bills and the available food?

The students will probably see differences in the effectiveness of different pliers types at cracking seeds and in the amount of force it takes to crack seeds of the same species. They may also see that although the average hardness of two seed types is different, the range of individual hardnesses may overlap. Thus, data can look like this:

SEED TYPE	PLIERS TYPE	AVERAGE CRACKING FORCE FOR 10 SEEDS
Millet	1	Group 1: 4 N
		Group 2: 4 N
		Group 3: 6 N
		Group 4: 20 N
	2	Group 1: 2 N
		Group 2: 5 N
		Group 3: 4 N
		Group 4: 35 N
Pecans	1	Group 1: unsuccessful
		Group 2: unsuccessful
		Group 3: unsuccessful
		Group 4: unsuccessful
	2	Group 1: 50 N
		Group 2: 47 N
		Group 3: 45 N
		Group 4: 120 N

Notice that group 4 has consistently high averages—much higher than the other groups. Using the questions above, let students consider such differences and what they mean.

Also notice that pliers type 2 is more efficient at cracking the larger, harder pecans, while pliers type 1 is better for smaller seeds.

Summary and Conclusions

How can you relate these differences to bird survival? (Since each pliers type is a finch species, and each seed species is potential food, some bird/seed combinations will survive while others cannot.)

For a bird trying to "make a living"—in this case, to feed itself—all these variations (in the strength and effectiveness of its bill modeled by the pliers and in the accessibility of the food inside a seed coat) are of vital importance. Each bird must take in a certain number of calories in order to survive and more calories in order to reproduce successfully.

In an environment with a wide variety of seed sizes, selection can have different effects. There can be specialization, with particular bird species specializing in particular seed species. The opposite can happen, with all birds taking all seed types. Or some combination of both can occur, with some bird species specializing in certain seed sizes and other species taking seeds of many sizes.

Similarly, in an environment with few seed types, selection can affect each bird species in a different way.

Optional EXPLORATION 2A GUIDE
Finch Bills, Pliers, and Newtons

You may want to hand this Exploration to students or just walk them through it, converting the newton readings they will have gotten using the spring scales into kilogram forces.

Optional Exploration 2a

FINCH BILLS, PLIERS, AND NEWTONS

Pliers, tongs, bird bills, and similar devices are excellent examples of the lever and its principles. A fulcrum is the pivot point between any object in which force or balance is involved. Recently in class you used a pair of attached levers—namely, pliers—to apply force to seeds and to mimic bird bills cracking seeds. In fact, you collected a considerable amount of data about the force necessary to crack different seed types. But do you understand those data? Can you translate the readings from the spring scale into a measure of force that makes sense to you?

Let's briefly explore the physics of a standard pair of pliers (see the illustration below) and then interpret the seed-cracking data in more familiar terms.

Materials

- The following **illustration**
- Two or more types of **pliers** per group
- Various kinds of **seeds**
- **Piping or tubing** to lengthen the pliers handles

Procedure

1. **Understanding the picture.**
   Carefully examine the labels in the picture, which is of a pair of pliers like those you used in Exploration 1 and Exploration 2.

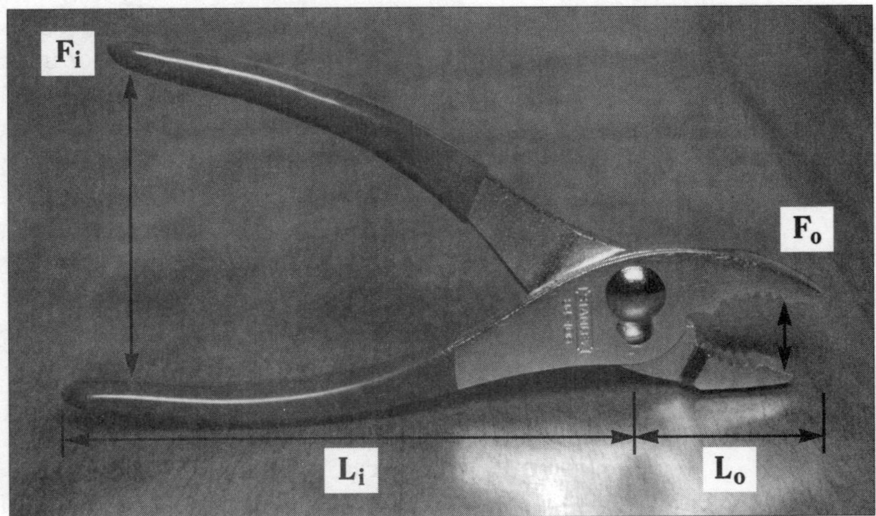

F_i = Force "in," the force applied on the handles by the pliers user. In your seed cracking, you measured that force using the spring scale.

F_o = Force "out," the force applied to the seed by the "mouth" of the pliers.

L_i = Length "in," the length of the handle, measured from the fulcrum (screws) to the end.

L_o = Length "out," the length of the jaws in front of the fulcrum.

2. **The physics of the picture.**
   There is a simple relationship between the "ins" and the "outs." This relationship is nicely summed up by the equation

$$F_o \times L_o = F_i \times L_i$$

The two sides of the equation will always balance, but each side is made up of two elements or quantities. How does this relate to nut cracking?

3. **What you control.**
The first thing to note is that in a pair of pliers, you can directly control only F_i and L_i. You control F_i by pressing harder, applying a greater force to the handles. You can do that by exerting more strength or by changing L_i. If you increase either of those two quantities, you will change the other side of the equation.

Here's the clever part: L_o is the length of the pliers jaws, which does not change. For the "out," or output, side of the equation to stay balanced when you increase the "in," or input, side, the only part that can increase is F_o, the output force that the jaws exert on something. That is why, if you lengthen the handles, you get more force with which to crack seeds. You are increasing the F_iL_i input side of things, while on the output side, only F_o can increase.

4. **Group data.**
Working in groups of three to five, try this with some real numbers and some real seeds. Start with the measurements from one pair of pliers and some input force, F_i. What is F_o? Now change L_i or F_i (making either one larger or smaller). What is the effect on F_o?

Try a second type of pliers, with different measurements. Keep track of your data.

Try various seeds, from soft to tough, large to small. How can you most efficiently use the pliers?

5. **Newtons to kilograms.**
Now you know something about the physics of levers and how that works with pliers. But what about your force data, which are in newtons? What is a newton (abbreviated N)? Talking about newtons is a bit like talking about foreign money, like Italian lire or Indian rupees. What is the exchange rate into dollars? If you have 600 lire, are you wealthy or not? (You are not.)

You can get some sense of how much force 1 newton (1 N) is by thinking about weight. Weight is a mass being accelerated by the earth's gravity or the gravitational force of whatever planet you are on. (That is another way of saying you would be lighter on the moon or Mars. Your mass does not change, but the force pulling you to the center of the planet does.) In the metric system, weight should be expressed as newtons, but people usually talk about weights in kilograms (1 kg = 2.2 lb). It turns out that 1 N of force exerted on something is equivalent to setting a mass of 0.1 kg on the object and letting gravity pull on it.

6. **Data conversion and seed cracking.**
In the case of seed cracking, it goes like this. If a seed cracks at 1 N, that is equivalent to your setting a 0.1-kg weight on the seed. If it takes 50 N to crack the seed, that is like having your 5-kg cat put all its weight on the seed. The conversion is easy: 1 N ≈ 0.1 kg. ("≈" means "approximates"; "=" means "equals" or "is equal to.")

For any seed you can substitute the appropriate values into the formula to calculate the force in kilograms exerted by that bill (pair of pliers). And more to the point, since the pliers applying the force are modeling a bill, you are actually calculating, in kilograms, the force that bird can exert with its bill. Some finches are far stronger than that and can exert nearly 300 N of force with their bills! (What is that in kilograms?)

7. **Class data and discussion.**
Pool the data. What patterns do you see? Do they follow the principles outlined above? If not, why might that be?

EXPLORATION 3 GUIDE

Get Selected: Bill Force and Seed "Crackability"

Students model individuals of one finch species, *Geospiza fortis*, experiencing a severe drought. The birds have to deal with highly limited food (seed) availability: only extremely large, tough seeds are still around. And only a small percentage of the birds, those with the largest, deepest beaks, can exert enough force to crack those seeds. This Exploration illustrates normal variations among individuals of a species, as well as possible effects of such variation under selection. Many individuals of this finch species do not survive the drought.

Materials

- **Pliers** of the same type for each group (since each student is now a member of the same bird species)
- A **list of bill strengths** (made in advance) to assign students. NOTE: The bill strength assignments must be such that 85% of the bills have a force below 30 N, that is, not sufficiently strong to crack the only seed now common in our experimental drought, the pecan. (Although there are no pecans on the Galapagos Islands, they are used to model, or stand in, for the seed species that were actually available during the drought of 1977.) Randomly assign a bill strength or force level to each student, either by telling each student his or her force-level number or by letting them pick numbered slips of paper from a bowl.
- Enough **pecans** that each student has three to try to crack

The Work and Discussion

Each student is now a finch and must try to crack three pecans without exceeding its bill force. Each student has already been assigned a maximum allowable force that he or she can use to crack seeds. To simulate the 85% mortality rate, 85% of the students must have bill force levels less than 30 N; only 15% can have force levels 30 and above. Any student/finch that cannot crack its pecans is dead and removed from the gene pool.

This Exploration models a real selection event in the Galapagos (see Reading 1: Natural Selection: A Severe Drought) when a severe drought altered the finch population. Natural selection eliminated all finches with bills of a size and cracking force less than 6 on the McGill nutcracker, that is, with less than about 15 kg force cracking power. This selection and its results persisted until the environment and, thus, selective pressure changed markedly, and, by chance, in the opposite direction (Reading 2: More Selection: A Flood and El Niño).

Students can see that food availability plays a crucial role in the survival of organisms and that survival may depend on very small differences (heritable variation) in size or shape, as with these bills. In this case, the difference between survival and death is a difference of 0.5 mm in bill depth.

Homework

At the end of this session, assign Reading 1: Natural Selection: A Severe Drought. It tells the story on which Exploration 3 is based. Also assign, or do in class, the Integration, which considers population implications of such a selection event and allows students to calculate changes in population numbers due to selection.

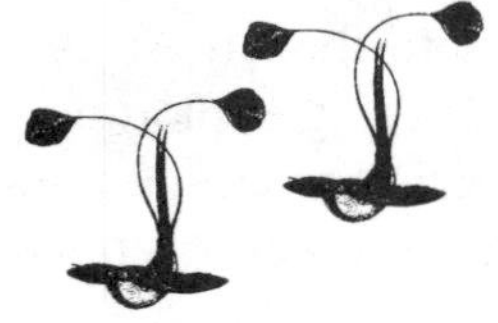

READING 1 GUIDE

Natural Selection: A Severe Drought

Students discover that the drought they modeled in Exploration 3 was real and that the difference between which birds did and which birds did not survive is small. Students may be shocked to discover that animals cannot necessarily survive; they might protest that all animals want to survive. While that is most likely true, it is insufficient, as they will come to see.

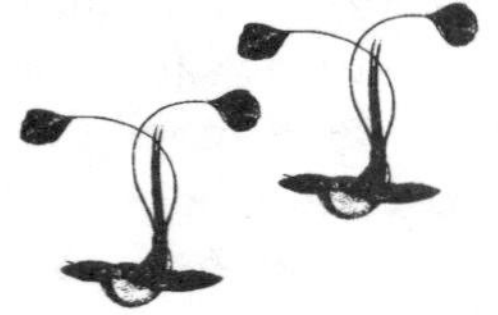

READING 2 GUIDE

More Selection: A Flood and El Niño

Conditions on the Galapagos Islands change drastically due to torrential rains and flooding. Finches with the bill shape that had survived the drought are now actually at a disadvantage and are dying. This vividly makes the point that survival is relative to particular conditions. There is no such thing as a perfect, all-purpose, or selection-proof finch (or any other organism, for that matter).

INTEGRATION GUIDE

Selection: Numbers, Not Need

Natural Selection within a Species

Let's consider a numerical example using the finch *G. fortis* again. We saw that under different sets of conditions, birds with different bill types survived. For "typical" times, there is an average bill of average size and average strength. Birds with average bills can get the largest number of seeds per unit time. Birds with shorter or weaker bills are not able to crack as large a range of seeds and so waste some time trying to crack seeds that are too hard for them. Birds with very strong bills also may have some difficulty finding enough seeds the right size for them and will lose some smaller seeds due to clumsiness.

Under typical conditions, these differences between birds in bill size and shape have little effect on their ability to survive. But during hard, extreme, or unusual times, as during the drought and during El Niño, the differences in birds' seed-gathering and seed-cracking abilities, in their time spent searching for seeds, and in the number of seeds they can get per day can be the difference between death and survival.

One aspect of evolution that some people find hard to understand is the irrelevance of desire, need, or volition. Whether an organism survives does not depend on whether it wants to survive. Survival depends on whether that organism is appropriately matched to its environment and conditions at that time and in that place. In terms of the Galapagos finches, does an individual bird have a bill shape that allows the finch to pick, crack, and eat enough of the seeds that are available at that time?

Work out the Integration example to demonstrate that finches with appropriate bill shapes soon outnumber the rest of the finches in the local population of that species. See also Science Background.

INTEGRATION
Selection: Numbers, Not Need

We have read about and modeled a natural selection event—the drought of 1977—and its consequences. Now, let's examine the effect on and change in the same population of *Geospiza fortis* caused by that natural selection event. That way, we can show ourselves numerically that evolution takes place through natural selection and reproductive success.

Materials

- **Calculators**
- **Graph paper**

Procedure

1. **Data for Year 1.**
Let's start our example under normal conditions and see the selective effects of drought on the population. Suppose we start with 50 bird pairs in each of three bill size categories.

	BILL SIZE AND STRENGTH		
	BELOW AVERAGE	AVERAGE	ABOVE AVERAGE
YEAR 1			
Number of pairs of adults	50	50	50
Number of chicks hatched	100	100	100
Number of chicks surviving	60	80	55

So, our population consists of three categories with 50 pairs in each category, for a total of 300 adults, plus all the surviving chicks.

END OF YEAR 1

How many chicks survive? __________

What is the current total population?

2. **Data for Year 2.**
Let's assume that 10% of the adults die every year (remember, these are imaginary numbers). Let's also assume that chicks become adults and breed the year after they are born. Thus, our second year's data look like this:

	BILL SIZE AND STRENGTH		
	BELOW AVERAGE	AVERAGE	ABOVE AVERAGE
YEAR 2			
Number of adult pairs surviving	40	40	40
Number of new adult pairs	30	40	22
Total pairs	70	80	62

So far, so good. But this is the year of the drought, and the number of birds that reproduce is much lower than the number in the previous year.

END OF YEAR 2			
Number of chicks hatched	0	0	0
Number of adults surviving	2	3	27

3. **Data for Year 3.**

	BILL SIZE AND STRENGTH		
	BELOW AVERAGE	AVERAGE	ABOVE AVERAGE
YEAR 3			
Number of pairs	1	1	13
Number of chicks hatched	2	3	30
Number of chicks surviving	2	3	27
Total number of birds in each class?	—	—	—

4. **Results.**
With the graph paper, make frequency histograms to show the change in the number of adults by the three bill-size classes across the three years. Here, write down your conclusions: who is and who is not surviving?

All the birds "needed" stronger, larger bills, but only those that already had them had a chance to survive the drought.

Discussion

A common misperception about selection and evolution is that they are about need. Suppose conditions change (say, there is a drought)—to survive, creatures also need to change. People tend to think that because the creatures need to change to survive, they can or will change. Although it may be true that creatures need to change to survive, that does not mean they are able to do so. Can a bird change its bill size just so? No. Thus, "need" is irrelevant to the mechanism of natural selection. Did the finches with less powerful bills try any less hard to survive the drought? Not likely. Did that make any difference? No. What made the difference? Hard physical realities about bill size and depth. In this case, birds with deeper, stronger bills were better equipped to survive under drought conditions and to reproduce.

Selection between Species

Natural selection occurs the same way between as it does within species. That is, we will come up with the same sorts of results whether the data in the three columns in the tables above pertain to three different species or to three different-size classes within a species. Indeed, many species that exist today are the outcome of the process we have been exploring throughout this Module.

Shocking, isn't it, to consider that organisms as different as the whale, ostrich, beetle, house cat, human, guppy, finch, snake, mosquito, shark, frog, and most plants, fungi, and microorganisms have come into being by the process of natural selection? Whole communities of organisms are interrelated and interdependent because they have been part of the dynamic process of evolution by natural selection.

Summary: Natural Selection and Its Three Conditions

We have considered several aspects of evolution by natural selection, so let's summarize our conclusions. Natural selection can result from effects of the external factors of everyday life on organisms, sometimes to their individual benefit (e.g., survival), sometimes to their detriment (e.g., death). For the finches, those factors include weather, food availability, and the presence of other species. Evolution is the consequence across generations of those forces—the outcomes of selection that are shown by which animals do and which animals do not survive.

So, for evolution to occur, what three conditions must be met?

SCIENCE BACKGROUND
More on Evolution by Natural Selection

Evolution by natural selection is a core principal of ecology. It is, if you like, a way of looking at ecology over time.

People sometimes get confused about how evolution happens, because they get confused about causality, the "if, then" part of the picture. There is an "if, then" part, but often it is misapplied or misunderstood.

It is not true that if an organism "wants" to survive or needs some characteristic to survive, then the organism can just demonstrate or acquire that characteristic. Can an individual finch change its bill shape because it "needs" to? Can a giraffe make its neck grow longer to reach leaves higher in the tree? No and no.

The correct "if, then" is something like this. If finches of a certain bill shape survive and produce more young than do individuals with a different bill shape, then those with the first bill shape will become more common than those with the second. Birds with both bill shapes presumably "want" to survive, but that is not how it works.

Actually, three "ifs" are necessary for evolution by natural selection to occur:

1. If there is natural variation in some trait (such as bill shape) in the population of creatures, and
2. if that variation has a genetic basis (and so can be inherited), and
3. if the trait involved affects reproductive success,

then that trait is available for natural selection.

Selection can act at various levels (molecular, individual, population) and in various ways. One way is a simple match or mismatch with the current environment, as we see in the finches.

There is also a body of research that suggests that much genetic change in organisms is neutral. That is, not every genetically determined characteristic is under genetic selection. Also, not every organism or every characteristic of any organism is the best possible match between the organism and its environment. It is just a good enough match for the organism to survive for now.

You may know that the absence of a perfect match between an organism and its environment is strong evidence against creationism. If a creature had been designed specifically to live in a certain way in a certain place, it would have been designed perfectly to match its circumstances. Instead, we find leftover, mismatched, and even unuseful characteristics or features. Ask students to name some; they include the human appendix, flamingos' upside-down feeding posture, and the panda's thumb.

There is also discussion over how much selection is due to the accumulation of tiny changes in, say, bill shape, versus a major change. Some plant species have suddenly come into being because incomplete mitosis caused them to keep a double set of chromosomes. That means they cannot reproduce with members of their former species and—voilà!—two species. For more, see especially Gould (The Panda's Thumb and The Flamingo's Smile) and Dawkins (The Blind Watchmaker).

REFERENCES

Dawkins, Richard. 1985. The Blind Watchmaker. New York: W. W. Norton.

Dennett, Daniel C. 1995. Darwin's Dangerous Idea. New York: Simon & Schuster.

Gamlin, Linda, and Gail Vines. 1991. The Evolution of Life. New York: Oxford University Press.

Gould, Stephen Jay. 1980. "The Panda's Thumb," in The Panda's Thumb: More Reflections in Natural History. New York: W. W. Norton. 343 pp.

— — —. 1985. "The Flamingo's Smile," in The Flamingo's Smile: Reflections in Natural History. New York: W. W. Norton. 476 pp.

Grant, B. Rosemary, and Peter R. Grant. 1989. Evolutionary Dynamics of a Natural Population: The Large Cactus Finch of the Galápagos. Chicago: University of Chicago Press. 350 pp., paperback.

Grant, Peter R. 1986. Ecology and Evolution of Darwin's Finches. Princeton: Princeton University Press. 458 pp., paperback.

Jones, Steve, Robert Martin, and David Pilbeam. 1996. Cambridge Encyclopedia of Human Evolution. Cambridge University Press.

Simberloff, D. S., and E. O. Wilson. 1969. "Experimental Zoogeography of Islands: The Colonization of Empty Islands." Ecology, 50: 278–89.

Weiner, Jonathan. 1994. The Beak of the Finch: A Story of Evolution in Our Time. New York: Alfred A. Knopf. 332 pp.

Williams, George C. 1966. Adaptation and Natural Selection. Princeton: Princeton University Press.

CARBON AND ENERGY

MODULE TWO OVERVIEW

The movement and transfer of energy within and among parts of an ecosystem are the foundation underlying all other ecological processes.

This Module describes how energy is stored and moved in the global carbon cycle. It considers energy transfer in communities and trophic pyramids via photosynthesis, feeding, predation, decomposition, competition. It explores questions such as: What is energy, biochemically and biologically? Why is food "relative," that is, why is grass energy for a cow but not for a cat? (And what differences in lifestyle go with that: how animals are built; their size; how they move; who or what they eat and digest; how they get what they eat; how many of them can live on 10 hectares?) How do desert- and water-living plants differ in energy needs and use (shape and size; how they fit into their ecosystem)?

The energy "Big Picture" (the global and ecosystem scale or level) is drawn by integrating smaller-scale energy pictures (although any complex picture is more than the sum of its parts). Thus this Module helps students explore energy at various scales—from the biochemical to the global scale—so they can develop tools and building blocks both to understand each scale independently and to integrate those blocks into an ever widening, cross-scale picture, ultimately yielding a Big Picture.

Carbon and Energy

Module Two Contents

Groupings and What They Mean

Unit 1

Groupings and What They Mean

UNIT 1 OVERVIEW

GROUPINGS AND WHAT THEY MEAN

This Unit helps students articulate their intuitive understanding of ecology. Every organism can be described variously and has multiple attributes and roles. Thus, a kangaroo is brown, furry, and a marsupial that carries its young in a pouch. That description is quite accurate, but "flat" or linear. A multilevel or dynamic description might include interactions (roles) of the kangaroo: it is a predator (eats plants), a grazer (specializes on grasses), prey (is hunted by humans and dingoes), and host (to assorted parasites and microorganisms).

By asking students to group the organisms listed, you and they will discover ideas they have about those creatures and whether and how they interact. At the end of **Chapter 1**, students likely have a real sense that ecology includes nonliving (abiotic) and living (biotic) things and that it is about the relationships and interactions

- among living things
- between living and nonliving things,

as shown by the arrows below:

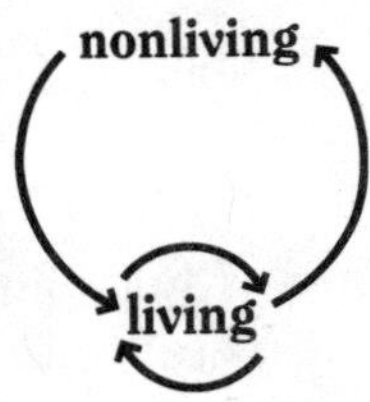

Those interactions form systems, which are both closed and dynamic. "Closed" means that (most) pieces of the system are recycled rather than used up, although they can take various forms. Thus, although grasses are eaten by the kangaroo, they are digested and broken down into different pieces (chemically and mechanically), which then become kangaroo flesh, get used as energy, or are excreted to get used by dung eaters. "Dynamic" refers to the continuous movement and change of state of, say, those grass blades.

Systems principles are by no means restricted to ecology. They are highly generalizable and can be applied to anything, from human relations of any sort to specific situations: a classroom, a factory, a family, a cultural or political group.

All the Units in this text include pedagogical as well as ecological principles or concepts. This first Unit, however, includes a few that are used throughout the text.

Having students group things and describe their reasons or criteria for those groupings is a powerful tool. Students presented with "raw materials" must respond to those materials directly and explicitly. In doing so, they reveal much of their attitudes, conceptions, and understanding of those materials. Set up well, an exploration that involves grouping most anything is empowering. Students discover that they do know something about the materials being grouped, whether it is that kangaroos have pouch babies, are furry, live in Australia, or are grass predators. Forced back on their own resources, students tend to discover that they actually have resources—which they otherwise are likely to deny or at least doubt. And you may be amazed at the novelty, depth, and breadth of those resources. Your students will come up with things you have not thought of, and we hope you will delight in their abilities.

The third major idea around which this Unit is built is that of being "right" or "wrong" and making intelligent approximations. Students will group organisms in very different ways, but ways that can be equally accurate, depending on context. It is essential in doing research to keep seeing things in different ways; we hope early experience with that mode of thinking and seeing things from different perspectives will help free students from preconceptions about "right" and "wrong" and the idea that there is always one "correct" answer. The **Technique: 21 Questions to Conclusions** reinforces aspects of this type of thinking. Asking questions does not mean you are dumb, it means you are thinking (**Chapter 2,** Case Study and Excerpt). And approximating things to an order of magnitude is a useful tool, not a sloppy or inaccurate way of doing things (**Chapter 1,** Reading: Answers in the Ballpark).

For more details, see the specific Session Guides in both chapters.

Connections with Other Units

Its breadth means that this Unit connects in essence to all others. Specifically, however, it deals with topics explored in more depth in **Unit 2** of this Module (**Carbon and Energy**). "Grouping" as a tool is used also in **Unit 2** of this Module (with plant types) and in **Unit 1** (**Groupings and What They Mean**) of the **Water Module**. The **Technique: 21 Questions to Conclusions** can be used with nearly any topic throughout the text, indoors or out.

THE "NATURAL LOOK" IS MANY-FACETED

CHAPTER ONE

CONTENTS

INTRODUCTION

The work of this Chapter has three major prongs: the doing of science, students becoming more self-aware thinkers/learners, and some concepts about ecological relationships. In the **Evolution Module**, students saw ecology as evolution taking place. In this Chapter, they are asked to take a different perspective, to look at ecology as interactions within a system. In the rest of this Module, much of our focus will be on the flow of energy and resources within a system: here, however, the students should think as broadly as possible about interactions among organisms and between organisms and the physical environment. Though we will not spend time on all possible interactions, they all are potentially important.

NOTE! The aim here is not to come up with a food web! This first chapter in the **Carbon and Energy Module** is intended to

- excite, interest, and empower the students
- set up or illustrate concepts or principles students will derive or encounter in the Module
- get students to raise questions about those concepts, which they will be able to answer as they progress through the Module
- be repeatable later in the Module, with students redoing the work in more depth, because they can build on what they have learned since their first encounter with it
- allow each student and you to assess his or her ideas about the topics
- get students to think about learning as asking questions, using tools like elaboration, renaming, making order-of-magnitude approximations, and thinking analytically

KEY CONCEPTS

- Ecology is the study of interactions among living things and between living and nonliving things.
- It is the study of systems, which are dynamic and have principles generalizable to most other systems.
- Given an open-ended assignment, students might think for themselves; see, not just look; discover they know something; and discover how to learn more.
- "Right" and "wrong" are not the only possible answers; thoughtful "wrong" answers may have more value for students' conceptual understanding—real learning—than thought-free "right" answers and "answers by rote."

MATERIALS AND PREPARATION

- Students' **homework groupings**
- **Paper** and **writing tools**
- Some **reference books** with information about the organisms (e.g., field guides, encyclopedias, books on plants, animals, ecology (See References.)
- **Whiteboard** or **poster paper** if you plan to record and post student thoughts and questions for future reference

SUGGESTED SEQUENCE OF SESSIONS (3–5)

Homework

Exploration 1 (Homework): Grouping: Plants, Animals, and Others. Working alone, students group a selection of organisms and write a brief explanation or rationale for their grouping(s).

Class Session 1

Briefly discuss groupings and rationale from homework; use them to introduce the topic.

Exploration 1 (Class): Grouping: Plants, Animals, and Others. Working in teams of three to five, students develop several groups of three to six organisms from the list and note why each group or set has been made: its defining characteristic(s) or how the organisms are related to each other.

Each team illustrates one or more of its groupings on the board and presents its rationale for class consideration and discussion. (This can carry over into the next session.)

Homework

Case Study: Solving Mysteries: Everything Has Many Names. Students find that adding names or roles to a thing adds to their understanding of that thing and how it fits into the world.

Class Session 2

Briefly discuss key point of homework reading: Case Study.

Continue class discussion from Session 1, if appropriate.

Exploration 2: Energy Relationships. Teams reconvene so students can consider their groupings from the point of view of energy use and transfer. Then the class discusses energy transfer and how that has affected some groupings and completely excluded others. (This session can also carry over.)

Homework

Reading: Answers in the Ballpark: Useful Approximations. Expanding the idea that learning requires thought, students encounter the tool of order-of-magnitude approximations and how it is used.

Class Session 3

Continue class discussion from Session 2, if appropriate.

Discuss homework Reading, especially as a tool for Exploration 3 (if students do that).

Optional Exploration 3: Relative Population Sizes. Teams consider relative (or absolute) population sizes of organisms involved in energy relationships, using ideas from the homework Reading on approximations. For example, how many prey (e.g., rabbits) might a family of predators (e.g., dingoes) need per day, week, or year?

Teams present their ideas, and the class reflects on the work so far, including questions and predictions to be considered as the Module progresses.

Integration

Students individually write up what they have learned about learning and about relationships among organisms. This can also be a Homework.

SESSION GUIDES, BY WORKSHEET

EXPLORATION 1 GUIDE (Homework)
Grouping: Plants, Animals, and Others

Students have worked individually on grouping the animals listed. Now, by way of introduction in class, have students tell you how they each grouped the organisms and why. Make neutral comments on the groupings; put some on the board. The point is to let students hear each other's thoughts about the organisms. Possible groupings can be ecologically quite sophisticated, biological rather than ecological, or based on things like shape, color, taxonomy, or anything students can imagine. (See Exploration 1 Guide (Class), next.) Rarely, the homework groupings are so sophisticated that doing Exploration 1 (Class) becomes essentially redundant; if so, just move ahead to Exploration 2.

How quickly you are ready to move on to the team work below depends in part on the diversity of groupings made by individual students and the liveliness of the discussion.

EXPLORATION 1 GUIDE (Class)
Grouping: Plants, Animals, and Others

Following the discussion, have students work in teams of three to five to explore further how the natural world is organized (grouped) and why. It is important that students do not feel that they are expected to know the answers to questions they are considering here. On the contrary, a primary goal of this activity is for students to discover how much they do know and to get a baseline reading of how they currently think about the concepts involved in these Explorations. Later in this Module, after they have worked in depth with related materials and acquired more tools to help make sense of the natural world, they will revisit these Explorations and reexamine their thinking.

Getting Started

If students have trouble thinking about kinds of relationships, encourage them to think first about just pairs of organisms or organisms and physical factors. This may get them started, so they can move on to multiple relationships.

Because issues will be raised that carry through the rest of this Module, you may want to set aside a section of blackboard or post some large sheets of paper on which to list and keep the questions handy for future reference.

Team Reports and Class Discussion: Kinds of Groupings

After fifteen to twenty minutes, have each team put its grouping and relationships on the board. Some of the organisms cited are geographically restricted (e.g., kangaroos occur only in Australia), while others occur in all the places included by this list (e.g., millipedes, earthworms). That means that, from the point of view of geographic distribution, the restricted animals cannot correctly be grouped with all other animals on the list, while the more widespread animals can.

It may well be, however, that the animals are grouped in a way that is ecologically valid, for instance, a carnivore is represented as eating an herbivore (e.g., a dingo eating a prairie dog). In fact, geographic distribution makes that impossible and a "wrong" pairing—but a correct pairing in that it shows some ecological understanding of the roles played by each organism.

It is, of course, important to encourage such ecological or "role" thinking while also being clear that the dingoes and prairie dogs do not coexist. This nicely makes the point that "right" or "wrong" can depend on context, and that there are multiple ways to look at or think about even something as apparently simple as a grouping of organisms. Possible groupings can include food eaten or trophic level (herbivore, carnivore, detritivore, scavenger); vertebrate/invertebrate; plant/animal; endotherm/ectotherm; large/small; furry/not furry; color; method of locomotion or sight; country of origin; and so on.

The two sets are listed here:

RESTRICTED DISTRIBUTION	UNRESTRICTED DISTRIBUTION
kangaroos–Australia	millipedes
dingoes–Australia	earthworms
emus–Australia	termites
badgers–North America, Europe	ants
prairie dogs–North America	bushes
foxes–e.g., North America, Europe	bacteria
ravens–e.g., N. Hemisphere	rabbits
owls–e.g., North America, Europe, South America	fleas
	grasses
	trees
	vultures

Questions Students Might Ask

Students are likely to raise two sorts of questions: those with simple answers ("What does an emu eat?" "What eats fleas?") and more complex questions ("Why do kangaroos and badgers not occur on the same continent?" "Why don't prairie dogs eat foxes?"). The first kind of question probably can be answered using reference materials in the class or with a visit to the library. Complex questions may be answered or become answerable as you progress through the rest of the curriculum and as students develop understanding of factors involved in ecological relationships, such as chance, body size, diet, and natural selection.

Help students make their ideas explicit—about relationships among organisms, about where their chosen organisms live, whatever. Have them use the reference materials if appropriate.

CASE STUDY GUIDE
Solving Mysteries: Everything Has Many Names

This Case Study considers one of three powerful tools used by ecologists and others, that of renaming things. Substituting names, putting together information or roles is an important way of revisioning—expanding one's vision—of an organism or a person. In their groupings and especially by Exploration 2, students expand their images and ideas of the organisms they are considering. This piece specifically articulates that tool and its value. It also uses an example of a math proof, to show students they have used this tool before and to help them connect their work here with previous work. Some students think such changing of names or roles is cheating—no actual work has happened. But its usefulness usually overcomes such feelings.

(One way you can monitor students' grasp of concepts in this Module is by the relative richness of their ideas about organisms. Do they describe a kangaroo simply as brown, furry, Australian, having pouch young? Or do they see multiple roles—an herbivore that is both predator and prey; an animal adapted to life in deserts; a marsupial with its unique form of reproduction?)

Most things have multiple roles or uses, each of which has a name. Thus, renaming or substitution helps develop more complex ideas about that thing because it evokes those multiple roles. What did you imagine when you considered "a flower"? Its roles include food source (for nectar and pollen eaters and herbivores, which eat the whole flower); farm product (there are many flower farms, for instance, in California, Holland, and South Africa); ornament (corsage, bouquet); and so on. You and your students probably thought of many other roles as well.

EXPLORATION 2 GUIDE
Energy Relationships

Biotic and Abiotic Energy Relationships

At this point, students will likely think about trophic relations—"X eats Y" is a well-known relationship. For "other things that organisms need," we are thinking about abiotic things, especially the sun but also water, earth, and so on. Pay special attention to students' thoughts about what might be missing from the system to make it a complete cycle. These thoughts will help you decide how to approach the topic of energy, since they may show what students call "energy" and how they perceive its movement, distribution, and transfer. A similarly useful point is student thinking about plants—where and how do students think plants get energy? Finally, some student responses may relate to the different kinds of cycles: matter cycles and is used and transferred in various states, but energy is dissipated or degrades. These profound ideas and concepts underlie much of ecology.

Roles of Student Ideas

By engaging students with these concepts in an open-ended way, several things can happen. Students interact with major concepts. They do so in a fresh way. Students articulate and thus become aware of their own thoughts about these topics. You learn about students' ideas, which puts you in a better position to enable students. And both you and the students have some record of their thoughts now, against which they will be able to continue to compare future thinking, to see how their ideas and understanding deepens and broadens.

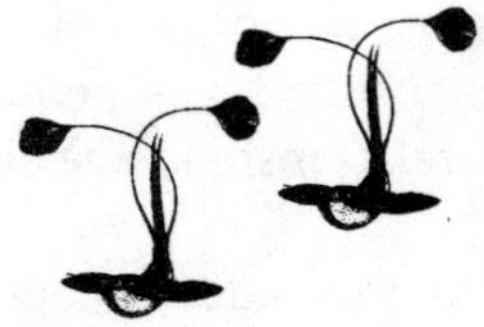

READING GUIDE
Answers in the Ballpark: Useful Approximations

To keep students thinking and learning, here they encounter a useful (and sometimes unsettling) tool: order-of-magnitude approximations. They may find it unsettling because it seems so imprecise, so "unscientific." Yet it is neither. As a first approximation, it is important to get the scope or scale of a question—to find its order of magnitude. Whether we are considering the size (length) of molecules (from 10^{-9} nanometers for water) or bacteria (10^{-5} nm) or mammals (10^{1} m), it frames our thinking to know these approximate size ranges. After all, molecules are influenced by things like electrostatic charges and capillarity, while mammals are subject to gravity. (For more on this topic, see the Reading in **Chapter 5** of this Unit.)

A first take on any problem requires some idea of its magnitude. This combination of educated guesses, facts, and common sense can be a powerful aid to framing a problem—whether about cows and hamburgers, stars in the Milky Way, or relative population sizes (Exploration 3). Many fields use such rough calculations. Some important caveats are:

- State the assumptions made at each step.
- Remember that the numbers are rough.
- Use them appropriately as approximations.
- Upgrade with direct data whenever possible.

There is also a big difference between sloppiness or imprecision and a rough approximation. While sloppiness is never appropriate, approximations are a good starting place for problem solving.

OPTIONAL EXPLORATION 3 GUIDE
Relative Population Sizes

This Exploration helps students become aware of relative population sizes and possible energy components of those sizes. These concepts are complex and more hierarchical than "who eats what." They raise questions for which students may have no answers—yet. So you may want to use this Exploration later, during the food web and trophic pyramid chapters in **Unit**

2: How Organisms Acquire and Use Energy. It is, however, productive and challenging to let students grapple with these concepts now and then redo this Exploration during those chapters. If you follow this latter route (which we recommend), make sure you and the students keep track of their work for subsequent comparison.

Population Sizes

All organisms that live in a given area are related energetically, directly or indirectly. They are not, however, all equally abundant. For instance, there are always more prey than predators. Ask students why.

Students can use the Reading on approximation here. For example, they might find information (in the reference materials you have provided or at the library) about related organisms: grass biomass per hectare of desert; numbers of kangaroos and dingoes in some area of Australia; and kilograms of flesh needed by a small wolf or dog the same weight as a dingo. They can "Fermi up" those numbers to produce a plausible set of population sizes. (For more on population sizes and trophic relationships, see also **Chapters 10** and **11** in **Unit 2**.)

Predation is one obvious mechanism that affects population size. Others include birth (of major importance in this context), death, and competition within or between species.

Next Steps

The next weeks will be spent on examining these kinds of relationships, better to understand where energy comes from, how organisms get it, use it, and transfer it to other organisms.

Again, students' thinking during this activity will help you plan the next section of the text as they develop their research projects.

INTEGRATION GUIDE

The Difference between Facts and Ideas

The work of this Chapter has three major prongs: the doing of science, students becoming more self-aware thinkers/learners, and some concepts about ecological relationships. You already have some measure of student progress with the first and third prongs from their work in Explorations 1 and 2. The second prong is addressed in the Reading and the Case Study and directly in the Integration.

Facts

The Integration directly addresses the issue of "facts" or "truth" and students' reactions. The discussion of "what is a fact" will likely raise numerous issues: relative and absolute truth, proof, sources and their validity or accuracy, what is knowable and how we know it. Help students develop a crude hierarchy of facts using their ideas about whether there are different kinds of facts. "The sun is shining" is an apparently simple and verifiable fact. But someone will (or you might) ask whether that is indeed the question. Technically, the sun always shines, but we cannot always see it. So what are the "facts" in this case? A genuinely simple question and answer might be, "Are you all in classroom number whatever-you-are-in?" How can they verify that? As they continue to work with this text, they will also expand their ideas about facts and truth. A key tool of analytical thinking is context: what is true under these circumstances and at this time might well not be true otherwise.

Feelings

Since the pedagogical approach of this book is somewhat unusual, you might find it interesting and helpful to follow students' self-reflection as learners and their growth as thinkers. Good science is the consequence of logical thinking, creativity, asking and answering questions, tolerating uncertainty, and the willingness to make mistakes. Some of these can be hard, and it is important for you and your students to know that. It is also important to know how students (and you!) feel about asking questions, about uncertainty, about relative truths and context-specific truth. Some people love uncertainty, some hate it, some are indifferent. Clearly it can be more difficult for someone who dislikes uncertainty to engage in open-ended work, just as it can be more difficult for someone who dislikes structure to follow detailed instructions. In our experience, however, this is much like playing an instrument, drawing, or participating in some sport. Everyone can do it, but some do it more easily and naturally than others.

Since much of the work to come will be done in small groups, you may find that mixed groups are more productive: an uncertainty tolerator with the opposite, a math hater with a number cruncher, an urban bug with a hiker nut, and so on.

You will see students' attitudes toward science and learning change over time. Ask them the same question after six weeks, after three months, and at the end of the year.

INTEGRATION
The Difference between Facts and Ideas

What is a fact? Is it what someone tells you? "No!" you probably shout, remembering things you have been told that were not true.

Well, is it something you read? No! You doubtless can also remember things you have read that did not agree with each other or with something you know. So which one is true? How can you tell? If you read things that contradict each other, it seems that one or the other but not both can be true. When is a fact not a fact?

Procedure

1. **What does a dictionary say?**

So, what is a fact? Look up a definition of "fact" in one or more dictionaries. Do they make sense to you?

Do you think there are different kinds of facts? If so, give an example of each kind.

Now look up "idea." What is the difference between an "idea" and a "fact"? Do the definitions help you answer the question "What is a fact?" Write down your thoughts.

2. **Ideas, facts, and thinking.**
We have been playing a bit loosely with "facts," with "right" and "wrong" answers, and with calculations in this Chapter. Why? Because thinking, learning, and science are rarely black and white. Like most things, they include lots of gray, lots of nuance, lots of "sort ofs," as well as facts, right and wrong answers, and highly precise calculations. But you have probably heard more about those latter things than the former ones. And although all are important, sometimes people focus on "right" and "wrong" and lose sight of the thinking, or they get too casual and lose sight of accuracy.

We especially do not want to lose sight of the thinking. Indeed, we are interested in all the above, and we have tried to design this curriculum accordingly. In fact, we believe all are necessary for good learning (thinking) and good science. (Mostly, we hope this curriculum will interest you in facts, ideas, and science, and how they all intersect.)

Now a question.

3. **Feelings about facts.**
How do you feel about facts and uncertainty? What describes your feelings about "knowing" or "not knowing"? Are those feelings any different since the class discussed various groupings in Exploration 1?

Some people dislike things not being black and white, or feel uncomfortable asking questions, or just want a straight answer, please! Others love puzzles, ambiguity, answering a question with more questions. No feelings are right or wrong—they simply are different, and it is useful to know your own reactions. Knowing your feelings will help you be a more self-aware, and thus a more successful, thinker and learner. If you feel uncomfortable with puzzles and like a lot of structure, try to work with students who have the opposite reactions. If you view Fermi calculations as a license to go wild, try to work with someone who has a more restrained attitude.

CLASSROOM VIGNETTES

This dialogue about Exploration 1 illustrates both the good results and frequent false starts that happen in thoughtful conversation.

About the Exploration "Groupings: Plants, Animals, and Others"

Students made various groupings, including these, with the organisms listed in Exploration 1:

- whether or not they are animals
- whether they are "close to my house"
- something that has to do with trees (earthworm in the soil under the tree, bird in it, etc.)
- things that live in the ground
- animals that are associated with Australia
- pests to humans
- four or more legs
- microscopic
- how some of the organisms interact (A student drew a diagram.)
- chordates
- birds
- insects (The student put millipedes in this group. When the teacher asked if anyone had any questions about that, the student herself answered that millipedes have too many legs to be insects.)

In-Class Discussion of the Homework

SER: Earthworms are mollusks.

TEACHER: They are?

RM: They're annelids.

RB: I just got a lot more stuff that lives in the ground (bushes, termites, prairie dogs).

S: Animals that have tails.

TEACHER: What do you notice about people's groupings?

[A few students say there are both similarities and differences.]

[Teacher points out that all the ways they came up with worked. "It's not as if there's just one right answer. That's what makes science interesting. There are lots of ways to look at something."]

TEACHER: If you take the same list and group them ecologically, how would you do that?

[M, P, and RB work together; S, RM, and SER work together.]

RB: How do you divide something into ecological relationships?

SER: Places they live.

S: Relationships.

RM: How they fit together on the food chain.

M: I think we should do something like an interaction.

RB: I agree.

M: Because you have loads of things that live together. We need interactions. If you think of just stuff that lives together, but they may not interact. It's a chain reaction.

TEACHER: There are some things on the list that are in Australia and live in other places as well. You could do a combination of things that live in Australia plus generic things.

> [The teacher is (too?) eager to have students move ahead and so "gives" them a specific approach rather than letting them continue the discussion until they find one themselves.]
>
> [What follows is a conversation among M, P, and RB about which animals interact.]

M: Do we want to do something with Australia?

RB: No.

M: Why don't we narrow it down to things that live in the desert?

RB: Can't we just put stuff that interact, but it has nothing to do with where they live?

P: Something about oxygen and plants.

M: Rabbits eat grass and bushes.

P: I'm creating my own. When you want an opinion, just tell me.

RB: Where does the tree come in?

P: I have grass, rabbit, tree.

M: What do owls eat?

> [M is drawing a picture of an owl in a tree.]

P: What good is that? Besides being a home for the owl, what good is the tree? The earthworm and owl pellets fertilize the tree and the tree releases oxygen.

RB: Shall I put the earthworm in? What do fungi eat?

P: Smaller microscopic organisms. Good bacteria help the tree grow.

RB: Fungi live in the ground and provide things to the tree and eat the bacteria. Are we allowed to use our biology book?

TEACHER: Of course

M: Do foxes climb trees?

> [This group is having trouble collaborating—all three students are working on their own pieces of paper. It is a good idea to stress collaboration and suggest that the members of each group work on one large piece of paper, preferably large enough to present to the class later so recopying everything on the board is not necessary. Or groups could work on transparencies to be projected on an overhead projector later for all to see.]

RB: Do fungi eat owl pellets?

TEACHER: Sure. There are different kinds of fungi, and some live on owl pellets.

RB: I want to get a complete cycle.

P: For a complete cycle, we need a complete set of organisms.

> [Teacher suggests that this group get together more, look over each other's work, and try to come up with one version.]

RB: What do earthworms eat?

[Having reference materials around is useful for this session. Students should feel free to use each other, the teacher, and other references to get the information they need.]

M: How did the fox die? Bacteria?
RB: Are there any fleas living on the fox?
P: Now it's starting to sound like a story.
RB: We can turn it into a song but keep adding on more organisms. What can we put in the fox's stomach?

[The idea of stories is a good one to help students both organize the information and share it. It probably won't appeal to all students, but it is worth suggesting as an effective way to talk about information.]

P: What's a badger?

[RB starts to look it up in her biology book.]

P: Maybe a fox is a vegetarian.

[The teacher asks them to go on to Exploration 2.]

RB: What direction would you have arrows going?

[RB hands her drawing to M, who starts to put some arrows in place.]

[The teacher suggests that each group put its drawings on the board and tells the students not to worry about doing this artistically. Once each group has put a drawing up, the class discussion begins.]

TEACHER: How does energy get into the system?
SER AND M: The sun.
P: So you'd have to add sun. Where would the arrow go?
RB: To the bunny.
P: To the bunny?
S: To the plants.
TEACHER: So the sun is what powers all the relationships. You'd also need water. What else?

[The conversation continues until the session ends. The students leave the room still discussing their ideas.]

Getting Hooked through Fieldwork

Chapter Two

Contents

Introduction

As described in User's Guide (pg. ix), the study of ecology should include close acquaintance with various habitats and some organisms, preferably in their natural surroundings. Nothing can substitute for such direct study, familiarity, and knowledge. Here, students begin connecting their in-class study with observations of some local area(s). This work makes two major points: first, ecology "is" everywhere and can be studied everywhere and, second, asking questions is the beginning of doing science.

The Technique you use to make those two key points is dubbed "21 Questions to Conclusions." It is used widely to introduce ecology students at all levels to the process of doing science and to a field site. It is deceptively simple; its power lies in allowing students to experience the reality that science is a process no more mysterious than asking questions and making and testing predictions. It gets students to raise questions, make predictions, and design ways of testing their predictions, of collecting and analyzing data, and of drawing conclusions.

The Technique can be used as a discussion tool about the process of doing research, or, in its entirety, it can be used to design, develop, and carry out a research project (of any duration).

The full version of the Technique perfectly encapsulates the process of research, without fanfare, jargon, or complication. That means it can also be used in the classroom about various topics or repeatedly in new field sites. Part of its success is that it differs substantially from any previous experience most students have had with "doing science," so—please—try to resist changing it.

Exploration 1 (the first field trip) is designed to introduce students to whatever local habitat is available, in a double period (although it can take more time, if you have it).

Exploration 2 (which is not in the student chapter) is intended to help you set up long or longer-term research projects at the same or another field site and to involve students in more systematic data collection. Projects can be of various durations—a series of 1-hour projects; projects that can be carried out over time, 1 hour at a time (e.g., per week); or long-term monitoring of various sorts (e.g., air or water quality, changes in plant growth or regrowth, seasonal changes in an urban landscape).

KEY CONCEPTS

- Ecology is everywhere—in urban, suburban, rural, and wild areas.
- Students can experience doing science in a fresh and engaging way, via the **Technique: 21 Questions to Conclusions**. This Technique perfectly encapsulates the research process and is a powerful conceptual and enabling experience for learners of all ages.
- Asking questions is an essential step in doing science. It does not mean you are dumb—it means you are thinking.
- Students can do actual research under apparently limited circumstances inside and outside the classroom.
- Students are far more likely to pursue and carry out a project that grows out of their own questions and ideas.

MATERIALS AND PREPARATION

In Advance

- Visit the site before the class trip and become familiar with its topography and components. You may find it helpful to bring a naturalist or an ecologist of some sort—ideally, someone who can help you identify different habitats, organisms, and ecological dynamics at work. See also References.
- Read the **Technique: 21 Questions to Conclusions**. Practice it with friends, colleagues, or ecologists if you can.

Safety

WARNING
Before the field trip, visit the site and note possible safety issues, such as broken glass, abandoned buildings or wells, cliffs, hornets' nests, and plants such as poison ivy or poison oak.

WARNING
Before the field trip, determine whether any of your students has a strong allergic reaction to plants or insect bites or stings (especially bee stings). Take precautions as necessary.

WARNING
Use the buddy system. Although students do the first part of this Exploration individually, remind them to remain in sight of someone else from the group, so they neither get lost nor are ever actually alone.

Materials

- **Time:** For Exploration 1 allow an hour in the field.

Per student:

- **Exploration 1: Your Local Site: Ecology Is Everywhere**
- **Paper and a surface to write on**
- **Pencil** (best for fieldwork, since it will not "run" if it gets damp)

You need:

- **Technique: 21 Questions to Conclusions**
- **Time:** (Plan accordingly for Exploration 2 or skip it altogether if you do not expect to do more fieldwork.)

SUGGESTED SEQUENCE OF SESSIONS (3–5)

Class Session 1

The class goes to a field site, and students work individually to compile a list of 21 questions about the site and the organisms on it. If there is time, the group discusses some of the questions at the site.

Homework

Case Study: Confessions of a Terrified Science Learner

Class Session 2

Discussion of the homework, especially how asking questions affects student work.

Students continue to share their field questions in a class discussion and to add questions that arise from hearing and talking about each other's questions.

If students will be doing field-based or related research, group their general questions by topic or area of work in a class discussion and let students choose a question group to pursue in teams of two to five.

Class Session 3

Continue Session 2, if appropriate. Students begin research or prepare for research.

Homework

Read Excerpt: The Having of Wonderful Ideas.

Class Session 4

Continuing discussion of asking questions and how to do science, including the Excerpt, the Case Study, and the **Technique: 21 Questions to Conclusions.**

Integration

This worksheet can also be used to get students started on their research projects.

Class Session 5

Continue previous session, if appropriate.

SESSION GUIDES, BY WORKSHEET

EXPLORATION 1 GUIDE
Your Local Site: Ecology Is Everywhere

Your work here has two parts: facilitating the process of asking and answering questions and facilitating thinking about ecology. Whether you work in your schoolyard or go somewhere less influenced by humans, you will find much to study—ant or pigeon behavior, distribution and frequency of native and introduced weeds, intertidal organisms, whether or how similar species (bird, squirrel, mouse, plant, etc.) compete or share the habitat, how isolated organisms or populations reproduce and disperse their young, and so on.

If you feel unfamiliar with the field site, preview it with a naturalist or an ecologist to help you see things and discuss ecological concepts. Read local guides. But remember that no one knows "all" about that or any site. Indeed, part of what makes such fieldwork interesting for you as well as your students is that you will be learning with them. It is important, however, to have some ideas about what you might see there, to help students think about some of their questions.

For the technique, see the **Technique: 21 Questions to Conclusions.**

CASE STUDY GUIDE
Confessions of a Terrified Science Learner

The Case Study continues to lay groundwork for students to think analytically. It raises issues about asking questions: why questions are often discouraged and why questions are essential for learning, especially in science.

The most important part of this Case Study, as with the Excerpt and the Technique, is actually your reaction. How do you, as a teacher, feel about student questions?

Questions Are KEY

Part of this curriculum's philosophy and approach is that questions are a key tool in thinking, learning, and especially doing science. While that may seem an obvious and laudable goal, it is not necessarily supported by the culture at large. As a teacher, you likely have encountered a parent or an authority figure who thinks that students asking questions is "lip" or disrespectful. Or that it is okay to ask questions about some things ("Is this the right answer?") but not about others ("Why do we go to church?"). It also tends to be true that a person who starts asking questions gets into the habit of asking questions, of thinking, and of analyzing things, and will also ask about topics other than those formally being studied. Not everyone is comfortable with that.

Your Feelings

So, how do you feel about student questions? Do they make you anxious because you may not know "the answer"? What if you tried the approach that you and your students are learners together? While you may have more background or information to offer, that certainly does not mean you do or should know everything. Together you and they can discover things. Part of true learning is figuring out how to ask and how to answer questions. You model half of this process—asking questions—anytime you do not know about something. So you are helping your students learn even when you cannot answer their questions, by showing them what to do with questions. You are helping them do science.

We have heard comments like the following from numerous teachers who let students ask more questions and take more of a leading role in the class.

> [About students doing "canned" lab activities] "I realized that they were just following directions. They didn't know what they were doing or why. And they didn't care. Now 50% of my labs are based on student questions. It's not much, but it's a start. And they're much more involved. They care."

"We [she and co-teachers] wish we had listened to students before. We've learned from them."

The Cat Food Analogy

As one high school principal said, "Teaching is like buying cat food: the consumer is not the shopper." Students are the learners, but they have little input to what they get to learn. When they ask questions, they become more involved, they stay involved, they work more and harder, and they come to enjoy their learning because it is self-reinforcing.

EXPLORATION 2 GUIDE
More Research—What, How Much, How Long

Ecology is a vast and complex domain about which we know very little. The list of issues, organisms, interactions, concepts that are unstudied far exceeds the list of those studied. And even what we do "know" is often only superficially or poorly known.

Two key factors contribute to our ignorance: the complexity of the natural world and the fact that many ecological processes take place in a time frame longer than that of most research studies. A master's program is just 1 or 2 years and often requires no research; a Ph.D. research project typically runs 3 to 5 years; a postdoctoral project might be 1 to 3 years. Yet biological or abiotic cycles can be far longer than any of those. How many generations of a tree species or the 17-year cicada can be encompassed in a researcher's lifetime? How many cycles of drought or high snowfall? The complexity of the natural world will begin to reveal itself as we work through this curriculum.

Short Term/Long Term

Research can be carried out on many time scales, from a few minutes to lifetimes. How you choose to work with your students might depend on external factors, like the distance to your site (behind the school vs. some miles by car), scheduling (rare vs. frequent double periods or project days), and your supervisor's attitude about the importance of research. Obviously, it depends on your interest and willingness as well.

Teachers we know have incorporated research into their classes in various ways. Some have focused on frequent short projects, inside or outside the classroom. Others have mixed short (1-hour) projects with longer (several hours a week for several weeks) projects. And a few have gone to the max. One team designed a 6-year project to be carried out by one class from their 7th through 12th grade years. Another designated 10th grade as the "ecology research year" and spent it studying many aspects of the natural world right by their (rural) school.

So consider whether you and your students are interested in a longer-term research project—from a month to a study that crosses years of students and is handed along to the next class. Maybe start small and expand as you feel comfortable.

Topics

But really, what would you do? Well, any of the questions that come out of Exploration 1 could be the starting point for a study. More broadly speaking, there is also a great need for careful natural history observation. When do the migrating birds come and go? Does it vary from year to year? Why might that be? Which native annual plants are thriving, and which are doing less well? Is it competition, invasion by nonnative species, increased average temperatures, effects of increased CO_2, or pollution? How might those effects be separated out from each other?

Start with a time frame within which you can work. Consider questions that can be studied in that time frame. Make predictions and test them by comparing different sites, different seasons, different years—or even by bringing your own predictions into the laboratory and testing them experimentally.

A Long-Term Research Site

Long-term research at a single site is rare and a valuable data source. A school is an excellent home for such a site, although different students might be involved each year. With some standardization of data collection and techniques, the site and studies can go on indefinitely.

Should you choose this route, realize that you have great latitude in what you study. Be sure to include questions that also give short-term answers and satisfaction. This term's students need to get some gratification from the work even if they cannot see, say, a full year in the life of a salamander.

Background Data

Whatever the duration of your research, you need to know things about your site, but you do not necessarily have to collect the information all yourself. A good picture of (parts of) your site can be assembled using the following: Climate data (average monthly precipitation, monthly temperatures, first and last frost); land-use data (how is the site used now? How has it been used in the past? How might that influence which organisms are or are not present?); and species inventory (which plant, animal, and other species live here now? How do they interact? What are their lifestyles and what does that tell you about the site?). Some or all such data might be available from your county extension office, newspaper, weather bureau, nature center, or conservation office.

One basic starting point

One way to begin is by cataloguing all the organisms that live on the site and build on that. In a paved schoolyard, you will find different species than in a lawn, park, or wooded area. Why? What can you learn about the site from the organism and vice versa?

Such close inspection of a site is similar to doing 21 Questions, and will likely also end you up with an armful of interesting questions.

Science Background discusses some important principles in ecology, to help you focus on possible research topics. Please see also the **Technique: Introduction to Research** (especially the first part) and the end of the **Technique: 21 Questions to Conclusions.**

INTEGRATION GUIDE

Turning Questions into Predictions

The Integration gets students to implement many steps of doing science, without calling it that. Students simply build on their interest in a particular (burning) question and end by designing a piece of research. They turn that burning question into a prediction, into a hypothesis (and alternate hypotheses), and (if they carry out the research) even some interpretation and conclusions.

For more on turning a question into a research project, see the **Technique: Introduction to Research**. It may give you fresh insights into parallels between what students are doing here and the process of doing science.

And if students actually carry out the projects they have designed with their Integration, how much the better!

INTEGRATION
Turning Questions into Predictions

After the fieldwork, we have lots of questions. Pick one that particularly interests you (or your group) and try to figure out how to go about answering it. The steps below might help you in this figuring. If any seem not to apply, skip them until later or discuss them with your group or the teacher.

Materials

- **Questions from Exploration 1**

Procedure

1. **Choosing a question.**
   My burning question from our field site is (or what I am going to find out is):

2. **Relevant background.**
   What I already know about this topic is:

3. **Expectations.**
   What I think will happen (turn out) is:

   I think this will happen because:

4. **Other possible influences.**
The following things might influence my data:

To keep track of their effects, I will:

5. **Research materials.**
The equipment I need is:

6. **Comparisons.**
If I am making some comparison, this table shows what I will change and what I will keep the same.

(Use the rest of this worksheet if you actually carry out the research you have suggested in order to answer your question. Answer these questions on a page in your notebook.)

7. **Results.**
What happened during my research or experiment?

8. **Expectations revisited.**
Is it different from what I thought would happen?

9. **What does my work mean?**
What have I found that I did not know before? Even if my work did not turn out as I expected, I learned:

SCIENCE BACKGROUND
Some Key Principles in Ecology

Ecology is a complex and multidisciplinary science. It is everywhere and includes, touches on, requires, many other topics or disciplines. Like the rest of the world, its principles are governed by the laws of thermodynamics. That means that at some levels ecology can be derived from first principles. It also includes more complex interactions, some of which can be explained by genetics, evolution, and natural selection. It includes patterns and interactions that we do not understand at all and probably others we do not even see or know about. What follows are a few broad concepts or principles about which we have some understanding.

THE LAWS OF THERMODYNAMICS

At all levels, from within organisms to global cycles, the flow of energy and matter follows the laws of thermodynamics. Matter (like carbon and nitrogen) cycles, while energy moves in one direction and is "lost." Biological systems are also inefficient at energy transfer; energy is lost (as heat) during every chemical reaction (energy transfer).

EVOLUTION BY NATURAL SELECTION AND GENETIC CONSTRAINTS

An organism has a family tree and a genetic background, which both limit a species (an ostrich cannot act like a mosquito) and provide variation among individuals so they are affected differently by their environment. Some individuals are more or less well suited to their current conditions and thus will survive more or less successfully (experience selection). (In **Module 1** we see that finches with beaks of a given size survive under one set of conditions but die under different conditions 3 years later.) Evolution represents the outcome of natural selection over time. Many studies focus on how evolution is "at work" under particular conditions.

SIZE AND SCALE IN TIME AND SPACE

For an organism, size is more or less genetically defined. It also determines which physical processes influence an organism. For example, organisms smaller than a dragonfly are affected by surface tension and air currents, not gravity; for a giraffe, the reverse is true. In terms of ecosystems, the concept of scale can be applied to many things. At what scale are we considering research? Are we studying an individual, a population, a species, many species? And over what time period might such a study need to be pursued? Time is obviously another scale issue.

Do we want to know how a thing looks right now, or at each season, or across years? How did this forest look 500 years ago? How will it look 500 years from now?

LIMITING RESOURCES

At various levels, there usually are some limiting resources. A plant might grow larger if it had more sunlight, water, nutrients, and space. A species might be more successful if it had more food, less predation, and less competition. A community might have more species if they were more specialized and thus less in competition.

UNUSED RESOURCES

It is also true that there can be resources not used by any species, which creates an apparent vacancy in a community.

INTERACTIONS

Given all the preceding factors and more, ecology focuses on interactions—within, among, between. Competition among individuals of a species and between species for water, nutrients, space, mates (within a species). Predation by species on others. Mating. Reproduction. Offspring surviving to reproduce. Dispersing those offspring. Interaction between the physical environment and organisms—how populations of a species that live in two places can differ. Mutualism. Parasitism. We understand little about many of these interactions, and all need further study.

ECOSYSTEMS ARE DYNAMIC

Not only are there interactions and interaction among interactions, they change with time and because of disturbances. Recently, human disturbances have become especially important, since the number of humans is so large and the land area rather small. How do humans affect ecosystems?

ECOSYSTEMS ARE SYSTEMS

Systems principles apply to ecosystems as to other systems. They are dynamic, have pools, flows, and reservoirs; they can be modeled and studied. What we learn about them might be applied to other systems, just as what we learn about other systems might apply to ecosystems.

EXCERPT GUIDE

"The Having of Wonderful Ideas"

This Excerpt tends to shock or excite readers, teachers as well as students. Its most striking points are that a student came up with a solution that had not occurred to the teacher (students tend to love this). And even more wonderful, the teacher listens to the student and lets him proceed—even though to do so he breaks a lightbulb.

Students can find the idea of open-ended exploration exciting, empowering, and scary. Their reactions will help you work with them most effectively—whether that means calming fears, encouraging independence, whatever. Your own reaction is also important. Can you freely listen to your students and genuinely hear what they say? Can you make space for real exploration, not just expected answers?

REFERENCES

Begon, Michael, John L. Harper, and Colin Townsend. 1990. Ecology: Individuals, Populations, and Communities. Boston: Blackwell Scientific Publications. 943 pp.

Biological Science: An Ecological Approach. 1987. BSCS Green Version. Dubuque, Iowa: Kendall/Hunt Publishing Company. 1,024 pp.

Duckworth, Eleanor. 1987. "The Having of Wonderful Ideas" and Other Essays on Teaching and Learning. New York: Teachers College Press, Columbia University. pp. 5–7.

Martin, Paul, and Patrick Bateson. 1993. Measuring Behavior: An Introductory Guide, 2nd ed. New York: Cambridge University Press. 222 pp.

Rezendes, Paul. 1992. Tracking and the Art of Seeing: How to Read Animal Tracks and Signs. Charlotte, Vt.: Camden House Publishing. 320 pp.

Smith, Robert Leo. 1990. Ecology and Field Biology. New York: HarperCollins. 1,001 pp.

———. 1990. Student Resource Manual to Accompany Ecology and Field Biology, 4th ed. New York: HarperCollins.

Weiner, Jacob. 1995. "On the Practice of Ecology." Journal of Ecology, 83: 153–158.

Wilson, Edward O. 1992. The Diversity of Life. New York: W. W. Norton. 536 pp.

How Organisms (except Plants) Acquire and Use Energy

Unit 2

How Organisms (Except Plants) Acquire and Use Energy

Unit 2 Overview

How Organisms (Except Plants) Acquire and Use Energy

This Unit considers energy at the level of whole organisms, especially animals, as well as at the level of bonds and biochemicals. Specifically, it considers energy use by individual animals and by groups (populations) for various species of animals. It also considers the energy that one organism makes available to another or that "flows" from one organism to another, such as when one animal eats a second animal or its dung. Finally, the complete picture of energy use and flow for a whole ecosystem—that is, for all the organisms that live together in a given place—is the sum of these movements of energy within and between individual organisms. That means that a good picture of the total energy flow can be obtained by adding up all those individual energy flows—although doing that is, in fact, more complex than what we will undertake here.

This Unit raises questions such as

- How much energy does an organism require?
- How does an organism use or expend that energy?
- How and why do different animals expend energy differently?
- How does energy move or "flow" through (the organisms of) an ecosystem?
- How can changes in population size affect energy flow from one species to another?
- What roles do detritivores and decomposers play in carbon cycling and energy flow?
- How does energy flow relate to carbon cycling in a system?
- What are the major reservoirs of carbon and energy in an ecosystem?

Students explore these questions through detailed study of energy budgets for various organisms from two ecosystems: a tropical grassland (the Serengeti in East Africa) and a temperate forest (the Northern Hardwood Forest). These energy budgets can be described by a brief equation called the **energy use equation** or the **balanced energy use equation**, which accounts for all the energy that moves through an organism per unit of time. The equation is

$$\mathbf{I = A + E}$$

where

I = **I**ntake of food, or food eaten
A = **A**bsorption, the part of the food that is digested
E = **E**xcretion (dung), the undigested remainder of the food

The energy that is absorbed, **A**, is used by the animal in two ways,

P = **P**roduction of tissue (growth, fat, offspring), or

R = metabolic or cellular **R**espiration

So, **A = P + R**, and the fuller, more detailed version of the equation is

$$\mathbf{I = P + R + E}$$

Typically, terms of this equation are described in units of energy, especially kilocalories (kcal), for a given weight of animal over a given amount of time. Depending on context, these units can be expressed as kilocalories per gram (kcal/g) per hour or other interval, up to kcal per animal per year, or even per lifetime.

The **R** term reflects energy used for respiration, which is eventually transformed to heat, a form of energy not usable by other organisms in the ecosystem. In contrast, the other terms (**E** and **P**) represent energy that either is not absorbed by the animal being studied and is thus directly available to other organisms as food (**E**) or is incorporated by the animal into new tissue (**P**) and is thus potentially available to other organisms, as they parasitise the animal, prey on it, eat its body, or eat the young it produces.

Because this powerful equation includes even the energy that is used by organisms themselves, it actually underlies all study of energy flow in an ecosystem. For that reason, it is the central focus of this Unit.

Students examine the terms of this equation in detail. In **Chapter 1** they consider Intake generally, focusing on how mammal teeth and skulls reflect the foods eaten by these mammals. Then students explore how they use the energy in foods they themselves eat (**Chapter 2**). This prepares them to consider how other organisms use, or allocate, their energy as individuals. Students work alone or in pairs, one per organism, and use data provided on the **Animal Cards** to construct energy budgets for animals from the two ecosystems, the Northern Hardwoods and the Serengeti (**Chapters 3** and **4**). (Each half of the class will study one ecosystem and its organisms.) Students consider terms of the energy use equation, exploring how an individual uses its energy absolutely (**Chapter 6**, respiration or **R**; **Chapter 7**, production or **P**). Students also compare animals to understand how differences in diet and body size affect relative food intake (**Chapters 4** and **5**).

Then students step back from looking at individual energy use to examine both molecular aspects of food quality, and to examine the energy animals make available to others in typical ecological interactions such as predation, excretion, scavenging, and decomposition. They carry out accurate, inexpensive measurements of calorie and carbon contents of various foods to understand how energy is stored, released, and transformed in different carbon bonds (**Chapters 8** and **9**). Then students examine ecological processes. They construct and analyze simplified food chains (**Chapter 10**); they explore energy transfer across the links of those chains, such as through predation; and they consider whether and how disturbance at one link affects other links (**Chapters 10–11**). Students also project from these simplified food chains to the whole grassland and woodland ecosystems. They compare these ecosystem-level patterns of energy flow to find striking similarities and differences between grassland and woodland (**Chapter 10**).

Connection with Other Units

The **Evolution Module** also considers getting and using energy, especially how abiotic (physical) factors affect success of individuals and competition among individuals. **Unit 3, How Plants Capture and Allocate Energy**, directly parallels this Unit, although the "balanced energy budget" for plants is analogous rather than identical to the balanced energy use equation for nonphotosynthesizers.

Similarly, the concept of a balanced intake/use equation can be applied to water (**Module 3, Water**), although rigorous research comparable to that on carbon and energy flows has yet to be done.

How the Chapters in This Unit Connect

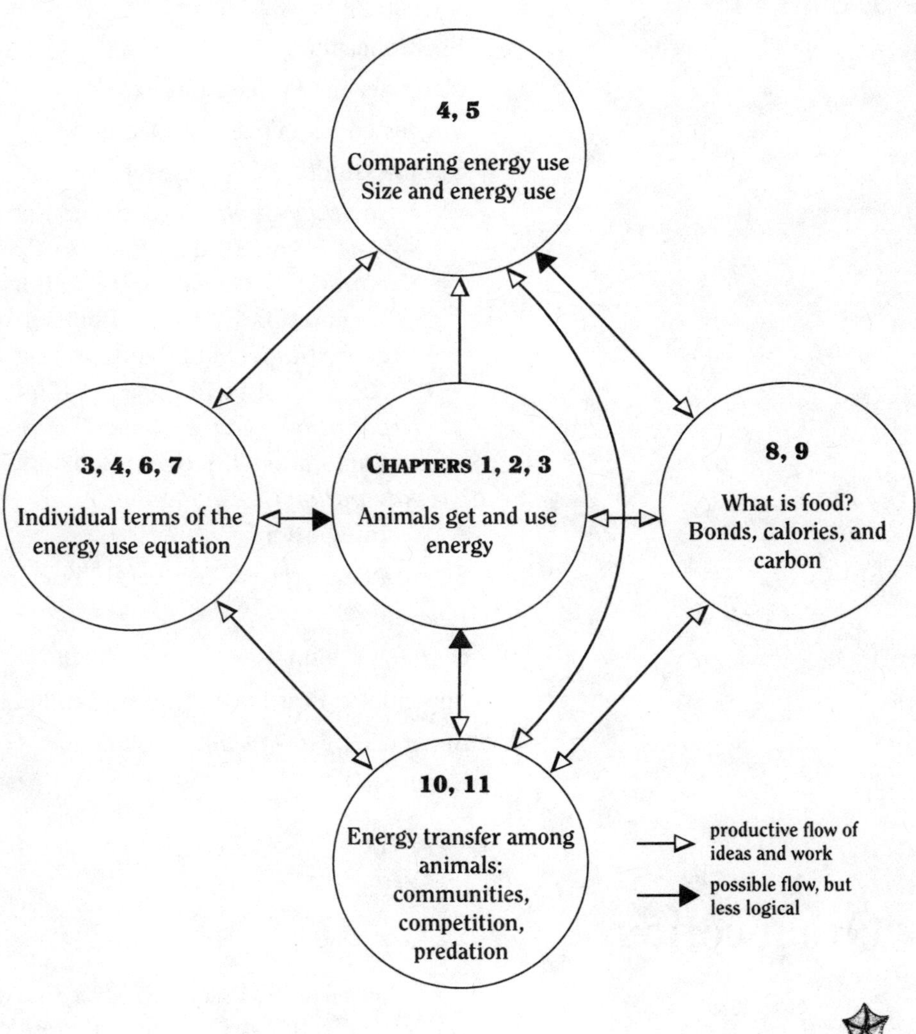

Bony Skulls
How Animals Acquire Energy

Chapter One

Contents

Introduction

Animal skulls and teeth come in a wonderful diversity of shapes, sizes, and specializations. They can be considered from several perspectives. We first consider "whatever"—that is, whatever students decide in their groupings of skulls. Then using those groupings, we focus more specifically on functional aspects of the skulls. How does a skull "work"? What do its form and teeth indicate about the lifestyle of the animal? What kinds of foods does the animal likely eat? Why? Does it chew or just tear off and swallow those foods? How can we know? Is smell or vision important for the animal?

Why? Yet another aspect of skulls is a taxonomic rather than a functional approach. Who is related to whom? How can we tell from skulls? Indeed, can we tell?

The skull is the part of the skeleton that encloses the brain; holds special sense organs for sight, hearing, smell, and taste; and forms feeding structures. Most animals actually take hold of and take in their food with these structures, which include jaws, teeth, palate, and teethlike structures. Within this broad definition, there is also considerable variety.

KEY CONCEPTS

- Getting or acquiring energy is a primary reason for eating, and nearly all animals must acquire energy by some sort of feeding behavior. This need to eat has important ecological consequences for the organism itself and for other organisms (it may eat them; they may eat it).
- Only plants and a few microorganisms can acquire energy from nonliving sources (namely, from the sun and from sulfur compounds, respectively).
- For organisms with heads, the size and shape of the head, skull, and teeth reflect much about the feeding behavior of the organism (as well as about the animal's general size and shape and even whether animals are ecologically similar or actually related).
- By examining and comparing a group of bony (vertebrate) skulls or photos of skulls, we can get a vivid sense of those animals, especially how they get food (and thus energy). This is a key aspect of an animal's ecology—of "how it makes a living" (as you remember from the **Evolution Module**).

MATERIALS AND PREPARATION

- **Skull sets**: 3 sets of skull photo cards, 2 copies of each set for up to 6 groups of students. Notice that skulls are uniquely identified by a letter and number; the list of numbered names is in the **Session Guide**. A simplified taxonomy ("family tree") is also there. (NHF means Northern Hardwood Forest; SEU, Serengeti Ecological Unit; dom., domesticated; herbi., herbivore; carni., carnivore; omni., omnivore; scav., scavenger.)

	SET A	SET B	SET C
Carnivores	bobcat (NHF) serval (SEU) jackal (SEU) wild dog (SEU) housecat (dom.)	lion (SEU) housecat (NHF) wolf (NHF) mongoose (SEU) dog (dom.) shorttail shrew (NHF)	leopard (SEU) caracal (SEU) bat-eared fox (SEU) shorttail weasel (NHF)

CONTINUED

	SET A	SET B	SET C
Scavengers/ omnivores	gray fox (NHF)	hyena (SEU)	raccoon (NHF) pig (dom.)
Herbivores	Eastern cottontail (NHF) wildebeest (SEU) impala (SEU) horse (dom.)	rock hyrax (SEU) Thomson's gazelle (SEU) giraffe (SEU) sheep (dom.)	deer mouse (NHF) white-tail deer (NHF) zebra (SEU) cow (dom.) muskrat (NHF)
WILD CARDS			
Marsupials	opossum (scav.)	opossum (scav.)	opossum (scav.)
Other	otter (carni.) vole (herbi.) human (omni.) skunk (omni.)	aardwolf (carni.) seal (carni.) gorilla (herbi.)	vervet monkey (herbi., omni.) beaver (herbi.) fruit bat (omni.)

- **Rulers** (flexible ones if students get into measuring skull volumes).
- **Appropriate field guide(s)**, anatomy books, atlas of mammals. You must have something with skull photos and illustrations for both the North American and East African mammals, preferably more than one copy of each. An atlas or similar book, such as MacDonald, Estes, and others (see References), will provide additional ecological and taxonomic data. For obvious reasons, you may have more difficulty finding pictures of the East African (Serengeti) mammal skulls. Fortunately, this is not a serious problem, since many skulls are unmistakable by family, no matter which species they are. So have students use the books of North American mammals to identify skulls to family, identify the species from the master list, and then do their research on the ecology of that particular species using the more general books.
- **Integration worksheets.** There are 5 different teeth. Make a copy of the worksheet text for each tooth picture and then enough copies of each pair of pages so that each student gets a picture and a page of text.
- **Skulls master list.** Make a copy for each student, so they have the names of all the skull photos in their text. Do not hand this out before the appropriate work in Exploration 2.
- OPTIONAL: If you have actual skulls, use dental carbon paper from your dentist to demonstrate how upper and lower teeth move "by" each other. (Dentists use such paper to check whether your upper and lower teeth match properly.)

SUGGESTED SEQUENCE OF SESSIONS (4–7)

Homework

Case Study: Feeding and Eating

Class Session 1

Discuss homework questions briefly; use them to introduce the topic. Working in teams of three to five, students group skull photos however they choose (Exploration 1: Grouping Bony Skulls).

Teams with identical photo sets briefly discuss their results with each other and try to come to a consensus.

Class Session 2

Teams present their groupings and rationale to the class, for a discussion of groupings and reasoning involved. This can carry over into the next session.

Homework

Reading: Skulls and Feeding

Class Session 3

Continue the discussion from Class Session 2, if appropriate.

Exploration 2: Name That Animal. Building on student observations, pose questions about tooth function and animal food types and lifestyle. Each student tries to identify one skull, to taxonomic family or general ecological group (carnivore, herbivore), using field guides and other references. Once a student has made serious efforts to identify the taxonomy of a skull, let him or her match the skull number to the animal name. With the animal name, students assemble information on the foods, lifestyle, and general ecology of the animal. (They may also reconsider their groupings and try to work out new relationships in light of new information.) This session can carry over to the next session.

Class Session 4

Continue work from Class Session 3, if appropriate.

Students individually integrate and write up what they have learned about their animal and about skulls in general, using all the information they have acquired. (Collect these writings for assessment if you want.)

Integration

This can also be a Homework; if so, move on to Class Session 5.

Class Session 5

Continue work from Class Session 4 and from Integration, with discussion if appropriate OR

Collect Integration for your independent reading and comments.

SESSION GUIDES, BY WORKSHEET

CASE STUDY GUIDE
Feeding and Eating

Begin by considering the questions from the Homework (Case Study: Feeding and Eating).

Nearly every living thing is eaten by some other living thing(s). And except for plants, nearly every living things eats other things. Why?

(To get energy, which is necessary for life.)

Do you remember how plants get their energy? How do plants and other creatures differ in their way of getting energy?

(Plants use energy from the sun, biochemically "fixing" energy in carbon-containing compounds through the process of photosynthesis. Nearly all other creatures must obtain energy by eating, either plants or other animals.)

EXPLORATION 1 GUIDE
Grouping Bony Skulls

Depending on your class size, ask students to work in teams of 2 to 5 per set of skull photo cards. There are 3 sets of 15 different skulls, with 2 copies of each set. That way there can be up to 6 teams of 5 students, and pairs of teams with identical skull sets can discuss their groupings. If you have some real skulls, you might want to keep them in a central location or give each team some time with them.

Ask students to group the skull photos into as many groupings as they need and to be able to explain how and on what criteria they chose those groupings. Ask them also to keep a list of questions that come up as they work. These questions can be raised during a wind-up discussion at the end of this session, and some of them will be answered through the work of the next Exploration. Some will require library or book work, as with the materials suggested.

Note that some skulls may be missing a tooth or have cracks. No animals were killed to obtain these photos. All these skulls are museum specimens, including zoo animals that died of age or illness.

Possible Groupings

Students may group the skulls in any of various creative ways. As with the **Groupings** work in **Unit 1**, this opener is to get students thinking as broadly as possible about the materials. They may quickly skirt the lack of focus and immediately move onto function, or they may be more "playful."

Groupings can be by size, superficial appearance, tooth shape or size, gaps in the teeth, number of incisors, and combinations of these characteristics. One group of learners came up with 19 attributes of their skulls (using real skulls) in about 10 minutes and then ignored all but three attributes for their actual grouping. They used incisor number, general tooth type, and general skull shape. They also had two skulls left over, that is, skulls they could not fit into their scheme and which they dubbed "aliens" (one was an armadillo, the other a turtle).

Size is often a grouping criterion. While animals of a given size can eat very different foods, in fact, same-size animals do have some ecological similarities. For example, as students will discover later (**Chapter 5**), small animals need to eat proportionately more than large ones. A small animal has a disproportionately greater surface area than does a large one, loses heat much faster, and must eat more to compensate for the heat loss.

Have teams with identical sets briefly discuss their results with each other.

Then have each team explain its grouping to the class, with the criteria it used. There may be disagreement among teams about placement of particular skulls: How and why did each team make its choice(s)? How can the differences be resolved? What does any group of skulls share? What might that feature or characteristic mean, functionally?

Possible Discussion and Questions

Questions from the class discussion might include:

Why are these animals a group/or not a group?

Are these animals related?

(Some are; check the phylogenies included below.)

What do they eat?

Are any skulls fake?

(None in our photos.)

Are any fossils?

(None in our photos.)

Are any of the skulls from babies?

(None in our photos.)

What is the purpose of the ridges or crests on some skulls?

(Crests increase the area of bone available for muscle attachment, and thus usually indicate considerable muscle strength along the area served by the crest. Gorilla or opossum skulls are good examples. Do not mistake a cheekbone for a crest!)

Do curvy long incisors and pointy canines have the same function?

(No.)

How does skull size relate to body size?

(Fairly consistently. That is, in vertebrates, heads tend to be in proportion to the rest of the body. Exceptions can include species in which the two sexes differ in overall size. Sometimes males are larger and/or have relatively larger heads [e.g., gorillas and various catlike animals such as housecats and lions]; sometimes females are larger [most lemurs]).

Do animals have different tongues?

(Different in what way? Ask students who have been licked by a cat or a dog how those tongues felt. All sizes of cats, or felids, have rough tongues, perhaps because they tend to open their prey by rasping skin away; they also groom themselves a great deal. Dogs, or canids, tend to have smooth tongues, perhaps because they tear open their prey. Some herbivores, such as giraffes and deer, have very agile tongues because as browsers they must manipulate twigs and leaves.)

See Classroom Vignettes.

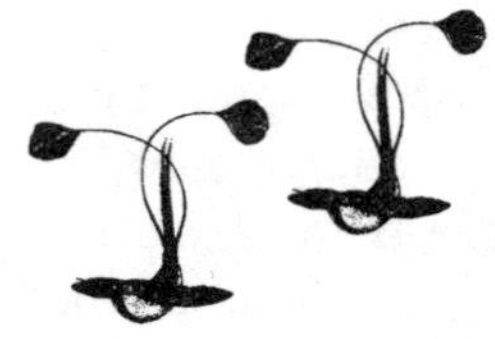

READING GUIDE
Skulls and Feeding

Students' thoughts about who eats what and how are articulated and amplified by this piece. It can coalesce their thinking about their skull groupings and about how skulls function. It also helps prepare students for the more detailed consideration of their specimens in Exploration 2.

EXPLORATION 2 GUIDE
Name That Animal

Students may have grouped skulls by size, similarity of shape, or similarity of teeth. Shape or tooth similarity likely reflects similarity in lifestyle of those animals, especially what and/or how they acquire what they eat. Such ecological similarity does not, however, necessarily reflect relatedness or taxonomic similarity. Now ask each student to take one skull and try to find its relatives. That is, using whatever the students have been thinking and the field guides, "family trees," and other materials available, can each student key out or roughly identify the skull—that is, can the student differentiate catlike skulls from doglike skulls from deerlike skulls, and so on?

Skull ID

Once a student has made a serious effort at placing a skull into the proper taxonomic family, let her match the skull ID numbers with the master list to find the skull's name. Looking up the name, the student can now find out more about the animal and how much of the team's thinking had been accurate and why. Let students write a paragraph or more about their skull, its ecology, and its place in the original grouping. See also the phylogenies under Science Background for a quick overview of how vertebrates are related.

Ecology and Taxonomy

Students may wonder about the relationship between ecology and taxonomy, so it may be fruitful to have a class discussion about that topic.

Animals not closely related but ecologically similar have evolved independently. That is, they have evolved independently of each other and have "come up with" similar solutions to ecological "problems"—or, as we have been putting it, with similar ways of "making a living." Such animals nicely illustrate a particular form of evolution by natural selection, which is called convergent evolution. Because those animals have evolved in similar habitats, they have converged on similar ways of "responding" to those habitats in their lifestyles, including evolution of their shape, the shape of their teeth or skulls, or whatever body parts are especially important to that lifestyle. One vivid example is that of the ostrich, the emu, and the rhea. These large (6-plus feet tall) flightless birds are only distantly related (they are all birds), but they look remarkably similar and share many aspects of their ecology. Yet they have evolved independently in the grasslands of three different—and distant—continents, namely, Africa, Australia, and South America, respectively.

Skull Comparisons

Now that students know which animals the skulls represent and something about the ecology of those animals, they can make comparisons among skulls. They may even want to rework their initial grouping. For example, within a skull group with similar teeth, such as herbivores, notice the relative delicacy and potential fragility of similar-size skulls. Although you cannot compare actual weight from photos, just consider mass. Grazers (grass eaters) have far more massive skull bones than do browsers (which eat leaves, bark, and various plant parts)—compare the deer or the giraffe with the cow or the sheep. Why might this be so, given their respective diets? What might skull size imply about the size of the rest of the animal?

Consider primate skulls, especially those of arboreal (tree-living) and ground-dwelling primates, such as the capuchin monkey and the gorilla, respectively. Where might you expect huge primates to live? Might a large heavy skull be an advantage or a drawback in the trees? Why? (See also the Reading.)

INTEGRATION GUIDE
Mystery Tooth

Give each student a copy of the Integration Worksheet and a copy of one of the five tooth pictures. Ask students to work alone. What do they think the animal eats? Why?

The teeth are molars from (1) an elephant, (2) a shrew, (3) a seal, (4) a bear, and (5) a cheetah. The worksheets show the typical shape and cutting surface of the molars of a herbivore (elephant), an omnivore (bear), a specialist that uses its teeth for grabbing rather than chewing (seal), a specialist that uses its molars for shearing (cheetah), and a carnivore eating mostly invertebrates (shrew).

Trying to work out jaw size and possible animal size, students may want to reuse their original team photo sets for comparisons. This can be a problem if the Integration is used as a Homework assignment, although students may be able to refer to their sketches as well.

Other work that can serve well as student or teacher assessment for this Chapter include the initial groupings, the paragraph each student prepares about his or her animal, and the group presentations of the groupings and the rationale for those groupings.

SKULLS MASTER LIST

NORTHERN HARDWOOD FOREST

DIDELPHIDAE
A1, B1, C1 opossum
(Didelphis virginianus)

SORICIDAE
B2 shorttail shrew *(Blarina brevicauda)*

CANIDAE
B3 timber wolf *(Canis lupus)*
A3 gray fox *(Urocyon cinereoargenteus)*

MUSTELIDAE
C2 shorttail weasel *(Mustela erminea)*
A4 river otter *(Lutra canadensis)*

PROCYONIDAE
C3 raccoon *(Procyon lotor)*

FELIDAE
A6, B4 housecat *(Felis domesticus)*
A5 bobcat *(Lynx rufus)*

CERVIDAE
C4 whitetail deer
(Odocoileus virginianus)

LEPORIDAE
A2 Eastern cottontail *(Sylvilagus floridanus)*

SERENGETI ECOLOGICAL UNIT

CERCOPITHECIDAE
C9 vervet monkey
(Cercopithecus aethiopis)

CANIDAE
A7 jackal *(Canis mesomelas)*
A8 wild dog *(Lycaon pictus)*
C5 bat-eared fox *(Otocyon pictus)*

MUSTELIDAE
B5 mongoose *(Herpestes ichneumon)*

HYAEDINAE
B6 spotted hyena *(Crocuta crocuta)*
B7 aardwolf *(Proteles cristatus)*

FELIDAE
A9 serval cat *(Felis serval)*
C6 caracal *(Lynx caracal)*
C7 leopard *(Panthera pardus)*
B8 lion *(Panthera leo)*

PROCAVIIDAE
B9 rock hyrax *(Procavi johnstoni)*

EQUIDAE
C8 zebra *(Equus burchelli)*

GIRAFFIDAE
B10 giraffe *(Giraffa camelopardalis)*

BOVIDAE
A10 wildebeest *(Connochaetes taurinus)*
A11 impala *(Aepyceros melampus)*
B11 Thomson's gazelle
(Gazella thomsoni)

DOMESTICS/WILD CARDS

PONGIDAE
B12 gorilla *(Gorilla gorilla)*

HOMINIDAE
A12 human *(Homo sapiens)*

CHIROPTERA
C10 fruit bat *(Pteropus sp.)*

CANIDAE
B13 dog *(Canis familiaris)*

MUSTELIDAE
A13 striped skunk *(Mephitis mephitis)*

FELIDAE
A6, B4 housecat *(Felis domesticus)*

PHOCIDAE
B14 harbor seal *(Phoca vitulina)*

EQUIDAE
A15 horse *(Equus caballus)*

SUIDAE
C11 pig *(Sus scrofa)*

BOVIDAE
B15 sheep *(Ovis aries)*
C12 cow *(Bos taurus)*

CASTORIDAE
C13 beaver *(Castor canadensis)*

MURIDAE
C14 deer mouse
(Peromyscus maniculatus)
A14 vole *(Microtus pennsylvanicus)*
C15 muskrat *(Ondatra zibethica)*

INTEGRATION
Mystery Tooth

The tooth pictured is actual size. It is a molar from a currently existing (not extinct) mammal species. What does the beast eat? Why do you say that?

As you have seen, most mammals have several molars in a row in their jaws. Given the length and the width of this molar (which you can measure from the picture) and knowing that there usually are several molars, what is a reasonable minimum length of that jaw?

Does that give you any ideas about what the animal might be? Can you check your idea using any of the reference materials?

Some other students have the same picture. Share your ideas with them and see if anyone has other thoughts. Are they helpful to you?

Check your "dietary diagnosis" for your photo with the teacher's master list. If you thought something different, why? What do you think now? Do you see where the difference comes from?

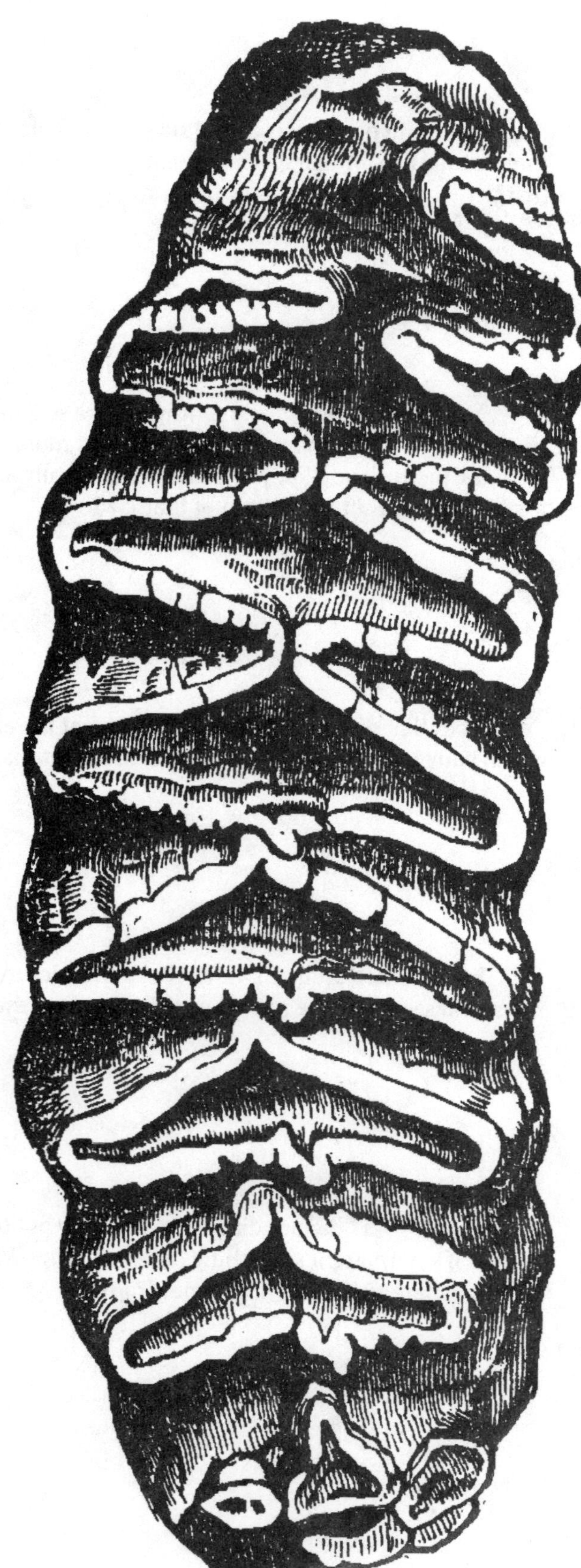

1.

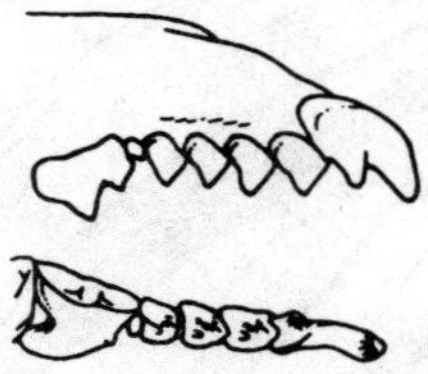

Magnified 3X Life Size

2.

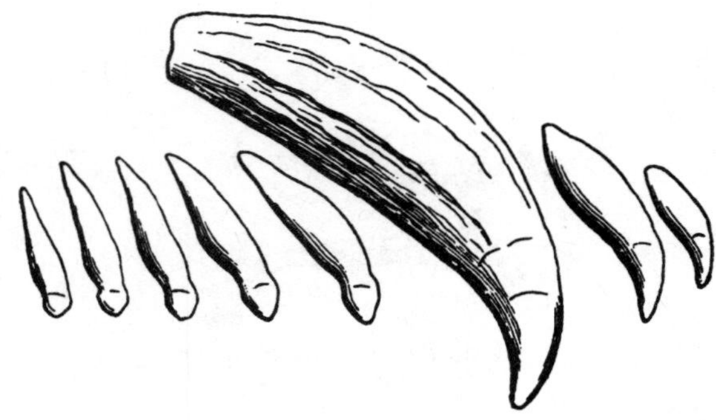

3.

4.

TOP VIEW

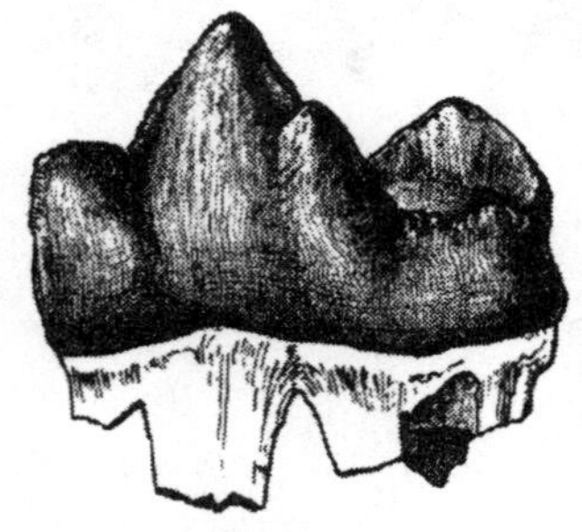

SIDE VIEW

5.

SCIENCE BACKGROUND
Teeth and Taxonomy

GENERAL ASPECTS OF SKULLS

Functionally, the most obvious and important pieces of a skull are the braincase and the jaws, including the separable lower jaw. These pieces are involved in many functions key to an animal's survival, especially taking in food and sensing the world. Observing a skull, we can ask many questions. Is the braincase fully closed, as in most mammals, or open, as in some reptiles? Where are the nostrils? If we peer into the nostrils, how much bony matrix is available to support smelling tissue? Are the eyeholes (sockets) large or small? Are they fully enclosed by bone and look like teacups lying on their sides, or are they open, like a cylinder or a teacup on its side and missing its bottom? What about bony ridges or crests, where muscles attach, for greater jaw leverage, which thereby increases jaw "crunch" pressure?

Things to Note about Skulls

1. General shape (round, long, etc.).
2. General size and what that implies about the size of the animal.
3. Sturdiness and bone thickness and what that implies about skull fragility, weight, and the likely heftiness of the animal attached to that skull.
4. Find the eyeholes, mouth, and place where the skull is attached to the backbone. Can you tell from the shape of the skull attachment whether the animal walks upright (bipedally), on all four (quadrupedally), or a mix? Why?
5. Is the skull smooth? Or does it have large protuberances, crests, ridges, cavities? What do they suggest? Compare the skull with a picture of the flesh-covered head.
6. How large is the enclosed part of the skull compared to the snout or jaws? How might that affect the animal's head shape? Make comparative sketches.
7. Where might the animal need strong muscles to make the shape of its jaw or head work?

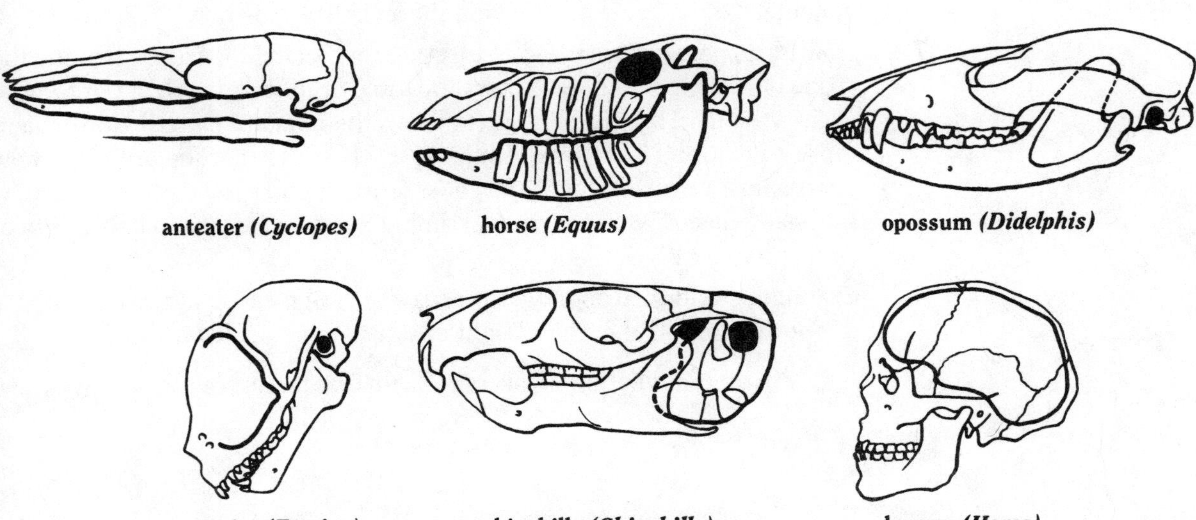

anteater *(Cyclopes)* horse *(Equus)* opossum *(Didelphis)*

tarsier *(Tarsius)* chinchilla *(Chinchilla)* human *(Homo)*

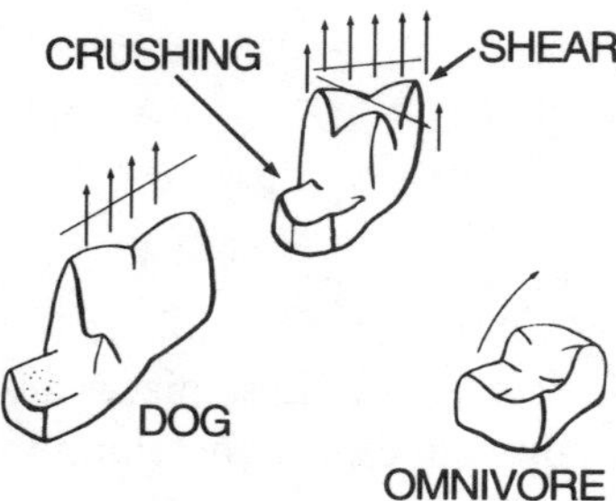

Tooth Shape and Function

The tooth or dentition literature is full of names for every crest, ridge, valley, and cone in teeth. Here are some simplified schema for tooth shape. Tooth shape affects how food is gathered and processed. There are four basic types of teeth among vertebrates: for crushing (typically for more omnivorous diets), for grinding (plant diets), for shearing (wholly carnivorous diets), and for piercing or catching (somewhat carnivorous diets). Animals with mixed diets also tend to have a mix of teeth. For example, the opossum, skunk, and human have canines for piercing and holding food as well as molars for crushing foods. Cats of all sorts, in contrast, have only piercing and shearing teeth and do not chew their food at all. They catch and kill it, then "cut off" pieces, which they swallow whole. Cats are the most wholly carnivorous land animals. Seals have mostly piercing teeth, a row of pegs with which to catch and hold fish, which they then swallow whole. Plant eaters (muskrat, cow, horse, deer), especially grass eaters, have teeth with lots of ridges, with which they grind the plant material.

Things to Note about Teeth and Jaws

1. The shape of the teeth, including whether there is a complete row of teeth or any gaps. From the inside and looking down onto the teeth tops, how many different shapes? Sizes? Gaps or absence of teeth?
2. Whether teeth are ever-growing.
3. The surface of the teeth when you look straight down at them.
4. How the teeth meet, that is, placement of tooth gaps in one jaw relative to the other. Is a gap in the lower jaw met by a matching gap in the upper jaw?
5. Similarity or lack thereof in size, shape, or number of teeth between upper and lower jaws. Also, placental mammals have four incisors, while marsupials, such as the opossum, have six.
6. Note the difference between shearing teeth, especially in cats, and side teeth of doglike animals versus grating teeth (the large-surfaced, flat-topped teeth of the herbivores) versus generalized crushing teeth (hind teeth of doglike animals, pigs, humans). If you have actual skulls, a nice way to study **occlusion**, or how teeth meet, is by gently closing the jaws on a piece of dental carbon paper and moving the lower jaw sideways.
7. How the upper and lower jaws fit together (or "occlude"). Are the size and the shape of the upper and lower jaws the same or different (e.g., a tighter or a wider V or U)? How do teeth meet when the jaws are closed? Do the jaws move only up and down or also sideways? What does that suggest about how the organism treats its food? How does any particular jaw motion affect how the teeth meet? What might this imply about types of food this animal could process? Why?
8. Examine specifically how the lower jaw is snuggled up against the upper jaw or the skull. Is the "joint" tight or loose? What could that mean?

For an examination of jaw movement and force, see the Extensions.

TAXONOMIC RELATIONSHIPS AMONG MAMMALS

The class Mammalia, or mammals, includes ecologically very different animals. Their hierarchical relationships to each other are presented here in table form and with a few illustrations of phylogenies, or "family trees." Students can use this information to help place their species, to discover more about each species' family and its typical characteristics, and to see how species are related to each other.

We use the standard hierarchy and names as established by Linnaeus and used ever since. (Remember the mnemonic King Philip Can Ordinarily Find Gray Socks—for Kingdom, Phylum, Class, Order, Family, Genus, Species.) Here we include Class, Family, and Species for the animals in our master list. Perhaps have students read about some characteristics of the Order as well as the Family of their species.

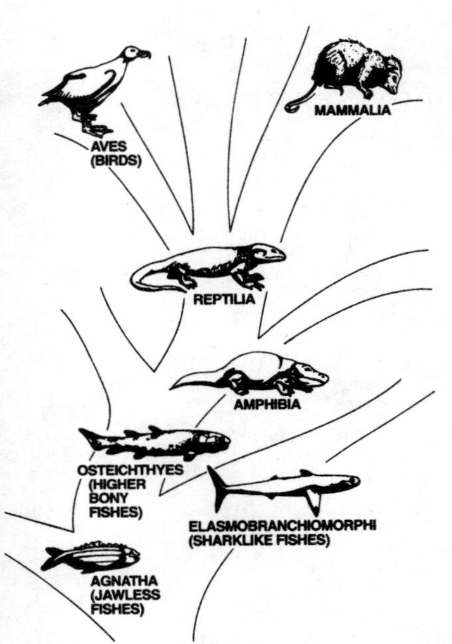

Where do mammals come from evolutionarily?

- Class **Mammalia**
  - Subclass **Metatheria (marsupials)**
    - Order Marsupialia
      - Family Didelphidae
        - *Didelphis marsupialis* (opossum)
  - Subclass **Eutheria (nonmarsupials)**
    - Order Insectivora
      - Family Soricidae
        - *Blarina brevicauda* (shorttail shrew)
    - Order Chiroptera
      - Family Pteropodidae
        - *Pteropus sp.* (fruit-eating bat)
    - Order Primates
      - Family Cercopithecidae
        - *Cercopithecus aethiops* (vervet monkey)
      - Family Pongidae
        - *Gorilla gorilla* (gorilla)
      - Family Hominidae
        - *Homo sapiens* (human)
    - Order Carnivora
      - Family Canidae
        - *Canis mesomelas* (black-backed jackal)
        - *Canis lupus* (timber wolf)
        - *Canis familiaris* (domestic dog)
        - *Otocyon megalotis* (bat-eared fox)
        - *Lycaon pictus* (wild dog)
        - *Urocyon cinereoargenteus* (gray fox)
      - Family Procyonidae
        - *Procyon lotor* (raccoon)
      - Family Mustelidae
        - *Herpestes ichneumon* (gray or Egyptian mongoose)
        - *Mustela erminea* (shorttail weasel)
        - *Lutra canadensis* (river otter)
        - *Mephitis mephitis* (striped skunk)

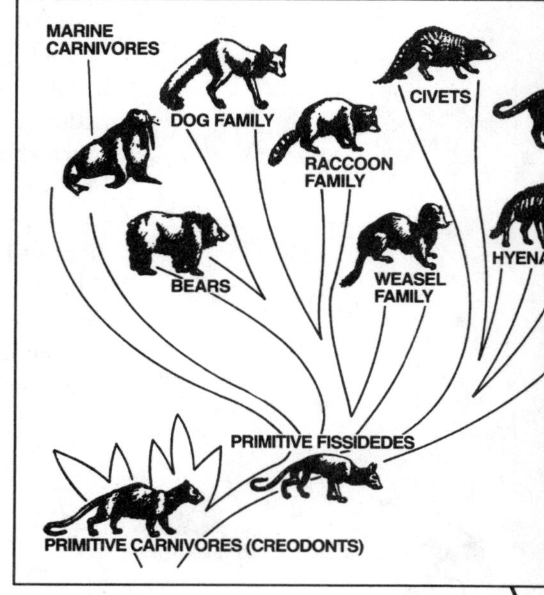
MARINE CARNIVORES
DOG FAMILY
CIVETS
RACCOON FAMILY
BEARS
WEASEL FAMILY
PRIMITIVE FISSIDEDES
PRIMITIVE CARNIVORES (CREODONTS)

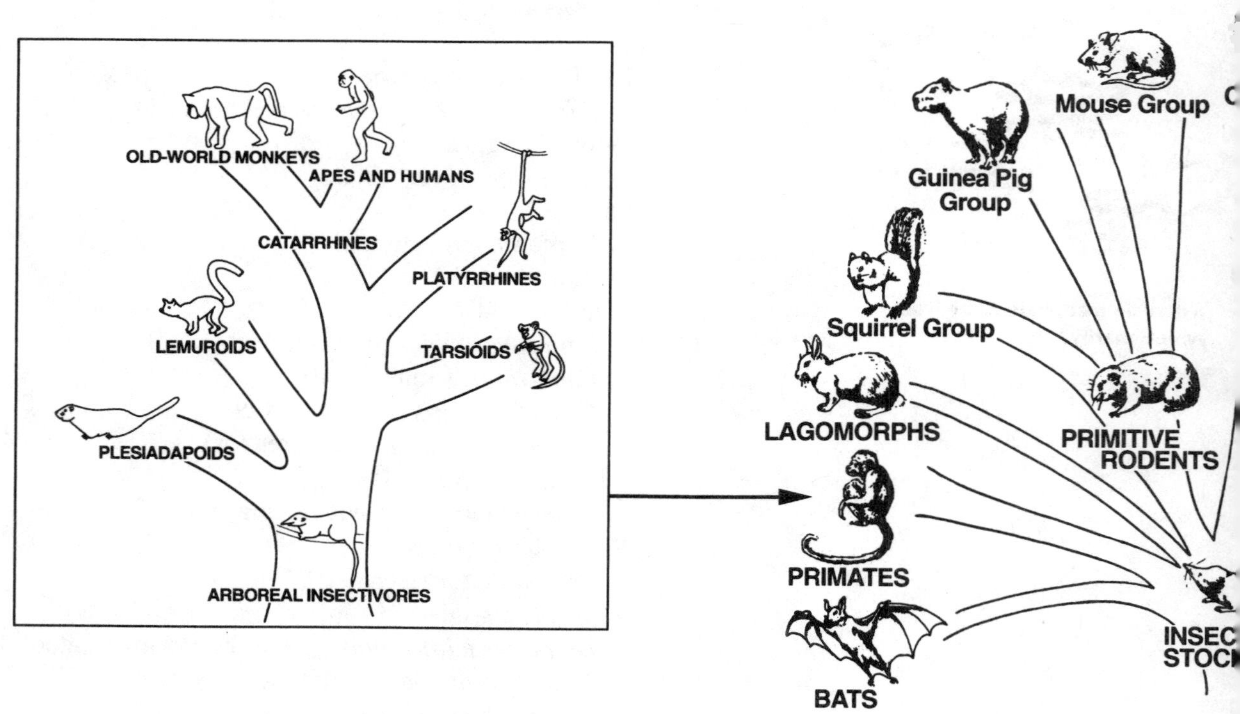
OLD-WORLD MONKEYS
APES AND HUMANS
CATARRHINES
PLATYRRHINES
LEMUROIDS
TARSIOIDS
PLESIADAPOIDS
ARBOREAL INSECTIVORES
Mouse Group
Guinea Pig Group
Squirrel Group
LAGOMORPHS
PRIMITIVE RODENTS
PRIMATES
BATS

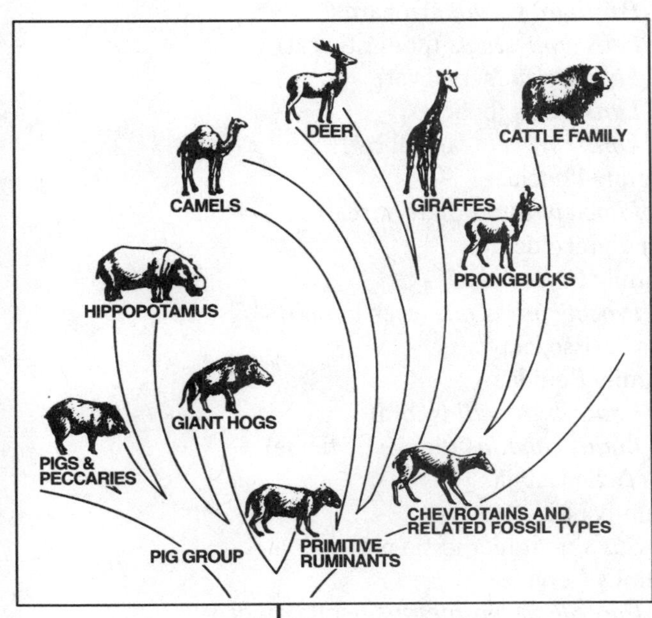
DEER
CATTLE FAMILY
CAMELS
GIRAFFES
PRONGBUCKS
HIPPOPOTAMUS
GIANT HOGS
PIGS & PECCARIES
CHEVROTAINS AND RELATED FOSSIL TYPES
PIG GROUP
PRIMITIVE RUMINANTS

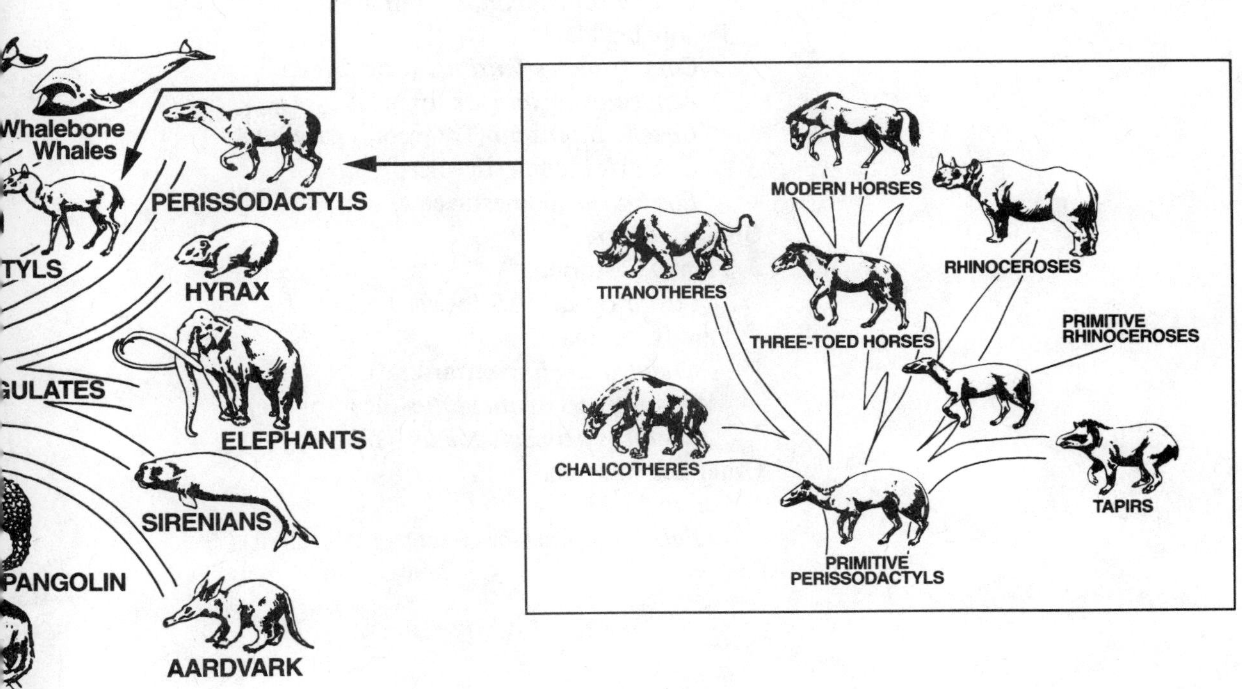
Whalebone Whales
PERISSODACTYLS
TYLS
HYRAX
ULATES
ELEPHANTS
SIRENIANS
PANGOLIN
AARDVARK
TES
MODERN HORSES
RHINOCEROSES
TITANOTHERES
THREE-TOED HORSES
PRIMITIVE RHINOCEROSES
CHALICOTHERES
TAPIRS
PRIMITIVE PERISSODACTYLS

Family Hyaenidae
Crocuta crocuta (spotted hyena)
Proteles cristatus (aardwolf)
Family Felidae
Panthera leo (lion)
Panthera pardus (leopard)
Felis domesticus (domestic cat)
Felis serval (serval cat)
Lynx rufus (bobcat)
Lynx caracal (caracal cat)
Family Phocidae
Phoca vitulina (harbor seal)
Order Hyracoidea
Family Procaviidae
Procavi johnstoni (rock hyrax)
Order Perissodactyla
Family Equidae
Equus burchelli (zebra)
Equus caballus (domestic horse)
Order Artiodactyla
Family Suidae
Sus scrofa (domestic pig)
Family Cervidae
Odocoileus virginianus (whitetail deer)
Family Giraffidae
Giraffa camelopardalis (giraffe)
Family Bovidae
Connochaetes taurinus (wildebeest)
Aepyceros melampus (impala)
Gazella thomsoni (Thomson's gazelle)
Ovis aries (domestic sheep)
Bos taurus (domestic cow)
Order Rodentia
Family Castoridae
Castor canadensis (beaver)
Family Muridae
Ondatra zibethica (muskrat)
Peromyscus maniculatus (deer mouse)
Microtus pennsylvanicus (vole)
Order Lagomorpha
Family Leporidae
Sylvilagus floridanus (cottontail rabbit)

REFERENCES

A combination of these references, or similar ones, is necessary for the work in this chapter. One way to choose is to pick at least one reference from those labeled **A** (North American mammals) and one from **B** (East African mammals). The titles in **boldface** are especially likely to be useful—check for details in the descriptions.

Also helpful, especially for the behavior and ecology of the East African animals, are the Animal Cards from **Chapter 3**.

A Burt, William H., and Richard P. Grosenheider. 1979. Field Guide to Mammals. 3rd ed. New York: Houghton Mifflin Company. 289 pp., paperback.
From the Peterson series of field guides, with illustrations of some animals, skull photos, range maps, and brief information on foods and behavior.

A Deblase, Anthony F., and Robert E. Martin. 1981. A Manual of Mammalogy. Dubuque, IA: Wm. C. Brown. 436 pp., paperback.
Excellent for taxonomy and phylogeny of mammals of the world; many illustrations.

B Dorst, Jean, and P. Dandelot. 1993. Collins Field Guide to Larger Mammals of Africa. New York: HarperCollins. 287 pp.
Illustrations of some animals, range maps, and brief information on foods and behavior. Excellent for ranges, field marks, some behavior, and ecology. No skull illustrations.

B Estes, Richard D. 1991. The Behavior Guide to African Mammals. Berkeley: University of California Press. 611 pp., paperback.
An excellent compendium of behavioral ecology of East African mammals. Well worth having, since it is helpful throughout this curriculum for the Serengeti mammals. Includes many illustrations, line drawings, and range maps, plus details of feeding, social, and reproductive behavior, as well as taxonomy.

A Jones, J. Knox, Jr., and Richard W. Manning. 1992. Illustrated Key to Skulls of Genera of North American Land Mammals. Lubbock, TX: Texas Tech University Press. 75 pp., paperback.
An outstanding key to identifying North American mammal skulls.

B Kingdon, Jonathan. 1989. East African Mammals: An Atlas of Evolution in Africa. Chicago: University of Chicago Press. 7 volumes, paperback.
An outstanding reference work, chock-full of animal, skull, skeleton, and other pictures, glorious illustrations, taxonomy, ecology, social behavior, evolution—everything. Fifteen years in the writing; a delightful, interesting, and useful series from someone who lived in East Africa.

A, B Macdonald, David. 1984. The Encyclopedia of Mammals. New York: Facts on File Publishers. 895 pp.
Social, ecological, and other general behavior; also taxonomy and phylogeny. Little on skulls themselves.

Maynard Smith, John, and R. J. G. Savage. 1959. "The Mechanics of Mammalian Jaws." School Scientific Review, 141 (March): 289–301.

A, B Radinsky, Leonard B. 1987. The Evolution of Vertebrate Design. Chicago: University of Chicago Press. 188 pp., paperback.
An especially readable, text-style book outlining function and shape of vertebrates and their change through evolution. It also includes some dinosaur and fossil data and has excellent line drawings as well as a delightfully nontechnical text.

A, B Romer, Alfred S., and T. S. Parsons. 1986. The Vertebrate Body. 6th ed. New York: Saunders College Publishing. 680 pp.
Detailed story of the development and evolution of the vertebrate body, with exemplary multicolor diagrams and illustrations. Numerous technical names

throughout, but all are explained or grounded with reference to illustrations. Much taxonomy and anatomy. Chapters of special interest may be 2, "The Vertebrate Pedigree"; 3, "Who's Who among the Vertebrates"; 8, "The Skull"; and 11, "Mouth and Pharynx, Teeth . . . ."

A, B Vaughan, Terry A. 1986. Mammalogy. Philadelphia: Saunders. 463 pp.
An excellent source of illustrations of mammal skulls, teeth, and skeletons, as well as some natural history of mammals.

Wake, Marvalee H. (ed.). 1979. Hyman's Comparative Vertebrate Anatomy. 3rd ed. Chicago: University of Chicago Press.
Embryology and evolution of vertebrate anatomy, with excellent illustrations. Especially useful may be Chapter 8, "The Endoskeleton: Comparative Anatomy of the Skull," by H. R. Barghusen and J. A. Hopson.

CLASSROOM VIGNETTES

We saw one team take the following route.

They deliberately set aside all previous knowledge and ignored obvious facts such as the presence in their set of skulls those of a human, some birds, a shark jaw, an opossum, and a horse, among others (eighteeen skulls in all).

They developed a simple grouping rule, based only on the number of rows of teeth. This gave them three groups of skulls: with one, two, and multiple rows of teeth. Most skulls fit into the first group, the skulls with a single row of teeth. The second group had double rows, thus including both the human skull and a pheasant skull. The former appeared to have two rows of teeth: it was a plastic child's skull, with milk teeth fully erupted and in place in the jaws and with the upper gums missing to show the incoming permanent teeth above the milk teeth. The final group contained only the shark jaws and a goose skull, the only skulls that had multiple rows of "teeth."

While their "tooth row" rule gave the students a clean way of organizing their skulls, they had to abandon it once they tried to include other characteristics of the skulls, even such simple ones as size and shape, not to mention tooth type (e.g., goose "teeth" are not teeth at all, while shark teeth are).

APPENDIX 1

Possible Additional Skull Sets

Comparisons depend on the skulls you have available and the points you want to emphasize. Possible sets include ones from the following lists. (Either real skulls or illustrations can be used, although the latter have the disadvantage that students cannot explore the movement of the lower jaw relative to the upper jaw, which tells so much about how an animal chews—or doesn't chew—its food.) In general, it is essential to have enough skulls of a given type that students can make satisfactory groupings—thus, having one herbivore is not sufficient. There should be several grazers and browsers (deer, camel, sheep, cow, horse, zebra, rabbit, woodchuck, mouse, muskrat, beaver, etc.), several carnivores (dog- and catlike animals, bears, wolverines, raccoons), and so on. It's also fun to include a few curve balls, such as armadillo, some birds, snake, turtle, frog, marsupial (opossum), porpoise, walrus, and so on.

1. Terrestrial Mammals

Flesh Eaters, by size and by type of flesh eaten:

a. invertebrate (e.g., insect) eaters: least weasel, shrew, various termite and anteaters such as sloths, pangolins, aardwolf, armadillo
b. vertebrate (bony animal) eaters: cats of all sizes, from domestic cat through ocelot and margey to cheetah, lion, and leopard; canids, or doglike animals, such as dingo, dog, wolf, and coyote; hyena; walrus; seal; otter

Plant Eaters:

a. browsers (leaf eaters): deer, some kangaroos, giraffe, rabbit, moose, hippo, some rodents, woodchuck, beaver, elephant, panda (a special case)
b. grazers (grass eaters): cow, horse, some kangaroos, zebra

Omnivores: raccoon, skunk, pig, opossum, human

2. Aquatic Mammals

Flesh Eaters:

a. invertebrate eaters: sea otter (eats sea urchins), baleen whale (strains water for zooplankton)
b. vertebrate eaters: dolphin, porpoise, whale

Plant Eaters: manatee or dugong

3. Birds by Bill Type

(See one of Roger Tory Peterson's field guides to birds or another excellent field guide to birds)

a. Darwin's finches and their specializations
b. seed eaters (finches)
c. scavengers, such as vultures
d. omnivores: jays, crows, ravens
e. insect feeders: warblers, swallows, hummingbirds (for their young)
f. nectar feeders: hummingbirds, sunbirds
g. filter feeders: flamingos, ducks
h. flesh eaters: hawks (look also at their feet), snail kite (a special example), curlew, gulls, woodpeckers, shrikes

4. Series of Mixed Vertebrates, including

a. bony fishes
b. birds

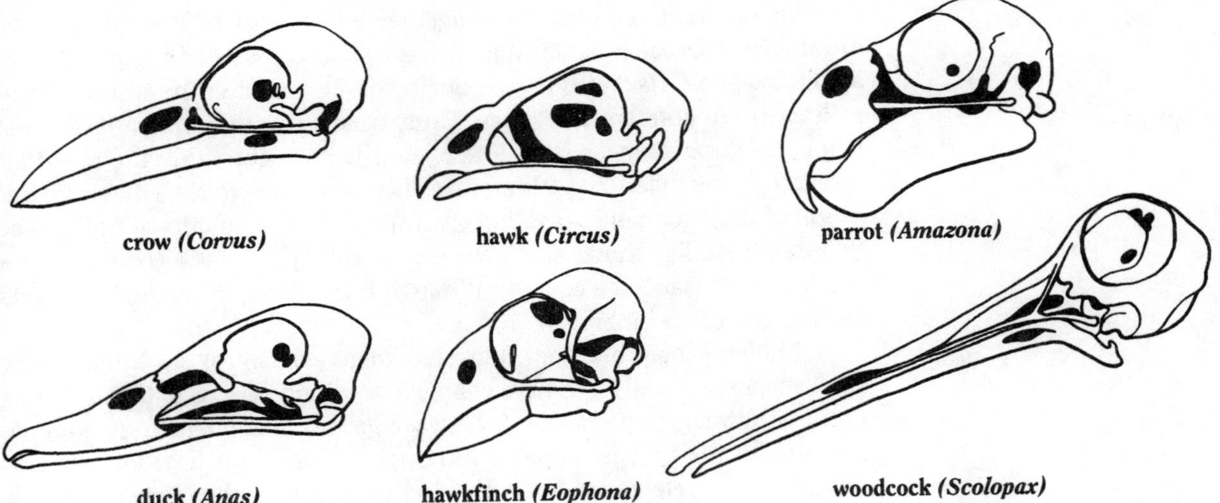

crow *(Corvus)* hawk *(Circus)* parrot *(Amazona)*

duck *(Anas)* hawkfinch *(Eophona)* woodcock *(Scolopax)*

c. amphibians: frogs, toads
d. reptiles: snakes, lizards, turtles
e. mammals

For easy contrast, compare a long-snouted plant eater versus a meat eater (e.g., deer, camel, cow, horse versus wolf, fox, dingo). Note the differences in tooth shape, number, and placement and in jaw fit and movement.

Similarly, compare a short-snouted plant eater versus a meat eater (e.g., a variety of monkeys versus cats).

APPENDIX 2

How to Obtain Skulls

- Check with local zoos, nature centers, museums, and universities, which might lend or donate skulls.
- Prepare skulls from roadkills. Preparation techniques include boiling carcasses or allowing scavengers and decomposers to eat the flesh off them. These include starlings, insects such as ants, microorganisms, or, if you have access to one, a colony of dermestid beetles, an intensely carnivorous beetle kept by museums expressly for cleaning flesh from skeletons.
- Get a grant to buy skulls from a biological supply company.
- Send letters home with all your students or advertise in the school newsletter for people to search their attics and basements for skulls. (You'll be surprised by what skeletons are in the closets!)

EXTENSIONS

Embryology—the study of where and how different skull parts develop—is a fascinating field. A classic reference is Romer and Parsons, 1986 (see References for full citations of texts mentioned here); another one is edited by Wake, the functional anatomy book from which we took the first excerpt. You can get a glimpse of the complexities studied in embryology if you consider the following. In the technical literature, you will see that the names we use are not necessarily those you will read. Although functionally we consider the skull and jaws together, they are, in fact, made up of different types of bony cells. That is, during development of the embryo, different cell types fuse together to form the functional units we are studying. Developmentally, in fact, the skull is the most complex part of a bony skeleton. Its pieces derive, during development of the embryo, from at least three different cell types. Thus, what we consider as a functional whole (braincase, upper jaws, lower jaws) is not necessarily the unit that researchers consider in the literature. They will refer to the embryological origin of skull components rather than simply to the functional unit. Since they serve similar functions, however, we call "jaws" both the "jaw" of a shark and the "jaw" of a cow, even though they develop from different parts of their respective embryos.)

Students may become interested in **phylogeny** or **evolution**—how skull shape, size, and teeth have changed over long periods of time within a group of animals (say, snakes) or between groups of animals (from a reptile ancestor to the first mammals). Although we focus on function, we also include some references for both phylogeny and embryology, especially

Romer and Parsons, Vaughan, Radinsky, and Kingdon.

The basic concepts of tooth function and animal lifestyle can be applied to dinosaurs as well; start with Radinsky.

Physics and **mechanics** describe how design and movement affect where and how much pressure jaws exert (and thus the kinds of foods that can be eaten), shear forces, the use of skull crests, and jaws as levers. This approach works best using real skulls, although basic mechanics and forces can be calculated from illustrations, as shown in the Extension. Such work can be done to compare any of the skull photos and makes an excellent integration with physics or math class. The following, which is summarized from Maynard Smith and Savage, 1954, can be photocopied and handed to students.

EXTENSION
Physics and Mechanics

How does the shape, structure, or mechanical function of an organism's anatomy affect its relationship to other organisms in its ecosystem? This is an important question because variations in measures like the ratio of surface area to volume (or fat distribution) affect the range, diet, behavior, and reproductive strategy of many types of organisms. These behaviors ultimately determine the organism's role in the local ecology. In this extension, we examine how the mechanics and morphology of the lower jaw relate to the trophic level of an organism.

The Reading: Skulls and Feeding introduces some ideas about how herbivore and carnivore jaws are different. Let's take a look at those points using jaw diagrams and force vectors.

These two diagrams show the force vectors of the temporal (T) and masseter (M) muscles and their moment arms (m1 and m2) about the point of articulation.

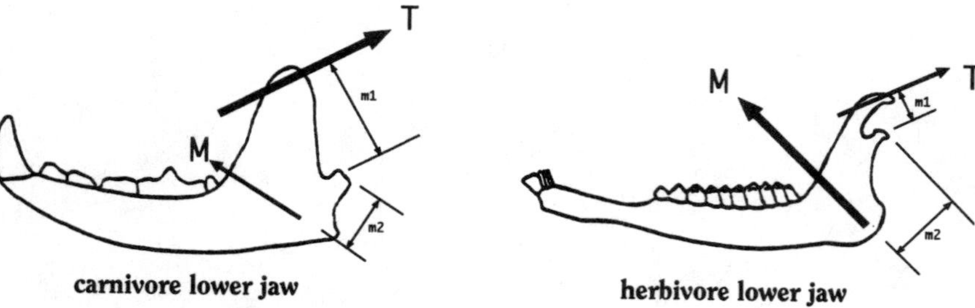

The main differences between the two jaws in the illustration include the following.

For carnivores, the temporal muscle is the main chewing muscle because its line of action is roughly opposed to that of the main load from biting down on prey (i.e., down and away on the front of the lower jaw). Using that muscle minimizes the net force at the joint.

The mechanical advantage of the temporal muscle in carnivores is increased by the relatively large distance between the condoyle and the action of the muscle (m1). For an everyday example, think about how it gets easier to lift a weight with a lever (say, a teeter-totter) as the lifting force is applied farther from the fulcrum.

In herbivores with a lateral chewing movement, the masseter is the main chewing muscle. The masseter muscle pulls the jaw toward the side on which the muscle is attached. Imagine that the force vector M in the diagram actually comes out of the page toward the attachment point on the skull.

The mechanical advantage of the masseter muscle in herbivores is increased by the relatively large m2, resulting from the high condoyle.

In either jaw diagram, it can be shown that if the animal were to use the auxiliary jaw muscle for prehension, the resulting force on the jaw would put considerable strain on the joint or on the jaw itself. Model this or see the referenced article for more information.

What You Eat and How You Spend Energy

Chapter Two

Contents

Introduction

This Chapter focuses on the **I**(ntake) and part of the **R**(espiration) terms of the balanced energy use equation (see **Unit Overview**). In general, we are considering how animals allocate the energy that they absorb from the food they eat. Recall that the energy use equation, **I** = **A** + **E**, can be expanded when we substitute **R** and **P** for **A**(bsorption):

Intake = **R**espiration + **P**roduction + **E**xcretion

Respiration means metabolic respiration, not breathing, and can be a surprising concept for students. They might think that if they are not overtly active, they are not using energy. It is hard to collect energy use data on other animals, so the Explorations use the students themselves as their own study organisms. They compile their own rough energy budget for a day—food intake and energy use or expenditure. They discover that their food intake is greater than their energy use, which sets them up for introduction to the other ways in which energy is used (other terms of the equation). In addition, they examine intake and energy patterns for the class and find some differences.

The basic sequence of events for this Chapter is a discussion of why energy intake and activity data might be related or interesting; how to collect and actually collecting the data; how to analyze and actually analyzing the data; comparing intake and activity numbers; and looking for patterns in each by age, sex, weight, and other factors. The Integration can simply be discussing patterns in the data or doing a full-blown charts-and-posters presentation of the data.

KEY CONCEPTS

- Getting or acquiring energy is a primary reason for eating. The need to eat has important ecological consequences for the organism itself and for other organisms (it may eat them; they may eat it).
- All energy going into and coming out of an organism can be accounted for. The uses or allocation and movement of the food energy in an organism can be described by the energy equation: I = A + E, with A = R + P.
- An animal engages in many kinds of activity (basic metabolism, moving, etc.), all of which require energy. But only some of these activities potentially provide energy as well (hunting, eating). Thus, the organism has finite energy resources.
- All organisms have the same needs (to eat, to reproduce, to survive), but they fill those needs or "make their living" in a great variety of ways.
- Simply being alive—breathing, digesting, sleeping, and so on—requires metabolic energy, so "activity" here means any and all life processes. "Respiration" refers to such metabolic activity and is not the same as breathing.

MATERIALS AND PREPARATION

In Advance

- **Carry out Explorations 1, 2a, and 2b yourself.** Keep your own activity and intake logs, and perform the necessary calculations on your data before class. Your data will expand the range of comparisons, your experiences might intrigue the students, and you will be better able to help them with their own research.

Materials

- **Calculators**
- **Reference materials for converting Intake data into kilocalories.** At least one copy of a good calorie table per group of students. We strongly recommend calorie tables that list prepared foods in the units that people tend to eat (e.g., by the cup, glass, sandwich, serving).
  - The Joy of Cooking has a reasonably complete and easy to use table.
  - The Handbook of the Nutritional Contents of Foods ($9.95, prepared for the U.S. Department of Agriculture and reprinted by Dover Publications, New York) is a superb reference. (It is a reprint of the Composition of Foods, Agriculture Handbook No. 8, which is no longer in print.) The handbook compares the contents of a standard amount, 100 g, of all foods it includes; this standardization enables students to compare caloric values of foods easily and directly. It lists the following information for over 2,400 foods: water content, calories per 100 g, grams of protein, fat, carbohydrate, and ash, as well as mineral and vitamin contents.
  - Various fast food chains provide nutrition information sheets that list caloric contents of their foods, as well as the amount of protein, fat, and carbohydrates.

SUGGESTED SEQUENCE OF SESSIONS (5–8)

Homework

Case Study: Two Lifestyles

Class Sessions 1–2

Discuss differences in the lifestyles of the two animals (Case Study) and the consequences. Start a list of energy intake and uses for the sloth and the penguin; use the list to introduce the topic of different uses.

If time permits, begin Exploration 1: Your Intake and Activity Log: Data Collection. Hand out data sheets (activity and intake logs), discuss issues of data collection, and ask students to consider how they might use such data to learn about themselves and compare themselves to other humans, to older or younger people, to other animals.

Class Sessions 2–3 or 3–4

Students convert their activity and intake data into a common unit, the kilocalorie (Exploration 2a: Your Activity Log: Data Analysis and Exploration 2b: Your Intake Log: Data Analysis). The former includes all necessary information plus a sample analysis; the latter requires reference materials you provide.

Homework

Reading 1: When Is an Activity Not an Activity? raises the idea that metabolic respiration or just being alive is an activity and costs energy.

Class Session 3 or 4

Continue calculations and conversions from above; when ready discuss Homework Reading 1.

Homework

In Reading 2: Energy in Foods: How It Is Stored and How You Get at It, students discover that energy can change form but is never "lost," and that such form changes are inefficient.

Class Session 5

Discuss Homework Reading 2, especially what was unexpected for students and what this has to do with ecology.

Class Sessions 6–7

Groups analyze and interpret their data with Exploration 3 (Class): Patterns in Intake and Activity Data. The class considers general patterns.

Class Sessions 7–8

Groups prepare formal presentations of some aspect of their results and present them to the class, using the **Technique: Preparing a Presentation**.

SESSION GUIDES, BY WORKSHEET

CASE STUDY GUIDE
Two Lifestyles

Herewith are some natural history and ideas that are important for your discussion. Both sloths and penguins are endotherms, which means they spend a considerable amount of energy maintaining a constant core body temperature by means of metabolic respiration. Clearly this presents different challenges in the Antarctic and the equatorial rain forest! Aside from being endotherms, the two creatures could hardly be more different in digestive system, reproduction, and general lifestyle. (And, of course, one is a mammal and the other a bird.)

The Emperor Penguin

The emperor penguin divides its year between nesting inland for several months and feeding at sea the rest of the time. During the breeding season, the penguin rarely eats and thus runs on an "energy deficit." It spends more kilocalories than it takes in and loses weight—lots of weight. Penguins can do this because during the other half of the year they eat much more (take in much more energy) than they require and store the extra as fat. Fat is an excellent tissue for energy storage because of its high carbon content and molecular structure (as we will see in **Chapter 8, Food Quality: Carbon and Energy Content**). The food penguins eat—fish—is highly concentrated, full of energy-rich fat and easily digested protein. That means a high proportion of Intake is Absorbed, so penguins can engage in efficient and high-intensity feeding.

The Sloth

The three-toed sloth, on the other hand, lives amid its food the whole year round. It eats leaves, which are not full of fat or protein—and thus not full of energy. Leaves also take a long time to digest, because they have lots of cellulose (what we call roughage). Overall, the sloth's diet does not allow the sort of highly efficient energy intake and fat assimilation allowed by the penguin's diet. Does that mean the sloth is "worse off" than the penguin? No, not at all. Each animal has evolved and is adapted for a very different way of "making a living."

Differences

Both the penguin and the sloth eat, maintain a constant body temperature, mate, have young, and care for those young. But they do those things in completely different ways, and each does them in a way that is internally consistent and suited to its environment. Penguins live in the cold; need lots of energy to thermoregulate and fast during reproduction; eat a very high-energy diet; have the teeth and digestive system for this diet; and have lots of fat, both for insulation and as energy reserves.

The sloth lives in a warm climate; can thermoregulate with far less energy (and moves in and out of the sun to help itself keep a constant body temperature); eats; can digest; and can live on energy-poor foods, for which it has appropriately specialized teeth and digestive system. It also moves relatively little and slowly, because it has little energy and because that way it also needs little energy.

Questions

Students may wonder: "Which came first: moving slowly or eating low-energy food; eating high-energy foods or living in Antarctica?" Good questions, which cannot be answered, at least not directly. But sloths are good at being sloths. Eating low-energy foods may seem a disadvantage, but the specific plants sloths eat are not eaten by many other animals. So a possible advantage may be lack of competition for food. By moving slowly, sloths also need less energy than they would otherwise, so they need less food. Penguins, by contrast, need lots of food and also must be much more active in order to catch so many fish. They are good at being penguins. Neither animal could survive in the other's habitat; each is well adapted to be where and what it is.

We will see over and over what we saw in the **Evolution Module** and now with these two animals. While all organisms have the same needs, they meet them in different ways and have a whole integrated set of characteristics with which to meet those needs—from digestive system, speed of movement, metabolic rate, and behavior to body size and shape, number of young, rate of reproduction, and even life span.

EXPLORATION 1 GUIDE
Your Intake and Activity Log: Data Collection

After discussing the Case Study, pass out intake and activity logs and have students read Exploration 1 or just discuss it with them. Exploration 1 is about two key aspects of being alive: energy intake and some ways that energy is used. Explain to the students that they are going to use themselves as subjects of observation, learn how one might calculate the amount of energy expended by an animal, and compare that expenditure with the animal's energy (food) intake. What must an animal eat to survive, and how does it use or divide up that energy intake?

Issues to raise with students before they begin data collection include why they are doing this; the purpose of the Exploration; how to collect the data; what defines activity; and using themselves as research subjects. Once students have read the Worksheet, consider with them ways they might pool the class data, that is, patterns they might look for and how they might use the additional data on weight, height, height last year, shoe size, age, and sex.

Do they have any predictions about intake patterns? (Taller or heavier people or someone involved with a sport may eat more; those not showing a growth spurt in height from last year may eat less.) Put the predictions on the board for future references.

Substituting Research Subjects

Students may be self-conscious about their own weight or food intake data. Let them substitute data from another person. This will certainly serve the same general purpose and may raise some interesting comparisons. For example, if the substitute person is an infant or an adult, several patterns may be quite different from those of the class as a whole, for example, food intake, amount of time spent active, and change in weight or height from a year ago. This allows for some discussion of differences among different individuals in their energy use and activities. Think briefly about infants versus young versus adults of, say, housecats or birds or fish.

The Data

You will know, if you have done this Exploration yourself, that the results do not permit construction of an energy use equation. The results include Intake and part of Respiration. The discussion guide to Exploration 3 helps draw out students about the life processes represented by other terms of the equation. Thus, by the time they get to the next chapter, they will already have a feel for those terms.

You will also know that various quantities for which you collected data were not exact (e.g., amount of time spent on an activity; amount of some food you ate).

Some students are troubled by this imprecision. You may want to explain that this is often the case with scientific work, certainly in ecological work. While it is important to be accurate, it is often not possible to be precise, especially in systems that are dynamic and complex, such as ecosystems. Remember the Fermi calculations in **Unit 1**—that often an order of magnitude calculation is quite useful? While that is not true for this

Exploration, it overlaps with a second important point about quantifying data, or preciseness of any sort. It is important to keep one's perspective about numbers and to use numbers that are of the same general degree of preciseness. Thus, it makes no sense to time one activity to hundredths of a second (a lap in the swimming pool), while others are precise to within five or ten minutes (amount of time spent moving between classes). This is an issue students likely have encountered in math and is worth coordinating a session or two with their math teacher, if possible. It is also considered in the **Technique: Introduction to Research**.

For other issues raised by students about Explorations 1 and 2, see also Classroom Vignettes.

DATA SHEET

Explorations 1 and 2a: Your ACTIVITY LOG for Data Collection and Analysis

PAGE 1

Name____________________ Date____________________

OUTSIDE CLASS		IN CLASS	
TIME SPENT	ACTIVITY	TIME SPENT	CALORIES

ACTIVITY LOG

PAGE 2

Name ____________________ Date ____________________

OUTSIDE CLASS		IN CLASS	
TIME SPENT	ACTIVITY	TIME SPENT	CALORIES

DATA SHEET

Explorations 1 and 2b: Your INTAKE LOG for Data Collection and Analysis

PAGE 1

Name ______________________ Date ______________________

TIME	FOOD OR DRINK	AMOUNT	CALORIES

INTAKE LOG

PAGE 2

Name ______________________ Date ______________________

TIME	FOOD OR DRINK	AMOUNT	CALORIES

SUBJECT'S HEIGHT: ____________ LAST YEAR'S HEIGHT: ____________

SUBJECT'S WEIGHT: ____________ LAST YEAR'S WEIGHT: ____________

SUBJECT'S SHOE SIZE: ____________ LAST YEAR'S SHOE SIZE: ____________

EXPLORATION 2A GUIDE
Your Activity Log: Data Analysis

Students will need the next one or two sessions to process their data: do the calculations and the conversions for energy use. The conversion of activities into kilocalories is straightforward; the student materials also include a fully worked example.

Students may need help in selecting equivalents for activities not listed in the Energy Expenditure Table. Students are likely to need some discussion of "activity." Often they consider only obviously active behaviors and do not realize that just being alive requires metabolic activity. This distinction is key here (and throughout this Unit) and so worth spending time on. You may want to skip ahead to **Chapter 3** for more.

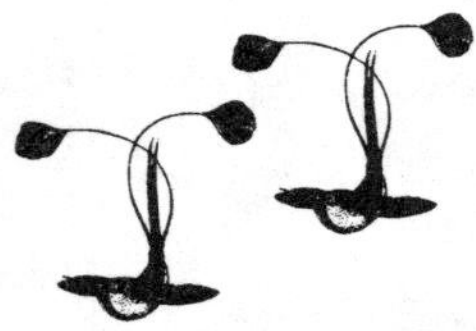

READING 1 GUIDE
When Is an Activity Not an Activity?

The key point of this reading is that just being alive takes energy. Student intake and activity energy data reflect this roughly in the energy use they report for sleeping.

Possible Confusions

Students might find two possible sources of confusion in this chapter: (1) between respiration as breathing and metabolic respiration and (2) between activity as action and metabolic activity. As this Reading suggests, breathing and action both require metabolic respiration. It is true, however, that when an organism is inactive (not moving), it is still metabolically active.

It may help keep these distinctions clear if you keep the vocabulary clear. Use the phrases "metabolic respiration" versus "breathing" and "metabolic activity" versus "action," "act," or "movement."

Basal Metabolic Rate

Basal, or baseline, metabolic rate (BMR) is an important tool for making energy use comparisons between organisms. In an obvious example, a running lion uses more energy than a resting lion. More subtle contrasts are between a digesting or pregnant lion and one that is neither. In those cases, the differences in energy use are not visible as action or movement, but they are real. In fact, a pregnant lion increases her energy intake and use by as much as 100% over her normal daily intake. Digestion is less dramatic—a digesting lion uses just a few percent extra kilocalories per unit of weight than its average basal metabolic rate.

So the formal definition of BMR is the amount of energy necessary to keep a typical, nonpregnant adult of the species alive when it is resting, that is, inactive, awake, not digesting food, and not gaining or losing heat. BMR does not include the energetic costs of any activities such as movement, pregnancy, growth, youth, illness, cold, or excitement.

EXPLORATION 2B GUIDE
Your Intake Log: Data Analysis

The conversion of food intake into calories involves quite a bit of looking up information in tables and doing calculations, but students generally find the work engaging. You might assign some of the work as homework, especially the calculations. We have found, however, that students often need teacher support to convert food intake to kilocalories, especially in choosing appropriate equivalents for foods not listed in standard calorie tables. (Ravioli and other pasta dishes seem to cause problems. This is because some tables list information for ingredients or whole foods, such as cheese, pasta, and tomatoes, while others list prepared dishes, such as the ravioli or macaroni and cheese one could make from those foods. Some, fortunately, include data for both.).

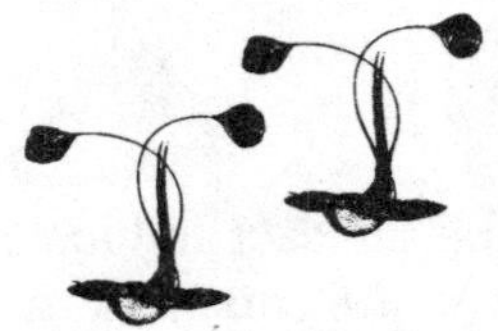

READING 2 GUIDE
Energy in Foods: How It Is Stored and How You Get at It

Key to this reading is students' grasp of the concept of energy and that it has different forms. We focus on metabolic energy because of our ecological perspective, but they may better understand the entire idea if they see where that fits in the whole energy picture.

It may be useful to refer students to their basic chemistry and remind them of how energy changes state but does not get used up. This principle of thermodynamics is likely one they have memorized but which they may not understand. Both biological and nonbiological processes use and release energy, that is, there are similarities and differences between combustion and metabolic respiration. Understanding those similarities and differences is essential to understanding energy as ecological currency and for making the distinction between energy being dissipated or used and carbon, the major carrier of energy in biological systems, being just recycled or reused.

Because this whole Unit is about how organisms get and use energy, some students grasp these concepts better if they are presented in a different order than we have chosen. You may find that students get ahead of where the materials are, or that you need to jump ahead to clarify something about the current work. This Reading in particular may raise some questions that may make you want to move more quickly to the next chapter or to do some of the bond energies work (**Chapters 9** and **8**, in this Unit).

EXPLORATION 3 GUIDE (Class)
Patterns in Intake and Activity Data

Once the numbers have been crunched, each student will have two numbers: kilocalories of food consumed and kilocalories of energy used or spent. If they do not notice it themselves, have them talk about the fact that they can convert two apparently dissimilar and unrelated things (eating and being active) into numbers with the same units, kilocalories. Remind students about renaming (**Unit 1**, **Chapter 1**). Ask them how activity and food are related and what the common factor is (energy).

Intake ≠ Activity

Students will likely also notice that the two numbers are not equal. Specifically, all will have taken in more kilocalories than they have spent. This is another good place to reinforce the concept of metabolic activity. (In the Classroom Vignettes, some students are surprised they use energy when sleeping.)

If students want to think about why their two numbers are not the same, discuss with them what biological activities and processes they have not considered. For instance, is digestion totally effective at getting energy out of food? What happens to the energy that digestion does not access? Similarly discuss the idea of metabolic respiration: What is going on in their bodies all the time? Does that require energy?

The next Chapter builds on this discussion and helps students construct the balanced energy use equation.

Patterns in the Data

For now, have students begin analyzing the data and looking for patterns of energy use or consumption. Have the students work in groups and plot their data to understand the relationships among variables. Use energy

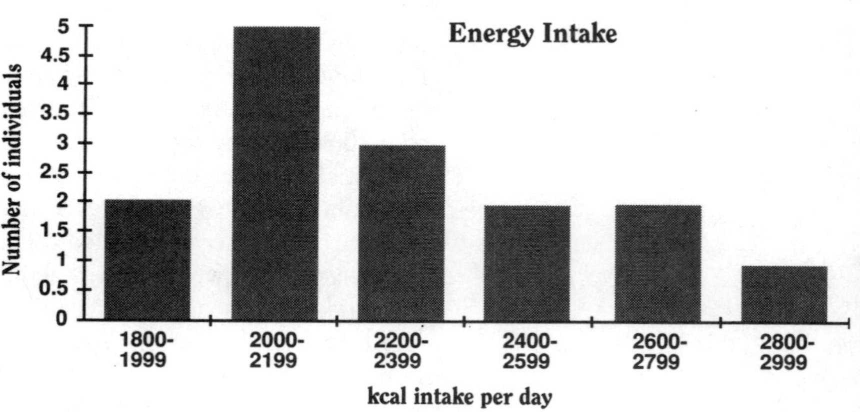

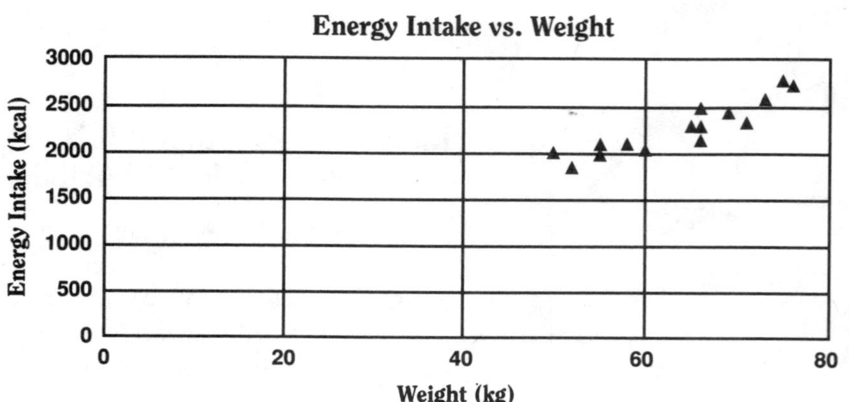

intake as the first dependent variable. Encourage students to use the other information they have, such as weight, height, foot size, growth rate, age, and sex.

- Who takes in the most energy?
- Who takes in the least?
- Are there clear patterns in energy intake? Is age a good predictor of energy intake? Does height, sex, weight, or growth rate correlate with energy intake?

INTEGRATION GUIDE
Presenting Your Data

This Chapter involves several data sets, any of which can be used for the Integration activity of data presentation. The most obvious sets are those from Exploration 3. Each student group can go through the **Technique: Preparing a Presentation** with one of those sets.

At each step of their presentation, students must articulate their ideas and expectations. So no matter which data they use, you and they will know clearly what they think and do or do not understand.

If possible, give the students time actually to make and present a poster (see the next section, Integration: Presenting Your Data) to an outside audience—another class or some teachers. The thrill of presentation, of feedback, and of discussion is intense, and students enjoy that process. They also learn from each other's work: about the subject, about data analysis, and about the entire process of doing science. For more details, see the **Technique: Preparing a Presentation** and the **Technique: Introduction to Research**.

INTEGRATION
Presenting Your Data

An important part of doing science is sharing results. We mentioned this when we talked about keeping accurate notes and data on your work, but because it is an integral part of the process of science, we return to it again in this context.

Now that you have collected, analyzed, and even interpreted your data, how can you best present them so others (teachers, class members, parents, etc.) can understand your work and conclusions? One way often used at scientific conferences is the poster.

Materials

- **Poster board** or **large paper**
- **Brief statements** about how data were collected, analyzed, and what conclusions were drawn
- **Graphs** and **tables** of your data
- **Your results**
- **Technique: Preparing a Presentation**

Procedure

1. **Read the Technique: Preparing a Presentation.**
2. **In groups, prepare a presentation of one data set.**
Pick one pattern in the data that you want to present to the class. Use the **Technique: Preparing a Presentation** to prepare the materials and your poster.
3. **Present your work.**
Perhaps you can have an open house and invite other classes, parents, or even the PTA, or another group during one of its meeting times.

SCIENCE BACKGROUND
Energy and Units

THE CALORIE

What is a Calorie? In general terms, it is a measure of energy. In specific terms, a Calorie, or a kilocalorie, is the amount of energy needed to raise a liter of water from 14.5 degrees Celsius° to 15.5°C. A calorie (small "c") is the amount of energy needed to raise a cubic centimeter of water from 14.5°C to 15.5°C. Thus, 1 kcal = 1,000 cal. A useful prop for discussing the kilocalorie is a liter bottle full of water—you can show students exactly the quantity of water that a single kilocalorie raises by 1 degree Celsius.

JOULES

You may wonder why we chose the Calorie over the joule as the unit of energy, since the joule is prescribed by the International System. We use the Calorie for several reasons:

- Its definition is more concrete and accessible to students, especially those with no physics background.
- Virtually all students have heard and used the term, even though they may not understand it scientifically—they know it has something to do with food value.
- The Calorie specifically as a unit of heat energy is appropriate for organismal biology.
- It has been used widely, whereas only recently has the joule become the standard in the ecological literature.

An enlightening discussion of this issue appears in The Hot-Blooded Insects, by Bernd Heinrich (see the References section). Heinrich reluctantly chooses the joule!

ENERGY

What is energy? Technically speaking, energy is the capacity to do work, where work is force times distance, and force is mass times acceleration. This topic encompasses many difficult concepts for students with no background in physics. Take the technical definitions only as far as you can; students probably bring a reasonable working definition of energy. A critical point for them to understand is that energy can be transformed: chemical energy can be converted to heat energy, either of those to mechanical energy, and vice versa—always with quite low conversion efficiencies.

REFERENCES

Heinrich, Bernd. 1993. The Hot-Blooded Insects: Strategies and Mechanisms of Thermoregulation. Cambridge: Harvard University Press. 601 pp.

Rombauer, Irma von Starkloff. 1975. The Joy of Cooking. Indianapolis: Bobbs-Merrill. 915 pp.

Watt, Bernice K. 1993. The Handbook of the Nutritional Contents of Foods. New York: Prepared for the U.S. Department of Agriculture and reprinted by Dover Publications $9.95.

CLASSROOM VIGNETTES

Discussing Intake Data

You can observe in this vignette that, as students carry out the work in this chapter, several kinds of processing are going on. Students are reflecting on their observations; since they have done some work in preparation for the discussion, they are "charged" and in a position to gain from the conversation. Definitions are processed by the group. Applications of the information are attempted over and over.

Everyone arrived with their food intake data sheets and Exploration 2b: Your Intake Log: Data Analysis. The teacher passed out some information about the number of calories in the food they ate to help them calculate their energy budgets later in the class.

The teacher began by asking students for reactions.

P: It makes you stop and think. How can a human being eat all this? [He is always talking about what a big eater he is; it is something he is proud of. There seems to be quite a difference between how the girls and boys feel about their food intake. The girls are embarrassed if they have eaten a lot. The boys, on the other hand, are pleased to have consumed great quantities.]

[Teacher asks for their reactions to recording their data. Answers are about both activity and intake.]

S: I noticed that I thought about what I was going to do.
P: I was about to watch the basketball game but decided that that wouldn't look good, so I went out and played basketball instead.
RM: I had trouble recording just what I did.
TEACHER: What did you put down in terms of sitting?
P: Fourteen hours.
TEACHER: Me too.
RM: It takes more calories to write.
TEACHER: I was shocked to find out what a slug I was.
RB: I figured out I walk a half an hour total between classes.
P: What is a kilocalorie?
TEACHER: Let's go over what a calorie is.

[RM repeats the textbook definition. Teacher brings out a liter bottle of spring water and asks the students how much water is in it.]

P: One liter.
TEACHER: There are 1,000 cubic centimeters in a liter, 1,000 cubic centimeters in a bottle of water. What would a kilocalorie be? How many kilocalories would it take to raise the temperature of water 1 degree?
RM: 1 kilo—that's 1,000 calories.

[Teacher asks about what freezing and boiling are in centigrade.]

RB: What's special about 14.5 and 15.5 [referring to the definition]?

[Teacher draws a graph of water density as a function of temperature on the board to explain how the density of water varies.]

Intake/Energy Use Considered Together

In this vignette, there is a mixture of questions and attempted answers, with the teacher or the students putting in facts. This collective effort allows the group to move toward an understanding that few of the individuals could have developed alone.

TEACHER: Let's talk about budgets. What might you expect to see after you add everything up?
S: What do you mean?
TEACHER: Did it seem right to use kilocalories for both input and output?
S: Yes.
TEACHER: Why didn't it surprise the rest of you?
S: Because they are both a measure of energy. You take in so much more than you burn off.
M: How many kilocalories in a pound? Would you have to burn 3,600 calories to lose one pound? It that true?
P: What does kilocalorie mean?

[Teacher explains again.]

TEACHER: So we're taking in a certain number of kilocalories and expending a certain amount. What might happen at the end of a day?
RM: We'll gain weight.

[S says something about being confused by calculating kilocalories and weight.]

TEACHER: What are the units for energy expenditure?
S: Kilocalorie per kilogram per hour.
TEACHER: Let's take an example from someone's chart.
P: Basketball for two hours.

[Teacher writes "2 hours × 9 kcal/kg/hr" and "140 lbs = 64 kg; 64 kg × 2 hr × 9 kcal/kg/hr = 1,152 kcal."]

M: That's how many calories burned.
RB: What's the canceling out [of units]?

[Teacher walks them through how he canceled the units but gets mostly blank looks. He says he'll go over this again later but for now everyone should work in pairs calculating their energy budgets.]

[P and SER look for how many calories P ate yesterday. They can't find blue tortilla chips. Teacher suggests they use potato chips. P finds spaghetti and wants to know how many cups of spaghetti are in a pound. He needs to know how much spaghetti, in cups, he ate. Teacher suggests he put down 1½ cups. Each group, as they work, has questions about quantities or appropriate substitutions on the list for what they ate. RB has a calculator, and P and SER use it to total P's energy intake. R and SER are enjoying themselves as the number of calories that S ate yesterday mounts up. P finds out that he burned more than he took in, which is a surprise given all our expectations that he would have eaten many more calories than he expended. He burned 2,590 and took in 1,268.

Now most groups have calculated the energy budgets of at least one member. There is lots of good-natured teasing of S, who apparently ate more than P and SER together.

Teacher wrote their data on the board:

P expended 1,292 more than intake

S took in 700 more than expended

M expended 1,375 more than intake

RB expended 227 more than intake

SER expended 1,074 more than intake

Teacher expended 350 more than intake

Teacher makes the point that people's diets change a lot from day to day. He asks if they all have complete faith in their numbers and says that it is really hard to estimate quantities.]

TEACHER: There are a lot of places we could have made mistakes. What would happen if day after day you spent more than you took in?

SER: You would lose weight.

TEACHER: What if this went on for a long time?

P: You would get sick and weaker.

M: Do vitamins have calories? [She apparently is starting to take vitamins.]

S: What about metabolism?

TEACHER: If you burn faster, the gap may be larger. What does this energy stuff mean for an animal in the wild?

M: They don't think about being fat.

TEACHER: What if they take in less than they eat?

M: Eventually they'll die.

TEACHER: Animals in the wild over the long haul either keep in energy balance or they die. If I'm a fox, it's very important to me that the rabbits are eating enough.

EXTENSIONS

Costs of Types of Locomotion (Moving from One Place to Another)

This Extension is particularly suited to integration with math, physics, and physiology classes. Moving around is a major "activity" (metabolically and otherwise) for most nonplant organisms. There are some interesting relationships between body size and the type and cost of locomotion. What relationships do you see in the following graph?

- The cost goes up with velocity.
- Different kinds of locomotion have different inherent costs, but these also depend on the mass being moved.
- Flying is more economical than walking, running, and swimming in terms of calories per meter, but it still incurs high metabolic costs.
- Long-term activity may require increasing heat loss.
- Not all locomotion is a direct investment in energy capture (foraging).

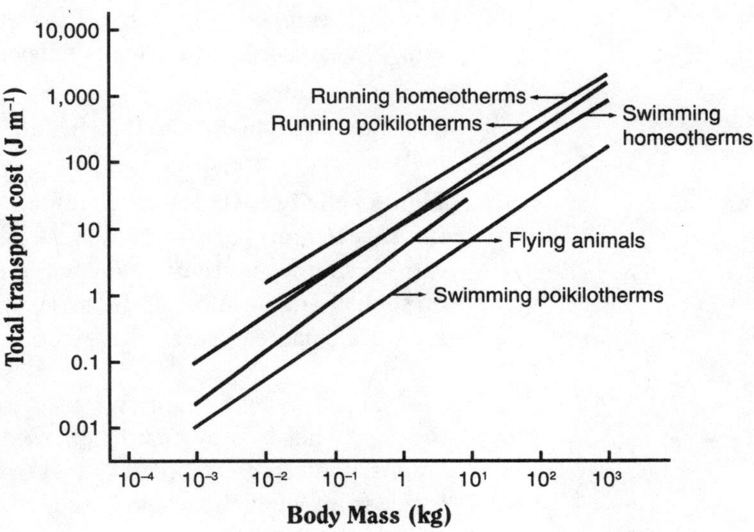

Transport costs (J m^{-1}) associated with swimming, running, and flying homeotherms and poikilotherms

References

McNab, Brian K. 1986. "The Influence of Food Habits on the Energetics of Eutherian Mammals." Ecological Monographs 56(1): 1–19.

Peters, Robert Henry. 1983. The Ecological Implications of Body Size. Cambridge (Cambridgeshire): Cambridge University Press. 329 pp.

THE ACTIVITY AND FOOD LOG OF AN ANIMAL

NOTE: This Extension, excluding Teacher Notes, can be photocopied and handed out as an Exploration.

You have used yourself as a sample organism to learn about activity and energy budgets. How does the activity budget of a very different organism look? The foundation of an answer to that question lies in the "simple" act of observation. Although it would be ideal to observe an animal's behavior around the clock for a whole year or its whole life, that is hardly ever done, and surely you don't have time to do that in this class!

For now, you and your teammates will choose an organism for which you will construct a 1-day (24-hour) activity log. Use those data to consider what the organism's energy budget might look like.

Procedure

1 **Choose a reasonable animal.**
By that we mean something that will be possible to observe. Some creatures, such as sea gulls and hawks, travel far, so people are rarely in a good situation to watch one for the whole day. Others, such as earthworms, are best observed in a laboratory setting.

2. **Work out a plan.**
You alone are not likely able to watch and take data every minute for 24 hours. So each team member will need to take a turn. There will also be

times when no one can watch. Plan when those times will be and consider how you can conjecture what is happening during that time.

3. **Take good notes.**
   See the **Technique: Animal Behavior** for some ideas about watching animals and collecting data.

4. **Figure activity costs for your animal.**
   It is easy to find charts that show the energy an "average" human expends on various common activities. You will not be surprised to learn that there are no such charts for most of the animals in the world—most species have not even been named yet, so there is much we still do not know about their biology.

   Because such information is scarce, some researchers have put together what is known and expressed the data in graph form. From such graphs, you can get estimates for your creature. Some animals are very different from what the graphs predict, but most creatures are more or less close to those values.

As we discuss elsewhere in the curriculum, it is always important to examine the sources of your data, rather than simply accepting all statements as facts carrying equal weight. Data in the graphs like these have been assembled from several different sources, and it is important for you to understand the differences among the sources. For instance, there are many different types of animals, most of which have not been studied directly. That is, they have not been the subject of an intensive investigation (or study). Therefore, some of the data that we want to include have not actually been collected for particular animals. For example, there are many animals for which energy use equation data have not been gathered.

In those cases, however we can use data that come from a model. Data that have been collected from some animals directly are used to build a model. Such a model allows us to make predictions about data for other animals that have not yet been studied. These predictions are a reasonable approximation of data for the unstudied animals. But data drawn from a model are not the same as carefully performed measurements on real organisms. Are we saying that data from a model are not useful? Not at all — in fact, data drawn from models can be very useful for giving you a sense of the differences among different types of animals. However, because they are not direct measurements from the animals themselves, we cannot be as certain about predicted data as about measured data.

Teacher Notes

Brainstorm about possible categories of behavior students may see. Much of what they see will fall into certain important categories: foraging and eating; sleeping; self-care (preening, cleaning of antennae, etc.); social interactions with own group or another group of the same organism; escape or hiding.

Students should be able to gather some information about the animal's food; later they will use the techniques of carbonometry and calorimetry to establish the energy content of the foods. The student teams can write a report on their results, including raw observations and their conclusions. They should be able to assign rough proportions of time the animal spent on the classes of behaviors observed and some information about the animal's food (although this may be surprisingly hard to determine). Remind them to seek additional information about their organism from field guides or other references, but only after their initial observations.

Conclude with a class discussion of the questions that came up and talk with the students about what surprised or confused them and what they would like to look for if they were to undertake another round of observations on their organism. What would they do differently?

A major gap in their conclusions will be their difficulty in converting activities into kilocalories and their behavioral observations into energy budgets. Later chapters will introduce them to the kinds of information they would need to do so. With this in mind, you might want to invite some students to return to this study toward the end of this Unit.

Reference

Martin, A. C., H. S. Zim, and A. L. Nelson. 1951. American Wildlife and Plants: A Guide to Wildlife Food Habits. New York: Dover Publications.

Dung Beetles and You
Building a Complete Energy Budget

Chapter Three

Contents

Introduction

Now we broaden our ideas about energy use: it is a general attribute of living things, and it takes many forms. Students try to discover all the ways in which live beings use energy. They use this information to reconsider why their intake and energy use data did not match. Putting these ideas together, students develop the balanced energy use equation.

For the Integration and in the next Chapter, the students "become" animals from each of two habitats. They use the balanced energy use equation to explore differences and similarities in the animals' energy use and lifestyles.

KEY CONCEPTS

- Organisms use energy on several time scales—every moment, daily, monthly, across a lifetime.
- In nonplants, those energy uses can be distilled to three "paths" that energy can take after it is ingested: (1) production (the energy is used to produce fat or new tissue in the animal or to produce the animal's offspring); (2) respiration (the energy is used for the tasks of daily living—moving, breathing, cell repair, sleeping, digestion; and (3) excretion (the energy passes through the animal's gut unused).
- Those energy uses can be represented in a succinct and informative way, the so-called energy use equation: **I**ntake = **R**espiration + **P**roduction + **E**xcretion.
- Biological processes such as respiration follow the first principle of thermodynamics: energy changes state but is not used up. Therefore, the energy use equation is balanced. When energy coming in (the **I** term, in kilocalories) is set to 100%, it can be accounted for by the sum of the three other terms (in kilocalories).
- Another way of categorizing energy uses is by short-term end-point: energy used by the organism itself and energy that the organism makes available to other organisms.

MATERIALS AND PREPARATION

In Advance

Devise a way of assigning animals from the "cards," one per student. There are thirty animals total, fifteen from each ecosystem.

Materials

- **Intake and activity data** from **Chapter 2**

SUGGESTED SEQUENCE OF SESSIONS (2–4)

Homework

Students read the Case Study and put life processes into place for each thing at different time intervals.

Class Session 1

A class discussion of the Case Study helps students understand that all living things perform the same processes, just on different time scales. And dead things do not perform any of those processes.

The discussion leads directly into group work on Exploration 1. Students discover that they seemed to take in more energy than they used because they did not account for all their energy use. Students integrate data from the Case Study, their personal energy use, and dung beetle food habits to develop a complete and balanced energy use equation.

Class Session 2

Continued from Session 1.

Homework

Reading: Who Balanced the Energy Use Equation?

Class Sessions 3–4

Continue class sessions as necessary, incorporating class discussion of the Reading. This helps students understand that energy can change form but is not "lost." Hence, the number of kilocalories on both sides of the equals sign in the energy use equation is the same.

SESSION GUIDES, BY WORKSHEET

CASE STUDY GUIDE
What Is It Doing?

This activity raises several themes that recur throughout the **Carbon and Energy Module**: life and nonlife; the importance of scale (size and time scale) to the understanding of ecological processes; and the idea that some life processes are continuous (such as metabolic respiration), while others are episodic (such as reproduction).

Here are a few questions to get students discussing these themes.

- What does each thing do?
- If you observed each one, what could you see happen? (with different tools and at different scales: if you looked at a cell or a small piece; at a hunk, an organ, or other big piece; at the whole thing).
- What activities does each thing carry out?

Following is a sample table; you likely will have additions to these answers. Notice that we have grouped living organisms as Plant and Animal. The responses need be scaled only to the life span of a specific plant or animal. Thus, responses for two common pets, cat and goldfish, would be similar. An indoor cat, however, has an expected life span of a dozen years, while the goldfish life span is about one year. (See Classroom Vignettes for some student reactions.)

What does each thing typically do during the course of each time interval?

	PLANT	ANIMAL (SEA CUCUMBER, PET)	ROCK
A minute?	Respire Transpire Grow	Breathe Respire Circulate blood Grow	Sit Weather
A day?	Photosynthesize Take up water + nutrients Change orientation toward the sun	Feed (forage) Excrete Sleep Move (some animals)	Sit Weather
A month?	Grow (some months)	Grow Move	Sit Weather
A year?	Grow Drop leaves Flower Fruit	Grow Mate Reproduce	Sit Weather
During a lifetime?	Germinate Reproduce Die	Be born Reproduce Die	Weather away

EXPLORATION 1 GUIDE

The Three "D's": Dung Beetles, Detritivores, Decomposers

Building the Energy Use Equation

Students discuss what happens to the large quantities of energy ingested by all animals, including humans, and, in the process, develop the energy use equation. The discussion as laid out here is linear, with students and teacher engaged in building the energy use equation. Students may, however, not think linearly. In that case, have them note all their activities on the board and work at collapsing or grouping those into categories. Students might come up with an exhaustive list of forms of movement ("run, jump, walk," etc.) but leave out reproduction or growth. Keep asking whether the list is complete for a lifetime's activities. Ask whether they are taller or larger than last year or have outgrown their clothes. If a baby is part of their household, has it remained the same size over time? Ask if any of the activities can be grouped (refer students to their Case Study data).

If the Discussion Starts Slowly

If the notion of grouping seems alien, ask students (as a class or in small groups) to consider repeated three-way comparisons of the activities listed. The triplets will include both like and unlike activities, which is a good approximation of group making. "Is running more like eating or more like jumping? Then let's put running and jumping together." "Is eating more like reproducing or more like running? OK, let's keep them all separate." Ask for reasons for each grouping or separation.

The Current "Equation"

The intake and expenditure of energy is the start of the energy use equation. At this point, the "equation" looks like this:

Ingestion ≠ Expenditure

Each term is expressed in units of energy, kilocalories. Remind students that metabolic activity is common to all other activities. So, by substitution, we can rewrite the equation as

Ingestion $\stackrel{?}{=}$ Respiration

(If necessary, refer to **Chapter 2** for information on respiration, activity, and so on.)

Clearly the equation still is incomplete. "Do you absorb all the energy you take in or eat? Where does the unabsorbed part go?" These questions can lead students to realize that humans and other animals do not absorb all the energy in their foods. (There may be some reluctance to address excretion. Use terms that are not part of street talk—fecal matter, excretion, dung, by-products of digestion, unabsorbed food. Ecologists tend to use the word "dung," even with reference to humans, and especially if they are studying dung beetles.

Expanding the "Equation"

Based on these considerations, we can expand the equation:

Ingestion = Respiration + Excretion

Is the equation complete now? "What about over your lifetime—are there activities you have not included in your daily list?" If necessary, remind the students of "What is it doing?" and an energy budget over the course of a lifetime. If students are not realizing that the production of new tissues (either the animal's own tissues or the tissues of offspring) require energy, you might ask more pointed questions, such as, "How tall were you last year compared with this year? Did that growth 'cost' anything?"

Another Term

Once students realize that the production of tissues is an energetic cost, the equation can be written as

Ingestion = Respiration + Production + Excretion

and is now complete. The left side of the equation stands for all the energy the organism has ingested; the right side for all the activities, actions, and behaviors it performs in its lifetime. We know both sides can be expressed in energy units of kilocalories, but how do we know the two sides are equal? Because all organisms are subject to the first law of thermodynamics—the conservation of mass and energy. More details follow next and in Science Background.

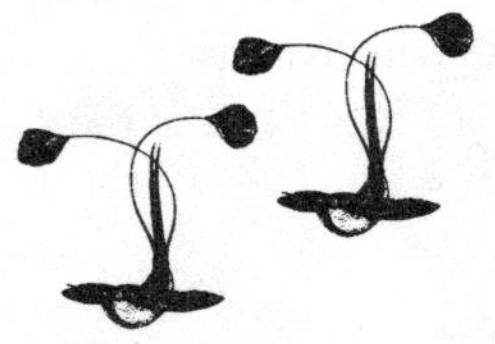

READING GUIDE
Who Balanced the Energy Use Equation?

The energy use equation "balances,"—all energy taken in can be accounted for. That is because neither energy nor matter is destroyed in biological processes. For more details, see Science Background.

If students have difficulty with this concept, you might want to back up to Reading 2 in **Chapter 2** or jump ahead to bonds and bond energy (**Chapters 9** and **8**).

INTEGRATION GUIDE
Absolute Intake of Some Organism

Assign each student one of the organisms on the animal cards in **Chapter 4**. Have them calculate the organism's absolute, or total, intake in kilocalories per kilogram per year. Ask them to calculate intake in kilocalories per gram, also. The animal data include average adult weight in kilograms and total food intake in kilocalories per animal per year. Students simply divide the latter number by the former. Ask them to bring their results to class for the work in the next Chapter.

NOTE: No Integration Sheet is included here since the assignment is simple enough for you to write on the board.

SCIENCE BACKGROUND
Energy, Organisms, and Thermodynamics

Let's step back for a moment and put this business of energy use into an ecological context. An ecosystem is a group of interconnected organisms and their environment; one major (if not the major) connection is energy. This includes how energy is acquired by organisms, how they use it, and how energy use moves between organisms. All possible energy connections can be put into one of two categories: the energy is used wholly for the organism itself, or some of the energy is available to other organisms. Although these categories may seem subtle, they are in fact pretty straightforward and make sense ecologically. They are also useful: they provide a logical way to group energy uses; they allow us to consider energy as it is acquired and used by a single organism; and they allow us to compare how various organisms get and use their energy. Finally, because an ecosystem includes a group of energetically connected organisms, by summing the energy uses of all member organisms, we can tally the (approximate) energy flow for the ecosystem as a whole.

CARBON AND ENERGY

So we are considering energy use by an organism. Some of the energy it takes in is used for the organism itself, the rest is available to other organisms. Although we have been considering this relationship primarily in energy terms, it applies to both matter and energy, in this case, carbon and energy.

CONSERVATION OF ENERGY AND STUFF

The balanced energy, or growth, equation is a convenient shorthand for discussing energy relations. The equation illustrates the first law of thermodynamics as it applies to living organisms. That is, neither energy nor matter (carbon) is destroyed in biological processes. Thus, what goes into an animal (matter and energy) must (in some form) come out. Matter (in this case, carbon) cycles, but energy "flows downhill." Every time energy is transformed from one form to another, some of it is lost as heat. Heat generally is not usable by organisms, and the efficiency of energy transfer is low. Typically 80% to 90% is heat, and only 10% to 20% is transferred as usable energy. This equation also forms the basis for all interactions involving transfer of energy or matter between an organism and its environment.

Chemical energy is the form used in biological processes. It depends on the arrangement of atoms in the bonds that make up those arrangements. (For more details, see **Chapter 8** or **9**.)

TERMS OF THE EQUATION

Intake or ingestion (**I**) equals whatever is absorbed (**A**) plus what is not absorbed but excreted (**E**). Thus,

$$\mathbf{I = A + E}$$

Energy that is excreted (**E**), as in dung, is clearly not being used by an organism itself and is available to other organisms. Energy that is absorbed is used for a few major categories: individual growth (production of tissue or fat), reproduction (pregnancy, nursing, etc.), and cellular respiration.

(Notice that we have turned around our approach to the energy use equation. Initially we built it up from the perspective of an animal's own uses. Here we are focusing equally on energy used by the organism itself and what is available to others.)

Respiration is a unique element in the balanced growth equation, because it is entirely a loss term. The energy of respiration is a one-way outlet for organic energy reserves. It is released as heat and is eventually lost to space. The matter associated with respiration is recycled as water and carbon dioxide, but the energy is dissipated.

Once it is taken in, energy in all organisms is channeled into either of two basic "directions": production or maintenance. Production is made up of all the energy uses by an organism that also provide possible food energy for other organisms. Maintenance is the energy uses by an organism that do not provide other organisms with possible food.

Thus, maintenance includes cellular respiration, breathing, eating, digesting, moving, generating body heat, and any activity—any use of energy by an organism that does not directly make energy available to other organisms. These activities are generally called "maintenance" energy uses, since they help maintain the body.

Production includes everything else: all tissue production (such as body growth and reproduction), any by-products of eating (such as dung, regurgitated matter, or just leftovers), and, ultimately, an organism's body after death. In all these examples, energy used by the organism being studied gives rise to or produces something containing energy that is, in turn, available to or can be "eaten" by other organisms. For example, a predator can eat the body of the study organism or of its young; a parasite can live in tissues of the study organism; dung beetles and microorganisms can feed on its feces; scavengers and microorganisms can feed on its carcass.

The following graphic shows the movement of energy through an organism. It might help students remember which categories do and do not provide potential energy for other organisms.

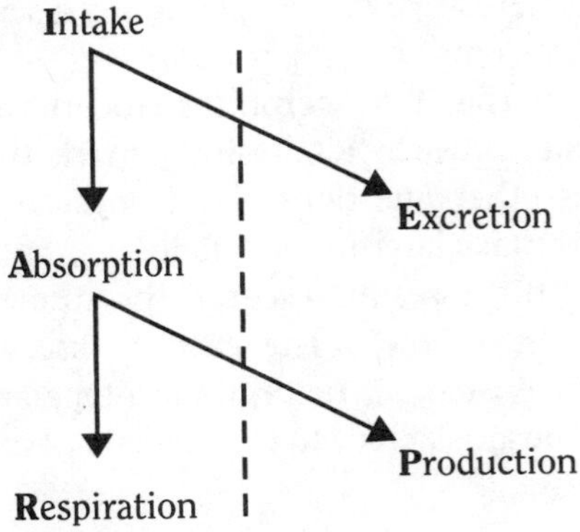

The energy uses to the right of the dotted line make energy available to other organisms. Respiration, to the left, does not.

Energy uses that yield or produce something containing energy that is usable by other organisms are called "production" or "biomass" energy uses.

Some people find it helpful to call maintenance energy uses "self" uses and production or biomass uses "other," as a way of indicating where the energy can go: only to the organism itself or also to other organisms. But some people find it confusing because "other" includes weight gain, which happens to the self.

Whichever names you use, you will be able to categorize an activity properly if you just ask yourself: Does this activity possibly make energy available to be ingested by another organism? Thus, movement?—no; weight gain?—yes; having babies?—yes; staying warm?—no.

ENERGY USES BY THE TWO CATEGORIES

MAINTENANCE	BIOMASS OR PRODUCTION
Cellular respiration	Generation growth: tissue production, growing, adding fat, gestation (pregnancy), lactation (nursing)
Movement	
Heat	By-products of feeding: feces, regurgitation, leftovers, carcass

NOTE: If you read elsewhere on the topic of energy use, you will notice the annoying number of units of measure that are used. Oxygen (O_2) is measured in milligrams (mg), cubic millimeters (mm^3), and milliliters (ml); energy in joules (J), calories (cal), and kilocalories (kcal); mass or size in micrograms, milligrams, grams, and kilograms in fresh (wet) or dry weight, and time in seconds, minutes, hours, and days. Approximate conversions are 1 watt (W) = 1 J s^{-1} = 0.24 cal s^{-1} = 0.05 ml O_2 s^{-1}. Oxygen consumption converts to kilocalories at about 4.8 kcal per liter.

CLASSROOM VIGNETTES

Here are two excerpts from a discussion of this Case Study among several students.

In the first excerpt, the students are beginning to explore time scales. As you can see by R's closing remark, the encounter with specific organisms raises other questions about physical and biological processes, questions that surface later in this Module.

In the second excerpt, the students continue thinking about plants, animals, and rocks. The teacher asks a very specific question, which triggers an unconsidered, regurgitation-type answer. That answer proves immediately unsatisfactory to the students, even to the person who made it.

I

S: We need to choose a specific animal.
SER: A rock is a rock.

[R wants to keep her pet mice in mind as she does this.]

SER: Shall we do a tree?
S: They have a long life, so let's do that. What kind of tree?
R: Sugar maple.
S: What does a rock do in a minute?
SER: Nothing.
S: Over a day.
SER: It depends where this rock is or what kind. Do you mean like limestone as it gets formed?
R: A rock in the water? On top of a mountain?
SER: A rock might become something different.
S: So in a month it may get smoother.
S: (reading down a worksheet): Over a lifetime?
R: It could decorate a sand castle.
S: It could become sand. Let's go on to other stuff. How about a mouse?
SER: It grows, develops, reproduces, dies.

[S wonders where to put growing for a mouse—under every minute, every day, or every month? They discuss where to put photosynthesizing for a plant and decide to put it under a day. Same with growing for a plant. They also discuss where sap production should go. SER says to put it under a month.]

R: The interesting part of a rock is when it's being formed. If it's not a living organism, it's not that interesting.

II

[After about 15 minutes, the teacher has everyone get back together to pool their results. The other group chose a daisy as their plant. The teacher points out that within the course of a year both plants (the sugar maple and the daisy) behave very differently.]

TEACHER (once all the results are on the board): Do plants, animals, and rocks require the same things?

P: They all respond to their environment. The rock erodes, the plant grows, animals move.

R: There are more similarities between plants and animals than with rocks.

TEACHER: What are the similarities?

R: They grow and die. They have cells.

[There is a discussion about what animals and plants require, with S saying they require light and water and that they both require energy.]

TEACHER: Did they also require oxygen? How does that work? Why do I need oxygen?

RM: You need it to get glucose.

S: We need oxygen to live.

TEACHER: If you put oxygen and glucose together, you need the oxygen to get energy out of it. As a bunch of six ecologists, what kind of features would you look for in an organism to study? Let's say we want to study energy use.

RB: I'd study *Euglena* because it has characteristics of plants and animals.

SER: An animal that's a model—something as an example.

Dung Beetles, Cheetahs, and Others

Chapter Four

Contents

Introduction

Each student "models" one animal from either the Serengeti ecosystem or the Northern Hardwoods ecosystem, learning about that animal from its animal card. Students develop a way of representing energy use data and then use their representations to compare and contrast energy use. They find patterns by animal diet, size, and various other things.

From this chapter you can either continue in sequence, exploring each component of the equation or skip ahead to bonds and atomic arrangements (**Chapter 9**) and caloric (= energy) and carbon contents of foods (**Chapter 8**).

KEY CONCEPTS

- Biological processes such as respiration follow the first principle of thermodynamics: energy changes state but is not used up. Therefore, the energy use equation is balanced. When energy coming in (the **I** term, in kilocalories) is set to 100%, it can be accounted for by the sum of the three other terms (in kilocalories).
- Another way of categorizing these energy uses is by the short term and end point: energy used by the organism itself and energy that the organism makes available to other organisms.
- Although the energy use of all organisms can be represented by the balanced energy use equation, organisms divide their energy differently among its terms. Animals can be grouped according to those energy uses. For example, animals that regulate their body temperature metabolically (like mammals) have much higher respiration values than animals that do not (reptiles, amphibians, insects).
- Those differences raise the idea of relative and absolute quantities. "Relative" and "absolute" embody a useful concept of comparison. They imply some measuring or quantifying—counting units of something and comparing those units against some standard or reference frame that is in the same units, such as units of size and time.

MATERIALS AND PREPARATION

- **Colored paper** (at least three colors to represent the different categories of the energy use equation)
- **Graph paper**
- **Large poster paper for group charts**
- **Colored pencils or markers**
- **Scissors**
- **Glue or tape**
- **Each student's animal card** and **Integration results** from **Chapter 3**
- **Calculators**

SUGGESTED SEQUENCE OF SESSIONS (6–8)

Homework

Students get introduced to the two ecosystems by reading the brief introductions.

Class Session 1

Ask students to predict which has more plant matter available as food, the grassland or the forest. How might that affect the animals they will find in each ecosystem? Each student models energy use of his or her animal. Using their **Chapter 3** Integration results, students work in small groups to represent and discuss their total or absolute energy uses (Exploration 1). Class discussion of the data shows patterns and extremes in animal sizes and energy requirements.

Class Session 2

Continue the discussion from Session 1.

Students move on to calculate the percent of their individual animals' energy—the relative amount—that animal allocates to each function represented by the **R**, **P**, and **E** terms of the equation (Exploration 2). They represent these relative energy uses for presentation and comparison. It may help to have a class discussion or discussion between pairs of groups about different ways of representing the energy use data. Students may also want to discuss what data are "good" or "good enough."

Class Session 3

Continue the discussion from Session 2.

Have students make within-group comparisons of energy use to find patterns and differences among animals in relative energy use.

Homework

Somewhere here, assign Reading 2 and a discussion of data types and quality. The timing of this assignment depends on where in their work students are.

Class Session 4

Groups present their data to the class, so students can see more and other patterns and categorize animals according to energy uses. They compare and discuss relative and absolute energy use and find some patterns.

Class Session 5

Continue the presentations from Session 4, as necessary.

Students make multiple comparisons between different kinds of animals (Exploration 3), for example, between carnivores and herbivores, and find several correlations with energy use patterns, including diet, body size, and type of thermoregulation.

Class Session 6

Continue the comparisons from Session 5.

Have the class discuss whatever could be a pattern, from energy budgets to diets. Group discussions begin to integrate all the discoveries about factors influencing animal "function."

Homework

Integration write-up of the factors discussed in Session 6, with each student using his or her animal.

SESSION GUIDES, BY WORKSHEET

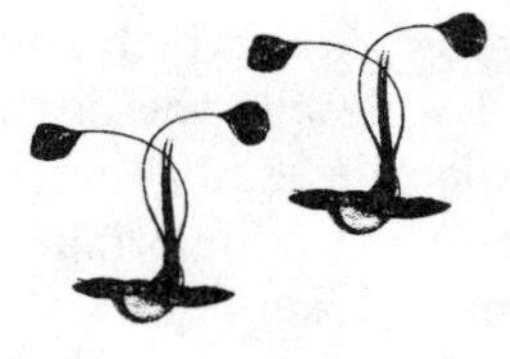

READING 1 GUIDE
Two Ecosystems

Students get a context or ecological frame within which to place the animals they are studying. They also begin to develop an awareness of differences between forests and grasslands. The latter have far more edible plant matter and correspondingly more animals and more different species of animals.

EXPLORATION 1 GUIDE
Comparing Absolute Energy Expenditure

Absolute, or total, energy expenditure is the amount of energy in kilocalories that an animal expends on respiration, production, and excretion. Using their Integration data, each group of 3 to 6 students makes a data table with the sizes of their animals in grams and each animal's energy expenditure in kilocalories. Students compare their animals' absolute energy expenditures.

Not all data are available for all animals. Note the caveat to the students about the data, which you may wish to discuss in the general context of data, sampling, and research. (See also the **Technique: Introduction to Research**.)

Group Composition

Discussion and comparison will be facilitated if each group comprises students whose animals are from the same ecosystem and include at least one of the following: an endothermic carnivore (from the Serengeti: lion, hyena, wild dog, leopard, cheetah, mongoose; from the Northern Hardwood Forest: weasel, wolf, fox, shrew, owl, blue jay); an endothermic herbivore (from the Serengeti: gazelle, wildebeest, topi, hartebeest, impala, zebra, hyrax, elephant; from the Northern Hardwood Forest: beaver, cottontail, squirrel, chipmunk, mouse, deer); an ectothermic carnivore (from the Northern Hardwood Forest: salamander, snake); and a detritivore (energy use data for the millipede, from the Northern Hardwood Forest, and the dung beetle, from the Serengeti, are included on the Exploration 1 sheet). (Some of the animals listed here are predominately carnivorous but may occasionally eat plants. Similarly, some are mainly herbivorous but may occasionally eat other animals. We categorized them according to their primary food source.)

Or just make sure each group includes both carnivores and herbivores and perhaps someone who understands the math more readily.

NOTE: If you are using just a subset of the animals, be sure to include the salamander.

Patterns in the Data: Class Discussion

When all groups have finished, make a list by animal size (in grams) on the board and ask students what comments they have about the data. They are likely to observe that there is a many-fold difference in the number of kilocalories eaten by different animals and allocated to various terms of the energy equation. In rough terms, these difference reflect the animals' size and thermoregulatory regime. (Exploration 2, in which students compare relative energy expenditures, shows that despite the disparity in the absolute amount of energy, in numbers of kilocalories, that different species of animals allocate to **R**, **P**, and **E**, there are some important similarities among groups of species in their relative energy use.)

One important trend is that energy intake and size do not track exactly. Animals of roughly the same size may have vastly different energy requirements due in large part to their individual thermoregulatory regimes. Among the animals represented, note the snake and the weasel.

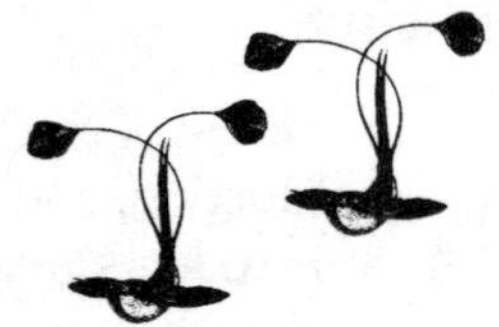

READING 2 GUIDE
Data Sources

Science as a way of knowing relies on creative and analytical thinking, asking questions, and accurate data. As we have seen already in the Reading Numbers in the Ballpark (**Unit 1**, **Chapter 1**) and our discussions of "facts" (Reading 2 and Integration, also in **Unit 1**, **Chapter 1**), data can be of various sorts. It is important to know the sources of data and to differentiate between numbers that come from a model and those that have been collected by direct observation. There are other subtleties as well: Who collected the data? What are that researcher's beliefs or even biases? When, where, how, and why were the data collected? Did the researcher have a point to make, or are the data objective? Recall also the brief discussion on averages in the **Evolution Module**.

Students might be shocked to discover that not all scientists are objective or that not all data are accurate (continuing the discussion of "when is a fact not a fact?") (**Unit 1**, **Chapter 1**, Integration). We bring up this theme periodically, because it is important and because people tend to accept too easily, without question or thought, what they hear or read.

EXPLORATION 2 GUIDE
All Energy Budgets Are Not Equal: Relative Energy Use

Relative energy expenditure is the proportion of an animal's total energy spent on respiration, production, and excretion. Working with the same students, animals, and data as in Exploration 1, students calculate the percentage of energy intake in kilocalories per year each animal "spends" on each of the processes represented by the terms of the equation. They discover important trends by animal size, thermoregulatory mode, and diet. (**NOTE:** Keep the student posters accessible for them to refer to in later chapters.)

Data Representation and Time

If possible, invite students to come up with their own ways of representing or displaying their animal's energy use in percentages. This work can take two or three sessions, depending on how much structure you give students. If possible, let the work be open ended, with students trying whatever occurs to them and rejecting things only after trying them. Or you may want to help the students assess their plans. Finally, you could provide students with some examples and let them choose among those.

Criteria for "Good" Data Representation

A fruitful class discussion would be to establish the criteria for "good" data representation. Our criteria included accuracy (Do the parts of the equation add up to 100%? Are the parts correct for that animal?), scale (Are representations by all members of a group to the same scale, so that easy comparisons are possible?), and clarity (Can the data be seen and understood easily?).

In addition, representation should be labeled with the name of the animal represented. It is also nice to include on the label intake in kilocalories per kilogram or per individual per year and perhaps average animal weight, for reference by those who do not recognize the creature.

Possible ways of representing the data include, but certainly are not limited to, pie charts (as used by our pilot test students), frequency histograms, and bar charts, examples of which are shown in Figure 1.

Students may get off to a slow start trying to understand how even to begin representing their animal's energy use in a pie chart. Once they understand what they are doing (expressing their animal's energy use as a percent), why using percentages rather than raw numbers is important, and how to go about doing this, they tend to become quite engaged with the material, to enjoy the process of making the pie charts, and to be excited by the results. This is an ambitious undertaking, which needs a lot of time and teacher support. Do not expect to move through this work quickly if students make decisions (with your support) about how to represent the data. Do expect them to be exhilarated at the results; this is heady material.

Possible Issues

This is a math-rich task that involves several issues, among them: why percents are appropriate; what is the whole of which these percents are part; why it is valid to represent data from a small animal with a pie chart (histogram, etc.) that is the same size as the pie chart for a large animal; how percentages can be represented visually; the difference between relative and absolute units of measure.

Percents

It may help students think about the usefulness of percents for comparison if you discuss the following or a similar example with them. One kind of question to ask your students is, "If an elephant puts 200,000 kilocalories into production and this is 1% of its total intake, what is its total intake?" Ask students not to look at the elephant's data as they think about how they would calculate total intake. There are several ways to think about this question, and it might be interesting for students to hear each other's ideas. Although high school students have worked with percentages before, some may not realize that taking 1% of a number is the same as dividing it by 100. Others may multiply 200,000 by .01. A more formal way of

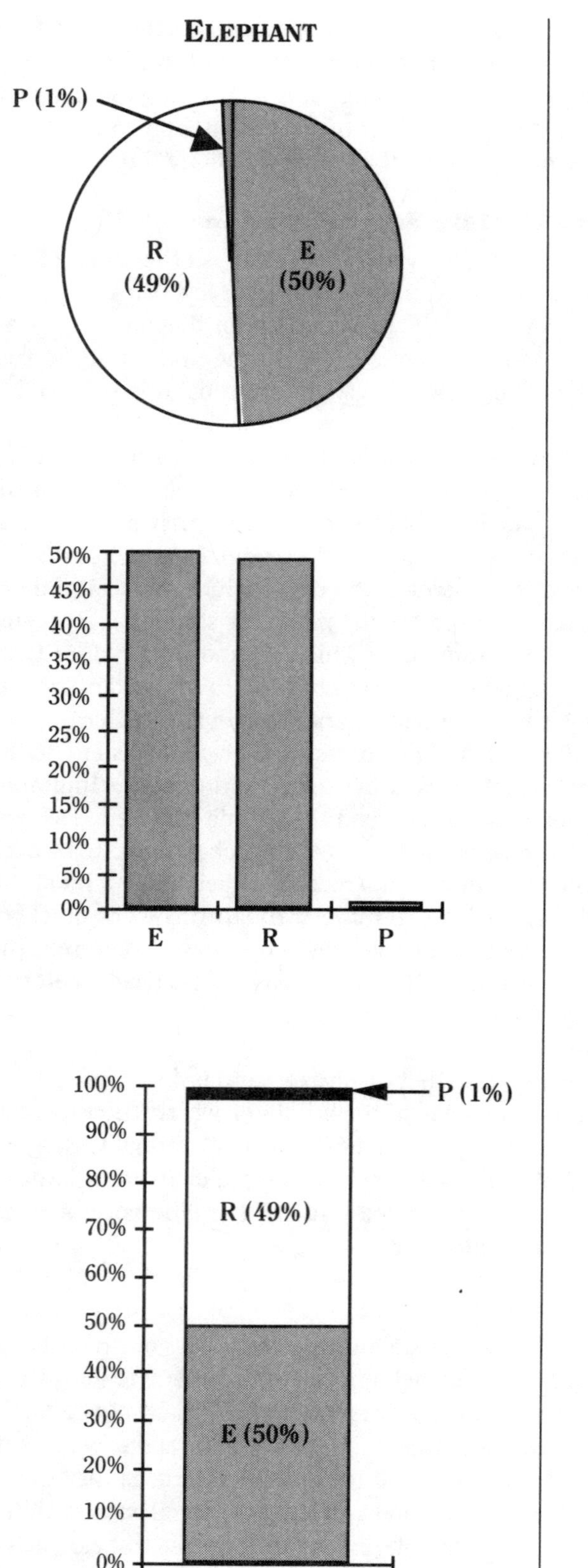

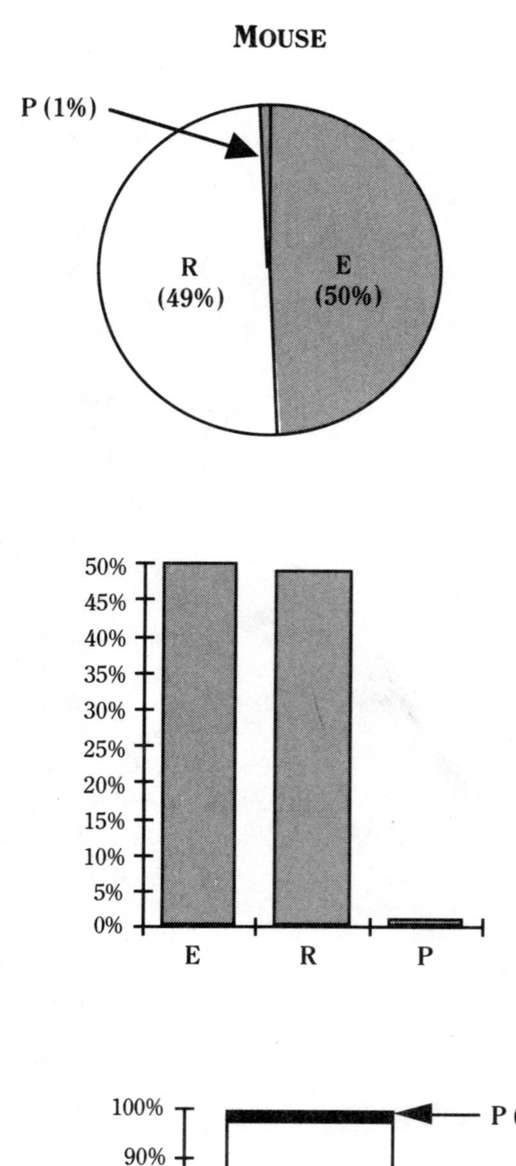

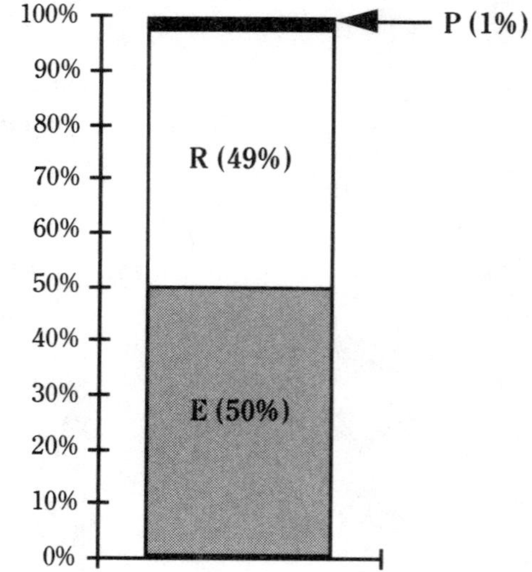

Figure 1. Sample representations of data.

approaching this problem would be to make production equal to 1% of intake:

$$P = 1\%\ I$$
$$200{,}000 = .01(I)$$
$$I = 200{,}000/.01$$
$$I = 20{,}000{,}000$$

After they have solved the problem, students may want to consult the elephant data.

Your students' understanding of how to solve such problems as turning kilocalories into percent of intake is also important in **Chapter 10**, when they trace the flow of energy from the sun, through plants and deer, and into a wolf.

If you like, photocopy and hand out the following problem:

> Try this experiment. Two of you go to a party at another school. The price of admission for each is 20% of the money in your pocket. One of you has a five-dollar bill, the other has $20. How much does each of you pay? Who takes a bigger hit? Why?
>
> Now which of you in proportion to, or relative to, the total amount of money in your pocket, takes a bigger hit? Why?
>
> Suppose that the price of everything at this party is set the same way, that is, some percent of the amount of money you had in your pocket when you arrived at the party. A soda is 15%; ice cream, 15%; pizza, 25%. Two sodas and two pizzas later, both of you are broke. Did you spend at the same rate? Did you spend the same amount? Explain.
>
> How does this example relate to intake data and using percents for comparisons? We set intake equal to 100%. In the case of your money, what equals 100%? How did you decide whether you both spent at the same rate or spent the same amount? This same reasoning can be applied to comparisons of the energy budget data.

Patterns in the Data

Once students have an accessible way of comparing their animals' energy uses, they begin to see patterns. (In fact, they may get ahead of Exploration 1 and be well into such comparisons already; see Classroom Vignette.) The most obvious patterns are between mammalian carnivores and herbivores, between vertebrates and the two invertebrates, and between mammals/birds and the salamander. The animals were chosen to provide a reasonable breadth of ecological and biological "types": carnivores and herbivores; large and small mammals; carnivores that eat invertebrates (insects, slugs, etc.) and carnivores that eat vertebrates; animals that do and those that do not maintain a constant body temperature. These "types" tend to have characteristic energy use patterns. For instance, herbivores have proportionately lower absorption values than do carnivores (50% versus 80%) and, thus, different excretion values. These differences are important to the animals themselves and to other species as well. Herbivore dung is a substantial source of food to other organisms (it still has half the caloric value of the original food), while carnivore dung is of relatively lower value.

The differences will raise questions about lifestyle, size, and method of staying warm. The clear correlation students can find from the animal data is between herbivores (high proportion of excretion) versus carnivores and between the two invertebrates and all the vertebrates. Remind them also of the tooth and skull differences they saw in **Chapter 1** and the dietary differences that go with those teeth and skulls.

"Relative" and "Absolute"

This work also raises issues of relative and absolute amounts of things. Sometimes students confuse a large proportion of energy being excreted (by the dung beetle versus the cheetah) as meaning that the dung beetle excreted more than the cheetah (see the Classroom Vignettes). Consider with them whether they are saying that a tiny dung beetle excretes more than a huge wildebeest or a large cheetah excretes less than a small millipede. What are they really saying? See the data representations in the Classroom Vignettes, which were made by the students discussing them.

Examples for Discussion

After discussing percentages, have your students compare relative energy expenditure data with absolute energy expenditure data. Begin these comparisons with a cheetah and a topi and ask this question: "How much of their intake energy goes to excretion, in absolute and relative terms?"

In one year, a cheetah typically takes in 2,400,000 kilocalories and excretes 480,000 kilocalories, which is 20% of its total intake. A topi takes in 2,300,000 kilocalories and excretes 1,150,000 kilocalories, which is 50% of its total intake. Thus, while a topi's total intake is smaller that a cheetah's, its excretion in kilocalories is quite a bit larger due to the large proportion of its intake that goes into excretion. A principal reason is the difference in the digestibility of the food each animal eats. Because a cheetah is more efficient at digesting its food, less energy is left unabsorbed.

Other pairs of animals to compare and talk about could be the following:

- Topi and deer. Like an elephant and a mouse, these two animals have different absolute energy expenditures but similar relative energy expenditures. That is due largely to the fact that both are endothermic and herbivores.
- Wolf and shrew. These two animals have very different absolute energy expenditures, but being endothermic, their relative expenditures are similar.
- Snake and weasel. Although the sizes of these two animals are comparable (about 200 g in each case), a snake has a much smaller absolute intake: 150 kcal as opposed to a weasel's 26,000 kcal. It would be interesting for students to speculate about what might account for such a significant difference in absolute intake, for example, that as an endothermic animal, a weasel's absolute intake needs to be much higher.

Presentations

Since students will be working with their animals for much of the rest of this Unit, it is helpful for them to become familiar at least with the other animals from their own ecosystem.

The obvious way for all students to see each other's data is to have each group present its data to the rest of the class. An alternative that ensures serious discussion is for two groups that used different forms of data representation to explain their choices and their data to each other. A third option could be for each group to affix its representations to a wall or board, so students can examine all the data either from their seats or by moving around the room.

EXPLORATION 3 GUIDE
Relative Energy Use: More Patterns

Students now build on Exploration 2 by continuing to sort animals by patterns of energy expenditure. They list their animal sets and make as many different sets as they can, describing the criteria they used for each. Once everyone has finished, ask students to share their sets and criteria.

Possible sets include the following:

Herbivores whose patterns of relative energy expenditure are generally similar. Their **E** term is relatively high since they eat a lot of roughage.

Carnivores, although their pattern of energy expenditure is more variable. Their **E** term is generally low, indicating that their food is more digestible for them than an herbivore's food is for it.

Endotherms, which typically have high respiration rates.

Ectotherms, which typically have lower rates of respiration and higher rates of production than endotherms.

Ask your students to speculate about what might account for the differences between the energy use patterns of millipedes and those of other animals. The smallest known endotherms weigh about 2 g, and there are only a few, such as hummingbird and shrew species. Below that limit, apparently it is not possible to eat enough to survive as an endotherm. By contrast, we do not know the possible upper limits to body size in endotherms. Some researchers say that dinosaurs that weighed over 100 tons were endotherms. So, actually, we do not know the upper limit to endothermic life on earth.

INTEGRATION GUIDE

Students have discovered that many factors are important to an animal's "lifestyle": natural selection and evolution, body size, diet, genetics and its "family" or who it is related to, its way of thermoregulating, where it lives and the abiotic factors of its habitat (such as temperature), and so on. Their writing should reflect some sense of integration among these factors at one or more levels.

THE ANIMAL CARDS

The animals are listed alphabetically by English name; each has its habitat listed (NHF is the Northern Hardwood Forest, and SEU the Serengeti Ecological Unit). There are 31 total, about half from each habitat.

BANDED MONGOOSE *(Mungos mungo)* NHF

Banded mongoose are highly social animals, typically living in packs of about 15 individuals (although packs may be twice that size). Breeding within a pack is synchronized, so that multiple females bear young within a few days of each other. The young suckle from any of the lactating (milk-producing) females in the pack, not just their own mothers. Both male and female adults in the pack "babysit" for the young while their mothers are out hunting; they also play with the young. In the process of such play, the young learn to socialize within the group and how to forage.

A mongoose that discovers an especially good food item, such as an ant nest, resists sharing the food with other members of the pack, squealing and growling at them. However, a mongoose that makes such a find generally cannot keep from making excited twittering and churring sounds, which immediately draw its fellow pack members to the food. As is usually the case, social life has both costs and benefits. (Consider also the lion or any of the dog family members: what are the costs and the benefits of their being social?)

A striking aspect of banded mongoose social behavior is their mobbing attacks. Fairly large predators, including large dogs, jackals, eagles, and vultures, can be repelled by one of these attacks. The mongooses cluster in a writhing, growling, spitting, snapping mass (with the young in the center) and advance toward their foes. Moreover, an individual mongoose will risk its own safety to free a fellow pack member from a predator. One male was seen climbing a tree to threaten an eagle that was about to eat a mongoose; the eagle dropped the captured mongoose, which survived.

Average adult weight: 1.5 kg
Size: head and body length, 30–40 cm; tail, 15–29 cm
Common foods: invertebrates, including beetles, millipedes, earwigs, ants, crickets, termites, plus some birds, eggs, and small vertebrates
Food intake: 1.0×10^5 kcal/individual/year
Energy use: $I = R + P + E$; $R = 78\%$, $P = 2\%$, $E = 20\%$; $I = 1.00 \times 10^5$, $R = 7.80 \times 10^4$, $P = 2.00 \times 10^3$, $E = 2.00 \times 10^4$
Offspring: 2–3 per litter (up to 6) and about 1–3 litters per year
Is eaten by: few species, although a number of medium-size mammalian carnivores and birds of prey sometimes try to hunt the mongoose
Population density: up to 18/km^2

BEAVER *(Castor canadensis)* NHF

Beavers are large rodents that are well known for their remarkable feats of engineering. Beavers can drastically alter their physical environment, creating new types of habitat in the process. When beavers build a dam across a small stream, they create a pond that can be many hectares in area (a hectare is slightly larger than two football fields). The pond floods and kills vegetation (often trees) that previously existed at the site, thus affecting both plant and animal life in the area.

Over time, the beaver pond fills with silt deposited by the stream and is then abandoned by the beavers (much the same process happens in reservoirs behind human-built dams). The filled pond becomes a meadow, creating an area of vegetation that is good browse for many species. As time goes by, bushes and then different tree species fill in the meadow, until after decades or centuries the meadow has become a forest. (Where do you think beavers go when their pond gets too big and they have used the available food trees? What risks might they run?)

Average adult weight: 18 kg
Size: head and body length, 62–76 cm; tail, 23–25 cm
Common foods: During summer: seeds, stems, roots of sedges and water grasses, and other aquatic plants. During winter: inner bark of tree branches stored during the summer; preferred species include aspen, poplar, birch, maple, willow, and alder.
Food intake: 6.2×10^5 kcal/individual/year
Energy use: I = R + P + E; R = 49%, P = 1%, E = 50%; I = 6.20×10^5, R = 3.04×10^5, P = 6.20×10^3, E = 3.10×10^5
Offspring: usually 2–4 per litter and 1 litter per year
Is eaten by: wolves; also hunted heavily by humans for their pelts
Population density: approximately 4/km^2 (increasing in the northeastern United States, where reforestation creates good beaver habitats but there are no wolves to help control the numbers of beavers)

BLACK-CAPPED CHICKADEE *(Parus atricapillus)* NHF

These lively little year-round residents of the Northern Hardwood Forest have a difficult time trying to eat enough to keep warm in winter. They have such relatively large surface areas that they lose heat very rapidly. On normally cold winter days, chickadees must spend most of the daylight hours looking for food to get them through the night. And, according to one study, at –40°C (which is the same as –40°F) chickadees must spend 20 times as much time feeding as they would during normal springtime weather.

Average adult weight: 10 g
Size: 12–14 cm
Common foods: insects, seeds, and fruit
Food intake: 3.5×10^3 kcal/individual/year
Energy use: I = R + P + E; R = 73%, P = 2%, E = 25%; I = 3.50×10^3, R = 2.56×10^3, P = 7.00×10^1, E = 8.75×10^2
Offspring: 6–8 per year
Is eaten by: owls
Population density: data not available

BLUE JAY *(Cyanocitta cristata)* NHF

These familiar birds have remarkably broad diets. They are among the most intelligent of birds and have excellent memories—they store large numbers of seeds and are able to find many of them. They also show good memory in laboratory situations. Feed them something red and bad-tasting once, and they avoid all red foods for a long time.

One of their springtime feeding methods makes use of their ability to mimic the scream of the red-shouldered hawk. When small birds hear this sound, they often flee for dense underbrush, thinking the predatory hawk is nearby. The jays then raid the birds' abandoned nests, sucking out the contents of eggs or eating the young.

Jays also mob other predatory birds, including hawks, crows, and owls. Several adults together repeatedly circle and attack a predator in the air, finally driving it away from the area. (Why do you think jays might carry out such so-called "mobbing" behavior?)

Average adult weight: approximately 77 g
Size: 28–31 cm
Common foods: feeds from ground to treetops on fruit, seeds, acorns, nuts, insects, spiders, snails, tree frogs, small fish, eggs, and young birds
Food intake: 1.5×10^4 kcal/individual/year
Energy use: I = R + P + E; R = 73%, P= 2%, E = 25%; I = 1.50×10^4, R = 1.10×10^4, P = 3.00×10^2, E = 3.75×10^3
Offspring: 4–6 per year
Is eaten by: owls
Population density: data not available

BUSH HYRAX *(Heterohyrax brucei)* SEU

Although they are mammals, hyraxes are notable for their poor ability to regulate their body temperatures metabolically. They are quite gregarious and live in colonies of 5 to 34 animals. These two aspects of bush hyraxes explain a great deal of their behavior.

Smaller than the closely related rock hyrax, bush hyraxes live on and in rocky outcrops that emerge from the plains. There, they live in groups deep among the rocks, using entrance holes too small for their predators to pass through. The temperature deep in their rock homes fluctuates far less than the outside temperature, which is a real advantage for them. They often sunbathe early on sunny mornings, presumably to raise their body temperature after the cool nights. Conversely, they avoid the midday sun, since they overheat under such conditions. Bush hyraxes feed mainly on the foliage of trees and bushes, especially acacias, and are excellent climbers.

Not only do bush hyraxes form colonies with members of their own species, they often share home territories, sleeping holes, and huddle in the sun with rock hyraxes. Such close association between two mammal species is also highly unusual for mammals. The only possibly similar examples may be some monkeys that live in multispecies groups. (What advantages and disadvantages can you think of for two species to share resources so closely?)

Average adult weight: 1.8 kg
Size: 30–47 cm length
Common foods: leaves of trees and bushes
Food intake: 1.2×10^5 kcal/individual/year
Energy use: I = R + P + E; R = 49%, P = 1%, E = 50%; I = 1.20×10^5, R = 5.38×10^4, P = 1.20×10^3, E = 6.0×10^4
Offspring: 1–4 per litter and 1 litter per year
Is eaten by: snakes, eagles, owls, jackals, and several different cats (including leopards and lions)
Population density: 2,000–5,000/km^2

CHEETAH *(Acinonyx jubatus)* SEU

Known as the fastest land animal alive, the cheetah can reach speeds of up to 90–112 km per hour (60–70 mph). However, the cheetah pays a price for this sprinting speed—it cannot run very far at high speed without overheating (remember that energy spent on metabolism ends up as heat). Cheetahs try to get to within 50 m of their prey before they begin their sprint. After a mere 300-m run, a cheetah's breathing rate may get as high as 150 breaths per minute, its body temperature goes way up, and it needs half an hour to cool down before its next chase. Although cheetahs are faster than Thomson's gazelles (their preferred prey on the Serengeti), gazelles make sharp turns that cheetahs often cannot match; after a few turns the cheetah may be so tired that it must give up. All in all, though, cheetahs are quite successful hunters, observed in one study as catching their prey in over 40% of hunts.

Being built for speed has one additional cost: their light build does not equip cheetahs to defend their kills against other large predators. Cheetahs lose at least 10% of the prey they catch to lions, hyenas, and other carnivores. They often also lose their cubs to the same predators and may well soon be extinct, at least in the Serengeti. (What might happen to the balance among mammals in the Serengeti if cheetahs become extinct?)

Average adult weight: 50 kg
Size: 70–90 cm shoulder height
Common foods: Thomson's gazelles, hares, young wildebeest, impalas
Food intake: 2.4×10^6 kcal/individual/year
Energy use: I = R + P + E; R = 75%, P= 5%, E = 20%; I = 2.40×10^6, R = 1.80×10^6, P = 1.20×10^5, E = 4.80×10^5
Offspring: 3–4 young per litter (range 1–8) and about 1 litter every 2 years
Is eaten by: cubs eaten by many large predators, including other cats and large eagles
Population density: 1–2/100 km^2

DEER MOUSE *(Peromyscus maniculatus)* NHF

Deer mice, which may be the most abundant mammal in their habitats, remain active throughout the year. They typically set aside a store of food for the winter, up to 3 liters in volume. Males often stay with the females and help raise the young. In fact, these mice are generally quite tolerant of others of the same species, and they may huddle in groups in winter. Such sociality is not always the case among rodents; some are quite aggressive toward individuals of their own species. (What might be advantages and disadvantages of such sociality within a species?)

Average adult weight: 27 g
Size: head and body length, 7–10 cm; tail, 5–12 cm
Common foods: seeds, nuts, acorns, insects
Food intake: 5.49×10^3 kcal/individual/year
Energy use: I = R + P + E; R = 49%, P= 1%, E = 50%; I = 5.49×10^3, R = 2.67×10^3, P = 5.49×10^1, E = 2.74×10^3
Offspring: 3–4 per litter (range 1–9) and 3–4 litters per year (in the laboratory, up to 14 litters per year)
Is eaten by: owls, weasels, foxes, domestic cats
Population density: 100–2,500/km^2

EASTERN CHIPMUNK *(Tamias striatus)* NHF

Chipmunks do not hibernate but survive the winter by eating food they have stored in underground burrows. Another help in getting through the winter is the ability of chipmunks to become torpid for 1 to 8 days. During such periods of torpor, their metabolism slows down considerably and their body temperature drops, so they consume far fewer calories.

As you may know, chipmunks have special enclosed cheek pouches that open into their mouths. A chipmunk can transport surprisingly large quantities of food in these pouches—one biologist counted 31 kernels of corn in a chipmunk's cheek pouches. When full, each pouch can be nearly the size of the chipmunk's head.

Average adult weight: approximately 0.1 kg
Size: head and body length, 12.7–15 cm; tail, 7–10 cm
Common foods: acorns, nuts, seeds, mushrooms, fruits, berries, and occasional insects, bird eggs, and small vertebrates
Food intake: 1.7×10^4 kcal/individual/year
Energy use: I = R + P + E; R = 49%, P= 1%, E = 50%; I = 1.70×10^4, R = 8.33×10^3, P = 1.70×10^2, E = 8.50×10^3
Offspring: 4–5 per litter (range 1–9) and 1–2 litters per year
Is eaten by: snakes, birds of prey, coyotes, foxes
Population density: approximately 500–1,000/km^2

EASTERN COTTONTAIL *(Sylvilagus floridanus)* NHF

The diet of the cottontail, a small North American rabbit, contains a wider variety of plant food than that of any other mammal in North America. They do not hibernate during winter but get through the cold months eating twigs and bark from woody plants.

Widely hunted by humans for sport, food, or to prevent damage to crops, the cottontail has been transplanted to a number of areas outside its natural range to improve hunting. Among the consequences of this human activity is the decline of populations of the New England cottontail (a related species), which is suffering a double disaster: loss of its habitat and out-competition by the Eastern cottontail. (What does it actually mean if one species "out-competes" another? Is that also what is happening between the African wild dog and some of its carnivore competitors, like lions and hyenas? How might humans help keep that from happening?)

Average adult weight: 1.5 kg
Size: head and body length, 35–43 cm
Common foods: large variety of herbaceous vegetation in summer, bark and twigs in winter
Food intake: 1×10^5 kcal/individual/year
Energy use: I = R + P + E; R = 49%, P= 1%, E = 50%; $I = 1.00 \times 10^5$, $R = 4.90 \times 10^4$, $P = 1.00 \times 10^3$, $E = 5.00 \times 10^4$
Offspring: 3–6 per litter (range 1–12) and 3–7 litters per year
Is eaten by: wolves, foxes, weasels, owls; killed by humans
Population density: approximately 1,000/km^2 in two studies

ELEPHANT *(Loxodonta africana)* SEU

Elephants have remarkable social lives. Herds of females and their young typically contain 9–11 individuals (range 2–24). These herds are distinctly matriarchal—they are led by the oldest female of the group and usually contain the matriarch's young, her grown daughters, and their young. The experience and leadership of the matriarch (who may be as old as 50 or 60 years) appear to be critical to the lives of elephants, so females often live well past the age of reproduction. This extended period of postreproductive life is highly unusual among animals, although humans also live past the age when they can reproduce. (Why do you think it might be unusual?)

Males can either be solitary or form herds that contain between 2 and 14 animals. Adolescent males (about 12 to 20 years of age) gradually separate from the herd in which they were born, eventually gaining membership in a bull herd.

Because an elephant eats about 4%–6% of its own body weight each day, a moderate-size herd can have a major impact on an area's vegetation. In Kenya's confined Tsavo National Park, the population density of elephants rose high enough during the 1960s and 1970s that a woodland was changed into a grassland by the elephants tearing up young trees and knocking over mature trees to get at leaves. These changes altered the food supply available for other herbivores, for example, other ungulates, insects, monkeys, and elephant populations then dropped by a quarter to a third during a severe drought.

These extraordinary animals can alter their surroundings tremendously if they cannot migrate away from areas such as some national parks where their food supplies have been reduced. On the other hand, in many areas elephant populations have been in serious decline lately; the animals were heavily hunted over the past 15 or 20 years as the price of ivory increased astronomically (several orders of magnitude per kilogram). Only with the recent ban on the international sale of ivory has this hunting been somewhat checked. Humans must learn how to deal with elephant populations somehow; to ignore the elephant is a choice that has major implications for entire ecosystems, as well as for the elephants themselves.

Average adult weight: 3,500 kg (males much larger than females)
Size: 2.5–3 m shoulder height
Common foods: grasses, herbs, and leaves of bushes and trees
Food intake: 2.0×10^7 kcal/individual/year
Energy use: I = R + P + E; R = 49%, P= 1%, E = 50%; I = 2.00×10^7, R = 9.80×10^6, P = 2.00×10^5, E = 1.00×10^7
Offspring: 1 every 4–9 years
Is eaten by: young elephants may be eaten by lions and hyenas; habitat loss and human killing account for most deaths
Population density: approximately 6/100 km^2 but varies greatly among regions

Garter snake *(Thamnophis sirtalis)* NHF

Like most reptiles, garter snakes do not maintain a high body temperature by metabolic means. They do increase body temperature by changing their behavior, such as by moving into the sunlight to warm up. In winter, when temperatures are so low that these snakes cannot move about, they hibernate, typically underground and often in groups. The snakes migrate to special hibernation sites in about October and return to their home ranges in March or April. Members of each hibernating population tend to be genetically related to one another, a loose family group. They do not, however, seem to show the same sort of social behavior as, say, a lion, elephant, or hyrax family group. (What advantages and disadvantages might there be for garter snakes to hibernate in such groups?)

Average adult weight: approximately 200–300 g
Size: 46–66 cm length
Common foods: earthworms (80% of food items eaten) plus many other types of small vertebrates and invertebrates
Food intake: 1.5 10^2 kcal/individual/year
Energy use: I = R + P + E; R = 72%, P= 8%, E = 20%; R = 1.08×10^2, P = 1.2×10^1, E = 3.0×10^1
Offspring: typically 14–40 per litter (range 3–85) and 1 litter per year. Garter snakes bear live young.
Is eaten by: owls, weasels, blue jays, to name a few
Population density: data unavailable

Gray fox *(Urocyon cinereoargenteus)* NHF

Gray foxes live in family groups of two parents and their offspring. Young foxes stay with their parents for several months, then forage on their own within their parents' home range for a few more months after that. Finally, they go off to find mates and establish their own territories. Females typically breed during their first year.

The gray fox is a remarkably good tree climber and is sometimes called the "tree fox." Their homes (dens) may be in piles of brush or rocks, burrows in the ground, or a hollow tree. One such tree den was found 9 m above ground level. When pursued by human hunters, gray foxes sometimes climb trees to escape.

(This species is in competition with the red fox, which was introduced a few hundred years ago by European settlers. What effects might this competition have had on the gray fox?)

Average adult weight: 5 kg
Size: head and body length, 53–74 cm; tail, 28–41 cm
Common foods: small vertebrates, insects, fruits, grains, and other plant materials (these foxes eat more plant matter than do other foxes)
Food intake: 2.0×10^5 kcal/individual/year
Energy use: I = R + P + E; R = 78%, P= 2%, E = 20%; I = 2.00×10^5, R = 1.56×10^5, P = 4.00×10^3, E = 4.00×10^4
Offspring: approximately 4 per litter (range 1–10) and 1 litter per year
Is eaten by: young occasionally eaten by birds of prey; adults and young killed by humans
Population density: 0.4–10/km^2

GRAY WOLF (TIMBER WOLF) *(Canis lupus)* NHF

Timber wolves are very social animals, typically living in packs of 5–8 (packs may contain as many as 36 wolves). It appears that success in hunting their large prey, such as deer and moose, depends on their ability to work as a group. In fact, pack size increases where the most common prey species is very large and where more wolves are needed to take part in the hunt. For example, on Isle Royale in Michigan, where moose are their main food, packs contain 15–20 wolves. Packs consist of a mated pair and their offspring of several different years. Large packs may split and eventually create separate territories. Alternatively, individual wolves may leave the pack and join another single wolf to begin forming a new pack.

Before being hunted heavily, the timber wolf had one of the largest ranges of any living land mammal; it was found throughout most of the Northern Hemisphere, including much of North America, Europe, and Asia, and even occurred in North Africa (although it did not live in dry deserts or tropical forests). Now, however, the wolf's range is much more restricted, and populations are greatly reduced. In the United States, for example, where wolves previously lived throughout most of the country, they are now found only in Alaska and small portions of Minnesota and Wisconsin, on Isle Royale in Lake Superior, and in a few remote areas in the Rocky Mountains. An experiment currently underway is reintroducing them to their native habitat in Yellowstone National Park.

Average adult weight: 45 kg
Size: 66–71 cm shoulder height
Common foods: deer, caribou, moose, and elk
Food intake: 2.0×10^6 kcal/individual/year
Energy use: I = R + P + E; R = 78%, P= 2%, E = 20%; I = 2.00×10^6, R = 1.56×10^6, P = 4.00×10^4, E = 4.00×10^5
Offspring: 5–7 per dominant pair in a pack
Is eaten by: heavily hunted by humans
Population density: 0.2–4/100 km^2

GREAT HORNED OWL *(Bubo virginianus)* NHF

Great horned owls are impressive predators, capturing a wide variety of prey, some of which outweigh the owls by a large margin. These birds appear to dislike other predatory birds nesting nearby; one owl was observed killing a red-tailed hawk that nested too close to its nest. In the far north, population densities of these owls are heavily influenced by the wide fluctuations in the populations of hares, which are key components of their diet.

Average adult weight: approximately 1.3 kg
Size: 46–63 cm
Common foods: wide variety of small and medium invertebrates, including skunks, minks, weasels, rabbits and hares, birds, mice, amphibians, reptiles, and scorpions
Food intake: 7.0×10^4 kcal/individual/year
Energy use: I = R + P + E; R = 77%, P= 3%, E = 20%; I = 7.00×10^4, R = 5.39×10^4, P = 2.10×10^3, E = 1.40×10^4
Offspring: 2–3 per year
Is eaten by: hunted only by humans
Population density: one well-studied pair had a 15.5-km^2 territory

HARTEBEEST *(Alcelaphus buselaphus)* SEU

Formerly very numerous, hartebeest populations have declined due to loss of habitat, hunting by humans, and competition with domestic cattle. Hartebeest typically live in herds containing up to 300 females and young; occasionally multiple herds join together in loose groups of up to 10,000. Adult males typically are not members of herds and can be either territorial or nonterritorial, while younger males often form large bachelor herds. Once young males mature, they set off to challenge for ownership of a good territory. Such territories contain a variety of plant types, good access to water, and several other features attractive to hartebeest. Competition for good territories is fierce, and males are usually able to defend and keep a good territory for only a few months. What might be advantages and disadvantages to belonging to each of the different social groups?

Average adult weight: 135 kg
Size: 107–140 cm shoulder height
Common foods: grasses
Food intake: 2.6×10^6 kcal/individual/year
Energy use: I = R + P + E; R = 49%, P= 1%, E = 50%; I = 2.60×10^6, R = 1.27×10^6, P = 2.60×10^4, E = 1.30×10^6
Offspring: 1 per year
Is eaten by: may be preyed on by lions, although not where wildebeest or zebras (preferred prey species) are plentiful
Population density: approximately 0.7/km^2

IMPALA *(Aepyceros melampus)* SEU

Impala herds typically contain 6 to 100 females and young. Multiple herds are loosely grouped into "clans." Clans are quite stable in their membership and quite faithful to their home ranges—they do not move very far.

Adult males typically are not members of herds; they can be either territorial or nonterritorial, with younger males often forming "bachelor herds" of 5–35 animals. Once these young males mature, they challenge mature males for ownership of territories. (What advantages or disadvantages might there be for a male to being territorial or nonterritorial?)

Average adult weight: 52 kg
Size: 40–90 cm shoulder height
Common foods: grasses when they are green; herbs and foliage at other times
Food intake: 1.0×10^6 kcal/individual/year
Energy use: I = R + P + E; R = 49%, P= 1%, E = 50%; I = 1.00×10^6, R = 4.90×10^5, P = 1.00×10^4, E = 5.00×10^5
Offspring: 1 per year
Is eaten by: leopards, wild dogs, cheetahs
Population density: 5/km^2

LEOPARD *(Panthera pardus)* SEU

These large, solitary cats are widespread, ranging from Africa to Korea and Java. Although they are capable of running at speeds of up to 60 km per hour, their hunting method is to stalk prey to a very short distance, less than 5 m if possible. From that point, they pounce. If they miss, they rarely chase their prey. If they do chase, they do not run more than 50 m.

A single leopard on the ground is no match for the social carnivores (lions, hyenas, and wild dogs), which readily take over a leopard's kill. To prevent losing their prey, leopards often carry their kills up into trees, where they can eat unmolested.

Leopards are listed as threatened or endangered throughout all of their range. (What do you think might make leopards more vulnerable to extinction than, say, lions?)

Average adult weight: 45 kg
Size: 55–70 cm shoulder height
Common foods: impalas, Thomson's gazelles, young wildebeest and zebras, hares, birds, even beetles; they also scavenge
Food intake: 1.2×10^6 kcal/individual/year
Energy use: I = R + P + E; R = 78%, P= 2%, E = 20%; I = 1.20×10^6, R = 9.36×10^5, P = 2.40×10^4, E = 2.40×10^5
Offspring: 1–3 cubs per litter and 1 litter about every 2 years
Is eaten by: Leopards have been heavily hunted by humans throughout much of their range for their pelts. Cubs are easy prey for other carnivores, and habitat destruction contributes to their decline.
Population density: about 4/100 km^2

LION *(Panthera leo)* SEU

Lions are the largest of the African carnivores. They are considered to be the only social cats—they typically live in close-knit groups of about 15 lions (the groups range in size from 4 to 37 animals). Living in groups enables lions to hunt in groups, and the success rate of group hunts is roughly 60% higher than that of solitary hunts. (About half of the hunts performed by lions involve two or more lions working in concert.) Of course, there is a trade-off here—group hunting means that more food can be brought in, but group living also means that there are more mouths to be fed. On average, however, group hunting is overall more efficient. (What other advantages and disadvantages might there be to living in a group?)

Although lions are able to reach maximum speeds of 48–59 km per hour, they rarely can sustain this speed for more than 100 m. Thus, lions must carefully stalk their prey and usually do not charge unless they are within 30 m of the animal they are hunting. (How might group hunting fit in with this need to stalk prey?)

Lions were once the most widespread wild land mammal. Ten thousand years ago, lions were found in most of Africa, Europe, Asia, North America, and northern South America. Their decline appears to have been due primarily to habitat destruction. Also important are competition from humans hunting the same prey species and humans hunting lions in defense of livestock or for sport. Because they reproduce readily and are relatively flexible about where they can live, African lions are not endangered in some parts of Africa. (The Indian lion is near extinction.)

Average adult weight: 170 kg
Size: 110–120 cm shoulder height
Common foods: wildebeest, zebras, Thomson's gazelles; they also scavenge a great deal
Food intake: 3.3×10^6 kcal/individual/year
Energy use: I = R + P + E; R = 78%, P= 2%, E = 20%; I = 3.30×10^6, R = 2.57×10^6, P = 6.60×10^4, E = 6.60×10^5
Offspring: usually 3–4 cubs per litter and 1 litter every 18–26 months
Is eaten by: cubs that have been left alone temporarily may be eaten by lions from other prides and by spotted hyenas; old and diseased lions may suffer the same fate. The primary killers of lions, however, are humans.
Population density: about 12/100 km^2

PLAINS ZEBRA *(Equus burchelli)* SEU

Zebras live in either of two types of social groups: families consisting of a male, 1 to 6 females, and their young; or small "bachelor groups" of stallions. In a family group, the dominant male is quite protective of the other members and will often stay behind in a defensive posture when predators approach, thus allowing the others to escape. Females usually remain in the same family group their entire lives. Although some stallion groups are stable for years, usually membership in those groups changes fairly frequently.

(What advantages might there be for a female to stay in her family group throughout her lifetime? What disadvantages?)

Average adult weight: 235 kg
Size: 127–140 cm shoulder height
Common foods: grasses
Food intake: 3.8×10^6 kcal/individual/year
Energy use: I = R + P + E; R = 49%, P= 1%, E = 50%; I = 3.80×10^6, R = 1.86×10^6, P = 3.80×10^4, E = 1.90×10^6
Offspring: 1 every 1–3 years
Is eaten by: hyenas, wild dogs
Population density: 8/km^2

RED-BACKED SALAMANDER *(Plethodon cinereus)* NHF

Which single vertebrate species contains the most biomass at the Hubbard Brook Forest in New Hampshire? Red-backed salamanders. Not only that, but red-backed salamanders make up more biomass there than all birds during their peak breeding season. Researchers have calculated that there are about 2,600 red-backed salamanders per hectare. Since a hectare is a bit larger than two football fields, that works out to over 1,000 salamanders in an area the size of a football field—a lot of salamanders!

The number of salamanders found in different areas of Northern Hardwood Forest probably varies, but these creatures are clearly important in the forests. (Remember Dr. Wyman's salamander-density data and hypothesis from the Reading on approximations in **Unit 1, Chapter 1.**) Salamanders appear to play a key role in nutrient cycling by eating many of the small invertebrates that mechanically break down leaf litter. By eating vast numbers of tiny detritivores, salamanders might markedly decrease the rate of nutrient cycling in these forests. In turn, salamanders form a high-protein food source for garter snakes, small mammals, and some birds. Thus, as both predators and as prey, these small, hard-to-see creatures play a major role in the energy picture of the Northern Hardwood Forest.

The single vertebrate species that contains the most biomass in the other habitat, the Serengeti, is probably the wildebeest or the two hyrax species. Compare the numbers to determine which habitat seems to have more biomass per square kilometer (km^2) of its top species. For salamanders, 0.7 g each × 260,000 animals per km^2 = 182 kg of salamander. What about the biomass per square kilometer of the wildebeest or the two hyrax species combined? Use 60 wildebeest/km^2, 2,800 rock hyrax/km^2, and 3,500 bush hyrax/km^2. Which habitat has more biomass in its top biomass species?

Average weight: 0.7 g
Size: 5.9–10 cm length
Common foods: large variety of invertebrates, especially mites and insects; also earthworms, snails, slugs, spiders, sow bugs, and millipedes
Food intake: approximately 4.0×10^0 kcal/individual/year
Energy use: I = R + P + E; R = 42%, P= 39%, E = 19%; I = 4.00×10^0, R = 1.70×10^0, P = 1.60×10^1, E = 7.0×10^{-1}

Offspring: 7–10 eggs deposited during summer
Is eaten by: garter snakes, shrews, ground-feeding birds
Population density: 260,000/km^2 at the Hubbard Brook Forest in New Hampshire

RED SQUIRREL *(Tamiasciurus hudsonicus)* NHF

Like the common gray tree squirrel, the red squirrel does not hibernate. (This is in contrast with many ground squirrels, which do hibernate.) Thus, red squirrels must either find food during winter (often a difficult task) or put aside stores of food to be eaten during the cold months. Red squirrels cache large amounts of food, especially entire conifer cones and mushrooms, for winter use. (A related species of red squirrel, *T. douglasii*, carries unopened cones to streams or damp spots under rotting logs, where it stores them. The wet conditions keep the cones from opening until the squirrel retrieves them later in the winter.)

The red squirrel's habit of burying seeds in the ground appears to have helped reforestation in areas that have been heavily deforested by humans. Although the squirrels are able to retrieve many of the seeds that they bury, some seeds germinate before the squirrels get to them. Thus, the squirrels can have a marked effect on their entire ecosystem.

Red squirrels live in forests rather than in the more urban areas favored by the gray squirrel, which was brought to this country by European settlers. (Could red squirrels live in more urban areas if larger gray squirrels were not there? How might you find out?)

Average adult weight: 0.25 kg
Size: head and body length, 17–20 cm; tail, 10–15 cm
Common foods: primarily pine and spruce seeds; nuts, buds, fruits, bark, mushrooms, sap, bird eggs and young; also mice and young rabbits
Food intake: 3.0×10^4 kcal/individual/year
Energy use: I = R + P + E; R = 49%, P= 1%, E = 50%; $I = 3.00 \times 10^4$, $R = 1.47 \times 10^4$, $P = 3.00 \times 10^2$, $E = 1.50 \times 10^4$
Offspring: typically 4–6 per litter (range 1–8) and 2 litters per year (spring and summer)
Is eaten by: hawks, owls, foxes
Population density: up to 700/km^2 in good habitat

ROCK HYRAX *(Procavia johnstoni)* SEU

Although they are mammals, hyraxes are notable for their poor ability to regulate their body temperatures metabolically. They are quite gregarious and live in colonies of up to 26 animals. These two aspects of rock hyraxes explain a great deal of their behavior.

These plump, short-legged animals live on and in rocky outcrops that emerge from the plains. There, they live in groups deep among the rocks, using entrance holes too small for their predators to pass through. The temperature deep in their rock homes fluctuates far less than the outside temperature, which is a real advantage for them. They often sunbathe early on sunny mornings, presumably to raise their body temperature after the cool nights. Conversely, they avoid the midday sun, since they overheat under such conditions. These animals are able to feed unusually rapidly for herbivores. They take large mouthfuls of grass and eat their fill in less than an hour a day. Such rapid feeding enables them to choose the times of day when they feed, rather than having to feed for long hours during both hot and cold times. It also means they spend less time in the open, where they are more vulnerable to many predators.

Not only do rock hyraxes form colonies with members of their own species, they often share home territories, sleeping holes, and huddle in the sun with bush hyraxes. Such close association between two mammal species is also highly unusual for mammals. The only possibly similar examples may be some monkeys that live in multispecies groups. (What advantages and disadvantages can you think of for two species to share resources so closely?)

Average adult weight: 3 kg
Size: 40–60 cm length
Common foods: grasses
Food intake: 1.8×10^5 kcal/individual/year
Energy use: I = R + P + E; R = 49%, P= 1%, E = 50%; I = 1.80×10^5, R = 8.82×10^4, P = 1.80×10^3, E = 9.00×10^4
Offspring: 1–3 per litter and 1 litter per year
Is eaten by: snakes, eagles, owls, jackals, several different cats (including leopards and lions), foxes, weasels, and mongooses
Population density: 500–4,000/km^2
Population density: up to 10/km^2 where prey animals are abundant

SHORTTAIL SHREW *(Blarina brevicauda)* NHF

If shorttail shrews were to have a motto, it would probably be "Live fast, die young." Few individuals survive past the age of a year, but they reproduce at an early age: females can mate 6 weeks after birth and males 12 weeks after birth. These animals are active throughout the year, spending much of their time scurrying along runways in leaf litter, snow, or underground. They can consume huge quantities of insect larvae underground. Since many of these larvae develop into plant-eating insects, shrews can help protect gardens and crops. They are, however, often killed by the pesticides people apply to the ground to kill the very larvae the shrews eat. (If you were a farmer, how might you figure out if you would be better off with more shrews and no larva-killing pesticide? What data might you need, and for how long?)

These tiny, quick animals (they weigh less than five nickels) are fierce predators. When they bite their prey, they inject a paralyzing nerve poison from special glands in their jaws. Shrew bites are reportedly painful for humans for several days.

Average adult weight: 23 g
Size: head and body length, 7–10 cm; tail, 1.9–3 cm
Common foods: insects, worms, snails, other invertebrates, salamanders, mice, and plant material
Food intake: 4.86×10^3 kcal/individual/year

Energy use: I = R + P + E; R = 78%, P= 2%, E = 20%; I = 4.86×10^3, R = 3.79×10^3, P = 9.72×10^1, E = 9.72×10^2
Offspring: about 5–7 per litter (range 3–10) and up to 3 litters per year
Is eaten by: extremely distasteful, so hardly ever eaten by anything; however, often killed by humans
Population density: 300–3,000 individuals/km^2

SHORTTAIL WEASEL (ERMINE) *(Mustela erminea)* NHF

This small, lithe animal undergoes two complete color changes every year. In winter, its fur is completely white, except for the tip of the tail, which is black. During that time, the shorttail weasel is typically called an "ermine" and is often trapped by humans for its fur. In summer, its back and sides become a chocolate brown (the underside remains white, and the tip of the tail stays black); in this color phase, it is often called a "stoat" and its fur has little or no economic value. (What advantage might such color changes offer? Think about where weasels live and the seasons there. Why might the summer coat have no value to human fur dealers?)

Females become sexually mature at the age of 2 or 3 months and sometimes mate during their first summer. As with many other weasels, the shorttailed weasel exhibits a remarkable phenomenon: the delayed implantation of fertilized eggs into the uterus wall. Fertilized eggs may go for as long as 9 months before implantation in the uterus and development of the embryos. Once development begins in the early spring, it is only about a month before the tiny young are born, weighing only 1.5–3 g at birth, or less than an $8\frac{1}{2} \times 11$ inch piece of paper. (Why might it be advantageous to bear young only during the springtime rather than later in the summer?)

Average adult weight: approximately 0.2 kg
Size: head and body length, 13–25 cm; tail, 0.5–1.2 cm
Common foods: mice and other small rodents, birds, eggs, insects, frogs, and occasional larger animals such as hares
Food intake: 2.6×10^4 kcal/individual/year
Energy use: I = R + P + E; R = 78%, P= 2%, E = 20%; I = 2.60×10^4, R = 2.03×10^4, P = 5.20×10^2, E = 5.20×10^3
Offspring: approximately 6 per litter (range 3–18) and 1 litter per year
Is eaten by: owls
Population density: up to 10/km^2 where prey animals are abundant

SLENDER MONGOOSE *(Herpestes sanguineus)* NHF

Unlike the banded mongoose, the slender mongoose is solitary in its behavior. Both sexes maintain territories; female territories seem not to overlap with one another, while male territories do. In addition, a male's territory is larger and typically includes the territories of two females. Being solitary, the slender mongoose does not have the option of threatening predators in a group, as the banded mongoose does. Instead, it becomes motionless or hides at the sight of predators such as eagles. Interestingly, these creatures show little fear of snakes and are willing to attack even poisonous snakes that threaten them. (Have you ever seen how fast a snake can strike—that it is almost too fast to see? What sorts of movements would a mongoose or any animal need to be successful in a "boxing match" with a snake?)

Average adult weight: 0.5 kg
Size: head and body length, 28–32 cm; tail, 28 cm
Common foods: rodents, lizards, snakes, birds, hyraxes, squirrels
Food intake: 5.4×10^4 kcal/individual/year
Energy use: I = R + P + E; R = 78%, P= 2%, E = 20%; I = 5.40×10^4, R = 4.21×10^4, P = 1.08×10^3, E = 1.08×10^4
Offspring: 2–4 per litter and about 2 litters per year
Is eaten by: eagles, snakes
Population density: no data available

SPOTTED HYENA *(Crocuta crocuta)* SEU

Spotted hyenas are typically the most abundant large carnivores in the undisturbed savannas of East Africa. Moreover, they are probably the most efficient carnivores when it comes to eating vertebrate prey: they eat everything, including bones, horns, hair, and skin. The only parts of their prey that they typically do not eat are the contents of the rumen (the first "stomach" of ruminants such as antelopes) and the heavy horn bases of large animals such as wildebeest. They also scavenge, eating dead prey of other carnivores or animals that have died of wounds, age, or illness. They will even take over a kill made by lions or other carnivores, chasing away the animals that actually made the kill.

Like most members of the dog family, hyenas live in family groups, packs of related animals. They also hunt in groups, which further increases their efficiency at getting food. (What do you think might make the spotted hyena less vulnerable to extinction than, say, the wild dog?)

Average adult weight: 58 kg
Size: 79–90 cm shoulder height
Common foods: wildebeest, Thomson's gazelles, zebras
Food intake: 1.4×10^6 kcal/individual/year
Energy use: I = R + P + E; R = 78%, P= 2%, E = 20%; I = 1.40×10^6, R = 1.09×10^6, P = 2.80×10^4, E = 2.80×10^5
Offspring: 2 per litter (range 1–4) and 1 litter every 12–18 months
Is eaten by: essentially no one
Population density: about 12/100 km^2

THOMSON'S GAZELLE *(Gazella thomsoni)* SEU

The Thomson's gazelle is a medium-size antelope that can sprint faster than any of its predators except the cheetah. These gazelles can reach speeds of up to 80 km per hour (50 mph), but they start to tire after running only 1 or 2 km. After a few kilometers of running, the gazelle's body temperature rises 5–6°C (remember, energy spent on respiration is transformed into heat), and the animal becomes exhausted. Hyenas and wild dogs have much better endurance than the gazelle (they pant while running to keep cool) and often catch up after the gazelle's initial sprint and bring down their prey.

Since they eat only green vegetation during the dry season, Thomson's gazelles typically move to areas of higher rainfall or near water in search of green plants. They also need to drink water, so when in dry areas, they travel up to 16 km every other day to get it.

Although these gazelles, with dark stripes along their flanks, are featured in nearly all nature films about the African savannahs, they are actually quite restricted in their distribution. They inhabit only the area around the Serengeti and two other regions in East Africa and only above 600 m in elevation. (How might this higher altitude affect their sunning and their heat production?)

Average adult weight: 20 kg
Size: 58–70 cm shoulder height
Common foods: grass (only when it is green); green herbs and leaves of bushes (when grass is dry and tough)
Food intake: 6.0×10^5 kcal/individual/year
Energy use: I = R + P + E; R = 48.3%, P= 1.7%, E = 50%; $I = 6.00 \times 10^5$, $R = 2.90 \times 10^5$, $P = 1.02 \times 10^4$, $E = 3.00 \times 10^5$
Offspring: typically 1 calf at a time. (However, because pregnancy lasts only about six months and females can mate two weeks after giving birth, two calves can be born in just over a year.)
Is eaten by: wild dogs, cheetahs, spotted hyenas, lions, leopards
Population density: approximately 25–30/km^2

TOPI *(Damaliscus lunatus)* SEU

The social behavior of the topi is remarkably variable. In some areas, mature males hold fairly permanent territories extending over 100–400 hectares. Each such territorial male maintains a group of several female topis and their young; intruding males are driven away by the resident male. In other regions, males maintain only small, temporary territories during the breeding season; such territories are about 1–3 hectares in extent. In still other regions, males form large breeding groups of up to 100 individuals. Females visit these groups (which are known as leks) to mate. The leks are located at the same places year after year, even though the topi herd moves around the plains almost constantly. Topi females and their young can either form small herds within a single male's territory or be part of a larger aggregation milling about the plains. (What might be advantages or drawbacks of the different types of territories?)

Average adult weight: 115 kg
Size: 104–126 cm shoulder height
Common foods: grasses
Food intake: 2.3×10^6 kcal/individual/year
Energy use: I = R + P + E; R = 49%, P= 1%, E = 50%; $I = 2.30 \times 10^6$, $R = 1.13 \times 10^6$, $P = 2.30 \times 10^4$, $E = 1.15 \times 10^6$
Offspring: 1 per year
Is eaten by: young eaten by several different predators; adults sometimes

preyed on by lions, although not where wildebeest or zebras (preferred prey species) are plentiful

Population density: 2/km^2

WHITETAIL DEER *(Odocoileus virginianus)* NHF

These large herbivores are well known for their hides, their meat, and their movie role, and as garden pests. The history of these widespread animals is quite interesting, and illustrates several of the different effects that humans can have on ecosystems.

Before Europeans settled in North America, whitetail deer populations were probably in the range of 23–40 million individuals. Native Americans hunted deer and actually managed many of the eastern forests by frequent controlled burning to improve habitat for deer and other game animals (deer like to eat many of the plants that colonize areas after fires). With the arrival of Europeans, several conditions changed. First, commercial markets developed for both venison (deer meat) and deer hides. These markets meant that hunters (now using firearms) were not simply supplying their families with food but might be fulfilling the needs of dozens or hundreds of people. In addition, with the spread of agriculture, the deer began to lose their preferred habitats—forest edges and regenerating forests. On the other hand, settlers were also eliminating wolves from much of the deer's range, thus freeing them from their primary animal predators. Overall, though, deer populations took a real beating. By 1900, deer were totally absent from most of their range; there were probably only 300,000 or 500,000 individuals left alive.

Around the turn of the century, regulations were enacted protecting deer, and states began management programs to increase deer populations (largely for hunting). In addition, with the abandonment of many agricultural areas in the east and the subsequent regeneration of forest in these areas, tremendous amounts of prime deer habitat were created. Finally, with wolves exterminated throughout most of the United States, the stage was set for deer populations to rise rapidly. The whitetail deer population is currently estimated to be 14 million, a far cry from where they were in 1900. In just a few centuries, humans nearly wiped this creature out by overhunting and habitat destruction and then enabled its remarkable comeback through creation of habitat and overhunting of its predators.

Average adult weight: 70 kg

Size: 91–107 cm shoulder height

Common foods: many types of leaves, including yew, hemlock, white cedar, and yellow birch, plus fungi, acorns, grass and herbs when available

Food intake: 1.5×10^6 kcal/individual/year

Energy use: I = R + P + E; R = 48.7%, P= 1.3%, E = 50%; I = 1.50×10^6, R = 7.31×10^5, P = 1.95×10^4, E = 7.50×10^5

Offspring: typically 1 fawn at a time (range 1–4) once a year

Is eaten by: wolves; fawns may be eaten by coyotes; adults hunted by humans

Population density: up to 25–50/km^2

WILD DOG *(Lycaon pictus)* SEU

Wild dogs are social animals. They live in packs that typically contain 10 individuals (6 adults and 4 young), although they can form packs of over 40 animals. Because they have specialized to feed on prey animals that are too large for a single dog to hunt efficiently, they must hunt in packs. By hunting in groups, wild dogs are remarkably effective: up to two kills per day, with success rates of up to 70–85% in their chases—a remarkable record.

Although wild dogs are slower than gazelles, they have much greater endurance than their prey animals. If the dogs can keep their prey in sight, working as a pack they can often run an animal to ground in a couple of kilometers. Although not sprinters, wild dogs can maintain a pace of 56 km per hour (35 mph) for a few kilometers without overheating (they pant while running to stay cooler). In addition, the hunting ranges of these animals can be very large; a single pack in the Serengeti may have a range of 1,500–2,000 km^2.

Despite this hunting efficiency, however, wild dogs are in severe decline and may be suffering from some disease, perhaps a domestic dog disease. Mostly, the survival rate of pups in the Serengeti is very low, due to predation by lions and hyenas. Unfortunately, these creatures are in grave danger of extinction. (Why do you think the hyena might not be similarly endangered?)

Average adult weight: 23 kg
Size: 60–75 cm shoulder height
Common foods: Thomson's gazelles, impalas, hares, wildebeest calves, zebras
Food intake: 7.5×10^5 kcal/individual/year
Energy use: I = R + P + E; R = 78%, P= 2%, E = 20%; $I = 1.50 \times 10^5$, $R = 5.85 \times 10^5$, $P = 1.50 \times 10^4$, $E = 1.50 \times 10^5$
Offspring: about 10 pups per litter and 1 litter every 12–14 months
Is eaten by: young eaten by hyenas and lions
Population density: 1 adult/200 km^2

WILDEBEEST (BRINDLED GNU) *(Connochaetes taurinus)* SEU

Wildebeest are large, powerful, and fast antelopes, with short curved horns and a beardlike tuft on their chins. An outstanding feature of wildebeest is their migratory behavior—virtually all of the 1.3 million wildebeest in the Serengeti migrate on a seasonal basis in search of green grass and water (they need to drink daily). Think of it: hundreds of millions of kilograms of wildebeest flesh moving en masse about the Serengeti. Over 1 million mouths—hungry mouths—all moving together. Over 4 million hooves bearing on the ground. What are the implications for grasses growing in the areas wildebeest migrate into? What are the implications for other herbivores? What are the implications for carnivores that prey on these animals? And for dung beetle populations?

The wildebeest, along with the other herbivores of the Serengeti, are the last great assemblage of large land mammals. In other comparable grassland areas (the North American grasslands, the South American pampas, and the Russian steppes), humans have taken over much of the habitat for cattle and feed production and/or have killed the native herbivores. Even the Serengeti is under severe pressure by humans for agricultural uses.

Average adult weight: 250 kg
Size: 115–138 cm shoulder height
Common foods: short grass
Food intake: 4.0×10^6 kcal/individual/year
Energy use: I = R + P + E; R = 49%, P= 1%, E = 50%; I = 4.00×10^6, R = 1.96×10^6, P = 4.00×10^4, E = 2.00×10^6
Offspring: typically 1 calf per year, with most calves being born during a 2- to 3-week period early in the rainy season
Is eaten by: lions, hyenas; wildebeest calves are eaten by wild dogs, cheetahs, and leopards
Population density: approximately 60/km^2; however, typically found at much higher densities since they form very dense groups

SCIENCE BACKGROUND

If necessary, refer to Science Background in **Chapter 3**.

REFERENCES

See also References in **Chapter 5** for more literature on body size and its effects.

Thomas, Roger. 1982. A Cold Look at the Warm-Blooded Dinosaurs. Boulder, CO: Westview Press.
This book is out of print, but it is a nice summary and can be found in libraries.

CLASSROOM VIGNETTES

Students compare the proportional energy uses by their animals. They find several parts of the work especially engaging: how best to represent the differences; how to interpret the differences (absolute vs. relative differences); and the magnitude of the differences.

RM: I forgot, what does production include?
S: Reproduction and new tissue.
P: I have the biggest production of everyone. [He is representing a wolf's energy use.]
TEACHER: Why do you think that is so?
P: Because of the terrain.
TEACHER: What else does a wolf have to contend with?
P: Keeping warm.
TEACHER: It takes a lot of energy to keep warm. Think of your heating bill. What else do you notice?

[The students examine the various pie charts they have made. See Figure 2. Note that they have rounded off some numbers for ease of calculation.]

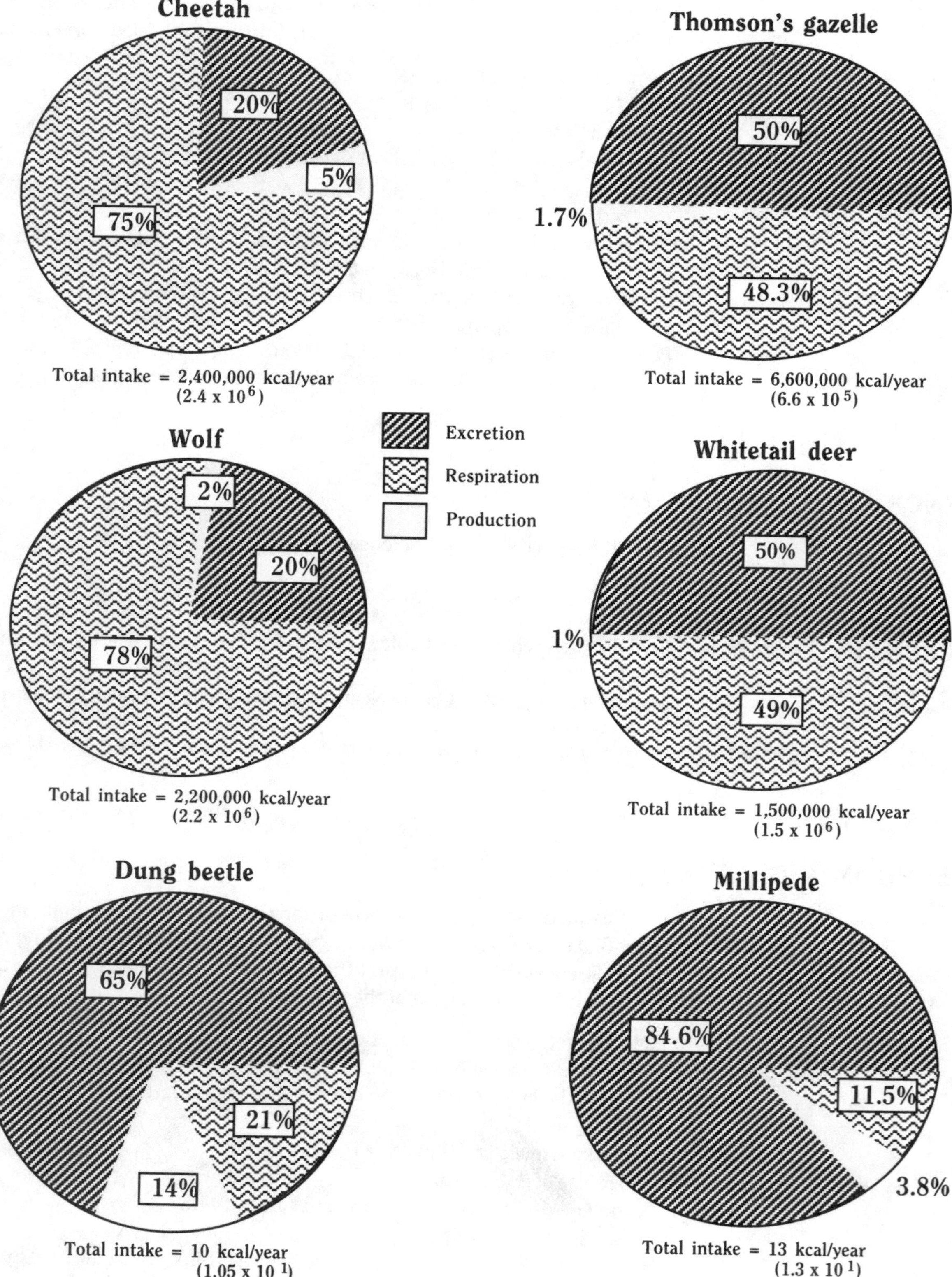
Cheetah
20%
5%
75%
Total intake = 2,400,000 kcal/year
(2.4 x 10⁶)
Thomson's gazelle
50%
1.7%
48.3%
Total intake = 6,600,000 kcal/year
(6.6 x 10 ⁵)
Excretion
Respiration
Production
Wolf
2%
20%
78%
Total intake = 2,200,000 kcal/year
(2.2 x 10⁶)
Whitetail deer
50%
1%
49%
Total intake = 1,500,000 kcal/year
(1.5 x 10⁶)
Dung beetle
65%
21%
14%
Total intake = 10 kcal/year
(1.05 x 10 ¹)
Millipede
84.6%
11.5%
3.8%
Total intake = 13 kcal/year
(1.3 x 10¹)

RB: The smaller the animal, the more excretion.
S: Production is so little.
RM: Production is similar (among all the animals).
P: The carnivores have approximately the same, the herbivores the same, detritivores the same.
TEACHER: Why would respiration be so different between carnivores and herbivores?
RB: Carnivores spend time chasing foods and their homes are complicated.
P: Excretion is the same between carnivores, herbivores, and detritivores.
RM: For herbivores, as they eat there is less nutrient values per ounce so they have to excrete more. For carnivores, they eat less nondigestible material.
P: Carnivores are respirating so much that they don't have as much waste as herbivores because they are using so much.
TEACHER: What about detritivores? What are they eating?

["Soil, leaves." The students pass over this topic.]

S: The smaller the animal, the more excretion.
TEACHER: It may look that way at first glance. But ask yourself this: "Are we saying that a millipede is actually producing more dung than a cheetah? Who is more efficient?"
P and RM: The dung beetle.
TEACHER: What do you think?
RM: If production is reproduction and cell rebuilding, they are going to get damaged. The other animals have fur to protect them.
RB: The dung beetle has very little else to do (than eat).
TEACHER: The dung beetle may produce 50 offspring, but carnivores just a few.
TEACHER: Looking at the Thomson's gazelle diagram, "what percentage will be available to its predator, the cheetah? How much energy will be available?"

[Several students say 1.7 percent because that is the amount being produced.]

TEACHER: The wolf and deer?
RM: 1 percent.
TEACHER: What's happening to energy? What percentage of the sun's energy is making it to the wolves and cheetahs?
RM: Very little. 1 percent or less. I can't remember.
S: You mean that reaches the earth?
TEACHER: What percent of that gets to those predators or to us humans?
RM: Very little.
TEACHER: In a sense, this whole unit is about energy lost.
RM: But why is it better to eat lower on the food chain?

[This last question is put on hold until the session on energy flow among organisms in **Chapter 10**, for which it provides a terrific opening question. Although we do not include a transcription of that pilot session, RM is able to answer her question satisfactorily. That is, she understands that eating plants (primary producers) is far more energy efficient for the ecosystem than is eating an herbivore (e.g., beef), not to mention eating a carnivore (e.g., dog or snake, as in some cultures). She is quite excited by her discovery, since her family is vegetarian.]

[The discussion ends here. Afterward, the teacher asks for reactions to the material, and gets the following responses:

"Very interesting."

"Fun."

"Hands-on great!"

"Interesting after all the aggravation [the math]."

"Once we understood the point, it was interesting."

"It helps a lot to see things visually, not just to look at the numbers."

"You can compare the differences with pie charts. Numbers show you something, but these charts show you a lot."]

Moose Are Not Mice—Size Matters

Chapter Five

Contents

Introduction

Body size is one of three key issues underlying an animal's energy use. The other two are diet—what it eats—and thermoregulation—whether, how, and to what extent the animal regulates its body temperature. If we know these three facts about an animal, we can predict many other things. For instance, a large mammal that eats insects (invertebrates) or plants will have a slower metabolism than a same-size mammal that eats other vertebrates. You remember from comparing the sloth and penguin intakes that, per unit weight, leaves have fewer kilocalories than fish and other penguin food (**Chapter 3**). Typically, a slower metabolism goes with lower-energy food.

That is not to say which came first, nor that a slower metabolism is "worse" than a faster metabolism. We cannot say whether a metabolism is slow because the animal eats invertebrates or, conversely, that an animal eats invertebrates because it has a slow metabolism. Moreover, there are advantages to a slower metabolism, such as you need less energy. (For more on this, see the Excerpt, "Size and Shape," and the delightful book by K. Schmidt-Nielsen.)

In the next several sessions, students consider aspects of body size. Beginning with a homework exploration, students compare small and large mammals by their relative food intake, that is, by how many kilocalories per kilogram of body weight per day each requires to "run" basic respiration. While it may be entirely obvious that total intake is greater for larger mammals than for smaller ones, it is surprising to learn that smaller mammals take in more energy per unit weight. In class students explore how surface area and volume vary for different sizes of cubes. They consider implications of those differences on processes like heat loss from cubes. Then they apply their insights to some large and small mammals. Finally, they integrate their understanding of size and heat loss with their understanding of energy loss.

KEY CONCEPTS

- Body size is an important aspect of animal energy use. Small animals lose body heat faster than comparable larger animals, because small animals have a disproportionately greater surface area.
- Surface area is a function of two linear dimensions of a body; volume is a function of three dimensions. Thus, surface area is a square power, while volume is a cube power. (To get an idea of how these vary, consider the graph in Figure 1.)
- At small body sizes, surface area and volume are more alike than they are at increasing body sizes. In other words, with an increase in body size, volume increases much more quickly than does surface area.
- "Relative" and "absolute" embody a useful concept of comparison. They imply some measuring or quantifying—counting units of something and comparing those units against some standard or reference frame that is also in units, such as units of size or time.

MATERIALS AND PREPARATION

In Advance

Make or get at least one **set of (paper) cubes** with side lengths of 8, 24, 40, and, if possible, 72 inches. Students will need the larger cubes for reference.

Materials

- **Some sugar cubes.** If you want students to work more with cubes of sugar cubes, there are 198 cubes in a standard box of sugar cubes ("dots"). That allows construction of one cube of maximum length side of five cubes ($5 \times 5 = 25$, $25 \times 5 = 125$; $6^3 = 216$ is just a bit more than one box).
- **Wooden blocks** are also helpful and less messy but larger.

In class students can build one or two paper cubes to work with or you can provide the following materials:

- **Paper** for making boxes
- **Scissors**
- **Sticking tape**
- **Ruler or tape measure**
- **Calculators**
- **Graph paper** (regular and log/log paper also, if possible)

SUGGESTED SEQUENCE OF SESSIONS (6–8)

Homework: Exploration 1

Students examine data on relative intake (in kcal) and animal size (in kg) to discover that small animals have greater relative intakes.

Class Session 2

Discuss the Homework (Exploration 1). Pay special attention to student ideas about relative and absolute intake.

Class Session 3

Students explore properties of cubes (which serve as model animals), from what a cube is to calculating its surface area and volume (Exploration 2). (If they make paper cubes, you will need another class session, Optional Exploration 2a).

Class Session 4

Continue Session 3 as necessary.

Class Session 5

Students work in groups to extrapolate from nonliving cubes to animals, or "living cubes." Working with moose and mice, they discover that animals also have a surface area and volume, which are subject to the same properties as those of paper or sugar cubes. Thus, small animals (and cubes) have relatively more surface area than large ones. Since heat leaves a body at its surface, small cubes (animals) lose relatively more heat.

Class Session 6

Continue Session 5 as necessary.

Assign the Reading as Homework or to be read in class. Students discover more aspects of animal lifestyles that vary with size.

Discuss and summarize the concepts.

Class Session 7

Continue Session 6 if necessary.

SESSION GUIDES, BY WORKSHEET

EXPLORATION 1 GUIDE
Relative Intake and Body Size

Students either do this Exploration in class or bring in their homework results (some arrangement of the relative intake data). Although they may find it trivial to discover the pattern (small animals have high relative intakes), they likely have not considered what that means or even quite what relative intake is. A brief class discussion can plunge them into both, as well as allowing them to practice data representation.

A Standard of Comparison

"Relative" and "absolute" embody a useful concept of comparison. They imply some measuring or quantifying: counting units of something and comparing those units against some standard or reference frame that is in the same units, such as units of size or time. We use "relative" and "absolute" with regard to intake. Thus, we compare intake in kilocalories per unit time per unit weight. Small mammals take in fewer kilocalories per year, total, than do larger mammals. In other words, the absolute intake of large mammals is greater than that of small mammals. However, small mammals take in more kilocalories per unit weight—that is, relative to their size—than do large mammals. These concepts are essential for understanding body size and heat loss. So a brief discussion of them is a good opener to the class. Refer back to **Chapter 4** and why percentages are a useful tool in exploring the concepts of "relative" and "absolute."

Discussion Guide Questions

These questions may already have come up in **Chapter 3**, Exploration 2. Questions about relative and absolute intake might include these: Are we saying that a (vole, hare, weasel) eats more than a (cheetah, wildebeest, kob)? What does "kcal per gram" actually mean? How does that information relate to the whole animal? What happens if we multiply kcal per gram by the animal's weight? How does that relate to total intake? What are the units of comparison? Draw a picture or write down what we are comparing. Is the idea of "total intake" helpful? What does "total intake" mean? Is that relative or absolute?

Data Representation

The data on mammal weight and relative intake can be represented in several ways, such as ranking or graphing. (Discussion of the concept of "relative" and "absolute" can also stem from student displays of their results on the board.)

Ask students to describe their data patterns verbally and graphically. If your students have implemented other sections of this curriculum, they will have represented more complex data sets before and likely will be ready to move on from this quite quickly.

Students may find help with data presentation and representation in **Chapter 4** or the **Technique: Preparing a Presentation.**

EXPLORATION 2 GUIDE
Size, Shape, and Energy Needs

Students derive some information about body size by studying stylized animals, that is, different-size cubes, same shapes (cube) of different volumes, and different shapes (rectangles) of a fixed volume. And they discover that physical laws apply to living as well as nonliving things.

Cubes: Same Shape, Different Volumes

Students can make at least two sizes of cubes from a regular piece of 8.5 × 11 sheet of paper (Optional Exploration 2a). They can work with blocks or paper cubes you have for them, or they can use sugar cubes ("dots").

Different-Size Cubes

If they make cubes from paper, students are likely to be quite absorbed by making cubes and will spend easily 20 minutes.

After their first study of the cubes, students may hesitate over their conclusions about surface area and volume of small and large cubes. Encourage them to continue calculating values for a range of cube sizes sufficient for them to trust the resulting patterns. They can also graph their values on log/log graph paper, graphing edge length (X axis) by area or by volume (Y axis).

The work with cubes can be expanded in several ways. Students can derive the formulas for surface area and volume (in which case, have them do so before they read the Exploration). And they can explore square and cube functions and their properties more generally.

They may also be uncertain what this has to do with ecology or even just living things. The relationships will become more apparent as students continue through the remainder of these materials.

Sample Data

Some sample data for different-size cubes follow:

	L	$SA = 6L^2$	$V = L^3$
"Small cube"	1.5	13.5	3.4
"Large cube"	3	54	27
Cube 3	6	216	216
Cube 4	12	864	1,728
Cube 5	24	3,456	13,824

As a first approximation of the relationship between SA and V, have students plot L^2 and L^3 for various lengths (Figure 1).

Remember that these values are not the same as SA and V, but that SA varies with L^2 and V varies with L^3. These are approximations, in the same way that we have been using squares and rectangular solids as approximations of animals. (**NOTE:** In Figure 1, the values in parentheses to the right of the L^3 line are L^3 values for L = 12, 16, and 20. These cannot be plotted here because the Y axis is not long enough.)

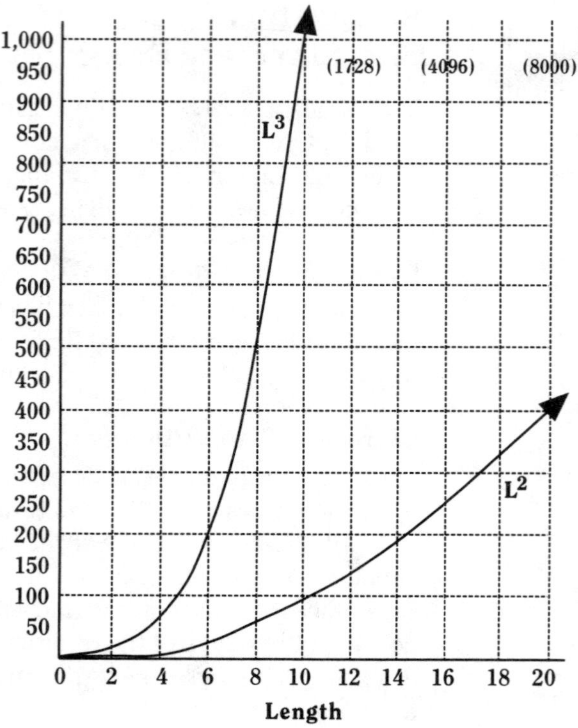

Figure 1

Rectangles: Same Volumes, Different Shapes

Although there is no formal activity in the Exploration on these shapes and their proportions, you may wish to pursue this work if students are especially interested or if you can do it in conjunction with a math class.

A set of possible rectangular "animals" whose volume is 24 cm^3 are pictured below, along with their dimensions.

After most students have finished making as many "animals" as they can and looking for patterns in the data, they choose one of their rectangular "animals" and decide whether it makes more sense for it to be ectothermic or endothermic. Students need to keep in mind that increased surface area increases heat loss. Thus, a snakelike animal with the dimensions $24 \times 1 \times 1$ would have higher energy needs due to heat loss and might more likely be an ectotherm. An animal at the other end of the spectrum, with the least surface area, say, one whose dimensions are $4 \times 3 \times 2$, would have less trouble staying warm and would therefore more likely be an endotherm. It may be helpful to have handy a few books with pictures of animals for students to look through as they think of real animals that resemble the rectangular ones.

L × W × H = 24 × 1 × 1; SA = 98 cm²; V = 24 cm³

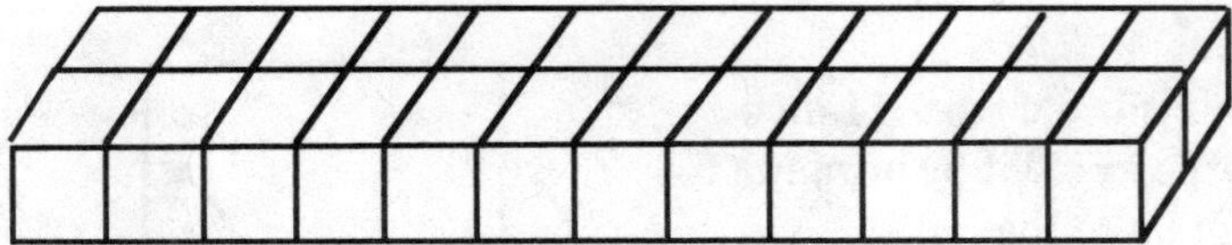

L × W × H = 12 × 2 × 1; SA = 76 cm²; V = 24 cm³

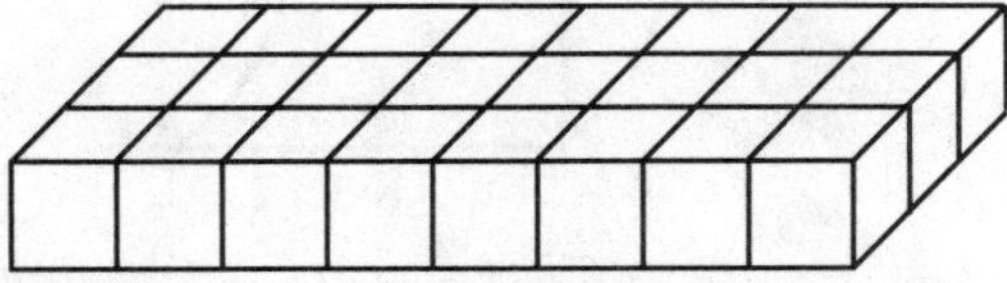

L × W × H = 8 × 3 × 1; SA = 70 cm²; V = 24 cm³

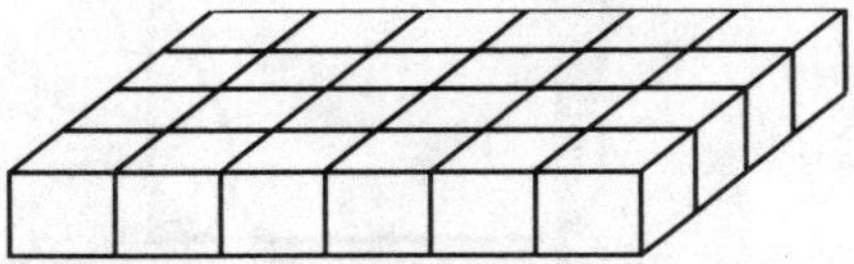

L × W × H = 6 × 4 × 1; SA = 68 cm²; V = 24 cm³

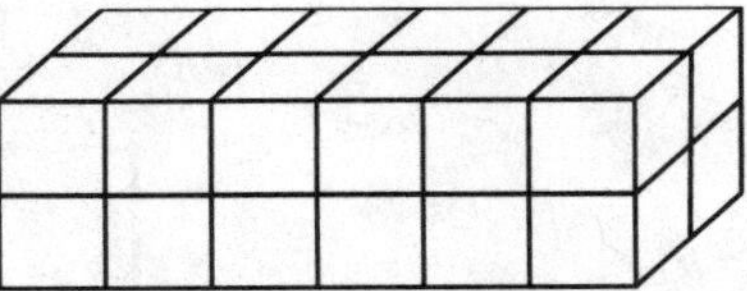

L × W × H = 6 × 2 × 2; SA = 56 cm²; V = 24 cm³

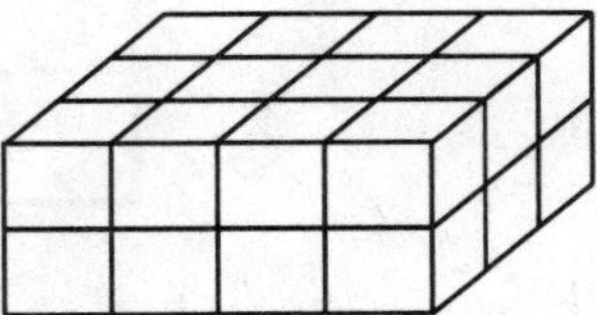

L × W × H = 4 × 3 × 2; SA = 52 cm²; V = 24 cm³

Optional Exploration 2a
BUILDING CUBES

1. Start with a normal 8.5 × 11 inch sheet of paper. Fold it by bringing the bottom up to the top as illustrated, with the fold on the dotted line. Now you have a double piece, 8.5 × 5.5 inches.

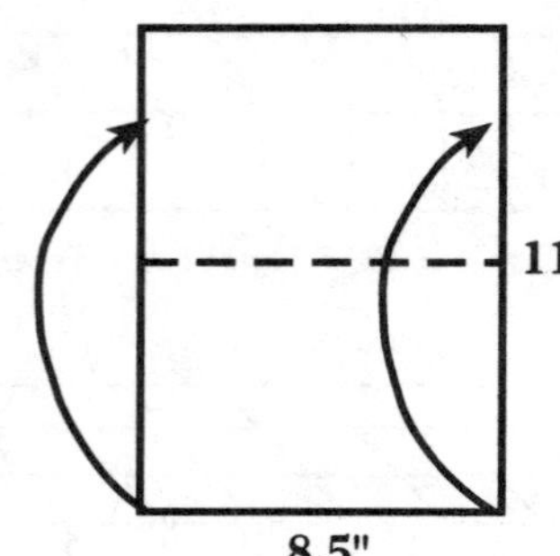

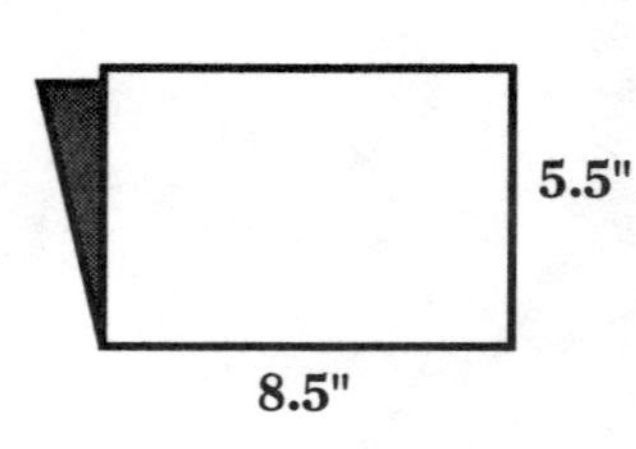

2. Repeat, bringing the bottom up again, to get a piece of 4 thicknesses, 8.5 × 2.75 inches.

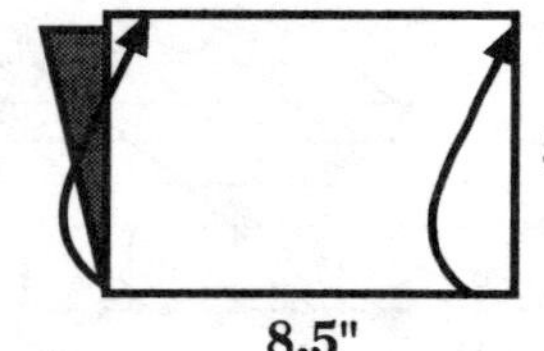

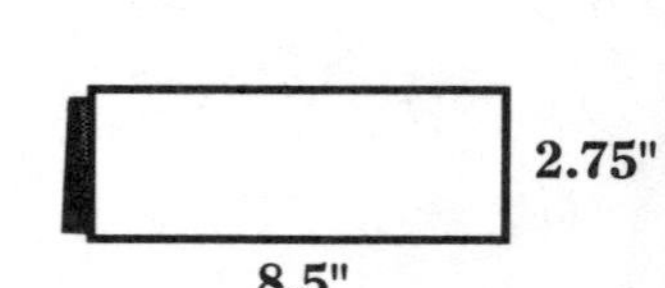

3. Now unfold the paper back to its original flat size.

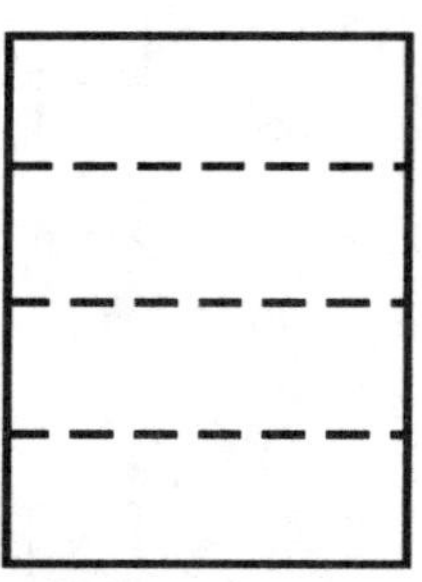

4. Make new lengthwise folds. Fold the paper twice, lengthwise, into three equal widths.

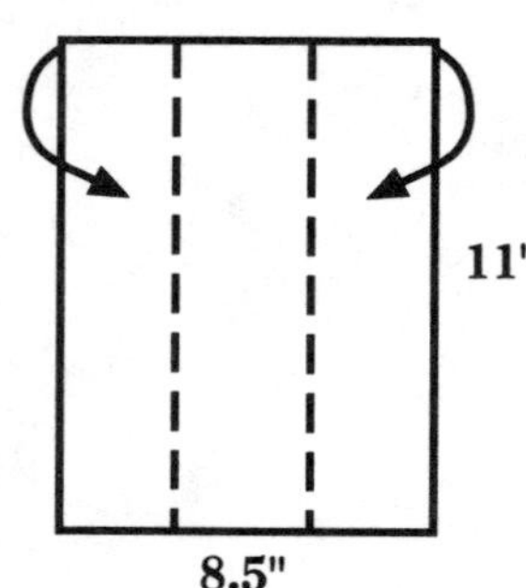

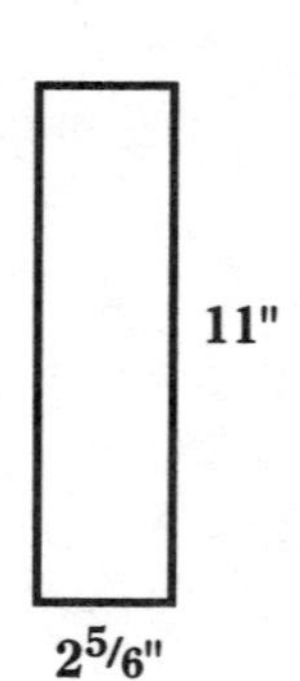

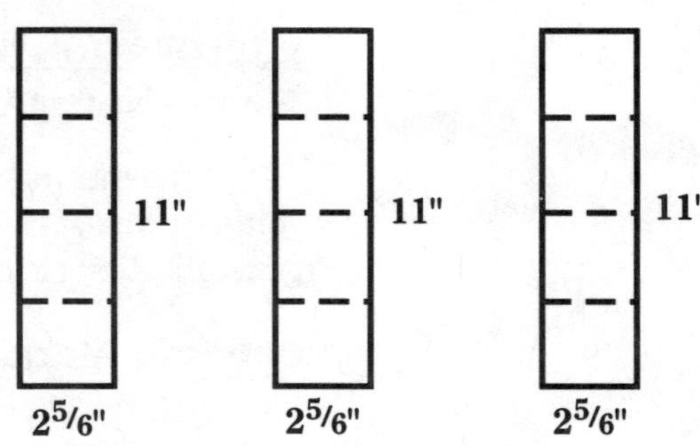

5. Cut along the lengthwise folds (or make the creases sharp and tear along them). Now you have three equal strips of paper, approximately 3 × 11 inches.

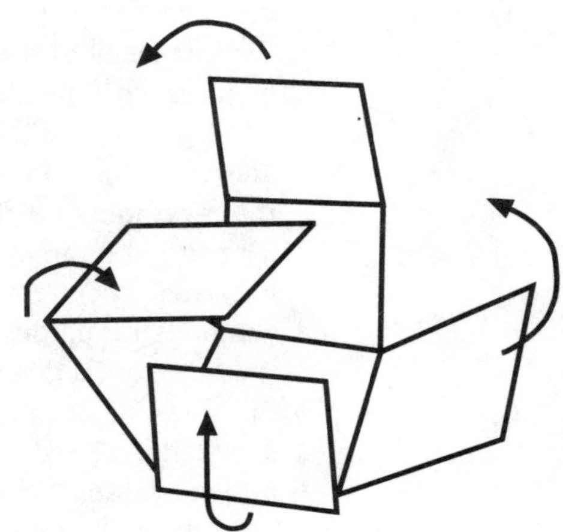

6. Using two of the strips, bend them along the creases from the first set of folds to form a cube. Some sides will have two thicknesses of paper. Tape the cube so it holds its shape.

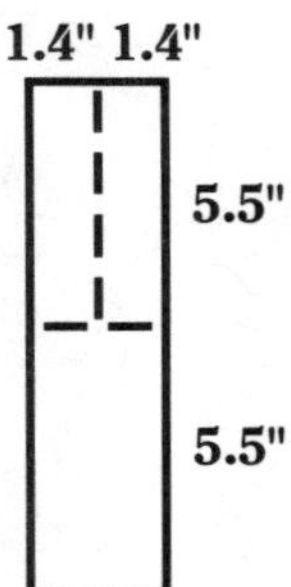

7. Cut the remaining strip two times, at the dotted lines.

8. With the two small narrow strips make a second cube, and tape it too.

EXPLORATION 3 GUIDE
Moose-Mouse Comparisons

Students may still be thrashing out their ideas about surface areas and volumes. To get the most out of this work, they should be able to make some generalizations about the two, vis-à-vis increasing cube size.

Cubes as Model Animals

Now the students consider two cubes of very different sizes and remind themselves that cubes are model animals, that is, they are alive and metabolically active.

The key to this work is integrating physical effects and their consequences with metabolism and energetics. That is, at smaller volumes, heat (cold, etc.) leaves the object more quickly. Animal bodies have volume, too, and are subject to the same effects as are nonliving volumes. That means that heat moves through a small-bodied animal faster than it does through a large-bodied animal. But mammals and some other animals actively maintain their body temperature. Humans maintain a constant temperature of about 98.6°F, domestic cats a temperature of about 101°F. This heat is a consequence of metabolic activity, that is, cellular respiration. Since small volumes lose heat more rapidly, small animals lose heat more rapidly. Thus, small animals require relatively more energy to compensate for this higher rate of heat loss. They must, therefore, eat relatively more.

Students may need help to remember that heat is a major product of cellular respiration. Remind them of the energy equation **I** = **P** + **R** + **E** and ask them about the energy represented by **R**.

The Data

An 8- × 8- × 8-ft moose has a surface area of 384 ft^2. The same weight of mice, 500 kg, at .03 kg per mouse = 16,667 mice. The per-mouse surface area is 6×2.5^2 or 37.5 in.^{2} × 16,667 mice for a total surface area of 625,012.5 in.^{2} ÷ 144 = 52,084 ft^2. No wonder the mice use 39,900 kcal/500 kg per day versus the moose's mere 3,000 kcal/500 kg per day.

Possible Discussion Points

If students have difficulty integrating the physical and biological aspects of this topic, it may be helpful to ask them about their own body postures when they are cold (all huddled up) and when they are hot (all spread out). "In terms of shapes and volumes, or what we have been considering recently, what about you is changed when you are huddled up versus all spread out? How might that affect the movement of heat?" Or ask about any animals they might have seen that obviously were hot or cold and the postures of those animals. (Of course, here we are considering behaviors that cause a change in surface area, while our original examples are about the unchangeable differences in surface area and volume between tiny and large animals. But considering change in surface area may be helpful to students, by throwing surface area into relief as the factor that varies with temperature.)

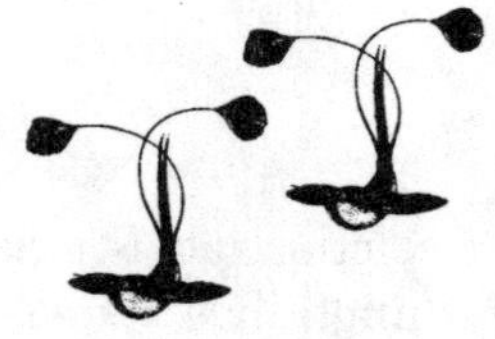

READING GUIDE
The Microworld and the Macroworld

Here we continue to see that an organism's size accounts for or is a constraint on most aspects of its life. This reading goes beyond the energy use issues we are considering, to the meta-level of gravity versus diffusion and capillary action. Students tend to have few questions.

You might remind them of their "ballpark answers," in the Reading on Fermi calculations (**Unit 1, Chapter 1**) for one more scale. See also the References if they want to pursue any of these ideas or give them the Excerpt.

INTEGRATION GUIDE
Mystery Animal: Who Am I?

Students are developing integrated pictures of organisms—about their sizes, habits, lifestyles, what they eat, how they regulate and maintain body temperature, and how all those things fit together. As students become more conscious of and articulate their thoughts and understanding, our materials become more open-ended and differently supportive.

This Integration presents numerous and complex concepts and how they are represented by specific organisms. The descriptions illustrate those concepts. And because the descriptions are written, students are better able to keep track of those ideas. But the students must juggle the concepts, integrating and reintegrating them until they resolve into some whole—a picture, an animal, or a kind of animal.

The animals we have in mind for each description are listed below, but your students will surely think of others that also fit. Good for them!

If this seems like too many animals to think about, choose (or let your students choose) some subset.

1. Polar bear (heat-conserving fur and behaviors)
2. Elephant (hippos weigh about 3,200 kg; Indian elephants—which have smaller ears, are generally smaller, and live on a different continent—are also an excellent match)
3. Tiger (cousin is Siberian tiger); note cooling behaviors
4. Catfish (scavenger fishes)
5. Shrew and shrewlike creatures
6. Lizard (monitor lizard is 450 lb)
7. Walrus (note heat-conserving adaptations)
8. Frog
9. Sphinx moth
10. Eagle
11. Panda (note the plant, i.e., bamboo, diet in a bearlike animal)
12. Mosquito (not vampire)

INTEGRATION
Mystery Animal: Who Am I?

Use the following clues to make some predictions about what animal is represented by each description and where it might live. Explain your reasoning. Then compare your thoughts with information from reference materials (including items in this book, such as your animal cards).

For example, if you think one description fits a penguin, read about penguins and see how your reasoning applies. Even if the animal you pick does not quite fit the description, is it ecologically similar?

NOTE: some descriptions apply to one or a few closely related species (e.g., penguins), others to larger groups of species (e.g., salamanders).

1. I weigh 540 kg (1,200 lb)
- am exclusively carnivorous
- hunt during the day
- am an endotherm
- am not black despite where I live
- go into torpor for periods of several days during the cold season
- raise one or two young and care for them for at least their first year

2. I weigh 5,000 kg (11,025 lb)
- am an endotherm
- eat coarse plant matter in huge quantities
- live in a hot climate but have several adaptations to help me lose heat (e.g., almost no hair, large ears)
- also cool off by getting wet
- have low body fat content
- tend to have one young at a time and care for it with the help of other group members for several years

3. I weigh 220 kg (485 lb)
- am exclusively carnivorous
- hunt at dusk or night to avoid heat
- live in a hot climate
- have an even larger cousin who lives in snowy regions
- am an endotherm
- ambush but rarely chase my prey (generates too much heat)
- am not social but care for my young for at least their first year

4. I weigh 2.27 kg (6 lb)
- am an ectotherm
- feed mostly on detritus
- have special feelers to help probe my food and have a good "nose"
- do not care for my young; just let the eggs develop and the young mature by themselves

5. I weigh 3 g (0.10 oz)
   - am an endotherm
   - must eat during all my waking hours to survive
   - am carnivorous in my feeding
   - have various heat-conserving behaviors, like nesting and rolling up
   - can have more than one litter a year and care for my young until they are semi-adult

6. I weigh 0.90 kg (2 lb) but have tropical cousins up to 130 kg (300-plus lb)
   - am an ectotherm
   - am usually carnivorous in feeding habits
   - have a four-chambered heart but with incomplete separation of two chambers
   - hibernate in winter if I live in cold climes
   - change my skin when I grow
   - usually let my young raise themselves

7. I weigh 1,000 kg (2,205 lb)
   - am nearly hairless
   - am an endotherm
   - have no external ears
   - am exclusively carnivorous in food habits
   - have high body fat content
   - am highly social

8. I weigh 170 g (6 oz), with cousins from 1 oz to over 1 kg
   - spend all my life in or near water or highly moist places
   - do lots of my "breathing" (gas exchange) through my skin
   - am an ectotherm
   - am wholly carnivorous in my food habits
   - tend to be tropical or have adaptations to deal with cold and dry
   - have a three-chambered heart
   - can be social or solitary, depending on my species
   - usually let my fertilized eggs raise themselves

9. I weigh about 1.5 g (0.05 oz); most of my relatives are smaller
   - am nectar-feeding
   - am able to regulate my body temperature metabolically during free flight
   - am typically considered an ectotherm
   - have insulative scales
   - can survive during very cold months as well as times of day
   - let my young take care of themselves through several growth stages and end by emerging as adults from pupae

10. I weigh 9 kg (20 lb)
- am an endotherm
- feed almost exclusively on animal flesh, typically fish
- go south for the winter
- nest in tall trees in inaccessible places

11. I weigh 150 kg (330 lb)
- am related to bears
- eat only plant matter
- must eat virtually all the time I am awake to get by on that diet
- am an endotherm
- live alone except for a brief mating period or when raising young
- have thick fur against the cold

12. I weigh 0.001 g (3.53×10^{-5} oz)
- am an ectotherm
- lay eggs in lots of places, like tree holes and old tires
- do not raise my young
- if the female in certain species, need a blood meal before laying eggs
- do not have a true circulatory system
- am not social although I can appear in seeming clouds of individuals

EXCERPT
"Size and Shape," by Stephen Jay Gould

Who could believe an ant in
theory?
A giraffe in blueprint?
Ten thousand doctors of what's
possible
Could reason half the jungle
out of being

—*JOHN CIARDI*

Poet John Ciardi's lines reflect a belief that the exuberant diversity of life will forever frustrate man's arrogant claims to omniscience. Yet, however much we celebrate diversity and revel in the peculiarities of animals, we must also acknowledge a striking "lawfulness" in the basic design of organisms. This regularity is most strongly evident in the correlation of size and shape.

Animals are physical objects. They are shaped to their advantage by natural selection. Consequently, they must assume forms best adapted to their size. The relative strength of such forces as gravity varies with size in a regular way, and animals respond by systematically altering their shapes.

The geometry of space itself is the major reason for correlations between size and shape. Simply by growing larger, an object that keeps the same shape will suffer a continual decrease in relative surface area. The decrease occurs because volume increases as the cube of length (length × length × length), while surface area increases only as the square (length × length): in other words, volume grows more rapidly than surface.

Why is this important to animals? Many functions that depend upon surface must serve the entire volume of the body. Digested food passes to the body through surfaces: oxygen is absorbed through surfaces in respiration: the strength of a leg bone depends upon the area of its cross section, but the legs must hold up a body increasing in weight by the cube of its length. Galileo first recognized this principle in his Discorsi of 1638, the masterpiece he wrote while under house arrest by the Inquisition. He argued that the bone of a large animal must thicken disproportionately to provide the same relative strength as the slender bone of a small creature.

One solution to decreasing surface has been particularly important in the progressive evolution of large and complex organisms: the development of internal organs. The lung is, essentially, a richly convoluted bag of surface area for the exchange of gases; the circulatory system distributes material to an internal space that cannot be reached by direct diffusion from the external surface of large organisms; the villi of our small intestine increase the surface available for absorption of food (small mammals neither have nor need them).

Some simpler animals have never evolved internal organs; if they become large, they must alter their entire shape in ways so drastic that plasticity for further evolutionary change is sacrificed to extreme specialization. Thus, a tapeworm may be 20 feet long, but its thickness cannot exceed a fraction of an inch because food and oxygen must penetrate directly from the external surface to all parts of the body.

Other animals are constrained to remain small. Insects breathe through invaginations of the external surface. Since these invaginations must be more numerous and convoluted in larger bodies, they impose a size limit upon insect design: at the size of even a small mammal, an insect would be "all invagination" and have no room for internal parts.

We are prisoners of the perceptions of our size, and rarely recognize how different the world must appear to small animals. Since our relative surface area is so small at our large size, we are ruled by gravitational forces acting upon our weight. But gravity is negligible to very small animals with high surface to volume ratios; they live in a world dominated by surface force and judge the pleasures and dangers of their surroundings in ways foreign to our experience.

An insect performs no miracle in walking up a wall or upon the surface of a pond; the small gravitational force pulling it down or under is easily counteracted by surface adhesion. Throw an insect off the roof and it floats gently down as frictional forces acting upon its surface overcome the weak influence of gravity.

The relative weakness of gravitational forces also permits a mode of growth that large animals could not maintain. Insects have an external skeleton and can only grow by discarding it and secreting a new one to accommodate the enlarged body. For a period between shedding and regrowth, the body must remain soft. A large mammal without any supporting structures would collapse to a formless mass under the influence of gravitational forces; a small insect can maintain its cohesion (related lobsters and crabs can grow much larger because they pass their "soft" stage in the nearly weightless buoyancy of water). We have here another reason for the small size of insects.

The creators of horror and science-fiction movies seem to have no inkling of the relationship between size and shape. These "expanders of the possible" cannot break free from the prejudices of their perceptions. The small people of Dr. Cyclops, The Bride of Frankenstein, The Incredible Shrinking Man, and Fantastic Voyage behave just like their counterparts of normal dimensions. They fall off cliffs or down stairs with resounding thuds; wield weapons and swim with olympic agility. The large insects of films too numerous to name continue to walk up and down walls or fly even at dinosaurian dimensions.

When the kindly entomologist of Them discovered that the giant queen ants had left for their nuptial flight, he quickly calculated this simple ratio: a normal ant is a fraction of an inch long and can fly hundreds of feet; these ants are many feet long and must be able to fly as much as 1,000 miles. Why, they could be as far away as Los Angeles! (Where, indeed, they were, lurking in the sewers.) But the ability to fly depends upon the surface area of the wings, while the weight that must be borne aloft increases as the cube of length. We may be sure that even if the giant ants had somehow circumvented the problems of breathing and growth by molting, their chances of getting off the ground would have been far worse than that of the proverbial snowball in hell.

Other essential features of organisms change even more rapidly with increasing size than the ratio of surface to volume. Kinetic energy, for example, increases as length raised to the fifth power. If a child half your height falls unsupported to the ground, its head will hit with not half, but only 1/32 the energy of yours in a similar fall. A child is protected more by its size than by a "soft" head. In return, we are protected from the physical force of its tantrums, for the child can strike with, not half, but only 1/32 of the energy we can muster. I have long had a special sympathy for the poor dwarfs who suffer under the whip of the cruel Alberich in Wagner's Das Rheingold. At their diminutive size, they haven't a chance of extracting, with mining picks, the precious minerals that Alberich demands, despite the industrious and incessant leitmotif of their futile attempt.

This simple principle of differential scaling with increasing size may well be the most important determinant of organic shape. J. B. S. Haldane once wrote that "comparative anatomy is largely the story of the struggle to increase surface in proportion of volume." Yet the geometry of space constrains ships, buildings, and machines, as well as animals.

Medieval churches present a good testing ground for the effects of size and shape, for they were built in an enormous range of sizes before the invention of steel girders, internal lighting, and air conditioning permitted modern architects to challenge the laws of size. The tiny, twelfth-century parish church of Little Tey, Essex, England, is a broad, simple rectangular building with a semicircular apse. Light reaches the interior through windows in the outer walls. If we were to build a cathedral simply by enlarging this design, then the periphery of the outer walls and windows would increase as length, while the area that light must reach would increase as length times length. In other words, the size of the windows would increase far more slowly than the area that requires illumination. Candles have limitations; the inside of such a cathedral would have been darker than the deed of Judas. Medieval churches, like tapeworms, lack internal systems and must alter their shape to produce more external surface as they are made larger.

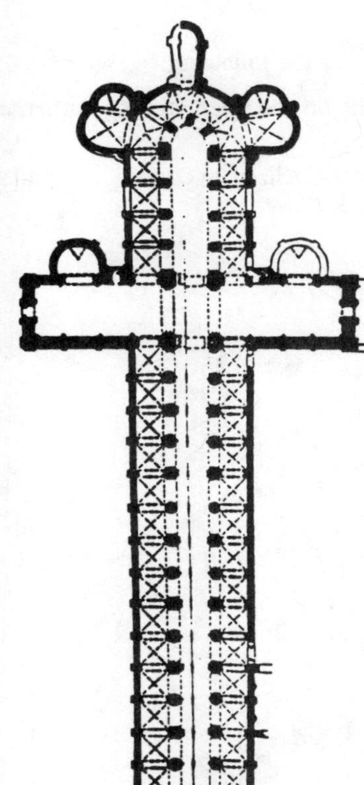

The large cathedral of Norwich, as it appeared in the twelfth century, had a much narrower rectangular nave; chapels have been added to the apse and a transept runs perpendicular to the main axis. All these "adaptations" increase the ratio of external wall and window to internal area. It is often stated that transepts were added to produce the form of a Latin cross. Theological motives may have dictated the position of such "outpouchings," but the law of size required their presence. Very few small churches have transepts.

I have plotted periphery versus the square root of area for floor plans of all postconquest Romanesque churches depicted in Clapham's monograph of English ecclesiastical architecture. As we would predict, periphery increases more rapidly than the square root of the area. Medieval architects had their rules of thumb, but they had, so far as we know, no explicit knowledge of the laws of size.

Like large churches, large organisms have very few options open to them. Above a certain size, large terrestrial organisms look basically alike—they have thick legs and relatively short, stout bodies. Large Romanesque churches are all relatively long and have abundant outpouchings. The invention of the flying buttress strengthened later Gothic buildings and freed more wall space for windows. Churches could then become relatively wider and simpler in outline (as in the Cathedral of Bourges).

The "invention" of internal organs helped animals retain the highly successful shape of a simple exterior enclosing a large internal volume; and the invention of internal lighting and structural steel has helped modern architects design large buildings with simple exteriors. The limits are expanded, but the laws still operate. No large Gothic church is higher than it is long, no large animal has a sagging middle like a dachshund.

I once overheard a children's conversation in a New York playground. Two young girls were discussing the size of dogs. One asked: "Can a dog be as large as an elephant?" Her friend responded: "No, if it were as big as an elephant, it would look like an elephant." I wonder if she realized how truly she spoke.

REFERENCES

For more on scaling and body size, see the following:

Gould, S. J. 1974. "Size and Shape." Natural History 83(1): 20–26.

Haldane, J. B. S. 1985. On Being the Right Size and Other Essays. Edited by J. Maynard Smith. New York: Oxford University Press.

McGowan, Chris. 1994. Diatoms to Dinosaurs: The Size and Scale of Living Things. Washington, D.C.: Island Press. 288 pp.

For more on body size, metabolic rate, and diet, see the following:

McNab, B. K. 1986. "The Influence of Food Habits on the Energetics of Eutherian Mammals." Ecological Monographs 56(1): 1–19.

Peters, R. H. 1983. "The Ecological Implications of Body Size." In Cambridge Studies in Ecology. New York: Cambridge University Press.

THERMOREGULATION
A LARGE PART OF R

CHAPTER SIX

CONTENTS

INTRODUCTION

Students explore a major piece of the **R** term of the balanced energy use equation through the control of body temperature, or thermoregulation. They do so by designing, building, and testing model "animals" that show either of two strategies for getting and staying warm.

Animals typically function best when warm (28°C to 32°C) and have various ways of getting to and staying at those temperatures. Generally speaking, animals raise their body temperature either by using an internal source of energy, metabolic energy (which is reflected in the **R** term of the energy use equation) or by using an external source of energy (heat).

By now students have seen various facets of animal design and lifestyle that affect **R**, from body size and diet to heritage, or, as it is properly called, phylogeny. So the Explorations here focus specifically on illustrating the two modes of thermoregulation and how they integrate with other factors studied so far.

KEY CONCEPTS

- There are two major methods for achieving and maintaining warm (and effective) body temperatures: endothermy and ectothermy.
- Endothermy and ectothermy each have advantages and disadvantages; neither method is inherently better than the other.
- Endotherms maintain high body temperatures metabolically, but they are locked into finding larger amounts of food to keep their metabolism running.
- Ectotherms need only a small fraction of the food intake of similar-size endotherms, but they may be limited in their movements when ambient temperatures are low.
- Many ectotherms thermoregulate quite well—by moving into and out of patches of sunlight and warmth they can maintain fairly constant temperatures.
- As we saw in **Chapter 5**, large objects lose heat more slowly than small objects. This difference has major implications for the energy budgets of animals.

MATERIALS AND PREPARATION

In Advance

We strongly recommend that you try building a couple of model animals yourself before your students attempt this project. It is especially useful to test the heating apparatus. We have included sketches of different designs of model animals in Exploration 1.

Materials

- **Cotton balls** (a couple of hundred)
- **Construction paper** of different colors
- **Thick woolen socks** (a few)
- **Heat-generating apparatus:** battery, resistor, and associated hardware. We used some D-cell batteries, battery holders, a little wire, switches, and 1-ohm power resistors from a local electronics and radio-type store. The resistor is a ceramic block about 7 mm by 7 mm by 20 mm. You will need a maximum of one set per group, but because groups tend to want to make endotherms, it may be easier to help students think "ectotherm" if there are not enough heaters. Be sure to have extra batteries.
- **Toothpicks**
- **Popsicle sticks**
- **Tape**
- **Glue**
- **Other materials** you think might be useful. Just remember to set an energy cost for each material to add to those listed in Exploration 1.

- **Watch**
- **Centimeter ruler or tape**
- **Thermometers** (one per group plus spares for breakage). Standard lab mercury thermometers are okay, but Microcomputer Based Laboratory temperature probes and computers are far more satisfying to work with. (Cheap digital thermometers may be inaccurate by over 1°C. If you use such thermometers, make sure to calibrate them against each other.)
- **Table lamps** with 60 or 75 W incandescent bulbs (several)
- **Film canisters.** Each model animal is built around a 35 mm film canister (the plastic container in which you buy the film), to provide a standard core for the body. Any photo store will likely give you dozens for free. Give all your students exactly the same size, shape, and color of canister, since the different colors and types of plastic have different thermal properties.

  Leave the covers on the canisters. Punch a hole in the bottom of each canister with an awl to allow a thermometer or temperature probe to be inserted in the canister. (See Figure 3, Exploration 1, in the Student Book.) (Try to make the hole just smaller than the diameter of the thermometer, so the thermometer fits tightly when inserted.)

Several of the materials that you provide for students will function quite well as insulators (e.g., cotton balls and wool socks). Insulating materials are quite useful for endothermic animals but actually are counterproductive for ectothermic ones. Fur, feathers, and a layer of fat under the skin all help endothermic animals retain the heat they generate. Similar insulating features on ectothermic animals, however, would insulate in the wrong way—they would insulate the animal's body core (which needs to warm up) from the external environment (where the heat is located).

Safety

WARNING

The heater apparatus is simple to assemble and fairly safe. Be careful when there is current flowing through the power resistor—it can get quite warm to the touch. To assemble a heater, place a D-cell battery in a holder and connect one of the wires from the holder to one of the resistor leads. We recommend that you connect the other leads from the battery holder and resistor to a switch, so it is easy to turn the system on and off. (Alternatively, you can simply twist the leads from the battery holder and resistor together when you want power flowing to the resistor.) Place the resistor inside the film canister, then close the cover over the resistor leads; the cover should keep the resistor in place.

You may find that more of your student groups want to build internally warmed ("endothermic") model animals. Make sure that about half of the groups build "ectothermic" animals, so there is a good comparison of the two lifestyles. You may want to restrict the number of heating mechanisms that you have available, so that not all groups can use this method.

SUGGESTED SEQUENCE OF SESSIONS (5–6)

Homework

The Case Study introduces students to the idea that the **R** term and animal temperature are different ways of looking at the same thing.

Class Session 1

Discuss the Case Study by asking students to refer to their animal cards and compare the **R** terms of endotherms and ectotherms (amphibian, snake).

Begin Exploration 1, designing the animals. Students build physical models of animals to study consequences of different modes of thermoregulation. Help students be clear about their goals, the building materials available for model animals, and that all building materials ("animal tissue") have an energy cost.

Class Session 2

Have students carry out their animal design and construction.

Class Session 3

Continue Session 2, especially testing different designs.

Class Session 4

Groups test energy costs of foraging by endothermic and ectothermic model animals (Exploration 2). Record data.

Homework

In the Reading, students discover other aspects of thermoregulation, torpor, and the deliberate failure, under some conditions, by endotherms to maintain a constant body temperature.

Class Session 5

Continue Session 4.

Calculate all energy costs and gains for each animal. Did they survive? Were they accurate to their intended thermoregulatory mode?

In a class discussion (optional), pull together all the components students have seen that are part of **R**.

Homework or Class Session 6

Copy and distribute the Integration.

SESSION GUIDES, BY WORKSHEET

CASE STUDY GUIDE
Hot and Cold: Thermoregulation in Animals

Discuss differences in **R** values of endotherms (large) and ectotherms (much smaller). Ask students to remind you of the sloth-penguin comparison in the **Chapter 3** Case Study. How do the penguin and the sloth fit into this picture? If students are unsure, wait and revisit this question after Exploration 2.

Be sure they know the difference between the two strategies of thermoregulation, and between raising and maintaining body temperature.

EXPLORATION 1 GUIDE
Design a Temperature-Regulating Animal

The two explorations demonstrate that both endothermy and ectothermy have advantages and disadvantages. Because endothermic animals provide their own warmth, they can forage for food and escape from predators regardless of the ambient temperature. The cost to this feature is that endotherms must take in large quantities of energy on a regular basis—they need to feed their furnaces continually, so to speak. Ectotherms, on the other hand, require far less energy intake than endotherms, since they are not burning energy staying warm. When their body temperatures are low, however, ectotherms move only slowly. They can neither forage for food effectively nor escape predators when cold. Many ectotherms actually do quite well at regulating their body temperatures by basking in sunlight to warm up, then foraging in the shade as their bodies slowly cool off.

For some notes on building animal models, see Materials and Preparation. Since we trust that you will have built and tested one or two "animals" before class, you can discuss with students issues that may arise in addition to those mentioned in Materials and Preparation.

The Role of Insulation

Ectotherms actually may be better off without external insulators such as fur or feathers. By analogy consider an insulated thermos jug. It can either keep a hot liquid from becoming cool (this is why endotherms invest in insulation) or prevent a cold liquid from becoming warm (which is why ectotherms do not invest in insulation). The bottom line on insulation is that students making endothermic animals will probably do well to insulate, while those making ectothermic animals should not. As students explore these design issues, try to relate their insights to the world of real animals, in which birds and mammals are insulated and amphibians and reptiles are not.

The Role of Color

External color is of major importance for ectotherms, whereas it is much less important for endotherms (if they carry insulation). Ectothermic models that are dark on the outside (either covered with dark construction paper or a bare black film canister) absorb heat much faster from table lamps than do light-colored animal models. (The dark animal models also tend to cool off faster, that is, radiate heat away faster, than do the light ones. Overall, though, dark ectotherms seem to do better thermally than light ones.) This, then, is another area in which students can explore differences and another place where they can speculate about the role of color in nature.

Testing Their Ideas

During the design and building sessions, students will need access to the thermometers (or Microcomputer Based Laboratory temperature probes), table lamps, and complete heater apparatuses so they can compare different designs.

EXPLORATION 2 GUIDE
Foraging: Your Animal Meets Reality

Now students go "live" with their model animals. Their main goal is to have their models spend as much time "foraging" (gaining energy) as possible. Animals can forage only when their temperatures are between 28°C and 32°C. When their temperature is outside that range, they must either warm up or cool down. Students record the amount of time that their animal's temperature is in the proper range and (for endothermic animals) the amount of time that the heater is on. At the end of the session, students total the amount of energy spent on building their animal, any energy they spent running the heater, and the energy gained while foraging (kilocalorie values for materials, heater, and foraging are in Exploration 1).

The Actual Foraging Period

For the foraging session itself, set up several table lamps around the room. When you announce that the foraging period has begun, students should turn on the heaters in the endothermic animals or place the ectothermic animals 5 cm away from the table lamp bulbs. Remember to have one or more periods of "night," that is, the table lamps are off, and no foraging can occur. During those periods, ectothermic animals can let their temperatures drop as much as they want, while endotherms must keep their temperatures at 27°C or higher.

Crunching the Numbers

Students will have time data (foraging, not foraging, and, for endotherms, with heater on and off), and energy data (animal building costs and foraging gains). They must calculate their costs and gains to see whether they have survived, that is, have a net gain.

One way that may simplify calculations is for students to designate energy costs (materials and running heaters) as negative numbers and foraging gains as positive numbers. Then all animals (ideally) show a positive balance (energy gained) at the end of the foraging session.

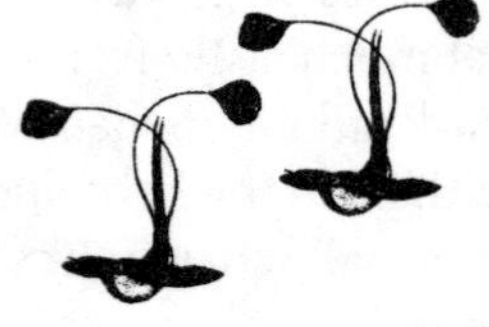

READING GUIDE
Stars and Oddballs in Body-Temperature Regulation

Students meet other examples of thermoregulation and a different aspect: the ability by some animals to drop and maintain lowered body temperatures deliberately under various conditions.

INTEGRATION GUIDE
"R"-Rated: How Body Temperature, Size, and Thermoregulation Mix

This integration actually includes concepts from the beginning of this Unit. Answers might include the following: Endothermic species can live in more different (and especially colder) habitats; they can process lower-quality food (but need proportionately more of it); they require a circulatory system and a four-chambered heart; they can be larger (but not smaller) than 2 g; they tend to invest more time and energy in raising young (they may need to feed their young, which have the endotherm's disproportionately larger appetites and growth rates); they have proportionately and absolutely higher **R** values in the balanced energy budget.

Endotherms tend to have fur or feathers; they often have clever heat-saving mechanisms (such as the countercurrent blood shunt in the legs of the Arctic fox or the optical properties of polar bear fur); their colors are more likely under selection for reasons of sociality, predation, or antipredation than reasons of thermoregulation.

Ectotherms are typically the reverse in all those respects.

There is debate over the absolute size limit of a terrestrial vertebrate, in part because it is unclear whether so large an animal could be or would need to be either an endotherm or an ectotherm (there are arguments both ways).

Fish are ectotherms. An interesting Extension might be to have students do some library work to understand how and why that is possible.

INTEGRATION
"R"-Rated: How Body Temperature, Size, and Thermoregulation Mix

By now we have explored various aspects of energy use: how it affects and is affected by every aspect of an animal's lifestyle. What an animal is (its evolutionary history, i.e., whether it is a penguin, an insect, or an iguana), where it lives, what it eats, how active and how big it is—all these factors are interrelated and affect one another.

Describe several circumstances under which it would be a benefit or a drawback to be endothermic. Explain your rationale. (What about the amount of energy required to care for or feed young?)

Now flip-flop. Describe at least five possible advantages and drawbacks to being an endotherm. Explain.

Are fish endotherms or ectotherms? Why do you think so?

Given the differences between the **R** values of endotherms and ectotherms, which do you predict might have a lower basal metabolic rate? Why?

Would you rather be an endotherm or an ectotherm? Why?

REFERENCES

Bernd, Heinrich. 1993. The Hot-Blooded Insects: Strategies and Mechanisms of Thermoregulation. Cambridge: Harvard University Press. 601 pp.

Schmidt-Nielsen, K. 1984. Scaling: Why Is Animal Size So Important? New York: Cambridge University Press. 241 pp.
This book also considers dinosaur size.

PRODUCTION
GROWTH, FAT, AND REPRODUCTION

CHAPTER SEVEN

CONTENTS

INTRODUCTION

What does it mean to "grow"? Getting taller, adding fat, and having babies are all included in the **P**roduction term of the energy equation. Our work with the energy use equation has shown us that while the **P**roduction term can range up to 40% for microorganisms, for vertebrates it is typically much less, and for mammals, just 1–2%. Students work with data on growth and energy intake in humans to demonstrate that key point.

We also consider why reproduction, although an even smaller part of the already small part of an organism's energy use, is the single most important criterion of "success," evolutionarily speaking.

KEY CONCEPTS

- All multicellular organisms grow, in at least two ways: they add tissue (get taller, larger), and they develop or mature (go through different life stages from infant to adult). The stages of development have various characteristics, for example, bones become more bony; the organism adds wood or lignin; the organism develops sexually).
- All organisms reproduce. Actually, not every individual organism necessarily reproduces, but all species reproduce in some way.
- The production of an organism's own tissue (growth, development, or the addition of fat) and reproduction (having babies, or producing the tissue that becomes another organism) both come from the same tiny part of the total energy budget.
- The energetic value of tissue is only a fraction of the energetic cost of producing that tissue. That is, if we put some seeds or insects or an egg into the calorimeter, we will know the energy in that tissue. But we still do not know how much energy was "spent" by the tree or the insect or the female animal to produce that seed, that body, or that egg.
- Even though the **P**roduction term of the energy budget is typically quite small for vertebrates (1–2% for birds and mammals, somewhat higher for others) and under 10% for most mutlicellular organisms, reproduction accounts for a large part of that energy. And successful reproduction is the definition of a successful life.
- Evolutionarily speaking, reproduction is the indicator of success. It is not just how many babies an organism produces, but how many of them successfully survive and reproduce. So the real question is, how many grandchildren does an organism produce? The more grandbabies, the more that organism spreads in the population, and the more successful it is considered by evolutionary ecologists.
- There are many different ways of using energy for reproduction. The two extremes are one-time reproduction (the big bang), with many, many offspring, which get no parental care and few of which survive (e.g., the mosquito), versus repeat reproduction, with few offspring, which get lots of parental care, and of which proportionately more survive (e.g., the hyena).

MATERIALS AND PREPARATION

- **Chalk- or white-board or poster board**
- **Animal cards (Chapter 4)**
- **Calculators**
- **Graph paper**

SUGGESTED SEQUENCE OF SESSIONS (5–7)

Homework

Have the students read the Case Study.

Class Session 1

The Case Study raises issues about some life history factors that might affect growth rate. Discuss students' graphs of the vole data (which likely have only two points); raise the issue of converting weight-as-growth to weight-as-energy. That concept is the focus of Exploration 1 and helps students make the connection between energy and tissue. Begin Exploration 1, with which students explore growth rate and compare it to caloric intake.

Class Session 2

Continue Session 1. As always, there may be questions about "sampling" and "averages" and what an average means. Refer to the section Averages in **Module 1**, Exploration 2 Guide.

Homework

Students discover that nonhuman organisms rarely are fat and are fat for specific reasons or periods of time only (Reading 1: Who Are You Calling Fat?). (In **Chapters 8** and **9** they explore properties of fats, e.g., different bond patterns and greater caloric value per unit weight, that help explain these cycles.)

Class Session 3

Discuss Reading 1, focusing on the idea that most organisms are never obese but periodically require additional fat (energy storage) at some times in their lives.

Begin Exploration 2: HOW Many Grandchildren? (If the class has already done **Module 1**, you will recognize this as the Integration. It may be worth redoing, since students may find that their understanding has become more sophisticated.)

Class Session 4

Continue Session 3.

Homework

Students discover that successful reproduction is energetically costly and an important part of an organism's lifestyle or life-history strategy (Reading 2: Reproduction: THEIR New Tissue).

Class Session 5

Students calculate effects of selection and survival (Exploration 2: HOW Many Grandchildren?). Evolution is the outcome of natural selection, survival, and reproductive success, not of an animal's need to change. And it is the number of successful offspring, that is, the number of grand- and great-grandchildren, that affects numerical success.

Class Session 6

Continue Session 5.

In a class discussion, pull together what students have learned about production—growth, reproduction, and fat—and how it is all about allocation of energy.

SESSION GUIDES, BY WORKSHEET

CASE STUDY GUIDE (Homework)
Some Growth Rates

Let students raise questions about the Case Study. They might wonder about any of the following. What is the difference between growth and growth rate? The Case Study suggests an absence of correlation between whether an organism is a vertebrate or an invertebrate and its growth rate. (Actually, roughly speaking, larger organisms have proportionately and absolutely slower growth rates, while invertebrates have faster growth rates than same-size vertebrates. We use extreme examples here without considering patterns.) Students might ask about evolution and natural selection. Are the cicadas "thinking" about their predators? Do the cicadas "mean" to outsmart predators? And so on. Remember that natural selection has nothing to do with volition or consciousness. (Review Science Background and the Readings from **Module 1** if they would help.)

Questions

If you want, briefly let students raise questions. Or ask them some. What is the difference between growth and growth rate? How do human growth rates compare to those of the seventeen-year cicada? How might an organism's life be influenced by its growth rate? And what does that have to do with energy use?

Vole-Growth Graph

Ask about graphing vole growth rates. The Y axis label might be in units of weight (grams) and the X axis in units of time, probably days. Ask students about their work and draw a sample graph (with two points) on the board, using the numbers for birth and adult weights from the Case Study. Detail is not the point here. Consider with students the concept that growth of new tissue can be expressed as an increase in stored energy instead of as an increase in weight. Since students have been thinking about energy flow, it is logical to think of growth as an accumulation of stored energy. A useful path from growth-as-weight gain to growth-as-energy accumulation is this: remind students that a gram of vole flesh contains or has an energy value of approximately 1.5 kcal. Ask, "How might we change our graph of vole growth over time to express growth as energy accumulation rather than weight gain?" We suggest that the class discuss the problem; students might discover the simplest and most powerful solution: that they can simply relabel the Y axis of the graph (weight in grams) to show kilocalories and relabel the numbers, since by the "vole conversion factor" there are 1.5 kcal/g.

Relabeling accomplishes two goals. Students see that growth can be measured in units of energy as well as in units of weight. And in terms of science process, students can start to see graphs in a new light. The appropriate manipulation of labels on a graph is a powerful way of changing how we look at patterns in nature. It is another example of renaming, substitution, converting.

Now that students can see growth in terms of energy content, it is possible to compare energy intake with production of new tissue, keeping both quantities in units of energy, as in the second part of Exploration 1.

EXPLORATION 1 GUIDE
Growth: OUR New Tissue

In groups or as a class, students plot the birth and adult weights of their animals (from **Chapter 4**), calculating the birth weight of an individual as 6% of average adult weight. These plots show considerable differences in absolute growth—how much the animals change from birth to adulthood—but nothing about growth rate—how fast and over what time course the growth occurs.

Average Growth Rates for U.S. Children

Students examine average per-year growth rates for U.S. girls and boys from birth to the end of high school. Because they have both the numbers and the graphs, students can compare the data whichever way is easier for them. Note in Figure 1 that males tend to be a little larger, except when girls have their puberty growth spurt; after both boys and girls have attained puberty, boys are clearly larger. If growth were constant, the lines representing growth rate would be straight, that is, have no dips or wiggles, and the weights per age would increase at a constant rate. (The data for both graphs are in the student chapter.)

Students calculate their cumulative caloric intakes simply by adding each year's intake to the sum of the previous years.

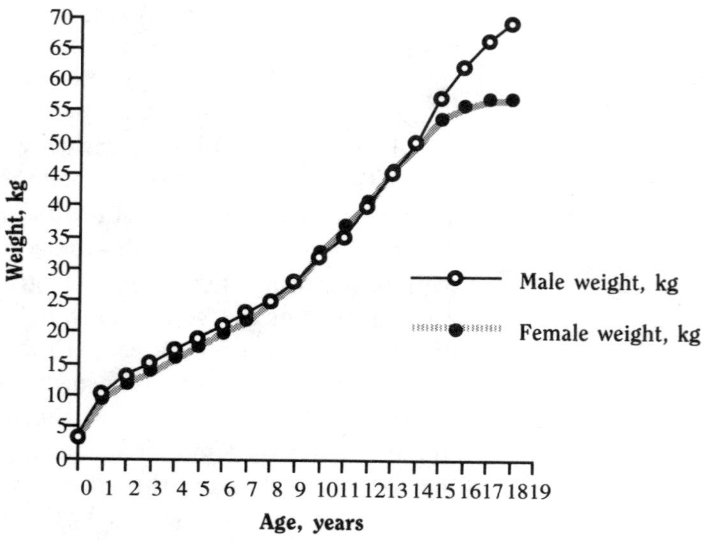

Figure 1. Average weights of U.S. boys and girls.

Weight to Energy

Students convert the values for accumulated tissue weight into units of energy, using the conversion factor of 1.5 kcal/g wet tissue (or 1,500 kcal/kg wet tissue). Having growth data in energy terms allows direct comparison with energy intake (the second data set) and standardizes the Y axis units. Briefly discuss their predictions concerning the relationship between growth rate and caloric intake. Some students might immediately make the connection between the numbers and the energy budgets, pointing out that growth rate must be tiny, while total intake will be enormous. Many will not consciously connect the two until they try to fit both sets of numbers onto one graph—the Y axes will be wildly discrepant in scale. We include both graphs, as Figures 2 and 3.

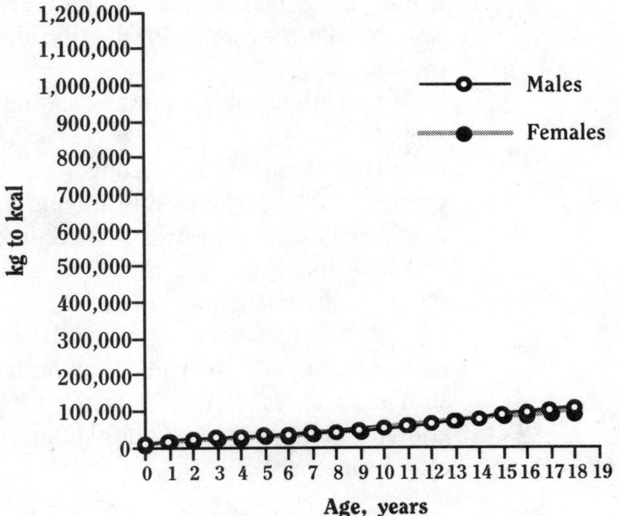

Figure 2. Conversion of tissue weight to energy.

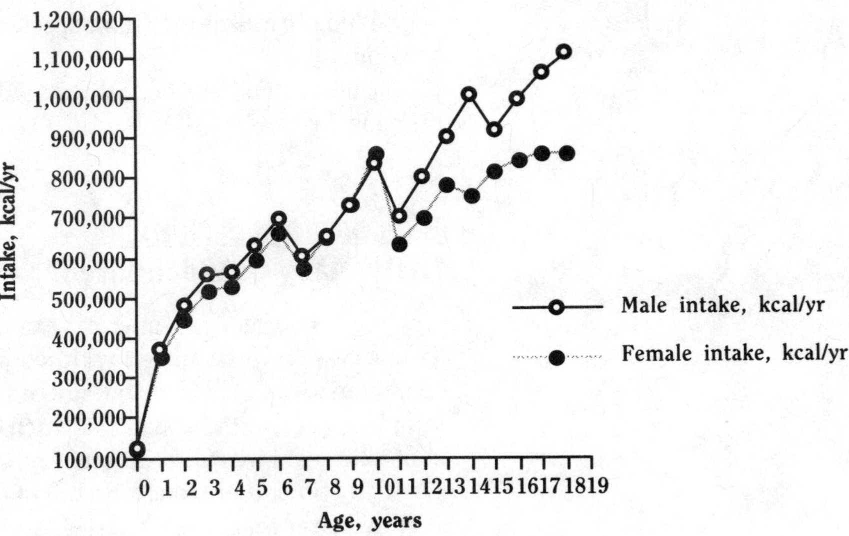

Figure 3. Energy intake.

Graphing the Data

Because both weight and intake are measured cumulatively, students can put both intake and growth (new tissue) on a single graph. This might take a little juggling by students. Because intake is generally two orders of magnitude higher than production, students have to plan their graphing carefully (the Y axis especially) to show both values on the same graph. It is worth doing, because graphing both data sets on one graph makes vivid the vast difference between intake and production for a model endotherm, the human.

Once students have made their graphs, let them roughly calculate the proportion of energy in tissue growth to lifetime energy intake. You may want to let them explore ways of performing this calculation, which is easy to perform. Students already have data on cumulative energy intake and production. To calculate the proportion of intake that became new tissue, simply divide lifetime production (current weight expressed as energy content) by lifetime intake. Production should be in the neighborhood of 1% of intake.

Growth is not the same as adding fat, although both can happen at the same time.

Once students have converted their data on weight in kilograms to energy in kilocalories by multiplying the number of kilograms by 1,500 kcal and have changed the Y axis to accommodate the intake data, their graphs will look like Figures 2 and 3. The difference between tissue energy and intake is obviously huge.

Finish by reviewing students' graphs and the implications of their data. Ask students to consider whether all organisms would have graphs similar to those they generated on human data. (In fact, an ectothermic animal's graph would be quite different, with intake and production much closer together.)

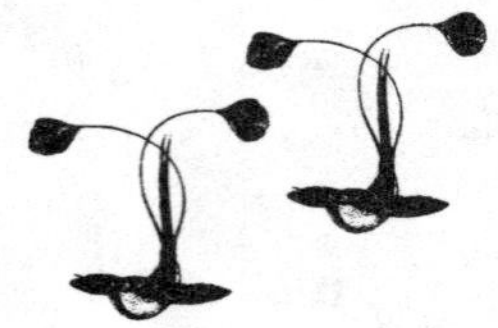

READING 1 GUIDE
Who Are You Calling Fat?

Wild organisms use fat for specific reasons, and their body fat fluctuates accordingly.

Obesity tends to be limited to domestic and zoo animals and some humans.

EXPLORATION 2 GUIDE
HOW Many Grandchildren?

Let's consider a numerical example of how natural selection affects the success (i.e., the spread within a population) of individuals possessing characteristics that are better suited to existing conditions. We use as our sample organism the Galapagos finch *Geospiza fortis*. Under different sets of conditions, birds with different bill types survive (for more, see **Module 1**). At any time, there likely is a bill of particular size and strength that does slightly better than other bill sizes and strengths. Birds with those bills can get more or better seeds, that is, more energy, per unit time than other individuals. For example, birds with smaller bills might not able to crack as large a range of seeds and so waste time trying to crack seeds that are too hard for them, while birds with larger bills might lose some smaller seeds due to handling difficulties.

Role of the Environment

Under typical environmental conditions, differences among birds in bill size and shape probably have little effect on their ability to reproduce or survive. But during "hard," extreme, or unusual times (drought, heavy rains, whatever), the differences in birds' seed-gathering and seed-cracking abilities, in the time spent searching for seeds, and in the number of seeds they can get per day can be the difference between failed or successful reproduction, even between death and survival.

Selection: Survivorship, Not Need

The single aspect of evolution with which some people have trouble is the irrelevance of desire, need, or volition. Whether an organism survives does not depend on whether it wants to survive. Survival depends on whether an organism is appropriately matched to its environment and conditions at that time and in that place. In terms of the Galapagos finch species, does an individual bird have a bill shape that allows it to pick, crack, and eat enough of the seeds available at that time?

Numerically Dominating a Population

Another aspect of evolution that gives people difficulty is understanding how survival and successful reproduction change the makeup of the population. Individuals that have more surviving young spread, begin to dominate, and (if things go on over a long enough period) take over the population. In our example, individual finches with larger-than-average bills outsurvive and outreproduce other individuals of the same species. With your students, work out the example to demonstrate that such finches do outnumber the rest of the finches in the local population within as few as three years, as shown in Figure 4. (For more, see Science Background in **Module 1**.)

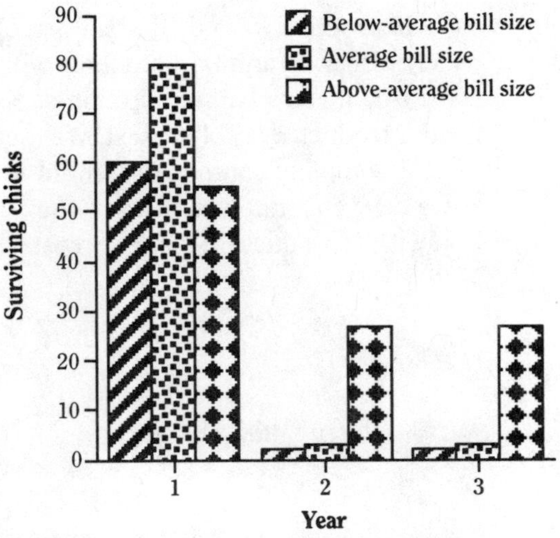

Figure 4. Surviving finch chicks by bill size.

By using such an extreme example, we might bias students to think that only under extreme conditions do individuals differ in reproductive success because of some physical differences among them. That certainly is not so. Natural selection goes on continuously, in small and large ways, about many characteristics. Sometimes it can affect two characteristics in one individual in opposite directions. There might be advantages from one characteristic and disadvantages from another characteristic in the same individual and at the same time. The overall outcome depends on which characteristic is under stronger selection.

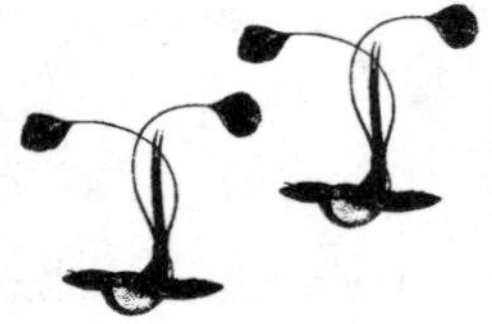

READING 2 GUIDE
Reproduction: THEIR New Tissue

By now, students likely are clear that being successful means leaving the most surviving, reproducing offspring. However, there are many different ways in which organisms have been selected toward that end.

Reproduction is another key component of any species' life-history strategy. In fact, organisms tend to fall into natural groupings based on mode of reproduction. Annual plants and insects reproduce seasonally and have non-overlapping generations. Most vertebrates and higher plants both reproduce seasonally and have overlapping generations. (For birds, mammals, and even some reptiles, overlapping generations are also tied into parents caring for their offspring.) Most organisms that produce continuously, that is, without regard for season, are single-celled organisms, the bacteria. They cannot be said to have overlapping generations, since they reproduce by division. The few other nonseasonally reproducing species do have overlapping generations: they include humans and fruit flies. The latter provide no parental care; the former provide it for many years, since humans have a slow growth rate and lengthy development period.

INTEGRATION GUIDE
Reproduction and Lifestyle: A Study in Contrast

Reproduction and lifestyle are obviously related; by comparing two widely disparate animals, students will see more about each because of the contrasts. If you want more particulars on reproductive strategies, refer to a good introductory ecology text. We mention two in References.

A complete comparison would include all or most aspects of lifestyle as we have encountered them in the curriculum so far, integrating production with reproduction—energy costs, biology, and social behavior.

INTEGRATION
Reproduction and Lifestyle: A Study in Contrast

Elephant and mosquito, salamander and ostrich, chickadee and crocodile, hyrax and honeybee, mongoose and ant, beaver and shark. How does each pair differ in its reproductive strategy?

Materials

- **Reference books, journals**

Procedure

1. **Picking a second species.**
By now, we know a good bit about the pieces of an organism's lifestyle. Let's add what we have just discovered about reproduction and production. Compare your own animal to some other, wildly dissimilar species, as unlike yours as you can imagine.

2. **Comparing lifestyles.**
Compare the two as deeply as possible. Try to answer questions like these: How many offspring do they have? How many times a year (or a lifetime)? How long do they live? Do the parents care for the young? How? What do the young eat? How soon are they independent? How many are likely to survive to reproductive maturity?
Some of these questions will be difficult to answer, because no one actually knows. If you get stuck, see if you can find data for a similar species.

3. **Writing it up.**
Write up your findings for both species in a way that allows you to illustrate clearly the differences and similarities between them, especially (but not only) with respect to reproduction.

REFERENCES

Begon, Michael, John Harper, and Colin Townsend. 1990. Ecology: Individuals, Populations, and Communities. 2nd ed. Boston: Blackwell Scientific Publications. 945 pp.

Ricklefs, Robert E. 1990. Ecology. 3rd ed. New York: W. H. Freeman. 896 pp.

FOOD QUALITY
CARBON AND ENERGY CONTENT

CHAPTER EIGHT

CONTENTS

INTRODUCTION

We have talked much about energy coming into and moving through animals, why animals need it, how different species expend it, and reasons for some of those differences. Here, we make that energy more directly visible, through the techniques of calorimetry, which measures the calories (energy) in items, and carbonometry, which measures their carbon. There is a direct link between the two; this Chapter focuses on establishing that link, while **Chapter 9** explores the bond energies that underlie and account for the link.

Students can also use these techniques as part of their work for other Units in this Module. We hope that students will ask themselves, "I wonder what would happen if I tested for carbon content?" "for energy content?" at many points throughout all modules.

KEY CONCEPTS

- All organisms eat to obtain some of the following: energy and ready-made molecules like amino acids, lipids, carbohydrates (or their component parts), vitamins, minerals, water, and (for vertebrates) roughage. In this Chapter and the next, we focus on energy: where it is, how much is there, and how it is arranged chemically.
- Although different organisms have the same general life requirements, individual species can also have quite different and highly specialized needs.
- Each species meets those similar and different needs by eating foods that other species do not eat and by processing them differently. That is possible because different types of species have different digestive systems, that is, different abilities, specializations, and efficiencies for dealing with particular food items. For example, herbivores, which get help eating plant material, are not very efficient (hence their high **E** values), while carnivores are more efficient but may have fewer food items available.
- Using the techniques of calorimetry, we can actually measure the amount of energy in any burnable organic substance. Burning breaks the bonds of the item and remakes stronger, higher energy bonds between the carbon in the item and the oxygen in the air. That energy is released as heat, which increases the movement of molecules in water in a container held over the burning item. That increased molecular movement (energy) registers on a thermometer in the water as increased temperature.
- Using carbonometry, we can measure the amount of carbon in an organic substance by burning the item, collecting the residue and the CO_2 produced by the burning, and then calculating the difference in CO_2 between normal air and the air collected from the burning.
- Both biological and nonbiological processes use and release energy. Both types of processes can start and end with the same materials, although the processes themselves differ markedly. For example, plant matter can be eaten and metabolized by an animal or burned—in both cases, the end-products are carbon dioxide and water.
- Energy differences between foods can be explained chemically. How carbon, hydrogen, and oxygen are arranged or bonded to each other tells how much energy is in a substance. (This is the real focus of **Chapter 9**, but it might be useful to you here as well.)

MATERIALS AND PREPARATION

Safety

WARNING

You will be working with burning matches, burning samples, and perhaps a nichrome wire–battery ignition system that gets very hot.

DO NOT ALLOW STUDENTS TO USE THIS TECHNIQUE WITHOUT ADULT SUPERVISION.

DO NOT PERFORM THIS TECHNIQUE IN AN OXYGEN-ENRICHED ATMOSPHERE.

DO NOT ALLOW THE TWO NICHROME WIRES OR ALLIGATOR CLIPS TO TOUCH EACH OTHER.

DO NOT TOUCH ANY BURNING, HEATED, OR RECENTLY BURNING ITEMS WITH BARE FINGERS OR ANYTHING BUT APPROPRIATE TOOLS. WEAR SAFETY GOGGLES DURING THE PROCEDURE.

In Advance

Discuss with students what they would like to test. If necessary, dry and prepare the samples yourself. You also may wish to assemble the calorimeters and carbonometers ahead of time. If the students are to assemble them, allow an additional class session.

Materials

- **Calorimetry apparatus**
- **Carbonometry apparatus**
- **Published caloric values** for the items students will analyze (see **Chapter 2**, References for suggestions)
- Molecule diagrams of lipids, proteins, and carbohydrates if you think they might be useful (A standard biochemistry or chemistry textbook should have some good diagrams.)

SUGGESTED SEQUENCE OF SESSIONS (7–10)

Homework

Have students read the **Technique: Calorimetry**.

Class Session 1

Discuss calorimetry and how to use it (Exploration 1 and the Technique). What do students want to examine for energy content—their own foods, foods of their animals (**Chapter 4**), or general categories of foods such as meat versus plant matter, insect flesh versus vertebrate flesh, wood versus grass versus nuts versus fruits, or any combinations? Ask them to explain their choices and reasoning. What are their predictions about which items will be high or low in energy? Why? Ask them to bring in samples or, if you prefer, provide the items yourself.

Class Session 2

Begin drying the wet items to constant weight. (To save time, you can do this ahead of time.) Begin assembling the calorimeters and carbonometers. Half the class can do one technique, the other half the other technique.

Once the apparatuses are prepared, begin testing the dried samples.

Homework

(Optional) Reading 1: They Eat WHAT? (You may wish to substitute Reading 3, which is a more detailed and broader discussion of the same general topic, or Reading 2, which better prepares students to analyze their data.)

Class Session 3

Continue testing samples. Reading 1 raises issues about who eats what. Reading 2 presents students with data on three classes of molecules they will encounter in their efforts to understand their calorimetry data. Reading 3 permits a discussion in which students can relate information on digestibilities of foods back to their animals' energy use equation (e.g., why does an herbivore have a higher **E** value than a carnivore?).

Class Session 4

Discuss energy values in the "calorimetrized" items. Ask students to consider patterns—what they are and why they might exist. Remember that lipid-rich foods have nearly twice the caloric values of either proteins or carbohydrates. Consider with them the three classes of molecules described in Reading 2.

Homework

Have students read the **Technique: Data.**

Class Session 5

The data are likely to be variable. It may help students bring order to them if they consider the **Technique: Data.**

Homework

Have students read the **Technique: Carbonometry** and Reading 2: The Big Three, to help them put their calorimetry results in perspective.

Class Session 6

Use the carbonometers to measure the carbon content of samples of the same items for which students have energy values (Exploration 2 and the **Technique: Carbonometry**).

Class Session 7

Continue Session 6 as necessary. Reading 3: Who Gets Energy, How? permits a discussion in which students can relate information on digestibilities of foods back to their animals' energy use equation (e.g., why does an herbivore have a higher **E** value than a carnivore?).

Class Session 8

As a class, assemble the energy and carbon data in a table. Students see the relationship between higher amounts of carbon and higher caloric values (Exploration 3). In **Chapter 9**, they will consider the actual bond types involved.

SESSION GUIDES, BY WORKSHEET

EXPLORATION 1 GUIDE
Calorimetry: The Condensed Version

The REAL Goal

The actual calorimetry technique is so simple that it can be easy to overlook its power or its purpose. Some students might believe the goal is to see how hot the water gets or to measure how long the sample burns. Be sure students understand that **the goal of calorimetry is to measure the energy content of the sample**. The probe, the device used for making those measurements, is a can containing a known quantity of water along with a thermometer to measure the change in water temperature due to combustion of the sample.

Also be sure students understand the actual procedure—what they do, when, and why.

You might start this class with a student-centered discussion about food quality and caloric content. The discussion might go in several directions: reviewing the most basic question, Why do animals eat? How do different animals meet their nutritional and energy requirements? How can calorimetry help find answers to these questions?.

Animals eat to get energy (key point), important molecules or their precursors, vitamins, minerals, water, and (for vertebrates) roughage. For more, see Science Background, at the end of this chapter.

Measures of Energy

Perhaps briefly review the concept that calories (and kilocalories) are measures of energy. If you have not done so before, you may want to show a liter bottle full of water to the students to demonstrate the amount of water that a single kilocalorie raises 1°C.

In this work, students measure the energy content of various items used as food by different animals. The technique shows that there is indeed energy available to be liberated in those items that they (and other animals) eat. In calorimetry, that energy heats water.

The Energy in Stuff

Although people talk a lot about calories and energy in foods in everyday contexts, this laboratory work gives students the opportunity to measure the energy contained in various foods and to see for themselves what a calorie is. The process should add to students' understanding of energy, foods, and the relationship between them.

A Range of Samples

Make sure the class as a whole has tested a wide range of plant materials (fruits, leaves, roots, seeds, stems) as well as some fats and protein-rich materials. Each student should test at least some of the food that one of the animals from the animal cards eats.

You may want to discuss various types of data with the students and the different ways in which they can analyze or present their data. Having your students do tests of statistical significance on their data would be great; however, we expect that in most classes students will work to achieve qualitative understanding of their data.

Analysis of Calorimetry Data

In the course of their investigations, students have collected quantitative data on the energy content of different foods and materials. While each sample could be considered separately (e.g., peanuts contain this much energy, corn flakes contain that much, and so on), students can learn much more from their data by using a second variable, such as the composition of foods, to help analyze their data. Without such a second variable, there is nothing to analyze but the average amount of energy in each type of food. By using information about the composition of foods, students can find correlations between energy content and composition.

Approximate biochemical compositions of items

Students should have access to data on the composition of foods in sources such as the nutrition labels that accompany foods or the Handbook of the Nutritional Value of Foods (**Chapter 2**, References). Information on food composition can be treated as categorical data, that is, classified as fats, mostly fats, protein, mostly protein, carbohydrate, or mostly carbohydrate (see the **Technique: Data**).

Alternatively, students could treat the composition data as quantitative. One way to do that is by considering the proportion of lipid in a food (in which case, foods range from 0% lipid to 100%).

Let students brainstorm about their data sets and how to analyze them for at least half a class period. It may not be obvious to the students that they have more information potentially available about each sample than just the caloric data they have collected. You may have to help them see the utility of consulting sources such as nutrition labels and the Handbook of the Nutritional Value of Foods. In addition, you may have to help students understand how to calculate the proportions of the different constituents in foods.

An example: The ubiquitous peanut

To calculate the different proportions of lipids, proteins, and carbohydrates in a given food, follow these steps. We use roasted peanuts.

Add together the quantities of protein, carbohydrate, and fat found in each serving. These quantities are readily available in either the nutrition information on a food package or the Handbook of the Nutritional Value of Foods. For salted peanuts, each serving (28 grams, or 1 ounce) contains 7 g protein, 5 g carbohydrate, and 14 g fat, which totals 26 g dry weight.

Divide each individual quantity by the sum of the three quantities per serving. That gives us the proportions of protein, carbohydrate, and fat. So, for our peanut, the proportion of protein is 7 g/26 g = 0.27; for carbohydrate, 5 g/26 g = 0.19; and for fat, 14 g/26 g = 0.54. To express those results as percentages, multiply each result by 100. Thus, the percentage of protein is 27%; of carbohydrate, 19%; and of fat, 54%.

Grouping like samples

Once students have ascertained the composition of their samples (in terms of carbohydrates, proteins, and lipids), they can group the samples according to that information. Thus, rather than saying, "Dried peanuts contain 6 kilocalories per gram," the group might be able to generalize, "Foods that consist of large amounts of lipids along with some protein and carbohydrate (e.g., potato chips, peanuts, sunflower seeds, and chocolate) contain 6 kilocalories per gram of dried material." Of course, students should report averages and some measure of variance for their data. For example, if several groups analyzed the energy content of peanuts (or nuts or fatty foods in general), the analysis team should calculate a mean for the grouped data and show the range of the data in their presentation.

The caloric and carbon contents of the three classes of biochemicals are as follows: lipids contain approximately 80% carbon and have about 9 calories per gram; proteins contain approximately 50–60% carbon and about 4 calories per gram; and carbohydrates contain approximately 40% carbon and about 4 calories per gram.

Reporting and Summing the Data

Each group reports its results. What are the caloric contents of the different foods they tested? What difficulties did they encounter in the testing?

What "wild foods" did they test? For which animals would any wild foods be appropriate (or even vaguely appropriate)? Clearly, students cannot test all possible foods for their organisms, but they might see that different types of seeds tend to have similar values and thus can serve as a first approximation of the food value of seeds; so also for tree leaves versus grass leaves, live leaves versus fallen leaves, and so forth.

Potential Roughness in the Data

Examining the data might be more brainstorming than hard data analysis. Although the students may have been able to collect data that are up to 70–80% accurate compared with published caloric or carbon values, there may be too much variation in the data for them to draw definite conclusions from some of their analyses.

Perhaps student values differ from published values in a consistent way. For example, students may consistently under- or overestimate. Or student values may differ from published values in both directions, that is, some values obtained by students will be lower than published values, while others are higher. It may be easier to think about values that are always lower or higher than expected, because they are probably due to one cause, for example, "Our calorimetry values are consistently low because we are not sufficiently careful about trapping the hot air."

Variable results are, however, still useful in the context of basic concepts. They also can be used to begin explorations of techniques and methodologies, such as why it is important to keep conditions as nearly constant as possible during laboratory procedures. (For more on this subject, see the **Technique: Data** and the **Technique: Introduction to Research**.)

Further Thoughts and Research

What experiments might students design based on their results? For example, how might they test whether an animal has food preferences? Does the animal prefer foods with the highest energy content? If the calorimetry value of a food is high, but the food is avoided by an animal that, it seems, should eat it, what factors might be at work (e.g., digestibility, palatability, size of jaws)?

Ask the students to refer to **Module 1, Evolution**, in which many of these issues come up in the context of natural selection. How might the pressure of natural selection apply to the students' own organisms?

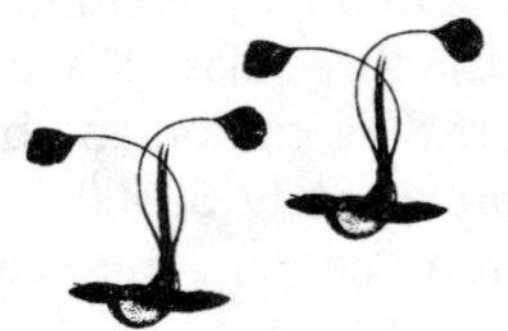

(Optional) READING 1 GUIDE
They Eat WHAT?

This reading portrays two very different scenarios in which the quality of available food interacts with the life-cycles of the animals in the system. In each case, the organisms need at least enough energy to survive and complete their life-cycles. The salamanders must complete their metamorphosis to adulthood; the survivors will reproduce the following spring. Clearly, if survival is enhanced by the ability to switch food types, this trait will be preserved by natural selection; the parallels with the Darwin's Finches example are straightforward.

The Serengeti ungulates also must survive and reproduce. The picture is a little more complicated, because these creatures are mammals, so their population includes a mixture of ages. Also, because the animals live long enough to reproduce in several seasons, adult survival this year at least makes possible reproduction in a later year. The grassland is tremendously productive, and a large percentage of the primary production is edible to the dominant herbivores. The grazers partition the resources, interacting with the plants' life-cycles.

Consider the questions about food quality and its connection with carbon content.

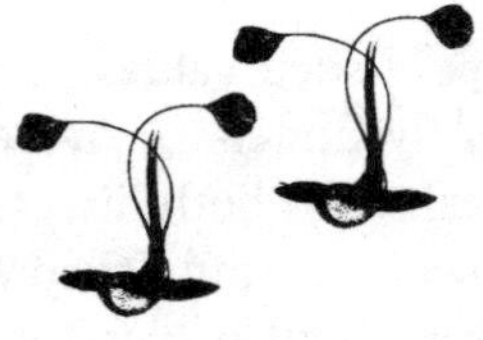

READING 2 GUIDE
The Big Three

Students can better handle their calorimetry data if they grasp the concept that most organic items are made up of three classes of biochemicals and that their energy contents vary according to the proportions of those three molecule classes.

EXPLORATION 2 GUIDE
Carbonometry: The Condensed Version

Although it may seem daunting to set up and carry out this (or even the preceding) technique, the carbonometry results should add a great deal to students' understanding of energy, the carbon content of organic materials, and the relationship between them.

It can be confusing to read the tubes, which are calibrated to report a unit that combines both parts per million and length of measurement in fractions of an hour. The sample reading and examples in the **Technique: Carbonometry** might help clarify this. The data analysis follows the same basic reasoning as that for calorimetry, except for conversion of the diffusion tube data.

Class Discussion of Data

Each group reports its results. What are the carbon contents of the different foods they tested? What difficulties did they encounter in the testing?

What "wild foods" did they test? For which animals would any wild foods be appropriate (or even vaguely appropriate)? Clearly, they cannot test all possible foods for their organisms, but they might see that different types of seeds tend to have similar values and thus can serve as a first approximation of the food value of seeds; so also for tree leaves versus grass leaves, live leaves versus fallen leaves, and so forth.

What ecological implications can students draw from the tests they made? What can they say about the "most desirable" kinds of food (of all foods tested and also within categories)? And desirable to whom, based on what they read in Reading 1?

Further Thoughts and Research

What experiments might the students design based on their results? For example, how might they test whether an animal has food preferences? Does the animal prefer foods with the highest energy content? If the calorimetry value of a food is high, but the food is avoided by an animal that, it seems, should eat it, what factors might be at work (e.g., digestibility, palatability, size of jaws)?

Ask the students to refer to **Module 1, Evolution**, in which many of these issues come up in the context of natural selection. How might the pressure of natural selection apply to the students' own organisms?

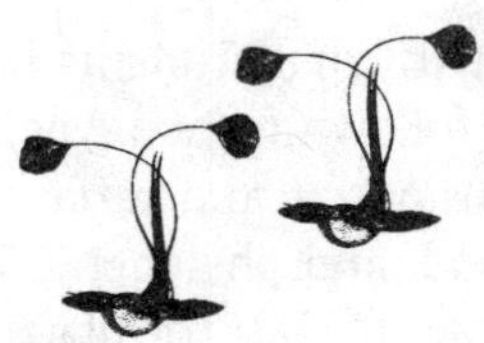

READING 3 GUIDE
Who Gets Energy, How?

Students can address or answer more of the questions that might have come out of their calorimetry data. They continue to piece together a working picture of how food, energy, habitat, and animal lifestyle interact.

In particular, this Reading raises issues about who can eat what and why. Although most species have the same general requirements from their food, they meet them in very different ways. That is, in part, because they have such different abilities, capabilities, and phylogenies.

EXPLORATION 3 GUIDE
Carbon and Energy: Class Data Patterns

To integrate the findings of their calorimetry and carbonometry studies, have students graph the results of each study as a function of the other. That way, students can see the direct relationship between the carbon and energy contents of foods. In general, the greater the carbon content, the higher the combustible energy, as illustrated in Figure 1.

Energy content

0 Carbon content

Figure 1

Discussion

By now, students have taken a series of empirical measurements of the energy and carbon contents of various items. The goal of this session is functionally to link those two sets of measurements and to address their links to the underlying molecular structure of the items themselves. Students have considered caloric value or energy content (via reading and calorimetry) and carbon content (from carbonometry). They have been teased with biochemical makeup (molecules such as proteins, lipids, and carbohydrates), component elements (carbon, hydrogen, oxygen), and the types of bonds involved. (These topics are covered in **Chapter 9**.)

Working as a class, students plot caloric versus carbon content of various materials. Carbohydrates and proteins contain a higher proportion of oxygen, less carbon and fewer calories per unit weight than do lipids. Foods that contain mixtures of these biochemicals will have intermediate values. The key question is: What is the link between carbon content and energy content?

To address that question, students must consider the carbon and caloric contents from the perspective of the molecular structures and bond energies of carbohydrates, lipids, and proteins. Since they have only casually addressed the molecular biochemical level, students should be fully primed to move on to the next chapter.

The caloric and carbon contents of the three classes of biochemicals are as follows: lipids contain approximately 80% carbon and have about 9 calories per gram; proteins contain approximately 50–60% carbon and about 4 calories per gram; and carbohydrates contain approximately 40% carbon and about 4 calories per gram. Students should see this trend in their data, and they can confirm it by calculating the energy in the molecular bonds of each type of molecule.

INTEGRATION GUIDE
Make a Creature

Anything goes, which is consistent with what students have come to know about the interactions among all the following: food type, thermoregulation, circulatory system, digestion, ratios of size and surface area to volume, how animals get and ingest their food, and phylogeny. They will be creative—and so must you—in playing "what if?" Test the plausibility of the fantasy creatures by asking, for example, "What if it walks and weighs 18 tons." Is there now, has there been, or could there be any animal like this fantasy creature? If not, why not?

INTEGRATION
Make a Creature

Create an animal. Give it size, weight, and shape. Give it a diet and a way of obtaining that food in sufficient quantities to survive. How does it raise and maintain its basal metabolic rate? Where does it live? How is it equipped to deal with its environment? And so on. We may have left out a few considerations, but you get the picture. Oh, and draw your creature, if you like.

Make sure you specify each of your animal's attributes and your reasoning. For example, if it swims, make sure you say how it gets enough calories to stay warm; if it flies, explain how it can be so large.

SCIENCE BACKGROUND
More on Reasons to Eat

ACQUIRING BASIC BUILDING MATERIALS

For example, twenty different amino acids are used to build proteins, but humans can synthesize only twelve of them. To make the proteins we need (including muscle tissue and the many proteins needed to run the cellular machinery of the body), the other eight must be acquired from the foods we eat.

ACQUIRING TRACE ELEMENTS AND VITAMINS

Animals need certain materials in very small quantities. These materials include vitamins (which are used to help run various reactions in cells and which cannot be synthesized by the body) and tiny amounts of necessary elements, such as copper, zinc, and molybdenum, that are important parts of certain enzymes.

ACQUIRING ENERGY FOR DAILY LIVING

It is expensive to run a body and even more expensive to grow. The expense is not one of money, but one of energy. It costs energy to move, to keep warm, to repair damaged tissues. As we know from **Chapter 3**, it even costs energy to sit still or to sleep—the cellular machinery of the body is always running.

BONDS
THE "GLUE" AND "SUPER GLUE" OF ENERGY

CHAPTER NINE

CONTENTS

INTRODUCTION

In this Chapter, students move from (bio)chemicals to the component bonds in those molecules. Now they have an opportunity to integrate their empirical results on carbon and calorie data with new knowledge of bond energies and the molecular structure of the different types of molecules. How are high- and lower-energy bonds formed? How are carbon and energy functionally related? How does that relationship map onto the foods organisms eat and the energy they can get from those foods?

The class considers their homework on how and how much energy is stored in and released from chemical bonds. Then the class calculates the energy released by methane combustion. Students work in small groups with magnets to demonstrate to themselves that the same few "atoms" (the magnets) can form weak and strong bonds, depending on which other atoms they are connected to. That is, the same kinds of atoms are in weak and strong bonds, but the molecules differ and their bond energies differ because their atoms have been rearranged.

KEY CONCEPTS

- The energy of bond formation: Chemical bonds release energy when they are formed; bonds require the input of energy to be broken.
- Not all bonds are equal; an energy "profit" can be made by breaking weak bonds and forming strong bonds among the atoms that are freed.

	WEAK BONDS	STRONG BONDS
In order to break—	Require less energy	Require more energy
Upon bond formation—	Release less energy	Release more energy

- Carbon (C), hydrogen (H), and oxygen (O) atoms make up the bulk of most "food" (things ingested by organisms). How those atoms are arranged or bonded and the ratios in which they occur affect whether a food supplies energy, and if so, how much, to the organism eating that food. Energy differences between foods can be explained chemically. That is, how C, H, and O are arranged, or bonded to each other, tells how much energy is in a substance.
- All organic matter is made up, in varying proportions, of three classes of biochemicals (plus other stuff). These compounds are lipids, carbohydrates, and proteins.
- Per unit weight, lipids contain nearly twice the amount of energy (number of calories) as proteins and carbohydrates. That is because the carbon atoms in fat molecules mostly share chemical bonds with hydrogen atoms and other carbon atoms, whereas the carbon atoms in carbohydrates and proteins often share bonds with oxygen atoms. Also, the carbon-carbon and carbon-hydrogen bonds are often in the form of high-energy double and triple bonds.

MATERIALS AND PREPARATION

- **Calculators**, at least 2 per group
- **Magnets:** 2 of the same strength to demonstrate that input of energy is required to break a bond; at least 4 (2 each of 2 strengths) per group of students for Exploration 3: Bond Strengths: Analogy with Magnets.

- **Plastic sandwich bags** (the type with a folded-over flap): 1 per group of students
- Many **small weights** (or a few hundred pennies) to measure the strength of attraction of 2 magnets

SUGGESTED SEQUENCE OF SESSIONS (4–6)

Homework

Students calculate the energy of different bonds between atoms that are common in organic compounds just by counting and adding from Figure 1 and a table of data.

Class Session 1

Discuss patterns students find in the bonds: which atoms are involved in more energy-rich bonds (carbon and hydrogen). Is there a relationship between the number of bonds and bond energy? (Yes—more bonds mean more energy.)

Turn to the results of the calorimetry and carbonometry work from **Chapter 8**. Can we see the same patterns for lipids, proteins, and carbohydrates? (For more, see Reading 1: Chapter 8 Revisited.)

Homework (or Class)

The Case Study Guide attempts to show relationships among the levels of bonds, whole molecules, and foods. Discuss the Case Study with students or read it together with them. (You might want to refresh your own chemistry by going through the optional Reading 2 [in the student chapter] and Science Background, here.)

Class Session 2

Continue Session 1 and the Homework, as appropriate. Keep students thinking across all three levels; only by such integration will bond energies make sense.

Revisit data from Exploration 3 and Reading 1 in **Chapter 8** to show those cross-level patterns and to reinforce the concept that the formation of strong bonds releases more energy and is energetically desirable.

Class Session 3

Continue Session 2, as appropriate.

In Exploration 2: Combustion of Methane, students see on paper how the combination of carbon and oxygen releases much energy.

Keep putting the specific work into the general picture: the same atoms in different molecules (i.e., with different bond types and numbers) have and release different amounts of energy.

Class Session 4

Different strengths of magnets and their attractions to each other model different amounts of energy.

SESSION GUIDES, BY WORKSHEET

EXPLORATION 1 GUIDE (Homework)
Powerhouse Bonds

Weak bonds are bonds that are rich in energy and tend to be made up of C–H and C–C single, double, and even triple bonds. Strong, energy-poor bonds include C=O and H–O bonds. The three classes of biochemicals represented here, fats (or lipids), carbohydrates, and proteins, vary markedly in the amount of energy they contain. Fats tend to have twice the amount of energy of proteins or carbohydrates. By considering the number of weak and strong covalent bonds in different molecules, we can gain a good understanding of the energy they contain. One approach to the situation is to count the number of weak, or energy-rich, C–H and C–C bonds and compare that number to the number of strong, or energy-poor, C=O and H–O bonds in the various molecules (Figure 1).

Note that in the fat molecule in Figure 1 very few of the carbon and hydrogen atoms are connected to oxygen atoms. That means that nearly every bond in the lipid can yield usable energy when an animals eats it. By comparison, in the carbohydrate pictured (glucose), each carbon atom has at least one bond with an oxygen atom, as do many of the hydrogen atoms.

A carbohydrate (glucose)

A portion of a protein

A triglyceride fat

Figure 1. Bonds in three classes of molecules.

Thus, fewer weak bonds are available to be broken, since many of the atoms are already involved in strong bonds.

What do all these bond energies mean in the real world, at the dinner table? Based on the preceding paragraphs, ask students which contains more calories per unit of dry weight: sugar (a carbohydrate) or margarine (a lipid).

Proteins, which are far more complex in structure than either lipids or carbohydrates, contain numerous C–O bonds, so they too yield less energy than lipids when they are eaten. (In addition, proteins contain nitrogen and a few sulfur atoms.)

CASE STUDY GUIDE
Food: Where Is the Energy?

Be sure students understand that energy is stored in chemical bonds, which one can calculate from the chemical formula for the substance, and that organisms liberate that energy for their metabolic needs by breaking weak bonds and forming strong bonds, primarily between carbon atoms and oxygen atoms. This is the fundamental idea behind cellular respiration, and it is this molecular behavior that drives animals' foraging behavior and makes possible (and sometimes necessary) all their activities.

Digestion and Assimilation

As we have seen, animals get their energy by gathering and digesting food, breaking weak chemical bonds in the food, and forming strong bonds in carbon dioxide (CO_2) and water (H_2O). Through this process, animals gain the energy they need to live, grow, and reproduce. However, no animals are able to use all the energy contained in food. In fact, animals typically waste most of the energy in the food they eat (remember our work with the energy use equation?).

As we know, a significant portion of food eaten passes through the animal's gut undigested, and the energy and nutrients in that material are lost to the animal. (The undigested material is, however, an excellent food source for detritivores and decomposers.) Furthermore, not all the food that is digested and absorbed through the gut wall is fully used. Nor are the chemical processes that take place in cells fully efficient at capturing all the chemical energy stored in food. Even the oxidation of glucose, a relatively efficient chemical reaction (actually, a long series of reactions), yields only about 38% of the chemical energy held in the glucose molecule. A great deal of energy is lost as heat during the biochemical reactions taking place in animals.

We know to ask, from our earlier studies, "Of the energy present in a food item, what proportion is the animal able to use?" "Of the energy present in a food item, what proportion does the animal turn into new tissue?" And we know the answers to both questions are that these processes are overall quite inefficient. (Refer to **Chapters 3** and **4**, if you wish.)

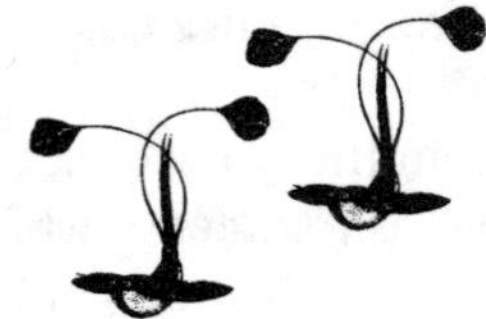

READING 1 GUIDE
Chapter 8 Revisited

Whatever their actual data, and even if students make graphs of published caloric or carbon values, these activities and discussion allow students to begin drawing together the various threads they have been exploring. Lipids contain more energy per unit weight than carbohydrates or proteins (as per the calorimetry studies and work with food). Lipids also contain more carbon per unit weight than proteins or carbohydrates (as per the carbonometry studies).

The punch line is that understanding bond energies and differences in molecular structure of lipids, carbohydrates, and proteins can help explain differences in both energy content and carbon content. Lipids contain relatively few oxygen atoms (hence the higher proportion of carbon). That means most of the carbon and hydrogen atoms in lipids are in weak bonds—specifically, they are not bonded to oxygen—so a great deal of chemical energy is available to be liberated from lipids. In contrast, many of the carbon and hydrogen atoms in carbohydrates and proteins already participate in strong bonds with oxygen atoms, so fewer weak bonds are available per unit weight to yield energy.

EXPLORATION 2 GUIDE
Combustion of Methane

Bond behaviors and how they relate to animals "making a living" can seem counterintuitive. It is key to help students keep practicing with every possible example until they genuinely understand why bond formation or creation releases energy and why bond separation or dissolution requires energy. (You may find it helpful to read the Classroom Vignettes.)

If possible, make this exploration more dramatic with a demonstration of burning natural gas (with a Bunsen burner), to show the process and products of methane combustion. Let's examine this specific example to illustrate the release of energy from the breaking and forming of chemical bonds. The simplest molecule that contains carbon and hydrogen is methane (CH_4), the main component of natural gas (Figure 2).

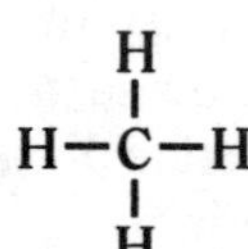

Figure 2. Diagram of a methane molecule.

In this thought experiment, we break each of the four weak C–H bonds in a molecule of methane and then place the freed atoms in strong bonds, that is, connected to an atom other than a carbon atom. (Keep in mind that the process of breaking and forming bonds actually is quite complex and that the atoms do not really float around free.) Overall, the process will release energy. What do we call this process of breaking and forming bonds? In this case, it is called combustion, or burning. We will look at what takes place inside the burner of a gas stove when natural gas burns.

Take a moment to consider the process of breaking a chemical bond. What is required? An input of energy is needed to break a bond. Once the bond is broken, what happens to the freed atoms? They may return to the same bond they were in before, giving off exactly as much energy as was needed to break the original bond. Or they might be able to participate in different, stronger bonds. If that happens, the bond formation will release more energy than was required for the initial breaking.

Let's relate this chemical-level description to what you know from your own experience. To create a fire, you need three things: a material that can burn, a spark or flame to start the fire, and oxygen. What is the initial energy input in this scheme? What role does the oxygen play?

We have a combustible material, methane, that contains four weak C–H bonds in each molecule (C–H bonds contain only 98.7 kcal/mole). To break a few of those bonds, we need the input of energy: a spark or the flame of a pilot light. Once the weak bonds are broken, stronger bonds can be formed with oxygen atoms (we also must break the double bonds of the O_2 molecules, which costs 96.1 kcal/mole). If we did not break the oxygen molecules, there would be no oxygen atoms with which the freed hydrogen and carbon atoms could form strong bonds. Without oxygen, the combustion or oxidation reaction would stop, and we would not make any "energy profit." (What does your own experience tell you about the role of oxygen in fires?)

Thus, the inputs for the reaction are methane, oxygen, and a small amount of energy. The outputs from the reaction are carbon dioxide, water, and large amounts of energy (Figure 3). Once the reaction is started, the energy released from the first methane molecule is enough to break the bonds of other methane and oxygen molecules, and the reaction continues without additional energy input. In this case, the chemical energy is released in the form of heat and light.

We must include enough oxygen to bond with the carbon atom and four hydrogen atoms that will be freed when we break the C–H bonds in the methane molecule. Thus, we will need two oxygen atoms for the carbon atom and one oxygen atom for each pair of hydrogen atoms, since we cannot have individual atoms floating around freely (see Figure 3).

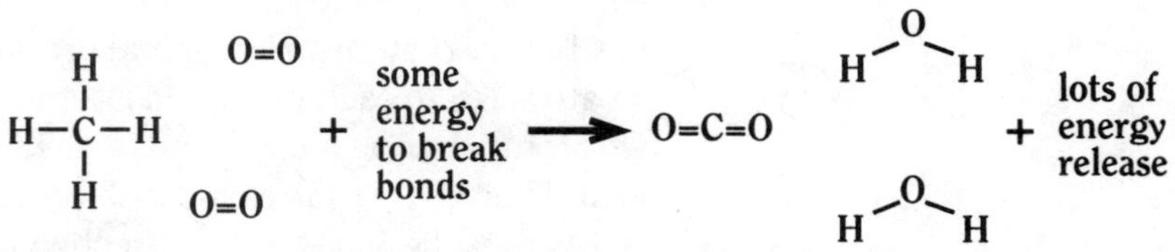

H–C(H)(H)–H + O=O + O=O + some energy to break bonds ⟶ O=C=O + H–O–H + H–O–H + lots of energy release

Figure 3. Breaking the weak bonds of methane and oxygen molecules, yielding carbon dioxide, water, and energy.

In summary, to release the chemical energy stored in the methane molecule, we need to break four C–H bonds and two O=O double bonds (since pure oxygen is typically found in molecules that contain two oxygen atoms sharing a double bond). Keep in mind that we will have to spend energy to break those bonds. However, when the strong bonds are formed between the carbon and oxygen atoms and between the hydrogen and oxygen atoms, a great deal more energy is liberated than was needed to break the original bonds. In other words, by finding relatively weak bonds (the C–H and O=O bonds) and investing energy to break them, we can create strong bonds (C=O and H–O) and release more energy than we spent.

The combustion of organic materials, such as methane and wood, proceeds rapidly, releasing most of the energy as heat and a small amount of energy as light. When organisms break down organic molecules, they do so in a complex series of biochemical reactions, releasing the energy of the chemical bonds slowly so that it can be captured and incorporated into other chemical bonds. While very few organisms can use methane as food, the general process of breaking C–C and C–H bonds and forming C=O and O–H bonds is how all animals gather energy.

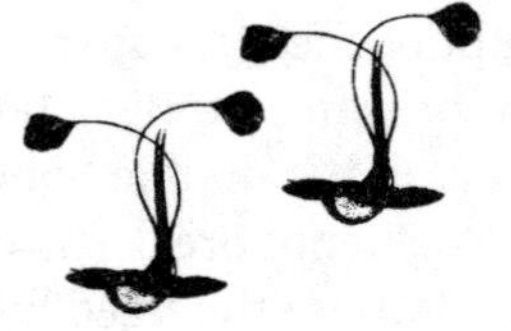

(Optional) READING 2 GUIDE
Bonds and Bond Types

Consider this material a chemistry refresher. Use it if you or your students would profit from having your memories jogged.

EXPLORATION 3 GUIDE
Bond Strengths: Analogy with Magnets

Chemical bonds, bond strengths, weak and strong bonds, and bond formation—these can be difficult concepts. To further illustrate these concepts, students model them using magnets. Certainly the principles governing magnetism are quite different from those governing chemical bonds. Several useful analogies can be made, however, that help explicate some aspects of chemical bonds. Students must experiment with magnets themselves.

Breaking Bonds Requires Energy

Students can have difficulty remembering whether the breaking of a chemical bond requires the input of energy or whether energy is released when a bond is broken. It will help them remember if they have used magnets to model atoms. Here, bond breaking is modeled by two magnets that are attracted to each other and are touching; the magnets are analogous to two atoms sharing a covalent bond. To break the bond, energy must be applied. That is, it requires muscular force to pull the magnets apart, just as energy must be added to break a chemical bond.

Demonstrate this or let students show it to themselves. Show your students two magnets (atoms) that are touching (modeling a chemical bond). Pulling apart the two magnets (breaking the bond) requires the addition of energy, that is, one pulls them apart by expending muscular effort.

Measuring Bond Energies

Students might not realize that chemical-bond strengths are not all equal. Analogously, certain pairs of magnets are attracted to each other more, or "bond" more tightly, than other pairs. This "bond strength" can be quantified by measuring how much weight can be lifted before the bond between the two magnets breaks. Quantitative comparisons of the strengths of bonds between different pairs of magnets are simple to make.

Not WHICH Atoms but HOW They Are Bonded

Energy is released when weak bonds are broken and strong bonds are created, and the same atoms can be rearranged from being part of weak bonds to being in strong bonds. It is difficult to find an exact analogy to energy release in the world of magnets. However, the strengths of the magnetic "bonds" are not transitive; that is, if you total the "bond strengths" of two pairs of magnets and then shuffle the magnets so they have new partners, you probably will find that the new combination has a different total bond strength. This can help model aspects of energy transfer in the breaking of weak bonds and the creating of strong bonds.

Example: Methane Combustion

Consider the example of methane combustion we discussed before. Initially, there is a collection of one carbon atom, four hydrogen atoms, and four oxygen atoms, arranged as one methane and two oxygen molecules. After the application of a small amount of energy (to begin breaking the bonds), we are left with exactly the same atoms that have been rearranged as one carbon dioxide molecule and two water molecules. Moreover, the total bond energies differ between the precombustion molecules and the postcombustion molecules.

Magnet Models

Similar effects are easy to demonstrate with magnets. By selecting the appropriate magnets, asymmetries of "bond strengths" between magnets that are attracted to each other can be shown. For example, select four magnets: two of one type, and the other two of a different type (by type, we mean size, strength, or shape). Call magnets of the first type A magnets and those of the second type B magnets. With most of the types of magnets with which we have experimented, it turns out that if you total the "bond strengths" when the two A magnets are "bonded" to each other and the two B magnets are "bonded" to each other, the total is markedly different from the total when each of the A magnets is "bonded" to a B magnet. That difference is analogous to the change in total bond energies from methane and oxygen to carbon dioxide and water.

Although students cannot measure the strengths of individual chemical bonds directly, here they can break "weak bonds," form "strong bonds," and sum the results using magnets.

An alternative method

Another way to measure "bond strengths" with magnets is to anchor one magnet firmly to a frame (perhaps with glue) and attach another magnet to a small spring scale (such as we use in **Module 1**). Add weight to the scale until the magnets come apart; the final weight recorded just before the break represents "bond strength."

NOTE: We have found that students really enjoy playing with their magnets. You may need to allow for a few minutes of giggling and quasi-mayhem, while the students get this out of their systems. Furthermore, students may tend to be more intrigued by the repulsion between magnets than their attraction (which is our analogy to a chemical bond).

INTEGRATION GUIDE
Same Atoms, No Calories

This simple activity forces students to articulate the concept that the energy content of an item varies with the arrangement of its atoms more than with the atoms it contains. Although the cookie and the carbonated water both contain carbon, hydrogen, and oxygen atoms, those atoms are arranged in completely different molecules, which in turn have different arrangements of the atoms in different bonds. And it is those molecular arrangements and the bonds of which they are made that result in the water having no caloric value, and the cookies lots of energy. The water is made up of H–O bonds with CO_2 for carbonation; the cookies include lipids and carbohydrates, with high numbers of carbon-carbon double and triple bonds and carbon-hydrogen bonds (refer to Figure 1 in Exploration 1).

INTEGRATION
Same Atoms, No Calories

You have been working hard all day, in school and out. You have been exercising a lot, so you go to a friend's house to chill out before going home to supper. You are hungry. Your friend says, "Check out the fridge, and help yourself."

You head for the kitchen, open the refrigerator. Inside there are just two things: a 1-liter bottle of carbonated water and a plate of chocolate chip cookies. It so happens that they weigh exactly the same (1 kg). You know that the carbonated water is made of carbon, hydrogen, and oxygen; the cookies are made of the same elements. Which one do you reach for to satisfy your hunger? Why?

CLASSROOM VIGNETTES

[The class is discussing magnets as an analogy for molecular bonds.]

TEACHER: So we're breaking methane bonds, which are weak with the input of energy, and rearranging them to get stronger bonds. . . .

[Teacher brings out the magnets. He puts two together, then pulls them apart.]

M: Oh yeah, put negative and negative together and they'll go apart.

TEACHER: Forget about negative and positive. Pretend these are two atoms. To pull them apart, I have to put in energy. To put them back together, some work is being done.

TEACHER: Take these four magnets, work in pairs. We're trying to find out what's stronger or weaker. Some of the bonds will be strong and some weaker.

[Teacher shows them how to measure the strength with pennies in a bag and magnets on either side of the bag.]

RB: So what are we trying to find out?

S: The strength of the bonds and how many pennies they hold.

TEACHER: So measure three kinds of bonds, big magnet with big magnet, small with small, and big with small. Record what you are finding.

[Students split into groups of three, count out stacks of pennies, and drop them into the bags. After about 10 minutes, the teacher has them call out their results:

	S, RB, AND SER	P, M, AND RM	AVERAGE
little/little	39	45	42
big/big	59	70	65
big/little	28	42	35

SER comments that the two small magnets hold more than the combination of a big one and a little one.]

TEACHER: Think about what this means for bond energies. Let's write these as a chemical equation using B and L. What would we write?

[No one responds. Teacher writes L–L + B–B > B–L + B–L.]

TEACHER: That looks very much like the carbon bonds we worked on before.

[He takes an average of the bond strengths and adds them up to get 107 > 70.]

TEACHER: So where is the release of energy?

S: When the LL and BB are formed.

RM: We're losing energy.

TEACHER: What if we change the direction of the arrow?

RM: We gain energy.

M: I would think it would take so much less energy to break apart.

SCIENCE BACKGROUND

TYPES OF ENERGY AND ENERGY TRANSFORMATIONS

Energy can be neither created nor destroyed. (Although it can be converted to or from matter. As Einstein's famous equation, $E = mc^2$, tells us, the conversion of matter to energy is the source of energy for nuclear power plants.) However, energy can change (or be changed) from one form to another. Most of the machines we use every day function only because energy can change form. Those changes, however, are never completely efficient, that is, some of the energy always ends up as heat, a rather unusable form of energy. For example, consider the ways in which energy gets transformed in your car and the various ways in which energy gets "wasted" as heat.

When you start your car, the car's battery changes stored chemical energy into electrical energy. Some of the electrical energy becomes heat, as the ignition wires warm slightly. The electrical energy becomes mechanical energy by turning the car's starter motor (and some of the energy is turned into heat because of friction in the starter motor). To keep the engine running, gasoline (which contains a great deal of chemical energy) is combined with air and a spark (electrical energy) to release heat. The heat causes the mixture of gases in the engine's cylinders to expand and push the pistons, thus changing the energy into mechanical, or kinetic, energy. The motion of the piston is transferred to the wheels via the crankshaft and the drive train, thereby propelling the car forward. As it moves, there is some friction between the tires and the road, and some of the mechanical energy becomes heat (that is why your tires get hot). Throughout this chain of events, energy is changed from one form to another; at each step, only a portion of the energy is transformed into the desired form—some of it becomes heat, which is not useful in moving the car forward.

MOLECULES, ATOMS, AND SUBATOMIC PARTICLES

Molecules, atoms, and subatomic particles are the building blocks of matter, the storehouses of energy. All matter consists of **atoms**. Atoms typically occur in more or less stable groups with other atoms; these groups are known as **molecules**. By describing these molecules as stable, we mean that they persist unless energy, such as heat, is added. Some molecules consist of just two atoms, while others contain thousands of atoms.

Atoms themselves contain a variety of subatomic particles. For our purposes, the most important of these particles are neutrons, protons, and especially electrons (Figure 4). Neutrons and protons, which are relatively heavy, are located in the center of the atom (in the region known as the nucleus), while the very light electrons form a cloud around the outside of the nucleus. As the outermost parts of the atom, electrons play a critical role in interactions with other atoms, as we will see.

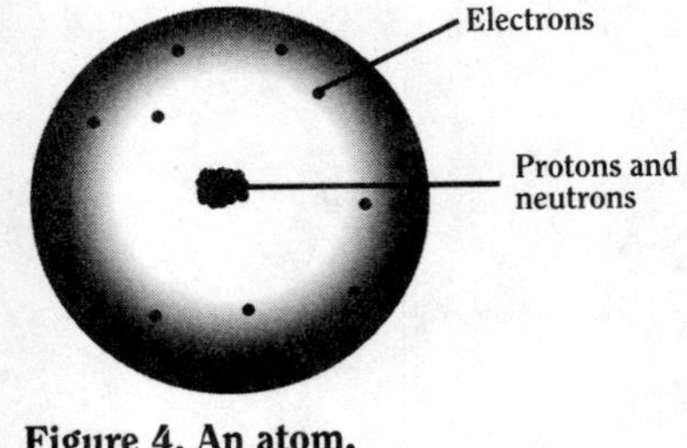

Figure 4. An atom.

Elements in Biological Molecules

Organisms consist almost entirely of a very few elements, especially oxygen, carbon, hydrogen, and nitrogen. If you understand how these elements are combined into more complex compounds, and how the atoms in molecules of these compounds are held together, you will understand a great deal about energy in the living world. It is worthwhile to compare the composition of organisms with the composition of the Earth; organisms contain very different proportions of the same materials that make up the Earth (Table 1).

Table 1 **Elements in the Earth's Crust and the Human Body**

ELEMENT	% OF EARTH'S CRUST BY WEIGHT	% OF HUMAN BODY BY WEIGHT
Oxygen	46.6	65.0
Silicon	27.7	Trace
Aluminum	6.5	Trace
Iron	5.0	Trace
Calcium	3.6	1.5
Sodium	2.8	0.2
Potassium	2.6	0.4
Magnesium	2.1	0.1
Hydrogen	0.14	9.5
Phosphorus	0.07	1.0
Carbon	0.03	18.5
Nitrogen	Trace	3.3

NOTE: Several other elements are also found in trace amounts.

For more on bonds and bond types, see Reading 2.

COMMUNITIES ARE SOLAR POWERED

CHAPTER TEN

CONTENTS

INTRODUCTION

Several concepts come together in this Chapter. Until now, we have focused on individual energy uses; here we step back one and two levels to look at (1) energy flow or transfer between organisms and (2) transfer of energy from the sun to plants.

We consider how species in an ecosystem are energetically linked. Nearly all nonplant species depend on other species for energy: all species eat and are eaten. We consider who eats and is eaten by whom, when. Energy transfers between species are, however, highly inefficient, and energy transfer from the sun to plants even less so. Those inefficiencies underlie the shape (and hence the name) of a trophic pyramid.

We also raise the idea of energy pools in an ecosystem. Each species can be seen as an energy reservoir, with energy moving into or out of the pool at different rates for different species. Thus, the lifestyle of one species might affect other species in subtle ways: its birth rate, death rate, how much it eats, and its population density all affect the amount of energy it does or does not turn over. For instance, many small ectotherms may eat little (use little energy), but because they are so numerous, they actually may contain a considerable amount of the ecosystem's energy in their biomass.

KEY CONCEPTS

- An ecosystem is an interrelated set of organisms and their physical (abiotic) environment. Ecology is the study of those relationships.
- Only a small proportion of the energy captured by any trophic level is available for transfer to the next level. (Remember the small values of the **P** term from the energy use equations?) Similarly, only a tiny amount of energy from the sun is actually absorbed by plants and used in photosynthesis. Here we develop some important generalizations about relationships between trophic levels. The typical ratios between plants and herbivores and between carnivores and herbivores reflect the typical energy use patterns of each group and thus also typical energy transfers between groups.
- Each type of ecosystem has a characteristic productivity (plant production) and set of organisms, which are interrelated in characteristic ways. We examine two ecosystems: a grassland, with grasses and little woody tissue, and a woodland, with the opposite vegetation patterns. Because grasses, unlike wood, are edible by many species, a grassland can support a huge biomass of herbivores. They, in turn, support carnivores, which eat them, and dung feeders, which benefit from the herbivores' inefficient digestion (remember that the herbivore **E** term is 50%).
- A food web is a qualitative representation of energy-based interactions among organisms. Here students place their own organisms into some ecological relationships with other organisms from the same habitat.
- The way in which a species allocates its energy expenditures has a major effect on the role that species plays in its ecosystem. Some species function as large pools of energy, even if little energy flows through them, while other species form small pools of energy through which large amounts of energy can flow.
- The interrelatedness among ecosystem parts is a key issue for wise management of an ecosystem. Unless we know how different parts interconnect, we cannot know what will happen if we alter or remove any single part.

MATERIALS AND PREPARATION

- **Calculators**
- **Rulers** (one or two per group)
- **Scissors** (one pair per group)
- 20–30 sheets of **graph paper** (some different grid sizes would be helpful)
- Several yards of **string**

SUGGESTED SEQUENCE OF SESSIONS (7–9)

Homework

Have students read Exploration 1, in which they learn that every plant and any nonplant species depends on and is depended on by others. Students illustrate their animals' connection to other organisms in their habitats.

Class Session 1

Discuss the Homework (Exploration 1) and have each student add the picture of his or her animal's interactions to one large picture (a partial food web) for each habitat (preferably on poster board or where the pictures can be kept for reference).

Homework

To flesh out their food web pictures, have students read Reading 1a or 1b, whichever is about the ecosystem in which their animal lives.

Class Session 2

Although bits of the readings have appeared before, here we focus on interactions between and among organisms and some effects of abiotic factors such as climate, season, and so on. The second focus is on energy flow among these ecosystem components.

Exploration 2 (optional) helps students think broadly about many aspects of their animals and how those aspects might influence the role or place of their animal in the ecosystem. You might find it too broad and wish to move on to Exploration 3, in which we calculate energy transfer across several links of a food chain, starting from an abiotic source (the sun) and moving through several biotic links.

Class Session 3

Continue Session 2, as necessary.

Class Session 4

Continue Session 3, as necessary. Students get engrossed in the data representation part of Exploration 3 and become animated at the magnitude of their results.

Homework

Reading 2: What Does a Food Web Mean?

Class Session 5

Discuss the Homework (Reading 2), which considers two animals up close to see what food webs and energy analyses might overlook if they rely on different scales of data and analysis.

Class Session 6

Continue Session 5, as necessary. Consider individual energy expenditures and population level expenditures for two contrasting species, the salamander and the chickadee. Individual chickadees turn over lots of energy, but because there are few of them they have little effect on ecosystem energy levels. Salamanders, by contrast, have little effect individually, but they are so numerous that they are a major energy reservoir.

Class Session 7

Continue Session 6, as necessary.

Discuss Reading 3, which is about flow and transfer in the two ecosystems. Note that the ecosystem with higher available plant production has higher amounts of energy and energy transfer. Woody plants just are not very edible. Also note that most of the energy is in plants, followed by the three Ds (detritivores, decomposers, and dung beetles). Have a class discussion in which students summarize key points of the chapter.

We offer two Integrations: one is included here, as usual; the second is a return to Exploration 3 of **Unit 1**. In that Exploration, students made guesstimates of relative numbers of predators and prey in the animals they had grouped by ecological relationships. It is instructive and empowering for them to return to that Exploration, to see how much they have come to understand since their first encounter with energy relationships. (They also may prefer it to the Integration in this chapter because it is less numerical, and they may be "calculated out" by that point.)

SESSION GUIDES, BY WORKSHEET

EXPLORATION 1 GUIDE
Food Webs: Is Any Species Independent?

Combining their knowledge about categories of energy sources and about organisms from each ecosystem, students work together in groups to develop for each ecosystem a food web, a picture of energy relations among the organisms. Your samples are here (Figures 1 and 2); the students' samples are embedded in Reading 2, so we do not give away the point of this Exploration.

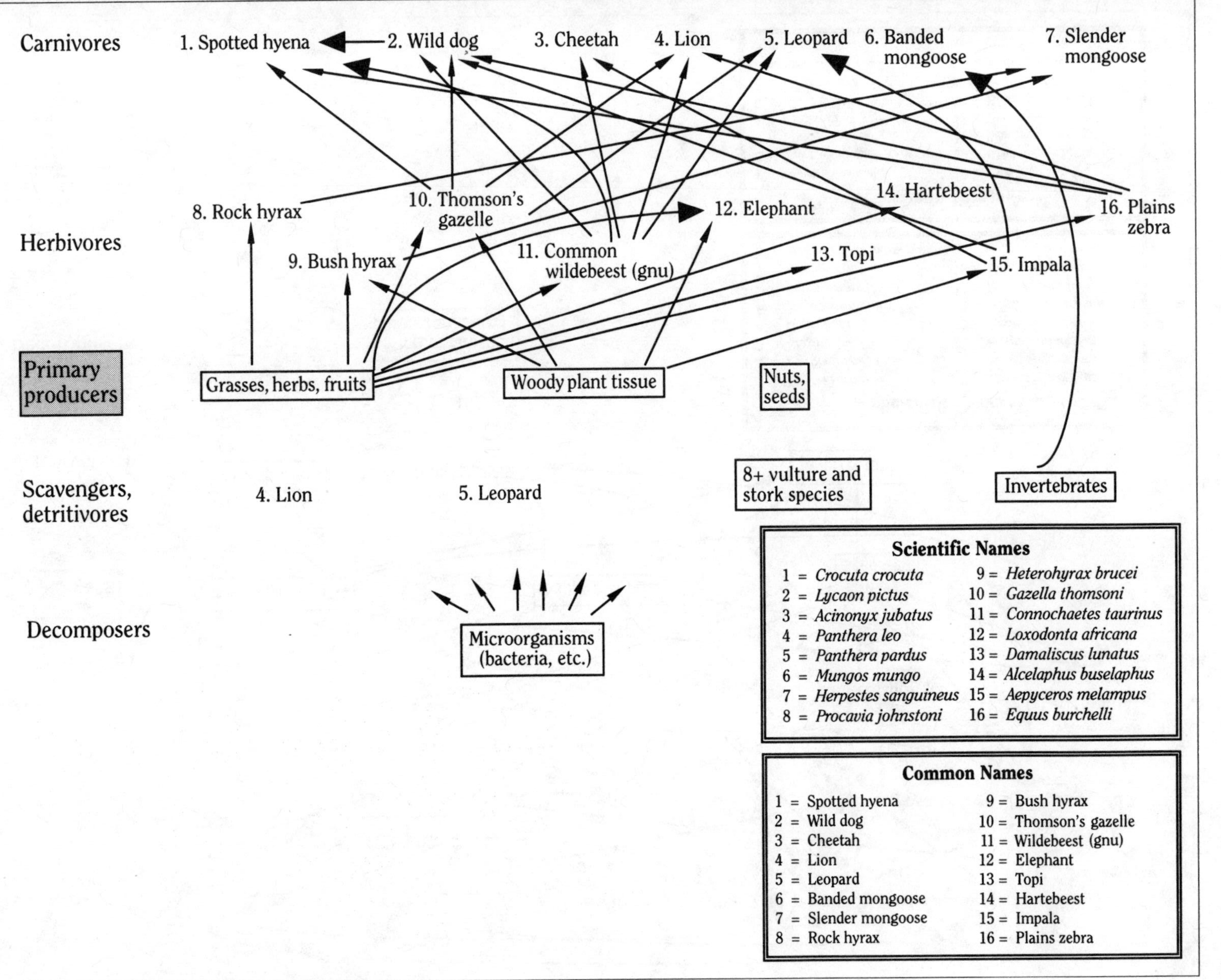

Figure 1. The Serengeti Ecosystem: Partial food web.

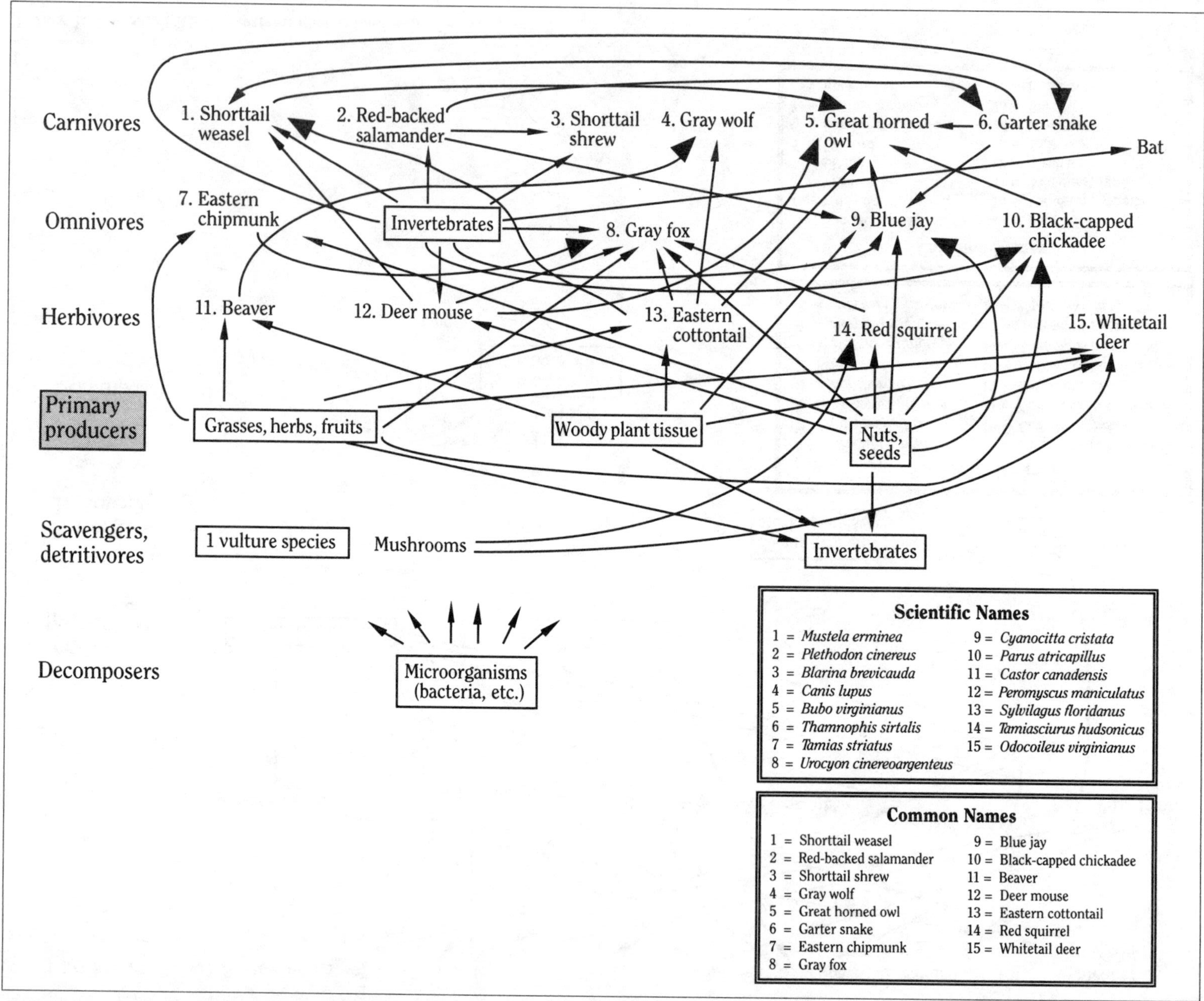

Figure 2. The Northern Hardwood Ecosystem: Partial food web.

Logistically, it may be helpful to split students by ecosystem and by trophic level within each ecosystem. Thus, the herbivores would work together, as would the carnivores.

Alternatively, through discussion with the class, develop a matrix of energy sources and trophic levels. Put one matrix for each ecosystem on a board or large sheet of paper. A flip chart is useful because it allows for the redrawing of things as they get complicated. Have each student place his or her organism on the matrix and draw arrows showing where that animal gets its energy and where its energy goes.

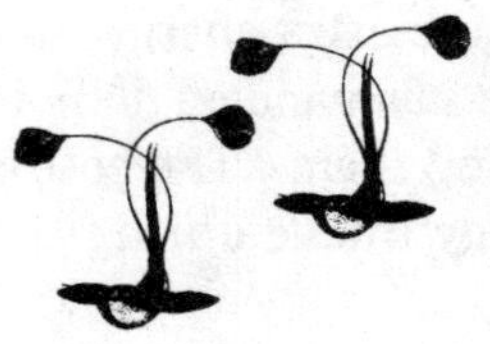

READINGS 1A AND 1B GUIDE
The Serengeti Ecosystem and the Northern Hardwood Forest

Having spent several chapters considering individual species and how they use energy, we now step back and begin to place those animals in an ecological context. Where do they live? How does a grassland differ from a woodland? How do those differences affect which animals live in each ecosystem? How do the animals affect each other? Where is the energy? What about energy flow or transfer between organisms? Where is it happening?

The class together builds a description of each ecosystem by striving to answer those and other questions, so the two systems are described and compared at the same time. (Alternatively, each half of the class, in groups, discusses its ecosystem, and then the class compares the two.)

Things they likely notice are that there are more species of organisms in the Serengeti. It is drier and hotter and thus cannot sustain tree growth, but it has much grass. Students may remember that wood is not a good food for most organisms, so they likely make the connection between animal numbers and plant productivity.

For more details on energy flow, see Exploration 4 Guide (but remember that students have not yet calculated energy flows).

(Optional) EXPLORATION 2 GUIDE
Lifestyle: Your Animal at Home

This Exploration helps some students contextualize their organism (i.e., pull together many aspects of its biology, physiology, lifestyle) and generally allows students to integrate what they have been learning, the concepts as well as the facts. It takes a little time and some discussion to get it going; there may be much referring back to earlier work as their ideas coalesce. We suggest small groups and then a class discussion. Here are sample answers, about salamanders and wildebeest, to the questions in the Exploration.

Red-Backed Salamander

Size: How big is your animal?

The salamander is quite small, 5.7–9.2 cm. It has very short legs, so it does not slither like a snake. As an ectotherm, it is not likely to move quickly for long and certainly not likely to move quickly in the cold. Its range is likely to be a few yards per day, and since it needs to be moist, it cannot travel great distances over land, except in wet weather. A typical salamander weighs just a few grams, or one ten-thousandth the weight of a 150-pound adult human. The salamander thus requires far fewer calories—orders of magnitude fewer. When its prey are plentiful, its normal density is high, up to six individuals per square meter.

Reproduction

Salamanders meet and mate in ponds (temporary or permanent) and will travel some distance to find a pond for mating. Such travel takes a lot of energy, and increases a salamander's likelihood of being eaten or squashed by a car. Another cost of reproduction is the extra energy the female allocates to eggs before she lays them. (Since salamanders do not take care of their young, adults spend no energy raising them.) The cost of producing eggs can double a female's normal energy intake during the months of reproduction.

Food and other resources

Salamanders eat small invertebrates that live in leaf litter and the upper levels of the soil. Different invertebrates—mites, worms, or sow bugs—are more or less abundant in different places. (Do salamanders have food preferences? That might be an interesting subject for experiment.) Another key resource is moisture; if a salamander's skin dries out, it cannot "breathe" (i.e., get oxygen and lose CO_2 via diffusion). Salamanders also need water for laying their eggs and for the hatching of those eggs. Some species live in water throughout their lives, while others leave pools (except for mating) as adults.

Other biotic factors

Salamanders are eaten by birds, small mammals, snakes, and numerous other predators. Over evolutionary time, they have been selected to have some effective defenses against being eaten. Common ones include tasting bad or being poisonous (because of chemicals in the skin), and having loosely connected tail bones, so the tail breaks off when a predator seizes it. Better to lose a tail than to be eaten. These animals typically regrow the lost tail, although the new one may be shorter than the original.

Abiotic factors: Climate and geography

As we have noted, salamanders require moisture at all times, which necessarily limits their geographic distribution. Because they are amphibians, they are also ectotherms and thus do not do well in cold temperatures. In fact, most salamander species live in warm, humid places. And those that do not have special adaptations to protect themselves against cold or drought—some burrow into soil or mud, while others live only one year.

Common Wildebeest

Size: How big is your animal?

A wildebeest is about 1.4 meters tall at the shoulder and weighs about 275 kg. Like most herbivores, they spend much of the day eating. Because they live in large herds, they must keep moving to find new grass—they clean out an area fairly fast. In the Serengeti, the bulk of the population migrates annually toward water and newly grown grass. Thus, although the wildebeest keep moving, they usually do not move far on any given day, just some hundreds of meters.

Reproduction

Female wildebeest typically have one calf a year. An unusual aspect of their reproduction is that females are highly synchronized, that is, most of them give birth within the same few weeks in January. Pregnancy is eight months long and begins in the drought. Perhaps when the young are born, there will be plenty of grass for them and their mothers to eat.

Food and other resources

The main food of the wildebeest is grasses. They do not need shelter, but they do need water. During the drought, they move to water holes and toward less dry areas in the Serengeti, both for the water and for the grass that grows there.

Other biotic factors

Males compete strongly for females to mate. Predation on healthy adults is rare; old, very young, and ill individuals are more likely to be prey. During the highly synchronized birth period in January, wildebeest calves are the favored prey of all carnivores large enough to kill them. There is likely little competition between wildebeest and other Serengeti herbivores, since each species tends to have different food preferences.

Abiotic factors: Climate and geography

Although wildebeest do not require moisture to breathe, as does the salamander, they do require it for their general metabolism. Thus, they cannot survive in deserts and are limited to grasslands. Geography affects their distribution because it affects plant distribution. Only in a tropical grasslands is the plant productivity sufficiently high that it can support as many wildebeest as live in the Serengeti (1.2 million). Although they are endotherms, wildebeest cannot withstand severe cold (e.g., frost). And, despite living in the tropics, they would overheat at desert temperatures.

EXPLORATION 3 GUIDE
Sun to Wolf: Energy Transfer!?

Students calculate the flow of energy through a simple food chain. They build on their knowledge of the energy use equation (**Chapters 2** through **4**), seeing how a series of inefficient energy transfers (from sun to plant to deer/gazelle to wolf/cheetah) turns out to be very inefficient indeed when considered from start to finish. The punch line is that a single carnivore requires a great deal of solar energy during a year, and the key is twofold: (1) at each stage (sun, plant, deer/gazelle, wolf/cheetah), no matter how much energy is present, only a tiny percent is available to the next stage; and (2) the production at each stage is the intake for the next stage (plant **P** is deer/gazelle **I**; deer/gazelle **P** is wolf/cheetah **I**).

Predictions and the Scene

Help your students flesh out the scenarios from Exploration 3. Have parallel scenarios for the wolf and the cheetah; the calculations and numbers are the same. Consider an adolescent wolf in the Northern Hardwood Forest. Over the course of the next year, it will add about 8 kg of new tissue, which contains 12,000 kcal of energy. Since students think about quantities of wolf and deer flesh, plant tissue, and sunlight throughout this exercise, it is useful to think about these disparate quantities in a single "currency," their energy content measured in kcal. (A kilogram of venison contains 1,260 kcal. Wolf tissue is probably quite similar in its energy content, so we consider the 8 kg of tissue to contain 8 kg × 1,260 kcal/kg = 10,080 kcal, or approximately 10,000 kcal.)

Sketch or name the key players on the board—the carnivores, the herbivores, some plants, and the sun. Ask students for ideas about the energy relationships among them. Add arrows to show those relationships (e.g., the wolf gets energy by eating deer, the deer get energy by eating plants, and the plants get energy from the sun).

Let each student predict how much solar energy (in kilocalories) is needed to support the carnivore and let it grow. Students write down their anonymous predictions twice, once for you and once in their notebooks. When you have all the predictions in hand, write some (or all) of them on the board to show their range. Save the predictions for reconsideration later.

Your Own Prediction

We recommend that right now you make the same prediction: how many kilocalories of solar energy are needed to support a growing, adolescent wolf/cheetah for a year. This problem is worth considering naively, as your students do, and once you have looked through these notes, you will never see the problem the same way again.

Getting Started

Divide students into groups of three, mixing students who have an aptitude for math with those who are less inclined. Although there is not much calculating necessary in this Exploration, some students find the math content difficult.

Refer students to the energy use equation, especially the relationship between intake and production of new tissues (Exploration 2 in **Chapter 4** and the appropriate animal cards).

The Calculations

Since students know that **P** is some small percent of **I** and that the wolf/cheetah adds 10,000 kcal (8 kg) of new tissue during the year, they can calculate the wolf/cheetah's energy intake over the course of the year. There are several ways to set up and perform these calculations, and different groups will probably use different methods. Some students may find the task daunting, perhaps because they are dealing with such large numbers. In fact, the calculations are quite simple; any difficulty tends to lie in whether students understand the energy-transfer relationships. A few sample calculations follow.

Sample Calculations for Wolf/Cheetah Intake

Wolf/cheetah production = 10,000 kcal (the 8 kg). From the animal card, we can calculate that wolf/cheetah production = 0.02 × wolf/cheetah intake. So, to solve for wolf/cheetah intake, wolf/cheetah production/0.02 = wolf/cheetah intake, so 10,000 kcal/0.02 = 500,000 kcal for wolf/cheetah intake.

A second way is this: 2% of some number = wolf/cheetah production, which means that wolf/cheetah production / wolf/cheetah intake = 0.02 = 2%. 10,000 kcal / wolf/cheetah intake = 0.02. So what is wolf/cheetah intake? Answer: A number 50 times greater than 10,000 kcal, or 50 × 10,000 kcal = 500,000 kcal = wolf/cheetah intake.

"Fermi-izing," that is, working with orders of magnitude, is yet another option. Assume that wolf/cheetah production is only 1% of wolf/-cheetah intake. It is easy to see that intake must be 100 times the size of production, or 1,000,000 kcal. Since wolf/cheetah production is actually 2% of wolf/cheetah intake, however, intake is only 50 times the size of production, or 500,000 kcal.

Once students have completed their calculation of wolf/cheetah intake, ask them if they want to revise their original estimate of the solar energy needed to support a growing wolf/cheetah for a year.

Deer/Gazelle Intake and Production

If necessary, remind students that we are talking about a deer/gazelle herd, not just a single deer/gazelle. Each year, a number of fawns are born, and adolescent deer/gazelle put on weight as they mature. Here we assume that the wolf/cheetah "harvests" all this new tissue produced by the deer/-gazelle herd. In nature, we might not find such an exact balance (although it has been demonstrated), but it is convenient for our calculations (for more, see **Chapter 11**). We have found that students often think the deer/-gazelle herd "attempts" or "tries" to create enough extra flesh for the wolf/cheetah.

Since all the year's new deer/gazelle tissue is being harvested by the wolf/cheetah, students know that deer/gazelle production equals wolf/cheetah intake, which they just calculated at 500,000 kcal.

They also know the relationship between deer/gazelle production and deer/gazelle intake, so they calculate the deer/gazelle herd's annual intake, just as they did for the wolf/cheetah. Deer/gazelle production = 500,000 kcal, deer/gazelle production = 1% of deer/gazelle intake (500,000 / 0.01, or 500,000 × 100). Therefore, deer/gazelle intake = 50,000,000 kcal. (Some students prefer to use exponents; others do not.)

Plant "Intake" and Production

Again, we assume that the deer/gazelle herd harvests all the new tissue production of the plants growing in a certain area (an unrealistic assumption except under highly unusual circumstances, such as during a long winter with deep snow, but it greatly simplifies the calculations). Plants do not absorb solar energy very efficiently; in fact, most of the sun's energy is reflected by plants, misses the leaves altogether, or is of the wrong wavelength to be used by a plant. Typically, only 1% of all the sun's energy reaching a given spot is absorbed by plants (this number varies from site to site, but 1% is a reasonable value for our calculations).

Plants, being alive, carry out metabolic respiration, just as animals do. In fact, plants spend about 50% of the energy they absorb on metabolic respiration, leaving about half of 1% of the solar energy they get for production of new tissue.

Since all the year's new plant tissue is being harvested by the deer/gazelles, students know that plant production is the same as deer/-gazelle intake, or 50,000,000 kcal. They also know the relationship between plant production and intake and can therefore calculate the plant community's annual intake of solar energy, just as before: plant production = deer/gazelle intake, or 50,000,000 kcal, so plant production = 0.005 × plant intake, or 50,000,000 / 0.005, or 10,000,000,000. Therefore, plant intake (of solar energy) = 10,000,000,000 kcal, or 10×10^{10}.

Data Conclusion and Prediction Comparisons

Returning to the original energy quantity, the annual production of new tissue by a single wolf/cheetah, we find that 10,000,000,000, or 10^{10}, kcal solar energy are needed to create just 10,000 (10^4) kcal of new wolf/-cheetah tissue. In other words, it takes one million kilocalories of sunlight to produce a single kilocalorie of new wolf/cheetah tissue (hence, the punctuation in our Exploration title—energy transfers are so inefficient, it seems that scarcely any is being transferred!).

Revisit the students' original (and revised) predictions and compare them with the calculated results. The purpose of the comparison is to illustrate the remarkable magnitude of inefficiency of energy transfer and the gap between initial off-the-cuff expectations and the reality of the situation. We have found that most biology teachers and biologists also are way off with their predictions—the magnitude of the results surprises nearly everyone who tries this Exploration.

Representing the Results

As striking as the results of those calculations are, we have found that some visual representation markedly enhances students' appreciation and understanding of the conclusions. It is well worth giving students the one or two sessions this work might take.

Each group of students decides on a method for representing their data. The student worksheet mentions several possibilities, such as using graph paper, lengths of string, or some type of weights or volumes.

Tips

Tell your students to start small and that even doing so they will be unable to represent the larger numbers. The difference between the amount of energy the wolf/cheetah uses on production and the amount of solar energy reaching the plants is huge—six orders of magnitude. If students use a large unit to represent carnivore production, they will run out of space for representing plant production and solar energy. No matter how small they start, students likely are to be unable to represent the larger numbers the same as they do the smaller ones—the differences are too great. So they might just write down the larger numbers and what it would take to represent them in the same way as smaller numbers.

Students should not use exponents or logs for displaying their data, even if they used them for the calculations. It is important that students use a single scale for representing their data. For example, if a square centimeter represents 10,000 kcal for the wolf, a square centimeter should also represent 10,000 kcal of solar energy; switching scales defeats the power of the data representation.

Examples of Scale and Representation

Clearly, students will need to improvise for the final numbers, or they will break your budget on graph paper and string alone! Here are two examples of data representation.

1 cm² = 10,000 kcal

	KCAL	CM²	COMMENTS
Wolf **P**	10,000	1	
Wolf **I**/deer **P**	500,000	50	1⁄10 of a piece of 8½-by-11-in. paper
Deer **I**/plant **P**	50,000,000	5,000	0.5 m², or 10 pieces of paper
Solar energy	10,000,000,000	1,000,000	100 m², or roughly the size of a small classroom

1 inch of string = 10,000 kcal

	KCAL	INCHES OF STRING	COMMENTS
Wolf **P**	10,000	1	
Wolf **I**/deer **P**	500,000	50	4 ft, or a bit over 1 m
Deer **I**/plant **P**	50,000,000	5,000	417 ft, or 127 m
Solar energy	10,000,000,000	1,000,000	83,333 ft, or almost 16 miles, or 25 km

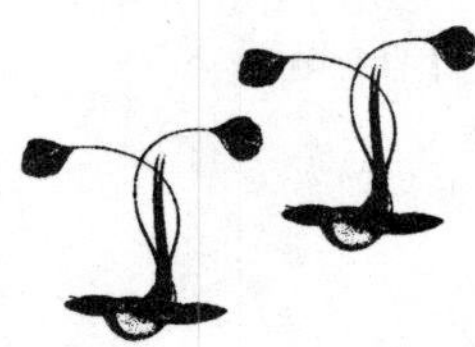

READING 2 GUIDE
What Does a Food Web Mean?

Referring students back to Readings 1a and 1b and to Exploration 3, ask them to think more about the pictures they have of their ecosystems, especially all that they had to leave out.

This reading raises issues of change over time, in both the biotic (organisms) and abiotic (weather, seasons, temperature, etc.) components of an ecosystem. Such changes also contribute to the picture of energy flow. Plants change by season; organisms vary their foods; young and old animals within a species might eat different foods; when some young are available, they might be eaten in preference to their elders. A drought or a flood—any abiotic extreme—affects all organisms. Our partial web is just a snapshot in time; unless we take many snapshots over time, we are limited to that moment.

Our web is also just one snapshot "in space," and has caught mostly the larger, more visible vertebrates and left out most of the biomass, and thus energy flow, of the ecosystems. While we chose those animals deliberately, it is important to recognize that they are not the main players, energetically or numerically. Even though there are 1.2 million wildebeest, each weighing over 250 kg, the invertebrate biomass is greater by several orders of magnitude.

Although all ecosystems are complex, one measure of complexity is the number of trophic pyramids. Only an ecosystem with very high edible NPP (plant productivity in grasses, not wood) can sustain many predators and the organisms they eat. In the Northern Hardwood Forest, there are perhaps only one-tenth the vertebrate trophic pyramids as in the Serengeti.

Some things not represented by our food web, then, include change over time in either biotic or abiotic factors, most of the organisms, most of the biomass, any microorganisms (which is where most of the heterotroph biomass resides), competition, specific species interactions, and amounts of energy transfer. Your students likely can add others.

EXPLORATION 4 GUIDE
Energy in Populations: Pools and Flows

Here students explore the population-level implications of various species' energy expenditure patterns. Low or high energy expenditure patterns affect species' roles in an ecosystem. Students work in groups to assemble and interpret a small data set on energy flow and storage through populations of salamanders and chickadees in the Northern Hardwood Forest. Groups write a short description of their understanding of the abundance and energy flow patterns they see.

Species Biomasses

As Table 1 shows, salamanders are several hundred times more abundant than chickadees in terms of biomass per hectare. But in contrast, the salamander population processes only about ten times the energy that the chickadee population does. In fact, compared with all songbirds at the site, red-backed salamanders contain about nine times the biomass of the birds. Yet the salamanders expend only an eighth of the energy expended by all the songbirds combined.

Table 1

Comparison of Chickadees to Salamanders

	WEIGHT PER INDIVIDUAL	NUMBER PER HECTARE	ENERGY FLOW PER INDIVIDUAL PER YEAR	BIOMASS PER HECTARE (WET WEIGHT)	ENERGY FLOW PER HECTARE PER YEAR
DATA SOURCE	**Chapter 4**	**Chapter 4** and calculations	**Chapter 4**	Calculations	Calculations
Red-backed salamander	0.7 g	2,600	4 kcal	1,800 g	10,400 kcal
Chickadee	10 g	0.3*	3,500 kcal	3 g	1,050 kcal
All songbirds	Not applicable	10	Not applicable	200 g	75,000 kcal

*Average of year-round data.

Perhaps conditions are better at the site for salamanders than they are for songbirds, thus leading to the amphibians' greater abundance. But, at least in terms of food, the birds are apparently doing quite well; they gather considerably more energy per year than the salamanders. The key to these differences may lie in the energy expenditure patterns of the different species.

Species-Typical Energy Expenditures

Students can draw on their knowledge of animals' energy expenditures from previous chapters as they compare the salamanders, chickadees, and all songbirds. As they know from **Chapter 4**, salamanders are remarkably efficient at producing new tissue; nearly 40% of what they eat gets turned into new tissue. (Studies of other species of salamanders have shown even higher efficiencies.) As ectotherms, salamanders spend virtually no energy keeping warm; thus, they keep their overall energy expenditures quite low. Furthermore, salamanders do not move far, and do not spend a great deal of energy on locomotion. By contrast, the endothermic chickadees expend a great deal of energy thermoregulating and only about 2% of their intake on production of new tissue.

In other words, for a given amount of intake, a great deal of salamander tissue gets produced relative to the amount of chickadee flesh that can be produced. On the other hand, a given quantity of chickadee biomass takes in and spends vastly more energy than the same quantity of salamander biomass.

Ramping Up: Individual to Population

Since living conditions appear to be good for both species at the site (Hubbard Brook, in New Hampshire), we see the energy expenditure patterns—the lifestyle—of individual organisms reflected in population characteristics for each species. Large quantities of salamander biomass roam the woods while processing surprisingly small quantities of energy each year. Birds, on the other hand, are scarce, yet massive quantities of energy flow through the bird populations.

The point of this Exploration is subtle: how the energy expenditure patterns of an individual of some species sum to patterns of population expenditures of that species.

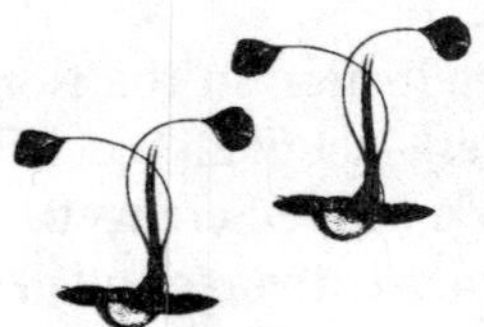

READING 3 GUIDE
Energy Flow in the SEU and NHF

There are several interesting differences and similarities between the patterns of energy flow in the two ecosystems. Here are some responses to the questions posed in this Reading.

Where does the energy flowing into an ecosystem "go"?

Much of the energy from the sun is not absorbed by an ecosystem's plants. This energy may not be intercepted by leaves, may be reflected, or may heat plants without helping with photosynthesis.

All living organisms (including animals, plants, fungi, and bacteria) use a significant portion of the energy they take in for respiration. This energy is released into the environment as heat, whereupon it no longer is in a form that can be used by other organisms.

Some of the energy is incorporated into living tissues of the organisms in the ecosystem. Detritivores and decomposers end up with a much higher proportion of an ecosystem's energy than do herbivores.

What are the similarities between patterns of energy flow in the two ecosystems?

In both ecosystems, the plants capture only a small amount of the sun's energy. Only a tiny portion of the energy striking either ecosystem gets to herbivores, detritivores, or decomposers.

Energy capture by the producers in a square meter of each ecosystem is quite similar, despite the fact that the Serengeti receives a greater amount of insolation over the year (NHF producers capture about 20% more than Serengeti producers).

What are the differences between the patterns of energy flow in the two ecosystems?

Herbivores in the Serengeti consume about sixteen times more energy per square meter than Northern Hardwoods herbivores do!

Detritivores and decomposers in the Northern Hardwoods consume a much higher proportion of GPP than those in the Serengeti. In addition, more energy is ingested by detritivores and decomposers in the Northern Hardwoods than by those in the Serengeti.

Producers in the Northern Hardwoods capture more energy per square meter than do producers in the Serengeti, but most of it goes into woody tissue.

What are some additional observations?

If we visited the Serengeti, we would be more likely to see the food web in action (large numbers of herbivores consuming plant matter and carnivores consuming herbivores) than if we visited the Northern Hardwoods, where a lot of the action in the food web happens in the leaf litter at a microscopic level. There are two main reasons for this difference: there are many more large herbivores and carnivores in the Serengeti, and because it is a grassland, the animals are much more visible than those in the thick forests of the Northern Hardwoods.

The multiple layers of leaves associated with the Northern Hardwood Forest provide more surface area to capture insolation than does the more simple physical structure of the grassland.

A higher proportion of the plant production in the Northern Hardwoods is generally unavailable to herbivores—about 25% of NPP is wood in these forests, compared with only about 5% in the Serengeti. These woody tissues are, however, eventually available to detritivores and decomposers.

INTEGRATION GUIDE
How Many Animals?

Data: Energy flow pyramid for an NHF food chain

Carnivore (wolf): One wolf eats 2×10^6 kcals/year.

Herbivore (deer): The yearly intake of one wolf is equivalent to about 30 deer. To calculate the energy transferred into those 30 deer: $30 \times (1.5 \times 10^6) = 4.5 \times 10^7$ kcal.

Producer (deer browse): The yearly energy intake of plant matter for 30 deer is 4.8×10^7 kcal.

Data: Energy flow pyramid for an SEU food chain

Carnivore (cheetah): One cheetah eats 2.4×10^6 kcals/year.

Herbivore (gazelle): The yearly intake of a cheetah is equal to about 180 gazelles. To calculate the energy transferred into those 180 gazelles: 180 gazelles $\times$ (6×10^5 kcals/year) = 1.08×10^8 kcal.

Producer (gazelle browse): The yearly intake of the plant material that 180 gazelles eat is 2.2×10^8 kcal.

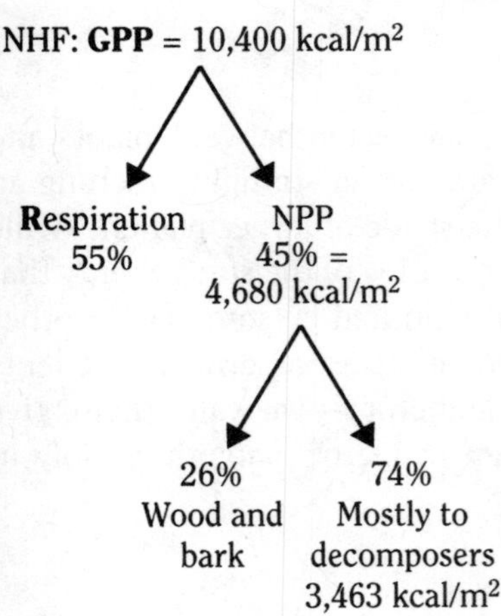

One area in the **Northern Hardwood Forest** has 6 wolves and about 500 deer. The wolf territory or ecosystem size is 115 km². Solar energy captured by a square meter (in GPP) is 10,400 kcal/yr; NPP is about 45% of that, of which about 10% is edible by herbivores.

The **Serengeti** has about 350 cheetahs and 600,000 Thomson's gazelles. The ecosystem size is 25,000 km². Solar energy captured by a square meter (in GPP) is 8,740 kcal/yr; NPP is about 50% of that, of which almost 100% is edible by herbivores.

A general energy flow pyramid is shown in Figure 3.

Wolf Territory Sizes

An adolescent wolf does not live alone but is a member of its parents' pack. Let's assume our wolf pack is fairly small—only five wolves. Even such a small pack, however, has a surprisingly large range. In the Northern Hardwood Forest, a pack that size might have a territory of 200 km². (Keep in mind that territory size is highly variable among packs. Summer ranges typically are smaller than winter ranges, when the pack has to search farther for food. Ecologists have reported range sizes for a wolf pack as small as 18 km² and as large as 13,000 km².)

Deer Populations

Within the pack's territory of 200 km², how many deer are there? As with wolves, the density of deer populations varies from region to region. However, there probably would be at least several hundred deer in an area that size, perhaps several thousand. If the deer population is small—in the

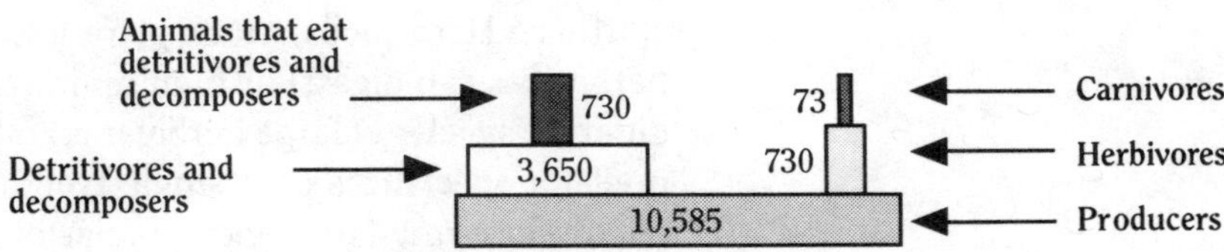

Figure 3. Energy-flow pyramid (kcal per m² per year).

hundreds—the wolves and the deer might affect each other's population sizes. For example, there simply may not be enough deer to feed more than five wolves; thus, the deer population may limit the size of the wolf population. Alternatively, the wolves may be such efficient predators that they keep the deer population from growing, despite all the fawns born each year.

Plant Populations

Even if the deer population is in the thousands, they probably have little effect on the plants of the region. Consider the plants found in the wolf territory of 200 km^2, an area 10 km by 20 km. Such a region contains tens of thousands of trees and millions of smaller herbs and shrubs. That is a lot of plants by any measure. In fact, studies performed in the Northern Hardwood Forest generally have shown that deer have little effect on plant populations or biomass (as we will see in **Chapter 11**). It should not be surprising, then, that lack of plants rarely limits a deer population.

The situation can be quite the opposite, however, in areas where deer are contained in small reserves of only a few square kilometers, where they are without predators, and where their densities are unnaturally high. In such circumstances, deer populations can explode, and the confined deer can strip a forest of virtually all greenery from ground level up to the highest level that deer can reach. Under natural conditions, predators help keep the deer population in check, and the deer can move to another patch of forest long before stripping an area completely.

Plant Productivity

Finally, we can briefly consider the relationship between plants and sunlight. Clearly, plants do not affect the amount of sunlight reaching an area (except for small plants growing in the shade of larger plants). While few plant communities utilize much more than 1% of the sun's energy that strikes the ground, plant growth typically is limited by some factor other than lack of light, for example, water, temperature, or crucial nutrients (think about how we care for houseplants and crops—we water them, give them nutrients in fertilizer, and keep them inside or plant them only in warm weather).

Gazelle-Cheetah Interactions

In contrast to the wolf-deer situation, the relationship between cheetahs and Thomson's gazelles is very loose. That is, although the gazelles are one of the main prey items of cheetahs, the population sizes of these animals are not linked, as far as ecologists can tell. Although 600,000 Thomson's gazelles roam the Serengeti, only 350 cheetahs are found on the plains. The reasons for the lack of correspondence between the two populations are not well understood, but certain factors appear to play a role. First, any grassland can support huge numbers of herbivores. In contrast, in the Northern Hardwoods, much plant tissue is in the form of wood (which few herbivores can digest) or high up in tree canopies. Second, there are many different species of large herbivores and large predators in the Serengeti. No predator specializes on a single type of prey, so it is less likely that a prey population would influence the size of a predator population.

INTEGRATION
How Many Animals?

We have just calculated how much of the sun's energy is needed to fuel one adolescent wolf's yearly growth. Energy appeared in many different forms (as wolf and deer flesh, plant matter, and sunlight), so we used the kilocalorie as a common measure of energy content for all those quantities. However, as useful as it is to think of energy flow in terms of kilocalories, in the field wolves, deer, and plants do not appear as bundles of kilocalories. Instead, they show up as individual, living organisms. How do our calculations look if we substitute real animals and animal numbers?

Materials

- Your **results from Exploration 3**
- **Calculators**

Procedure

1. **The carnivore.**
We are starting with one animal, by definition, and its 10,000 kcal of intake. Use the wolf if your organism comes from the Northern Hardwood Forest, the cheetah if your organism is from the Serengeti.
2. **How many ungulates?**
We know that wolf/cheetah **I** = deer/gazelle **P** for some number of deer/-gazelle. How many deer/gazelle per year is that? How do you figure that? You may want to refer to your data on each species' energy use equation and the diagrams in Exploration 3.
3. **How many plants or how much land?**
Serengeti edible NPP is between 19% and 35%, depending on the season; Northern Hardwoods edible NPP is about 5%. The Serengeti ecosystem is about 25,000 km^2; the Northern Hardwoods is about 115 km^2. Calculate the total amount of energy passing through the two food chains.

CLASSROOM VIGNETTES

Students explore the transfer or flow of energy between parts of an ecosystem (the Northern Hardwood Forest). They consider the sun striking plants, which are eaten by deer, which are eaten by a wolf. The first vignette is of students making predictions about and then doing calculations for the amount of solar energy necessary for production of 12,000 kcal of wolf; the second is of students representing their results.

Exploration 3: Predictions and Calculations

TEACHER: Today we will discuss energy flow through ecosystems. We will figure what percentage of the sun's energy ends up in the production of a new wolf or another animal in the system.

[Students make predictions.]

P: Is there a formula, or do we just take a wild guess?

RB: Alternatively, we could use a formula. . . .

TEACHER: Well, this is interesting [puts numbers on board]. . . . Let's see the range of answers: 15%, 10%, 8.39%, 3%, 1%, 0.002%. Several orders of magnitude range here. How did you get these?

S: In my biology class, we learned that 2% of the sun's energy is utilized by plants, then I figured the wolf was a secondary consumer, so I moved the decimal over.

SER: I put 10%, since it's a forest, trees get energy from the sun, and the remainder is eaten by animals.

RB: Plants take in 10%, and one-half of that the deer eats.

P: But there's lots wasted.

RM: I said 10% because they take in about 10% for production, then the primary consumer gets 10% of that, then the wolf gets 10%, so that's 1% [sic].

[Working in two groups (RB, M, and SER) and (RM, S, and P) with the readings and data from the two ecosystems, students begin their calculations.]

P: Isn't what the deer loses what the wolf eats?

S: Plants don't get 100%.

RM: How much do plants get?

P: 80%.

RM: Of the sun's energy?

S: We use 100% of the energy that hits the whole earth. Or do plants take in 100%?

P: What else could they do with it?

S: Respiration, excretion? It's not used. . . .

P: We're seeing how much of this field [115 km^2] gets captured by plants. Do deer eat plants' excretion?

RM: Deer breathe in plants' oxygen. Deer can't absorb all the energy in plants.

P: How much of this 100% is the plant getting?

RM: 100%

OTHERS: OK. . . .

P: From plant to deer. . . .

RM: How much does the deer get?

S: Some is used—not available to the deer, used for respiration, growth, not production, so the energy is lost.
RM: Deer do not get energy from the sun directly.
P: I guess 75%. Think about a plant—they don't waste as much as animals.
RM: Deer take in all the plants' energy but don't use it all and only put a small part into stuff a wolf can eat. Remember that little purple piece [referring to the production portion of her animal's energy allocation chart]? Wasn't it 2% that the deer put into production?
S: But we're not talking about production.
RM: Deer had 75% respiration. . . . Some of the plant is excreted. . . .
S: How much energy is left in the plant?
RM: 75% R, 2% is tissue, the rest is wasted.
S: But we're talking plants, not animals.
RM: Plants get 100% and need to use some for growth.
S: I'm confused.
RM: A plant gets 100% from the sun—is everything it uses 100%, or stuff from the sun 100%?
S: Yes.
P: So, we're figuring what is wasted, so we know how much the deer gets.
S: We didn't do [energy use] pie charts for plants. What percent here is used by plants for P?
RM: Let's take a wild guess.
P: We're guessing excretion—the opposite of that goes to the deer.
S: Production?
RM: Energy is used to grow what isn't reflected in production, auxin causes growth—energy is used and cells get bigger.

[The teacher worries that the students are too bogged down in the numbers and tries to focus back on the larger picture.]

TEACHER: Let's talk about the process as a whole group. Let's forget about the numbers for now and think in diagrammatic terms.
RM: Give us five more minutes?

[RM's group writes: Production, Respiration, Excretion and begins to diagram energy flows on paper.]

RM: So, the deer gets its energy from plant production, so the deer gains from the plant's work. Energy goes into the deer, then the deer has Production, Respiration, Energy. . . .

P: It's respiration that does not go to the wolf, just production. So now we just need to put some numbers on the diagram.
RM: So how much energy goes into production for plants? More because it's lower on the food chain, I think.
P: Let's guess 75%.
RM: Okay. So how much does the deer get?
P: 2%, or so.

[They refer to their percentage data.]

P: 1.5% goes into the wolf?

[They ask for a calculator and start to punch in numbers.]

RM: So the wolf uses 1.5% of the deer's intake energy? What was the cheetah's production? Let's say 2%. So, what is 2% of 1.5%?

S: 0.03%.

RM: You were close.

TEACHER: Can you put your diagram on the board?

RM: Exclude excretion, respiration, since they don't count, really.

TEACHER: Put it all up on the board.

[While one group of students puts diagrams on the board, the others wait, talk about their final exams, etc.]

TEACHER: The 100% is the energy hitting our 115 square kilometers, not 100% of what is going into plants.

RM: This is hard to do, 'cause we didn't do [energy budgets of] plants last week. We don't know.

TEACHER: Now we're going to see what all these arrows mean—get a flavor of where all the energy is going. [He reviews their diagrams.] In both cases, you start with 100% from the sun. The plant [in the diagram] gets 75%, 25% is excreted or respired. What is excretion for a plant?

M: Like shedding?

SER: Energy is wasted.

TEACHER: Over here [other diagram], we see that 50% of the sun's energy goes into plants. Where does the rest of it go?

M: Some of it just bounces away.

RB: Trees and plants have "uneaten" stuff that doesn't go into the next organism.

M: Wolf production is 1%.

[The teacher asks the students how to make the calculations easier.]

TEACHER: This gets confusing. I find myself getting confused. Would this be easier if we just drew arrows?

P: Yes, the numbers were our complication.

RM: We had to make too many guesses. It wasn't fun. We were illiterate on what they should be.

P: With just arrows, it's easier.

RB: Start with arrows, then give them percentage data, then let them use real numbers.

RB: The initial 100% was confusing. How much goes to plants?

RM: We had a problem with the starting point—100% of what the plant gets or 100% of the sun's energy?

TEACHER: So we agree only a small percentage of production goes into the wolf (or whatever). Were your final numbers close to your first predictions?

RM: The number is close to 0.002—far from the other stuff.

TEACHER: What is the percentage of production for the wolf?

RM: 1–2%, more production than the gazelle or deer.

[Teacher draws arrows on the board and puts up some numbers. If the wolf is 1% efficient at producing, then we get 0.00008 as what percent of the sun's energy is represented by a wolf's growth. The other group gets 0.03% as their percentage.]

Exploration 3: Data Representation

TEACHER: Let's express 50 as the product of 5 times 10, make a box that is 5 times 10. Let's express 5,000 as 50 times 100. If we want 50 quarter-inches lined up, how many inches must we have?

RB: 12.5 inches.

TEACHER: So mark this off on the board.

TEACHER: P, please cut out what we'll need to show intake. What do we need for this 2.5 million?

RB: 500,000 times 500,000.

TEACHER: Let's check that. . . .

RB: No. . . .

TEACHER: Too many zeros.

TEACHER: What if this were 1 million?

RB: 1,000 times 10,000?

TEACHER: 1,000 times 1,000, let's express this on the board. . . . We're rushing through this, guys, sorry. Let's take our time. So 1,000 quarter-inches is. . . .

S: 250 inches.

TEACHER: So we have 250 inches. Let's do it with the calculator. . . . For our NPP, we'll make a box 2,500 inches by . . . gives us a box for deer intake. How many feet is this?

SER: 52.5 feet?

TEACHER: Yes. And 250 inches?

S: 21 feet.

TEACHER: Let's measure that box—the box to get NPP. [Passes out string.]

M: We need 52.5 feet? Where do we measure this?

[RM, P, M, and SER get up with string.]

TEACHER: [to RB] You seem disengaged. What's up?

RB: I'm not doing anything. . . .

[Teacher apologizes, puts her to work with S.]

TEACHER: What kind of a box do we need? What are we representing now?

S: NPP?

TEACHER: Production of plant matter—we measured almost the whole room as representing NPP.

S: Wow!

TEACHER: How many steps in this?

S: Two: plants to deer to wolf.

TEACHER: How big is the box of total solar input?

RB: 10,000 by 50,000.

TEACHER: How many feet is this?

S: 833 feet.

RB: 4,167 feet.

TEACHER: What is 4,000 feet? Approximately?

RB: 1 mile?

TEACHER: So, almost one mile by one-fifth of a mile is how much energy comes in to make one wolf unit.

P: Wow!

TEACHER: Where is the extra energy going?

RM: It's intangible. It "goes away" as heat.
TEACHER: . . . and stuff that is not eaten.
RB: Into millipedes and dung beetles!
P: . . . and that starts the process all over again.

[After the class session, an evaluator asks some questions about the chapter.]

Q: Did this last demonstration [the visual data representation] **work?**
RB: Yes, gives you visual idea of energy wasted.
S: Gets beyond the numbers.
P: The math did not help.

Q: What new things did you learn?
SER: It takes lots of energy to make a little matter.
S: The scale of it is amazing.

Q: Did you have any math difficulties?
S: The calculations are confusing. What you wanted us to do was confusing at first, but it was clarified later with the size-shape exercise.
M: I'm visual—the measuring helped and made the numbers more real.

Q: What were the most interesting parts?
RB: The final shapes, measuring the numbers out.
RM: We were confused in the beginning, didn't know what we were supposed to measure or calculate. The measuring out helped us see.

REFERENCES

Please see References in **Chapter 1**, this Unit.

EXTENSIONS

Your students may want to explore some implications of their calculations in Exploration 3.

Humans and their foods

Consider humans in place of wolves and cattle in place of deer. Which is energetically more effective for humans: to eat mostly beef or to eat mostly plant parts, such as grains? Given that there are over five billion humans on the planet and that population experts expect the earth to hold over ten billion sometime in the next century, how should we use our arable land, a very limited resource?

How many deer does the wolf eat? How much plant matter?

Your students may be interested in translating the energy content of the deer herd and plants into quantities of deer meat and plant tissue. If so, you can use the following information for calculations, along with the data on body sizes from the deer animal card: deer meat contains 1,260 kcal/kg; leaves contain roughly 200–400 kcal/kg (values vary considerably among plants).

PREDATOR AND PREY
WHO EATS WHOM?

CHAPTER ELEVEN

CONTENTS

INTRODUCTION

This Chapter expands on the ideas of the entire Unit so far, especially **Chapter 10**, about food chains and food webs. Students consider whether species regulate each other directly or indirectly through predation. If so, does the predator regulate its prey or vice versa? If two predators eat the same prey, do they regulate each other? Finally, students consider potential community-level effects of such interspecific interactions by debating or writing about some drastic perturbations to ecosystems.

KEY CONCEPTS

- Although ecology is the study of interactions between and among species (as well as between organisms and their physical environment), we actually know little about such interactions. There are so many, and so few have been studied.
- There are three apparent types of predator/prey interactions: some predators regulate their prey; some are regulated by their prey; and some predators and prey seem independent of each other.

MATERIALS AND PREPARATION

- **Paper** for diagrams
- **White or poster board**

SUGGESTED SEQUENCE OF SESSIONS (8–10)

Homework

Students read the Overview.

Class Session 1

Discuss the Overview, tying it back to students' work with food chains in **Chapter 10**. Then, working in teams of three to five, students study one famous example of predator-prey interactions, the snowshoe hare–lynx cycle (Exploration 1). Which species seems to be driving the cycle? (Answer: the hare.)

Homework

Reading 1: Hare and Lynx: Other Factors.

Class Session 2

Continue class discussion from Session 1, including the additional information from Reading 1. The hare is itself a predator, on plants, which may be controlling the cycle through chemical responses to overgrazing by hares.

Homework

Reading 2: What Kind of Data and What Does That Mean? (optional) may change students' perspective by examining the source of data for the hare-lynx example.

Class Session 3

Continue from Session 2, as appropriate. Discuss whether Reading 2 affects students' reactions to the original data. If you passed on Reading 2, begin Exploration 2. Students integrate information about hare health and energy use during a downslide in their population numbers with the energy use equation.

Class Session 4

Divide the class into three sets. Each third works in groups, studying one of the three example sets to decide which species in that set is controlling the predator-prey interaction. Then, as a class, students discuss and compare their examples.

Class Session 5

Continue Session 4, as appropriate.

Homework

Reading 3: Epilogue.

Class Session 6

Student groups present their conclusions and discuss categories of predator-prey interactions: how they might have come into being; how they might affect their communities; what kinds of ripples change in one population can have on other species.

Homework

Either have students write about one of the case studies in the Integration or let them read one or more case studies for a class debate and discussion. Alternatively, let each group pick a case study, read it, and prepare a presentation for class discussion. You likely will need two class sessions for the last alternative.

Class Session 7

Discuss part(s) of the Integration, considering how a change in any part of an ecosystem has many effects and at many levels.

Class Session 8

Continue discussion from Session 7, as appropriate.

SESSION GUIDES, BY WORKSHEET

EXPLORATION 1 GUIDE
The Hare-Lynx Cycle

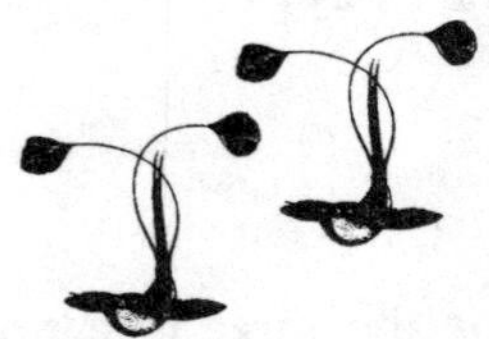

READING 1 GUIDE
Hare and Lynx: Other Factors

These two pieces tell the full story of the hare-lynx cycle, which is sufficiently complex that it is best taken in parts. The main points are these:

1. A drop in the hare population is actually a response to decreased food supplies. As hare populations increase, hare predation (feeding) on their prey (plants) also increases. The plants respond by producing defense chemicals, which make them undesirable or unhealthy for hares and keep the hares from eating those plants.

2. Since the plants continue to produce their defense chemicals for several years, hares have inadequate food supplies for the same period of time. Hare numbers continue to drop markedly.
3. The lynx population numbers follow the hare numbers but with a bit of a time lag. At first, when hares have inadequate food, they are easier to catch, and lynx numbers can keep increasing for a while. But as hare numbers keep decreasing, the lynx numbers also decrease.
4. Grouse, which are the lynx's substitute prey, show cycles like those of the hare, but also with a time lag.

Other effects are not considered here, such as effects on the plants eaten by grouse, on other predators of grouse, on invertebrates that feed on any of the plants, on any parasites, fleas, or microorganisms that live in or on the major players in this drama, and on the detritivores and decomposers that live on their leavings.

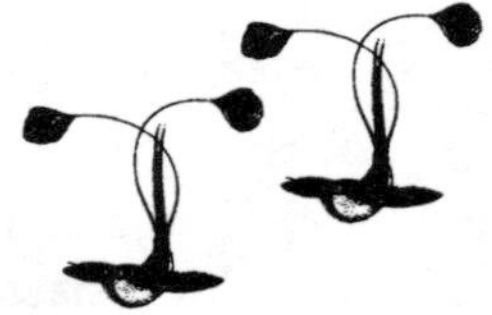

READING 2 GUIDE
What Kind of Data and What Does That Mean?

We continue to examine the sources of data and to differentiate between causality and coincidence, observation and experimentation. Students sometimes wonder whether raising these questions undercuts the reliability of the data. Actually, it enhances the data's credibility, since the sources are unambiguous, and the data can be more fully evaluated.

EXPLORATION 2 GUIDE
Energy Balance during Hare Cycles

Ecologists tested the hypothesis that observed effects on hares were due to too little food, in two ways. First, they performed experiments in which hares were fed too little. Underfed hares did, indeed, show the same characteristics as wild hares during a drop in the hare population. Second, ecologists measured amounts of food available to hares in the wild. They found that there are shortages of food during times of decreased numbers of hares.

EXPLORATION 3 GUIDE
Who Controls Whom: Predator and Prey?

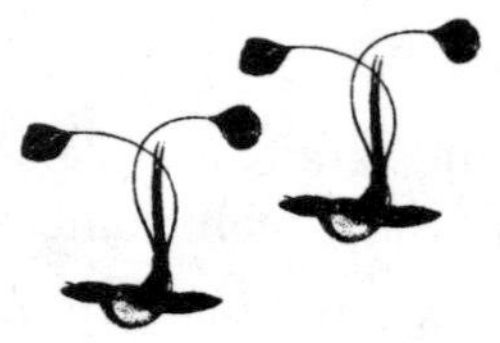

READING 3 GUIDE
Epilogue

Exploration 3 and Reading 3 examine the three categories of prey-predator interactions and provide food for a class discussion. Ask each group to put the diagrams of their set of interaction(s) on the board and explain their reasoning about who is "regulating" the interaction. Lively discussion may ensue. The third category can be most difficult to grasp, since it seems not to make sense. Point out how it might work. Note too that apparent independence does not mean there are not subtle aspects to those interactions that we have yet to realize.

Prey Apparently Regulate Their Predators (Category 1)

Pairs in this category tend to have several things in common. Each predator has one major or preferred prey species (so changes in the population of that prey affect the predator population). Despite that effect and even strong fluctuations in population sizes (several-fold decrease in animal numbers from cycle highs to lows), the situations are stable over time. Neither species has caused extinction of the other.

Ask students what might buffer a cycle from ending in extinction. Changing food species, such as the lynx switching to grouse, and the grouse to other plant species, is one example.

The type of oscillation between predators and prey looks similar for both vertebrate and invertebrate pairs. Prey numbers increase (to the maximum their environment can sustain); predator numbers increase; prey numbers exceed some threshold and drop; after a lag, predator numbers drop.

Predators Apparently Regulate Their Prey (Category 2)

These pairs also share equilibration in their respective numbers, but regulated by the other half of the pair. It continues to be a source of study whether, and under what conditions, such pairs lead to extinction of the prey species. The starfish in the Australian Barrier Reef was said to be wiping out its prey populations. More recent study suggests other aspects of the ecosystem might be involved, such as pollution by humans and a possible epidemic in the prey species.

Predator and Prey Numbers Seem Independent (Category 3)

A particular form of seeming independence between predators and prey is that in which prey populations cycle without their predators. Certainly populations of some prey species cycle. These include (among vertebrates) grouse, lemmings, and voles, and (among invertebrates) locusts and gypsy moths. These cycles, however, do not seem to have direct effects on their predator populations. Nor are the cycles as clearly linked to an explanation as is the hare cycle. In fact, lemming and vole cycles are so complicated that they are believed to involve at least ten major factors.

The predator population (tawny owls) maintain constant numbers, despite cycling in their prey species.

A predator that eats many different prey species might not be dependent on any one. Thus, if one prey species is cycling, the predator is relatively unaffected. Alternatively, if the relative numbers of prey are huge compared to predator numbers, the two species may have little direct effect on each other. Both circumstances may apply to the cheetah: Thomson's gazelles make up 40% of cheetah kills; there are about 350 cheetahs to 600,000 gazelles in the Serengeti.

Another possibility is that the data are incomplete, that is, they cover too brief a period, are too small a sample, or do not adequately consider the complete owl diet (what else do they eat and in what proportions?).

Class Discussion: So What Is a Predator?

We have considered several types of predator-prey interactions among different kinds of organisms. In fact, in the hare-lynx case, we see two connected predator-prey interactions: the hare as predator on its plant prey and the lynx as carnivore predator on its herbivore prey species, the hare and the grouse. Plus we have considered mite and insect predators.

Ecologists apply the same reasoning and words to invertebrate predators (such as insects) and their prey, whether those prey are plants or other animals. So the word "predator" applies simply to any organism that feeds on another organism that is not already dead. Thus, a predator can be a vertebrate or an invertebrate, a pathogen, even a plant. Prey can also be vertebrate, invertebrate, plant, or pathogen. (Except for viruses, pathogens also are alive and thus eat and are eaten.)

Parasitoids

Some ecologists consider host-parasitoid interactions a special form of predator-prey interactions. We were not quite accurate in calling the wasp that "preys" on the adzuki bean weevil its predator. In fact, the weevil is a host and the wasp a parasitoid (which is like a parasite, in that it lives off of another organism). A parasitoid differs from a parasite in that only the immature form lives in the host and consumes the actual flesh of the host until it ends by killing the host. So it is not the adult wasp that lives off the weevil. Adult female wasps lay their eggs on weevils. Once the eggs hatch, the growing, grub-like immature wasps (the larvae) then feed on the flesh of the weevil, until it dies.

Models

In addition to studies in the wild, ecologists have examined predator-prey interactions with computer simulations or models, with mixed results. Sometimes model assumptions simplify the relationships between organisms so much as to make the simulations unrealistic. In other cases, the models match reality but explain just one or a few examples rather than all the different kinds of matches we have seen. But there are some excellent pencil-and-paper and computer simulations of predator-prey interactions that are quite realistic and lots of fun to use.

INTEGRATION GUIDE
Perturbations: Events That Disturb Ecosystems

Perturbation is a fact of ecological life. In the past two decades, ecologists have gradually ceased looking for the ideal, unperturbed system. That realization has enabled us better to see factors that shape ecosystem function and community features such as species composition and abundance.

Students have studied some dynamics of trophic relations, including how species can affect each other. Using that background, let them consider the effects of some perturbations. Here are five cases of perturbations that have had or continue to have ripple effects on various parts of the systems in which they occur. A few include some human participation, but the spotlight should be on the way the "machinery" in the systems responded to the perturbation.

Background

Perturbations play an integral role in ecosystem functioning. They can have immediate effects on one aspect of an ecosystem, but because of the complex interactions within a system, the effects are likely to spread widely through the system. Perturbations may or may not be related to human actions. Human actions, however, can increase the severity of an otherwise natural perturbation, cause a perturbation, or increase the likelihood of some kind of perturbation event.

Logistics

Give students the worksheet to read overnight and prepare for the discussion the next day. Either have students write about one of the case studies in the Integration or let them read one or more for a class debate and discussion. You may wish to assign the cases to specific students, have all the students work on two or more cases, or divide the cases according to the ecosystems whose organisms the students have been learning about and using in earlier chapters.

We suggest that you introduce the basic notion of perturbation to the class and help the students see the integral role of such rare or occasional events in the life of an ecosystem. You may be aware of other examples that would be of interest to your class, such as the 1988 fires in Yellowstone National Park, the eruption of Krakatoa in 1880 (described in considerable detail in E. O. Wilson's Diversity of Life), the accidental introduction of the zebra mussel into the Great Lakes, or the intentional introduction of the Nile perch to Lake Victoria. Local events might be unusual rain patterns, severe drought, a major windstorm, or various human activities with clear ecological consequences. Students may have cases they would like to discuss, which we encourage you to have the students consider in addition to or instead of our examples.

Students' Objectives

- To discuss the case from the point of the trophic dynamics we have been examining in this unit.
- To conjecture about possible effects of the perturbations. They may wish to seek additional information or suggest experimental approaches to the testing of some of their ideas.
- To report to the class on their ideas and lead a discussion on those ideas or to write about their case (as you decide).

You may want to limit the Integration work to one class, or you may want to give the students more time to think and work on the cases. Another alternative would be to assign students a case study some time before the reports are brought to the class, as a finale to the Unit. You may want to use written reports on their ideas about the cases as a final assessment piece. Look for a clear understanding of trophic relations and a consideration of all levels (primary producers, consumers, and detritivores/decomposers).

Following are some notes on each case.

Rinderpest

In 1890, the viral disease rinderpest reached the Serengeti. The disease was carried by domestic cattle, for whom it was deadly. Unfortunately, it also proved fatal for several wild species; in two years 95% of the wildebeest and buffalo were dead, as were 95% of the domestic cattle.

Consequences included a great increase in NPP of grass and small trees (since so many herbivores had died—over 1.2 million), a decrease in competition among grasses, and an increase in populations of other grazers, such as Thomson's gazelles, and their predators, such as the cheetah. The increase in small-tree growth also increased giraffe populations.

As wildebeest populations slowly recovered, the effects were reversed. Today the wildebeest dominate the grasslands in herbivore biomass (with the possible exception of the hyraxes), and other species have returned to preperturbation levels and interactions.

Gypsy moths

This case is one in which the effects we see depend on the scale at which we look. On a large scale, the effect is not great. Much of the forest mosaic is relatively untouched. Even if the caterpillars take a significant proportion of NPP for the season, it is a temporary effect on a system that produces vastly more than is consumed by herbivores.

On the other hand, what are the trophic elements that process most of the energy that comes into a hardwood system? Detritivores and decomposers may, in fact, experience a drastic reduction in input; NPP in trees may be reduced somewhat. On a local scale (in the middle of a hard-hit forest), the effect can be temporarily great. Some other herbivores may have to migrate or may be locally outcompeted. Predators can probably move elsewhere (or really feast on gypsy moths!).

Mountain lions

Adding a large cat to an area might lead to a regulation of or decrease le density of prey to that of, say, the Serengeti: the cat will have to range over quite a large area; cats are not very efficient hunters compared with, say, canids (cats score a success in about 40% of their attempts at a kill); and their populations do not concentrate. Overall, therefore, there might not be much change from the point of view of ecosystem function, though it would certainly add to the interest of the eastern woods.

Mount Pinatubo

There may be an overall decrease in NPP because there is less sunlight. This could ripple up, decreasing all population sizes. The effect might be rather small, at least small enough that it would be hard to measure.

On the other hand, atmospheric scientists believe that the Pinatubo cooling effect has masked the global warming trend for those few years, though it should not have a long-term effect on the trend. Further, the aerosols from Pinatubo seem to have had a deleterious effect on the ozone layer in the higher latitudes. Increased ultraviolet B light has been shown to slow primary production by plankton in the south polar seas. If production continues at even a 5% reduction, consequences would be serious all along the food chain.

Tsavo elephants

The elephants so thoroughly overused their source of browse as to cause local short-term desertification and the destruction of some topsoil. That depleted and disrupted the communities of detritivores and decomposers, further impoverishing the soil. The effect on the elephant population was dramatic, with starvation and disease killing 25–50%. The threatened black rhino population was affected and crashed; the trees were gone, and any creature depending on trees for food or shelter also was displaced or perished. Finally, the elephants and other animals tried to do what they always had done when an area was no longer hospitable—they moved outside the park and foraged in what had become completely agricultural lands. That led to direct conflict between elephants and humans, with the result of some human and many elephant deaths. With the reduction of the population of large herbivores, the pressure on the trees was reduced, so the land is beginning to recover. Elephant populations probably are still above sustainable levels; the area is simply too small for those numbers.

How Plants Capture and Allocate Energy

Unit 3

How Plants Capture and Allocate Energy

UNIT

3

CONTENTS

UNIT 3 OVERVIEW

HOW PLANTS CAPTURE AND ALLOCATE ENERGY

This Unit considers energy flow as it relates to plants. It makes concrete and quantitative the notion of terrestrial "primary producer." It also introduces some basic design constraints that shape plant evolution and life histories with respect to energy capture. It moves from plant form at the level of species, to global distribution of plant community types, to energy allocation in plants. Since plant productivity largely defines land ecosystems, it is an important measure of many aspects of ecosystem function.

The Unit considers such questions as:

- How much solar energy is actually available to an ecosystem?
- What limits the amount of that solar energy that is fixed as plant tissue?
- How does energy capture relate to the great variety of plant form?
- How do we describe plant communities, and how do plant community types shape the environment for the consumers in an ecosystem?

We use two simple physical systems to model energy-capture processes. The "design a plant" activity that leads off **Chapter 1** introduces design constraints in a simple cost-benefit model. "Design," of course, is accomplished by means of natural selection, not plant need or desire.

Solar cells provide a way of exploring the amounts of solar energy arriving on a given area. We examine plant properties vis à vis solar energy first by modeling them and then by comparing models to the real thing (**Chapter 1**). Plants respond to most external stimuli by changes in growth (amount, form, amount of leaf, root, and wood). Such response explains both plant shapes and their distributions; plants have responded to external factors over evolutionary time in ways that explain the geographic distribution of plant shapes (**Chapter 2**). Students develop their own schemes for classifying or grouping plants by form and compare them with a standard scheme. Details of these forms tell us much about the plant's life history, its environment, and where and how carbon and energy move through the plant part of ecosystems (**Chapter 3**).

Plants also provide a good system in which to study costs of reproduction. Numerous species can be used in the laboratory to estimate reproductive success under various growing conditions, and to impose, experimentally, selective pressures that result in easily measurable phenotypic changes.

We recommend that students describe and compare habitats or communities, including parks, lawns, roadsides, or sidewalk tree-wells, as well as other systems less severely shaped by human activity (**Chapter 4**).

Using the simple measures of species composition, plant life-form spectra, and plant biomass, students can undertake a wide range of ecological experiments and field studies, including many of real scientific relevance (Extensions, **Chapter 4**).

DESIGN A PLANT
ENERGY CAPTURE AND ALLOCATION

CHAPTER ONE

CONTENTS

INTRODUCTION

In this Chapter, students work with physical models to think about what plants have to do to get the energy they need. We focus on light as a resource whose availability is limited temporally (e.g., by day length and seasonal variation) and spatially (e.g., by the presence of other plants that may cast shadow). Plants do not forage for their energy the way animals do, but they do grow so as to maximize their intake of solar energy.

As with animals and other organisms, a plant's cells respire constantly, and the plant has a minimum energy requirement it must meet in order to survive. To grow and reproduce, the plant—like animals—must exceed that minimum requirement. This roughly corresponds to the basal metabolic rate (BMR), discussed in **Unit 2.** The manufacture of new tissue carries its own "overhead" as well—new tissue "costs" both the energy in the molecules that constitute it and the energy to manufacture those molecules. (See Science Background for details.)

The plant's physical growth form plays a crucial role, because it dictates how a plant gets its energy and also what it cannot do. Root and shoot growth are necessary if the plant is to find the resources it needs. Unlike animals, the plant cannot move to avoid competition; growth rates and stress tolerance are its principal weapons against competitors.

This Chapter focuses on the leaf as a solar collector and on the plant as a composite of real populations (see **Chapter 3**, Case Study) of many solar-collecting modules—the construction plan for the activity progresses along those lines. Exploration 1 introduces the notion of plants as solar collectors. Explorations 2a and 2b use photovoltaic cells and thermometers to explore the ideas of energy transformation and the efficiency of energy capture. The text then moves on to geographical effects on the solar budget: differences in sun angle, both on a small scale and with reference to latitude. This lays the groundwork for designing an experiment estimating the efficiency of energy capture by plants.

Before that, however, we look at plant form as a way to think about plant communities and biogeography, and then biomass as a convenient way to measure the effects of environmental and genetic factors on plants (and organisms in general). By the end of the Chapter, students should be able to demonstrate what happens to the solar energy striking a plant and analyze ways that energy capture shapes plant form and ecology.

In Advance for Chapter 3

If you plan to grow your own seedlings for the work in **Chapter 3**, you need to start them now. They need about a month to reach adequate size. See **Chapter 3** for details.

KEY CONCEPTS

- Light is plants' energy source. The light that strikes a plant includes wavelengths that are used for photosynthesis. Other wavelengths are either absorbed (e.g., as heat, causing a rise in temperature) or reflected.
- Each individual plant must maximize energy capture, balancing it against the cost of tissue production and maintenance. Discharge of excess heat also is important.

- In a plant community, plants compete in three-dimensional space for access to light. Increase in photosynthetic area may require an increase in nonphotosynthetic support tissue.
- Leaves also serve as organs for absorption of CO_2 from the atmosphere. More trade-offs are caused by the need to limit water loss through the stomates that admit CO_2.
- Plant life forms and morphologies have evolved largely under the pressure of those trade-offs, while making economical use of water and nutrients gathered below ground.
- We can study aspects of plants' function and the constraints on them by using physical or conceptual models, which then can be used to design experimental or field studies of actual organisms.

MATERIALS AND PREPARATION

Materials

For Exploration 1

- **Scissors** (1 pair per student)
- **Green construction paper** (10 sheets per student)
- **Transparent tape** (1 roll for each group)
- **Scale** that weighs in grams
- **Graph paper**

For Exploration 2a

- **Thermometers** (2 per group)
- **Light meters** or **sensors that record visible light** (optional)
- **50- to 100-watt lightbulbs**, with lamp shades or reflectors (1 for each group)
- **Assorted colors of construction paper**
- **Meter stick**
- **Corrugated cardboard**
- **Masking tape**
- **Clock** or **watch**

For Exploration 2b and 3a

- **Solar cells** (1 per group in Explorations 2a and 3a)
- **Multimeter**, or amp-meter (1 per group in Explorations 2a and 3a)
- **1-ohm (1-Ω) resistors** (1 per group in Explorations 2a and 3a)
- **Measuring sticks** (for sun-angle measurements and positioning of sensors)
- **Protractors**
- **Relief globe, map,** or **atlas** (of the United States, at least)

You can use an MBL (Microcomputer-Based Laboratory) setup with a light probe (such as those produced for the TERC Star Schools Weather Unit or the IBM PSL™ system) to calibrate the solar cells for watts per square meter, which can then be converted to calories (1 W = 0.2388 cal/sec). Otherwise, use the maps attached to Exploration 3b: Geography and Plant Growth to figure the approximate amount of insolation at your latitude. Note that the measurements in the maps are in langleys (1 langley = 1 cal/cm^2; multiply by 10,000 to get kcal/m^2). The measurements also represent total insolation, which is about 50% photosynthetically active and 50% infrared and ultraviolet.

In Advance

Exploration 2 and Exploration 3 divide the class into halves. Each half carries out complementary aspects of each Exploration. You may want to divide the class into different proportions, depending on the availability of materials or on other factors. Exploration 2a looks at the conversion of light energy to heat energy; 2b at the conversion of light to electrical energy. In Exploration 3a, students quantify the effects of the changing sun angle on the supply of light to plants over the course of a day. In Exploration 3b, they study the effect of latitude on the light supply.

Encourage duplicate groups to compare their results. You may need to help them consider what generalizations they can draw from the differences or similarities of their findings. When the two halves of each Exploration report to each other, guide the discussion in such a way that the whole class profits from the division of labor by asking each half to integrate their results with those of the other half.

Safety

For Exploration 2b and Exploration 3a

> **WARNING**
> **When taking solar measurements, do NOT look at the sun directly! It can damage your eyes!**

> **WARNING**
> **Never set the meter to read ohms (Ω) when it is attached to the photocell. Doing so can cause permanent damage to the multimeter.**

SUGGESTED SEQUENCE OF SESSIONS (8–10)

Class Session 1

Introduce Exploration 1: Design a Plant and begin on the first task, a single plant module.

Class Sessions 2–3

Continue Session 1. Students develop and test their multimodule plant models and evaluate them for effectiveness as interceptors of solar energy. As homework or in class, students write their wrap-up reports for Exploration 1. Discuss the reports in class.

Homework

Reading 1: Sun Leaves, Shade Leaves, and Tree Shapes.

Class Session 4

Based on the Homework Reading, students revise their models for efficiency.

Class Session 5

Students report on their models and discuss the relationship between their work and Reading 1: Sun Leaves, Shade Leaves, and Tree Shapes.

Class Session 6

Exploration 2a: Transforming Light to Heat Energy and Exploration 2b: Transforming Light to Electricity use simple physical models in parallel to study the transformation of light into heat energy and into electrical energy.

Homework

Reading 2: Light Striking Vegetation: Reflection, Transmission, and Absorption.

Class Session 7

Groups report on their results from Session 6 or complete their data collection. Discuss Reading 2 and how plants can respond to solar energy by changing their leaves, shapes, and so on.

Class Sessions 8–9

Students explore the effects of sun angle, which has both seasonal and geographical components. Half the class collects new data on light and sun angle throughout a day and estimates the supply of light at that location. The other half looks at published data on the differences in light supply according to latitude.

SESSION GUIDES, BY WORKSHEET

EXPLORATION 1 GUIDE
Design a Plant

Have the students work in groups of two or three. For each group, provide paper, tape, scissors, graph paper, and pencils. Remind them to bring their notebooks.

In design work like this, it often is the case that one student will dominate a group, so that student's ideas are tested or logic is followed. This is to be discouraged on two counts. First, it may exclude others in the group, whose involvement will be less as the "star's" involvement is more. Second, the tendency is to take one idea, work it to the point of diminishing returns, only to arrive at a dead end. Encourage groups to brainstorm about the design task. Suggest that they list several possibilities, make sketches, or jot down notes to focus their thinking and give themselves several options to try.

Students' evaluation of their models has two parts. In the first part, they calculate shade area, which implies how much light was caught and is available for photosynthesis. You might ask students to discuss why a plant might be at a disadvantage in competition with another plant that casts no larger a shadow, but a darker one. It also is worth asking what the implications are of a flat surface intercepting a lot of light, thus raising the question of heat stress and related physiological questions.

The second part of the evaluation lies in the estimate of the efficiency of the designs. What is the ratio of leaf area to sunlight intercepted? What is the relation between leaf area and the amount of materials used? How about the relation between shade cast and the amount of materials used?

One design constraint that may be a challenge is the free-standing one. If students are having too much trouble with this in the single-module stage, have them skip it until the multiple-module stage. The point is for them to see that supporting structure has a cost and is an integral part of a plant's "capital investment" in photosynthesis.

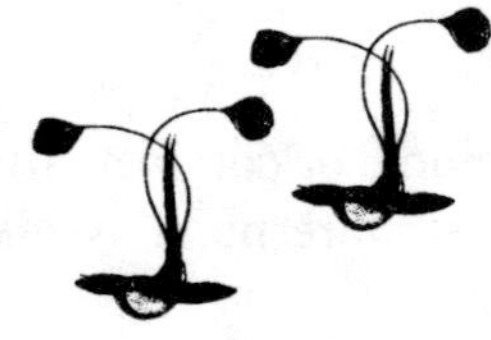

READING 1 GUIDE (Homework)
Sun Leaves, Shade Leaves, and Tree Shapes

This Reading addresses the basic idea of evolutionary strategy. Light may seem to be an abundant resource, but it is actually in problematic supply since plants capture so little of it in primary production. Reading 1 points out that many plant species, especially trees, have evolved the ability to respond to large-scale variation in light supply, so they can balance light capture, heat control, and conservation of water.

Tree form is itself one evolutionary solution to the need to maximize photosynthetic area unshaded by competitors. Of course, the multiplication of modules leads to self-shading, and growth in forests means that trees of the same and of different species shade each other as well. Such competition for a limited resource has driven the evolution of different tree shapes. The evolutionary acquisition of very large woody stems has brought with it a whole cascade of other ecological characteristics. Varieties of tree shape are easily observed, once you know what to look for, and it is exciting to see such variety as an outgrowth of evolution in action. (You might want to refer in the discussion to **Module 1: Evolution**.)

Of course, most plants will not reproduce and distribute their seeds in ideal conditions, so those "offspring" will try to take root and survive in habitats that range from ideal to challenging for the species. Plasticity—the ability to change growth patterns in response to environmental conditions—is an important strategy for individuals as well as species. Thus, trees like sugar maples, which tend to be found in shady forest sites and whose leaves appear as monolayers, grow as multilayer trees in sunny locations. Such plasticity can be expressed at the level of the species, the individual, or the module (say, a leaf).

EXPLORATION 2A GUIDE

Transforming Light to Heat Energy

The capture of light energy in an ecosystem is constrained by characteristics of the abiotic elements (sunlight, temperature, moisture, atmosphere, etc.) and of the biotic elements (the plants themselves, the autotrophs). It often is said that organisms obey the laws of thermodynamics, but because the biological consequences are rarely specified, they generally remain obscure to high school students (and most other people, even professional scientists). A critical point is the finite supply of solar energy and the relative inefficiency of biological systems that capture and use that energy.

Solar energy has several effects on living systems: only a small part of the solar spectrum is photosynthetically active, and much of it imposes a heat load on living systems, with various metabolic consequences. (Plant response to heat load is also considered in **Module 3: Water**.)

This Exploration has two parts, which run in parallel. Each half of the class carries out one part. The groups in each half prepare and present their findings to the entire class. This stimulates a whole-class discussion to construct an initial energy budget for a generalized green plant.

Students use model systems to explore links in the chain from sun to living tissue. They also examine plants' role in the system from the plants' point of view, as well as the role of the secondary producers, the consumers.

What Happens to Light That Hits an Object?

The most important point of this discussion is that energy from the sun (or from a lightbulb) comes in the form of electromagnetic radiation. When that radiation strikes the surface of an object, some of the radiation is reflected, some is absorbed, and some may be transmitted (i.e., pass through the material). Exploration 2a illustrates that light/radiation from the sun can be absorbed and increase the temperature of an object.

Collecting the Data

The experimental setup is simple. It is important to standardize the size of the lightbulb and the distance between the light and the receptive surface. The idea that darker things absorb more heat generally is well known. Students may discover it harder to demonstrate this fact than they might think, because factors that affect absorption of light are multiple. Most of them are relevant to plant biology: reflectance, heat loss by evaporation, and reradiation. Figure 1 is a sample data sheet.

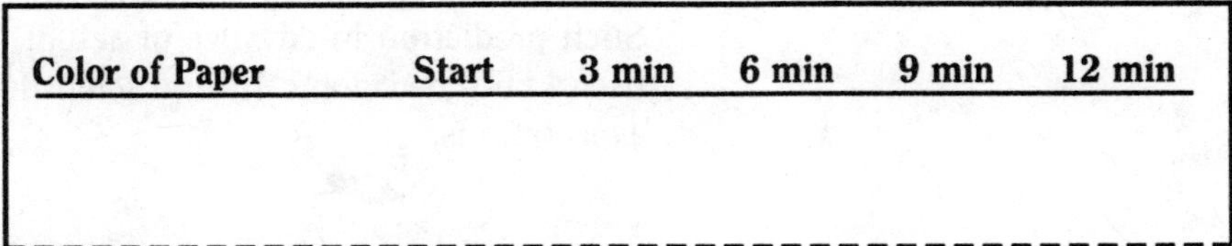

Color of Paper	Start	3 min	6 min	9 min	12 min

Figure 1. Sample data sheet for Exploration 2a.

If you have access to light meters, you might suggest that as the groups collect the temperature data some students take measurements of the light reflected from the absorptive surface.

The purpose of using different colors is to contrast the absorptivity of different surfaces based on color. This exercise helps students add understanding about radiation into their current knowledge. In photosynthesis, the chemical difference in objects—the presence or absence of chlorophyll—explains the differences in absorption of radiation.

Another variation of this Exploration can be built on the following question: How might you quantify the amount of energy that is striking the black paper? The earlier work with calorimetry may suggest trying to heat water using the heat captured by the different heat-capturing setups.

Presenting the Data

Students may get off to a slow start trying to understand how to represent their results graphically. Once they understand what they are doing (expressing temperature change as a function of time for each color) and how to go about it, they tend to enjoy the process of making graphs and to be excited by the results.

If possible, invite students to come up with their own ways of representing or displaying their data. Each student can "specialize" in a color. That way, students can help each other, but each is responsible for one set of data, and the group has a built-in comparison. It might be helpful if each group includes students who understand the math more readily. The students in each group also need to agree on a standard way of representing their data. (They may find it helpful to read or review the **Technique: Data.**)

Class Discussion: Integrating the Data

This session can vary somewhat, depending on how much structure you give students and thus how much time you allocate to this work. If possible, use two sessions and give students lots of latitude about finding their own ways of representing their data. The work can be open-ended, with students trying whatever occurs to them and rejecting things only through trying them. Or you may want to help them assess their plan or help them make decisions about scale. Finally, you could (although we hope you would not) provide some examples and let students choose among them.

Students can also address the issue of data representation even before they collect real data. They can make—and represent—predictions about temperature increase over the 12-minute experiment. They can label the Y axis "temperature," with just a few points: room temperature, starting temperature, and final temperature. The label on the X axis can be "time," with the start and end times of the experiment in intervals of 1 or more minutes. Such prediction in advance of actual implementation of an experiment is useful both pedagogically and scientifically—it clarifies one's thinking and expectations.

EXPLORATION 2B GUIDE

Transforming Light to Electricity

The capture of light energy in an ecosystem is constrained by characteristics of the abiotic elements (sunlight, temperature, moisture, atmosphere, etc.) and of the biotic elements (the plants themselves, the autotrophs). It often is said that organisms obey the laws of thermodynamics, but because the biological consequences of thermodynamic laws are rarely specified, they generally remain obscure to high school students (and most other people, even professional scientists). A critical point is the finite supply of solar energy and the relative inefficiency of biological systems that capture and use that energy.

Solar energy has several effects on living systems: only a small part of the solar spectrum is photosynthetically active, and much of it imposes a heat load on living systems, with various metabolic consequences. (Plant response to heat load is also considered in **Module 3: Water**.)

This Exploration has two parts, which run in parallel. Each half of the class carries out one part. The groups in each half prepare and present their findings to the entire class. This stimulates a whole-class discussion to construct an initial energy budget for a generalized green plant.

Students use model systems to explore links in the chain from sun to living tissue. They also examine plants' role in the system from the plants' point of view, as well as the role of the secondary producers, the consumers.

What Happens to Light That Hits an Object?

The most important point of this discussion is that energy from the sun (or from a lightbulb) comes in the form of electromagnetic radiation. When that radiation strikes the surface of an object, some of the radiation is reflected, some is absorbed, and some may be transmitted (i.e., pass through the material).

Exploration 2b introduces another analogue, the photovoltaic cell, or solar cell, which converts radiant energy into electricity through a photoelectric reaction.

Calibrating the Solar Cell

Students calibrate their solar cell by using some numbers for W/cm² for the distance from a 75-W and a 60-W lightbulb. Then they develop a regression relating the current from their solar cell to the power from a source using the values in Table 1.

Table 1 **Values Used to Calibrate Solar Cells**

	POWER (W/CM²)	
DISTANCE (CM)	75-W BULB	60-W BULB
5	314	195
10	186	47
15	91	23
20	68	15

Voltage Readings

A simple formula (power = voltage^2) relates voltage readings to the power (in watts) that is being generated. Students should keep track of the distance from the light source and the voltage readings. A table like the one in Figure 2 facilitates calculating the power value for each voltage reading.

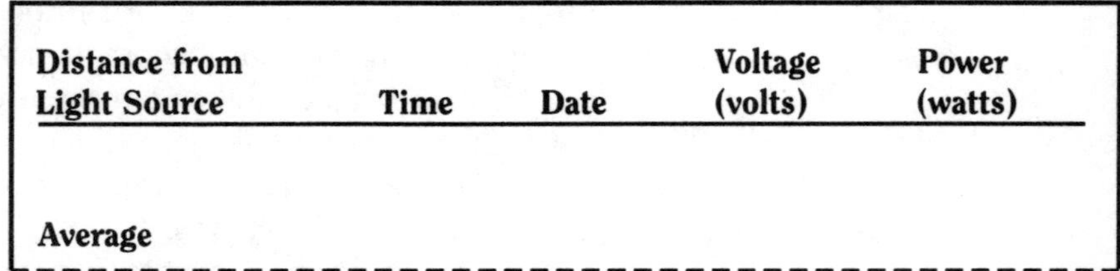

Distance from Light Source	Time	Date	Voltage (volts)	Power (watts)
Average				

Figure 2. Sample data sheet for Exploration 2b.

Estimating Efficiency of Energy Capture by Photocells

Energy transformation always has a cost, as described by the laws of thermodynamics. It is possible to measure, or at least estimate, the "performance" of any energy-transforming system. (We encourage you, at the end of this Unit, to have your students design an experiment to estimate efficiency of photosynthesis in a laboratory system, using the biomass added by laboratory plants under a light source of known [or estimated] power. The basic thinking of the photocell work in this Exploration provides the skeleton for that experimental design.)

Input and output

To determine the efficiency of energy capture by a photocell, we must compare input to output. We assume input from the sun to be 1,000 W/m^2, or 0.1 W/cm^2. That is our given.

For output, we need to know how many watts per square meter are produced by the photocell. First, we measure the area of the sensor generating the power. Next, we get a measure of the power and calculate a power per unit area. By dividing the power per unit area by the input, we get an efficiency of energy capture. A sample calculation follows.

A worked-through example

The sensor is a half-circle with a diameter of 7.5 cm and therefore a sensor area of 22.089 cm^2. In full sun, the sensor provided 0.2234 W of power.

To find power per unit area, we divide the power by the area of the sensor and get 0.01011 W/cm^2. Then, to calculate the percentage efficiency, we divide the output by the input and multiply by 100. Our measurement of the efficiency of the transformation is 0.01011 / 0.1 = 0.1011, or 10.11% efficient. This efficiency is similar to that of very efficient plants, such as some varieties of corn.

Reports and Class Discussion

There no doubt will be variations in the readings from the different groups. Such variations reflect, for example, the source of light, the performance of the solar cells used, and the positioning of the cells.

Different models show some important aspects of plants as collectors: the instrument (the leaf) collects varying quantities at various efficiencies. A leaf has a lifetime, just as a whole plant does. Over a lifetime, the leaf's effectiveness as a photosynthesizer changes, rising to a peak as the leaf matures and decreasing as the leaf ages. Genetic variation also plays a role within individuals of a species and between species. Some individual leaves (refer to Reading 1), some individual plants, and some species are more efficient than others. That variation means that some species—even individuals within the same species—are more successful than others in particular locales or conditions, which may give them a competitive advantage.

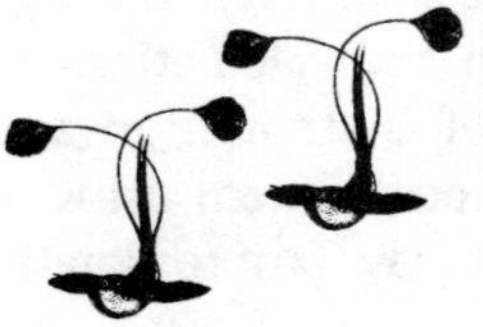

READING 2 GUIDE (Homework)
Light Striking Vegetation: Reflection, Transmission, and Absorption

This reading rehearses some basics about what happens to light that strikes the surface of an object. Students who have not taken a physical science course or who took such a course awhile ago will profit from the reminder. It helps them see that there is biological significance of an apparently abiotic set of events: the amount of light affects primary production, as do the water condition, heat balance, and circulation of plants. The fact that only a subset of incident sunlight is photosynthetically active and that the total amount of available light is limited by geographic, seasonal, and community characteristics should be increasingly clear to the students. This Reading helps them draw those conclusions. In the class discussion, make sure students understand both the abiotic facts and their biological implications, especially for primary productivity.

EXPLORATION 3A GUIDE
Figuring the Angles in Your Location

Primary production is the fundamental route by which solar radiation becomes available to the organisms in all ecosystems. Solar input varies around the globe, both seasonally and daily. The earth's shape, rotation, and revolution cause some of the most important variations in sunlight. Relatively simple observations can enable students to understand those factors.

Explorations 3a and 3b can take one or two class sessions, depending on whether you use homework time for some of the data analysis. The work is designed in three parts. The first two parts are done by groups, in parallel. Exploration 3a focuses on daily variation in insolation, while Exploration 3b focuses on latitudinal and seasonal variations. The groups report on their results to each other, and a class discussion of perhaps 20 minutes pulls the two strands together. The work introduces students to some important facts about the sun's behavior as we perceive it here on earth and raises a lot of questions to which students return. These Explorations also provide a lot of opportunity for Extension projects, for example, on the efficiency and practicability of solar power in your latitude; on plant leaves and sun angles; and on related biological, technological, or astronomical questions.

Divide the class so that half the students work on Exploration 3a and the other half on 3b. Then subdivide the halves—groups of four work well. Replication is good, because there undoubtedly will be differences in results, which can be fruitful grounds for investigation. (Why did we get only 60% of your result? How can you interpret your results that way?)

Timing

You may wish to telescope the work and have most of it done outside of class, with a 15- to 20-minute preparation time and then a session of reports and discussion. Alternatively, you can devote a double session or two successive sessions to data collection and analysis and to discussion.

In Exploration 3a, students measure solar angle throughout the day. The students may need some help with the calculation of sun angles, although the procedure on the worksheet is straightforward. We recommend that students experiment with a model system using a lightbulb as the source before going into the field. You may want to skip this session, or perform a demonstration.

When it comes to conjecturing about mechanisms to explain what they see, students might not realize that tilting a collector (or any surface) affects the density of insolation or that it is a geometric matter. As Figure 3 shows, a given "volume" of rays of light coming in at an angle is spread over a much larger area than rays at the same density but coming directly (not at an angle). Thus, the density of light striking any one point is lessened by the slant. (This is a case in which a sensor can transform our understanding of a phenomenon, since our perceptions of the sun's effect on us are complicated by many other factors.)

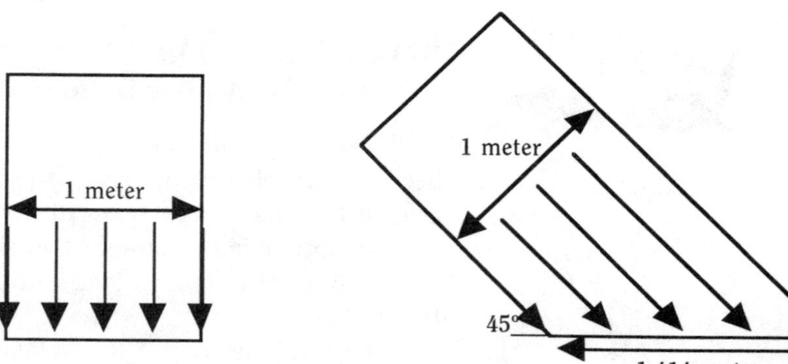

Figure 3. Comparison of light rays arriving directly and at an angle.

EXPLORATION 3B GUIDE
Geography and Plant Growth

While half of the class is taking data on the amount of solar energy available at one site on one day, the other half is looking at the same phenomenon, only on a larger scale of time and space. The time scale is a year, and the spatial scale is the western hemisphere.

As students look at the data in Exploration 3b, they may take some time to reach the conclusion that latitude is an important factor in the amount of insolation available at any one point. They might have a harder time conjecturing about reasons for the patterns than in seeing the patterns themselves. The examples from Alaska and Hawaii may help clarify this point. The conceptual difficulty mentioned in the Guide for Exploration 3a is relevant here: why should the angle of incoming radiation make any difference? It is helpful to have a globe handy, so students can see a representation of the earth's curvature. Then they realize that on a global scale the differences in density created by differences in angle can be significant. (Compare Figure 4 to Figure 3).

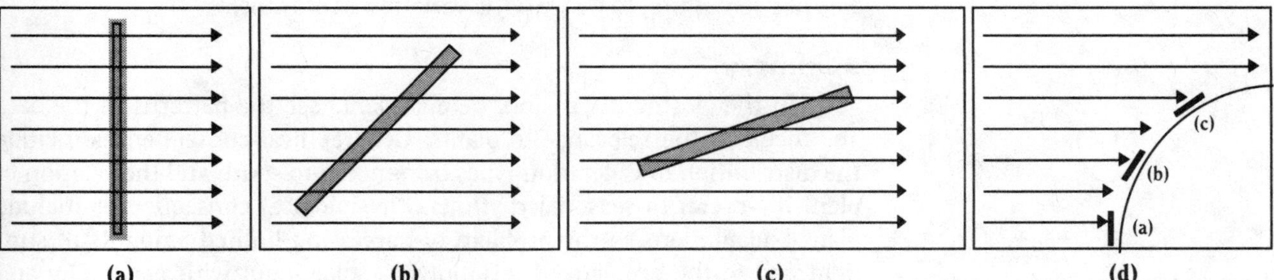

Figure 4. Differences in density created by differences in angle: (a) corresponds to the equator, where insolation comes in directly; (b) at roughly 45°, corresponds to temperate latitudes; (c) corresponds to the Arctic (or Antarctic) Circle; (d) Compares (a), (b), and (c). As the incident angle declines, the density of energy also declines. That is why, even allowing for the midnight sun, Alaska does not collect as much sun as, say, Quito, Nairobi, or Lahaina.

In the class discussion, students should be helped to see that differences in location have a profound effect on the solar energy supply for plants. On a local scale, north- or south-facing slopes have more light available (depending on hemisphere). On a global scale, the closer to the equator you are, the larger and more steady the supply of solar energy (which may well be a contributory cause of the extraordinary species diversity of tropical ecosystems).

INTEGRATION GUIDE
Revisiting Your Designer Plant

You can use the Integration as homework or as the basis of an in-class discussion.

Students now have had a taste of several aspects of the ecology of light as a resource. From a plant's point of view, we can regard light as a resource, like water. It flows more often at one time than at another; it is more accessible in some locations than in others; its availability varies from season to season in most parts of the world. Further, a plant's size and shape reflect the importance of light in two general ways. First, plants evolve to make the most effective use of some portion of the light striking their area. Second, that evolutionary division of the energy pie is a constraint because light as a resource is not available in unlimited supply.

An Afternote: Why Seasons?

Sun angle is a crucial variable on a daily and a seasonal basis. One point we have not addressed directly is the reason for the seasons. That is, students readily understand that seasonally there is less light available during short-day periods, but they may not be clear about why days get shorter in the first place. The classic misconception is that cold weather comes because the earth gets farther away from the sun in the course of its revolution around it. Consideration of day length as a co-varying phenomenon may raise a question about the plausibility of that theory. In any case, students cannot deduce the fact that the earth is actually closer to the sun during the winter than in the summer (in the northern hemisphere). If you tell them this fact, they then may be able to deduce that the earth's tilt on its axis has something to do with the variation in seasons.

Summary

In the closing discussion, help students see the patterns in the data and focus on the relevance to plants. Geographical consequences include the distribution of vegetation types from north to south and the relation of plant life-cycles to seasonal rhythms. Physiological consequences include plants' adaptations to the problem of harvesting limited amounts of sunlight and to the problem of variations in solar input with geography and during the day. These types of consequences are explored in more detail later in **Chapter 2**.

All these points can be used to stimulate what students know or think about biogeography and plant life-cycles. Help students keep track of questions that come up, which they can then review later in this Unit.

INTEGRATION
Revisiting Your Designer Plant

In the Explorations, you encountered and experimented with several factors that affect how much light is available to plants at particular spots on the earth's surface. A plant's challenge is more complex than just capturing the light from a strong lightbulb shining from one direction.

What are some factors that limit how much light a plant can collect over the course of a day? A year? Its lifetime?

What changes would you make to the plant module you designed or to the arrangement of modules in the whole-plant model you designed? Make a sketch if you want.

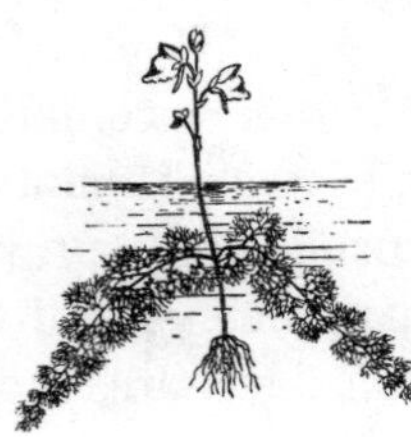

Do you think your plant might be better suited for one environment than for others or for one part of the world than for others? Why?

SCIENCE BACKGROUND
General Aspects of Plant Production

If you are acquainted with plant physiology, you probably can think of several ways in which we oversimplify the factors that should be considered in the design of a functioning plant model. We do not ask the students to consider below-ground structures or features such as hairs or stipules, to add reproductive tissue, and so on. We also do not raise the issue of physiological responses (strategic and tactical, phenotypic and ontogenetic), such as shade versus sun leaves or lower or higher compensation points.

Chapters 2, 3, and **4** address several aspects of the plant ecology that lies behind the activities.

PLANT MORPHOLOGY

Plant species evolve in the context of other plants as well as of herbivores. Insolation can be a limiting and limited resource, for which the plants have to compete and perhaps not get enough of. Plants have a number of strategies for getting as much of this resource as they can. For example, some plants allocate energy to supporting structures, which allows them to overtake their competition and provides a good "spread" between layers of their own branches or leaves. Other strategies include leaf arrangement and leaf shape.

Leaf Arrangement

If the resource is scarce, leaves are arranged so there is minimal self-interference. If there is more than enough light, the leaves are arranged in layers. Each layer takes a portion of the light coming from above and transmits a portion to the layer below.

Leaf Shape

If there is so much light that leaves are saturated quickly (and thus have a greater temperature load), the leaves are smaller in area, either by reduced linear dimensions or by lobes and divisions in the leaf blade.

MEASURE OF LIGHT USE

The leaf-area index allows us to measure how completely the available light is being exploited per square meter. In many habitats, a high leaf-area index means high plant production and usually high primary productivity. Simply calculate the surface area (in square meters) of the leaves in the air space above a square meter of ground. Typical leaf-area index values for various types of vegetation are listed in Table 2.

Modular Structure

Unlike animals, plants can be considered populations of modules, each module consisting of a leaf or branch and its node. This modular structure gives plants a great deal of flexibility in their response to stimuli, even to the point that different branches of the same tree may have leaves of

Table 2 **Typical Leaf-Area Index Values**

TYPE OF VEGETATION	LEAF-AREA INDEX
Rain forest	10–11
Deciduous forest	5–6
Boreal conifer forest	9–11
Grassland	5–8
Tundra	1–2
Desert	1
Agricultural area	3–5

different shapes or may flower at different times. It is possible to construe many developmental changes in plants as the result of competition or compromise between different modules of the same plant.

ALLOCATION OF RESOURCES

The structural or morphological responses of a plant are expressed in the way the plant allocates its resources, especially photosynthate. Under particular conditions, a plant may be helped or hindered by allocating more to roots than to shoots, to secondary compounds, to leaves rather than stems (or vice versa, of course), to vegetative versus reproductive parts.

There can be competition among the ways a plant allocates its resources. That is, allocating to the stem diminishes the amount of photosynthetic area that the plant has. Allocation to leaves and branches raises the possibility of self-shading, which may lead to a waste of resources.

We can use simple models to explore such questions and to make conjectures; then we compare the models with real plants (or real whatever). That approach of starting with models can be very powerful.

ENERGY COSTS OF PRODUCTION

Table 3 lists the energy costs (in grams of sucrose per gram of carbohydrate manufactured) of tissue construction in two types of trees.

Table 3 **Energy Costs of Tissue Construction**

TYPE OF TREE	TISSUE TYPE	COST
Pine	Needles	1.57
	Branches	1.49
	Bark	1.6
	Roots	1.47
Eucalyptus	Phloem	1.45
	Sapwood	1.36
	Heartwood	1.4

We can estimate the energy-cost values for other plants if we know the composition of the tissues involved:

COMPONENT TYPE	COST
Lipid	3.02
Lignin	1.9
Protein	2.35
Complex sugar	1.18

One study showed that, while plants "turn a profit" during the day, in several herbaceous species 30–60% of the day's photosynthate was expended in dark respiration. In tropical countries, 70–80% of the day's total intake can be lost during the dark hours, because of the high night-time temperatures, which speed metabolic rates.

REFERENCES

Bernhardt, Peter. 1989. Wily Violets and Underground Orchids. New York: Vintage Books.

Kricher, John C., and Gordon Morrison. 1988. Eastern Forests. Boston: Houghton Mifflin Company.

Larcher, Walter. 1995. Physiological Plant Ecology. 3rd ed. Berlin: Springer-Verlag.

Perry, David A. 1994. Forest Ecosystems. Baltimore: Johns Hopkins University Press.

Waring, R. H., and W. H. Schlesinger. 1985. Forest Ecosystems: Concepts and Management. Orlando, FL: Academic Press.

Abiotic Factors and Plant Distribution

Chapter Two

Contents

Introduction

The Explorations in this Chapter introduce several concepts that are important to an understanding of carbon cycling and energy flow in ecosystems. They are based on the use of plant life form as a descriptive tool, because plant form is closely linked to the competition for light in three dimensions above ground. "Life form" refers to species characteristics of growth, often coupled with reproductive or life-span characteristics. Some examples of life forms include trees (tall, woody), shrubs, herbaceous (non-woody) perennials, herbaceous annuals, and aquatic plants. In Explorations 1 and 2, the students themselves develop some categories based on their own observations. They apply a version of the classical system (Raunkiaer's famous life-forms system) to the plant community in their field site and compare that site to plant community types around the world. Such descriptions are linked to issues of energy flow and biomass in a community or ecosystem.

The Explorations also raise questions outside the scope of this text that you or your students can pursue through field or laboratory studies. Plant physiology and community ecology (the study of interactions between and among the plants in a particular location) can be developed to only a limited extent in this course, but they provide rich opportunities for research. We mention some branching points in the Extensions.

LIVE PLANTS

We wish to emphasize that your students should have as much chance as possible to work with living plants, both in the laboratory and in the field. One approach includes learning plant identification and developing an inventory of the plants growing on a nearby site, whether woods, abandoned field, or parking area. Any such place provides opportunity for comparison with other systems and for questions about plant co-occurrence, distribution, and abundance.

PLANT FORM

Plant form is a concrete way to develop the idea of the niche and of processes of evolution. The focus of this Module is carbon and energy, and the consequences of a plant's effectiveness in gathering solar energy can be related directly to its reproductive success and, ultimately, its evolutionary fitness. Many ways of measuring plant growth and fitness rely on biomass measurements of various kinds. Since plants respond to most stimuli by altered rates of growth and reproduction, these measurements provide tools to answer many questions of plant ecology.

KEY CONCEPTS

- Light is a critical resource, and plants have evolved in their form and behavior to compete for light energy.
- Plant species are shaped by that competition, and by other selective pressures, from abiotic conditions (such as climate and soil type) to interactions with other organisms, including herbivores, pathogens, and pollinators.

- The vegetation in an area can be categorized according to the relative proportions of life forms of the species present. Those categories of forms (e.g., tall woody, low woody, herbaceous annual, herbaceous perennial) represent different evolutionary strategies: each species exploits some portion of the available resources under the limitations imposed by the climate and by competitors.

MATERIALS AND PREPARATION

- **Notebooks**
- **Pencils and pens**
- **10-meter measuring tapes** (to measure field sites)
- **Poster paper** or other large-format paper for class presentations
- **Markers**
- **Field guides** to trees and flowers (optional)
- **Plants** (vegetables from the grocery store, potted plants, pressed specimens, etc., for Exploration 3)

The sources of climate information for this activity will be various. A good place to start is a reference like the World Almanac. Weather bureaus sometimes can provide information about monthly averages for various climatic variables. An agricultural extension office may also provide such information.

Information about phenological patterns (e.g., the timing of flowering, fruiting, leaf fall) is sometimes available from botanical gardens, agricultural extension offices or laboratories, or wildflower societies. If such information is not available, the class could compile it for a few species in the area. Observations might include the date of first appearance of the species or first new leaves, date of first flower open and last flower, date of first fruit release, date leaves begin to fall, and date when last leaf is gone.

Safety

WARNING

Before your first site visit, determine whether any of your students has a strong allergic reaction to plants or insect bites or stings (especially bee stings). Take precautions as necessary.

WARNING

Preview the site before the class visit. Note possible safety issues, such as broken glass, abandoned buildings or wells, cliffs, hornet's nests, and plants such as poison ivy or poison oak.

WARNING

When students do fieldwork, they should always work in pairs at least and use the buddy system.

SUGGESTED SEQUENCE OF SESSIONS (8–9)

Homework

Reading 1: Reading the Signs introduces important ecological processes to watch for during the field trip in Session 1.

Class Session 1

Exploration 1: Describing a Plant Community: A Field Trip. The class goes to a field site, and each group observes and takes data on one section of the site. The data are of two kinds: impressions of the field site (for possible future projects) and data on the relative abundance of plants in student-constructed categories (to be used later in Exploration 3 and the Integration).

Class Session 2

Students analyze the results of the field trip. As a class, discuss some questions about how their study sections fit in with the whole site and about the ecological processes they may have seen at work there.

Homework

Reading 2: Abiotic Factors Constrain Leaf and Plant Shapes

Class Session 3

The class discusses Reading 2, which introduces links between plant physiology and plant ecology in relation to geographical distribution and the structure of plant communities (like the one seen on the field trip).

Class Sessions 4 and 5

Exploration 2: A Plant's Year in Your Part of the World. In groups, students develop descriptions of the yearly variation in several climatic variables important to plant growth. The class produces a composite of all the variables and considers the effects of climate on plant growth (and thus primary productivity) in your area.

Class Session 6

Exploration 3: Plant Forms: Patterns and Differences. Student teams group plants by criteria that make sense to them. They develop the classification scheme using their observations of plants in the field and classroom and the illustrations in this text.

Homework

Reading 3: Raunkiaer's Classification System. Students see another classification scheme—the first systematic attempt to relate plant form to plant physiology and climate.

Class Session 7

Exploration 4: Plant Life Forms around the World. Students use Raunkiaer's descriptions of plant forms for several diverse ecosystems. That helps them correlate his plant-form system with geographic factors (rainfall, temperature, and latitude) and better understand both their field site and their own plant classification system.

Class Session 8

Integration: Putting Your Field Site on the Map. The students use their (possibly revised) classification schemes to describe their study sites and build a composite description of the ecological characteristics of the whole field site. They might start the Integration as homework.

SESSION GUIDES, BY WORKSHEET

A study of ecology should include close acquaintance with some organisms, preferably on site. Nothing can substitute for that knowledge. Plants are distributed across the landscape of an ecosystem, in both horizontal and vertical patterns, reflecting both abiotic factors and the influence of the plants on each other. Current distributions represent the outcome of those processes of influence and the plants' responses to them.

Here the students lay the groundwork for several later activities on light and energy capture and also begin their introduction to plant communities. The students work in groups on different parts of the study site, to describe the vertical and horizontal arrangement of the vegetation and to count or estimate the proportions of plants with different life forms.

This field trip provides background information and initial data for the plant-form activities later in this segment (and for the second field trip in **Chapter 4**). More important, though, it provides an opportunity for students to begin observing organisms in detail and in the field.

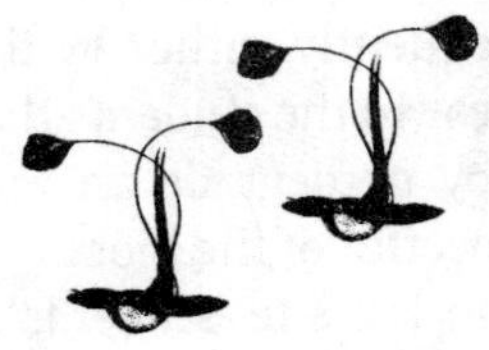

READING 1 GUIDE
Reading the Signs

This Reading introduces the basic idea of succession, in preparation for the trip to the field site. You may want to discuss it with your students; if so, assign it before the actual field trip. Help students see that the organisms in a particular place must make use of whatever resources exist there. Each organism that establishes itself there has obtained access to some share of energy, space, water, and so on. It is handy that the vertical and horizontal distributions of plants show the results of that partitioning of resources. Every change (e.g., a tree fall or a fire) might result in damage to one member of the community but provide sudden opportunity for others already there or a foothold for a wholly new organism. What you see is a snapshot, a freeze-frame of dynamic processes (which sometimes occur on a time scale different from ours).

Preview the Site

You should preview the site and plan where to direct each group. As you see from the activity, the groups should work on sections or plots that differ from each other as much as possible, to reflect the diversity of the location. Note interesting features of the flora, such as marked transition zones, unusual species, areas solely covered by a single species, and changes relating to gradients of light, water, elevation, or other recognizable features.

EXPLORATION 1 GUIDE
Describing a Plant Community: A Field Trip

Organizing the Work

Use one area for all field work. More recent or intensive human activity will require more interpretation, in that the processes of succession may be inhibited or directed by human actions, such as destruction, removal, or planting of vegetation.

Students work in small groups, each group responsible for a segment of the field area. There are various ways to do this. As you work out your preferred method, help students think about sampling techniques and other strategies for community description. Depending on the area, you might have them work on quadrates (squares) of a standard size; if the area is very accessible, each group might work on several sections within the site. During our pilot tests, we assigned groups to plots roughly 10 m by 10 m (paced off), a good general size. In our area, that size site included a few trees, some bushes, and an herb layer that was not too dense. If the herb layer is very rich in a study section, the groups might also sample 0.25 m by 0.25 m^2 plots, but that size probably would not include some growth forms, like trees.

Marking and Caring for the Field Site

Mark off the study site, using sticks and string or flags at the corners of each plot. If the area is to be visited frequently, either by the class as a whole or for small-group projects, make clear to the students that even educational and scientific activity can destroy or degrade an area, so their movements should be economical and respectful of the biota.

In looking for evidence of animals on the site, students may need a reminder that insects and other very small animals carry on their lives largely ignoring human observers. Vertebrates, however, tend to be conspicuous by their absence and detectable only indirectly—by burrows or nests, marks on vegetation, dung, fur or feathers, remains of food. We have to look sharp to detect such evidence.

Using the Data

Data collected during this field work are essential for Exploration 3 and the Integration, unless you are able to make another trip expressly for Exploration 3. Alert the students about the importance of careful notes and expressive sketches, which can be interpreted later.

Discussion

Discuss the questions at the end of Exploration 1. Student understanding may grow during the discussion. For example, they may be able to answer quickly that their study plot is not typical of the whole area. On the other hand, it might take more thought to characterize the similarities or differences. If you ask them where the carbon is—in what kinds of tissues are the largest reservoirs of carbon—they may be inclined to focus on one aspect of the plant community (e.g., trees) to the exclusion of others (e.g., the grass or herb layer). Again, asking about the evidence or rationale behind their replies can lead to deeper consideration of the question.

For example, students testing this curriculum were asked what they thought was the most important category of plant they saw in the sample area. All but one instantly named the trees. None mentioned the grass in the lawn on which they all were sitting and which covered the largest actual surface area. Yet when asked to think about what might be most important for supporting animal life, several replied, "The grass." Grass seemed more palatable to them than all the woody tissue on which they had been focusing. The system looked different, depending on their point of view.

Possible Extensions

The field work may well raise questions whose answers require more research, in the library, the laboratory, or the field. (If you would like students to carry out research projects during this ecology course, field work is a rich arena for research topics.)

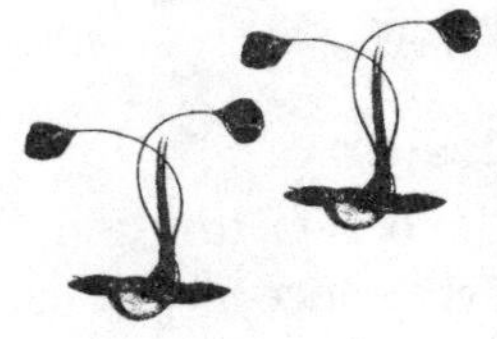

READING 2 GUIDE
Abiotic Factors Constrain Leaf and Plant Shapes

This reading introduces and considers some physiological processes that underlie the ecology of plant form and biogeography. Light as a resource is not in unlimited supply. Even when a lot of light is available, other factors (such as temperature and plant structure) may limit photosynthesis and thus primary productivity.

EXPLORATION 2 GUIDE
A Plant's Year in Your Part of the World

Students consider factors that control plant distribution by examining climate variables in their own area. The major patterns of vegetation distribution and thus the major bioregions (e.g., deserts, evergreen forests, grasslands, tundras) can be explained largely by variations in temperature, precipitation, and latitude. Although vegetation patterns are complicated on a regional or local level by factors (like topography, soil composition, and human activity), temperature, precipitation, and latitude control photosynthetic rate and transpiration and are fundamental.

Introduction and Choice of Factors

Give students an overview of the session flow. Remind them that plants, as primary producers, are the controlling biotic element in terrestrial ecosystems. Not only does the local productivity set limits on the amount of energy available to other organisms, but the kinds of plant life supported by the system have other effects on the biota. For example, animals rely on vegetation for more than food (for hiding, for dens or nests, as a place to display to potential mates, or to mark territory). The climatic conditions controlling plant life have implications for animal life as well. Ask students to consider differences between a forested area and a desert or a grassland.

Then ask them to brainstorm about factors that affect plant productivity. Eventually reduce the list to the top four or five in importance. They might include temperature, precipitation, day length, seasonal variations in insolation, and plant phenology (growth and reproductive patterns). Various factors are interrelated, but such overlap might help students see the dependencies between, say, day length and insolation.

Data Collection and Representation

Have groups of several students each study one factor. Specifically, they should describe the annual change in that factor in your area. So, month by month, what is the rainfall (day length, temperature, etc.) where you live? Let students discuss and decide on the format in which to display their information. You may need to help them consider whether their displays allow comparisons of the sort needed for this work. If students come up with representations other than graphs, you might suggest that they also try graphs for standardization so data for all the variables can be compared directly. Ease of interpretation also is important.

Data Presentation and Class Discussion

Each group presents a "year in the life of a factor" and discusses the possible effects of that factor on plant growth. Once all the data have been presented, integrate them to develop a composite picture of your area from a plant's point for view. Do the maxima for some variables coincide with the maxima or minima of others? For example, is a lot of light available at a time when a lot of water (or very little water) is available? Or is there a lot of precipitation at the coldest time of the year? How does that coincide with plant growth?

What are the times of the year in which a plant is likely to add the most new growth? When is mortality likely to be highest? Why? The aim is to understand how climatic patterns affect plant growth. In the next Exploration, students use the same reasoning to analyze and describe differences for nonlocal plant communities in annual cycles and climatic conditions.

EXPLORATION 3 GUIDE
Plant Forms: Patterns and Differences

In Exploration 1, students collected data on plant area, the life forms on their sites, and estimates of the relative abundance of each form. Now students use that information to group plants and design a scheme for classifying plant forms. They compare their scheme with a famous system and consider their classification from an ecological perspective.

The Groupings

Students group or classify plant forms for several reasons. Like any grouping work, it makes students look at the items (plants) carefully. Specifically, we ask them to think about plant organs and where growing plants allocate resources—to leaves, shoots, roots, flowers. It is important to let students brainstorm about these ideas, as long as they are making reference to actual plant materials. Are they seeing carefully? (Remember that classification for ecological purposes is not the same kind of work as systematics. It has a different aim, although the two kinds of classification clearly support each other.) Students might also come up with other criteria for their groupings; when they encounter the standard system, let them reconsider their criteria in light of ecological importance and plant survival across a year. Refer them back to the local plant's year (Exploration 2) and ask whether or how their criteria are related to a year in the life of any plant. How does allocating more energy to roots affect possible survivorship? What about flowering profusely and then dying? (Remember "big bang reproduction" from **Unit 2, Chapter 7**?)

Logistics

Have students work in the same groups as they did for Exploration 1 (the field trip) and use their data field sheets. Have some field guides, horticulture books, and other plant illustrations available, so students can see something of the great variety of plant forms. You may also want to bring or have students bring in plant samples of a wide range of shapes—a visit to a grocery store might be in order. The idea is for the groups to develop as comprehensive a classification as possible. The more actual plants, the better, of course, but good photographs or line drawings are fine. Make sure they are not all local vegetation. The Private Life of Plants, by Attenborough (see References), is a good place to start.

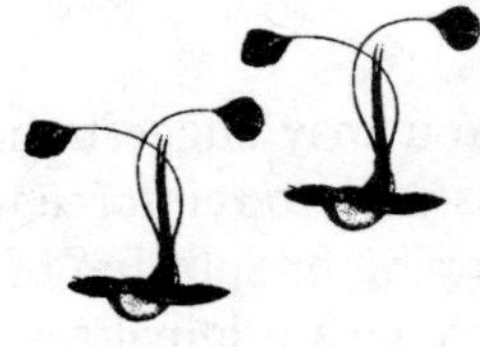

READING 3 GUIDE
Raunkiaer's Classification System

Now that the students have developed their ideas about classification, Raunkiaer's theory will help them make the link more strongly among plant form, associations of plant forms in differing proportions, and geography. It also formalizes an approach that allows us to compare different bioregions and even sites within an ecosystem.

Surviving the Hard Time

Raunkiaer's classification focuses on the parts of the plant that survive the harsh times of year, which have strong effects on a plant's energy allocation and storage. You may find it easier to discuss this topic by focusing on the life histories of flowering plants. Emphasize, if the class does not, the major events of germination, seedling growth, flowering, fruiting, and seed distribution. The timing and the amount of time in which these events take place strongly affect resource allocation and other life-history characteristics (as becomes clearer during the work).

In class, discuss Reading 3. Have each group describe its classification or grouping scheme and especially what criteria were used. Ask the groups to describe problems they encountered or questions they would like to pursue.

Different Tissues and Energy Allocation

Have the students speculate on the relative energy importance of each growth stage. One way to do that is to refer to the energy use equation, **I** = **P** + **R** (see **Unit 2**). How much energy does the plant put into **P** (up to 50%) versus **R**? (We return to this equation for plants in **Chapter 3**.) Another way to estimate allocation to different plant tissues is by actual weight. Usually dry weight is used, as we did in **Chapter 1**. What are the proportions of the weight of stems (which provide elevation), of leaves (which perform gas exchange and photosynthesis), and of roots (which anchor the plant, collect water and water-soluble nutrients, and provide energy storage in some plants)?

Almost all the dry weight of a plant is carbohydrate. Each gram of carbohydrate contains an average amount of energy (about 4.5 g, as we remember from **Unit 2**, especially **Chapter 8**). Seeds and fruits, however, often are higher in protein and fat than other plant tissues. Students may have relevant results from **Chapter 8** in **Unit 2**. (We consider carbon storage again, in the Integration and in **Unit 4: Global Carbon**.)

EXPLORATION 4 GUIDE

Plant Life Forms around the World

Bioregions have characteristic sets of plant forms, which arise in response to local conditions (as well as for historical, evolutionary reasons). Those sets, in turn, affect how the ecosystem looks and functions, and what other organisms can live there.

Raunkiaer: An Overview

Consider data from different sites. You may suggest that students refer to Figure 7, the Whittaker diagram, as well, to reinforce the climate-biogeography link. (In considering the lumping or splitting of categories, the students might like to know that Raunkiaer's original system has ten categories, but that other ecologists since then have developed systems with 70 to 200 categories!)

The Biological Spectra

Although the biological spectra here are from very different regions of the world, they do not cover all possible terrestrial bioregions. You may use them in class in two ways: (1) delegate different parts of the work, including the data representation, to groups or individuals, or (2) do some of it yourself and focus the class on discussion and analysis. The first method is likely to lead to more student involvement, while the second may save you class time, if that is an issue. In either case, make sure that students get some idea of the location and the climate of each place—tropical, temperate, or arctic? Wet or dry?

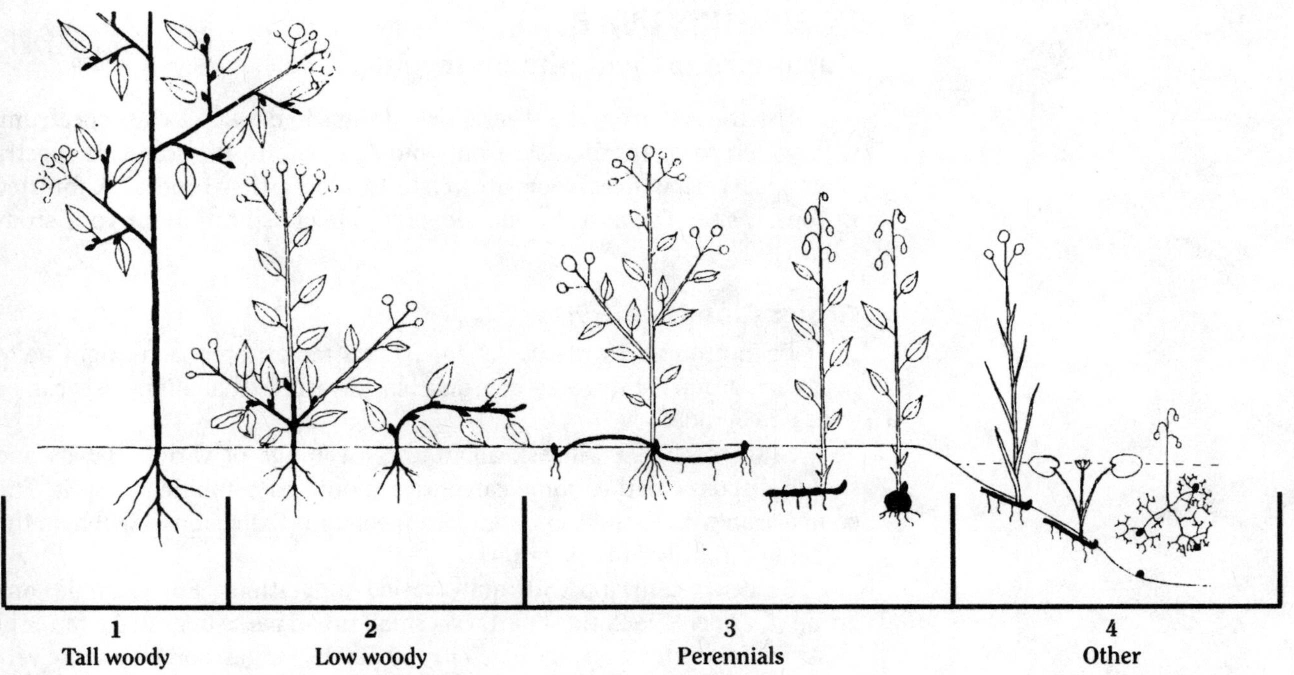

(From The Life Forms of Plants and Statistical Plant Geography by Raunkiaer, © 1934. Reprinted by permission of Oxford University Press, Oxford, UK)

Method 1: Groups present the data

Divide the class into groups and have each group work out a representation of the spectrum from one area. They should start by finding out where the place is. This whole activity should take about 10 minutes, if some students do the reference work and others work on the graph. Have each group present in turn, then proceed with the class discussion.

Method 2: You present the data

Put the spectra on the board yourself, in bar-graph form, and describe the location of the place. Ask students to discuss what the vegetation at each site might look like and why.

Class discussion of the data

Consider the general ecology of each site. Have students conjecture (for each site) where the biomass is concentrated, in general terms. Is it mostly in leaves, which turn over their carbon to the environment relatively quickly? Or is it mostly in wood, which turns over slowly? Point out that colder temperatures slow down cellular and chemical activity of all kinds (as they do digestion and animal metabolism—**Unit 2, Chapter 6**), so that turnover in both wood and leaves is slower in colder places. The abundance of water affects the richness and activity of microbial communities, which also help cycling of nutrients and energy materials. Finally, speculate with students about how to relate Raunkiaer's plant spectra and locations to the conditions of your local study site and region (Exploration 2). Do the patterns fit? What abiotic factors seem most important in your area versus Djakarta or the Seychelles?

INTEGRATION GUIDE

Putting Your Field Site on the Map

Use the data from the several field groups to develop a class spectrum, with which to relate the data from your field site to the standard spectra (Raunkiaer). How does your site relate to a desert? A tundra? A forested European site? The aim is to develop a usable classification for your study site.

Group Classification

Each group presents its scheme. The simplest approach might be to have each group list its categories on a blackboard, so that all the lists can be seen side by side.

Students likely will ask about the meanings of various labels and should discuss whether some categories should be combined or split. The comparison with Raunkiaer's standard spectrum (Extension 1) will help the students think about their criteria.

Students come up with quite varied suggestions. For example, one group of students looking at parts of a small urban park suggested a range of classification schemes, some explicitly by height ranges, some by some version of vegetation type: tree, shrub, bush, evergreen, little leafy things, grass-type things.

Patterns of Carbon Allocation

Once the classification is done, consider patterns of allocation and biomass (although that work may already have been done as part of the criteria for the classification. If so, skip ahead.) That is, where does each kind of plant allocate new growth? What parts are discarded every year (e.g., the leaves of deciduous trees, flowers, and fruits), every few years (e.g., needles on a conifer), or much more often (e.g., root hairs, nectar)?

Consider how these patterns relate to biomass distribution. If 10% of the species in an area are large woody plants, and 90% are herbs, does that mean that 90% of the area's biomass is in herbs? What does the biological spectrum not tell us about carbon and energy reservoirs in the vegetation of a system? How would we go about getting that kind of information? (See also Extension 2.)

Finally, relate this back to students' work on carbon and energy content. What are the energy and carbon contents of such materials? Which are relatively costly (assuming that each gram costs not only the raw materials, but 1.2–2 times more in metabolic costs)?

Now you have a composite scheme, based on the students' work and the standard classification schemes. Write it down so everyone has it and can use it for other research.

INTEGRATION
Putting Your Field Site on the Map

You have seen ways to compare the climates of different areas. You have developed a classification scheme for the vegetation you are acquainted with. How can you combine the two to compare patterns in different parts of the world—to compare your study plot with a study plot in, say, Denmark or Africa?

Materials

- **Field notes** from Exploration 1
- **Notes** from Exploration 3, step 4
- **Raunkiaer's system** (Reading 3)
- **Reference materials**

Procedure

1. **Relate your grouping or classification scheme to Raunkiaer's.**
In your field groups, review your notes about plant types on the field site. Relate your classification of vegetation types on your study site to the four Raunkiaer categories, as described in Reading 3. You may have to look up or guess for some plants. (Later, more field work might allow you to check your decisions.) For now you are doing two things: relating a large-scale scheme to your actual, local site, and in doing so, constructing a scheme for the vegetation types of your area, with an accompanying set of ecological factors.
2. **Represent your results.**
First, put your results into a table, something like this:

LOCATION	TALL WOODY	LOW WOODY	PERENNIAL HERB	ANNUAL HERB
Plot #1	20%	25%	45%	10%

Then put the results into a bar graph, like this one:

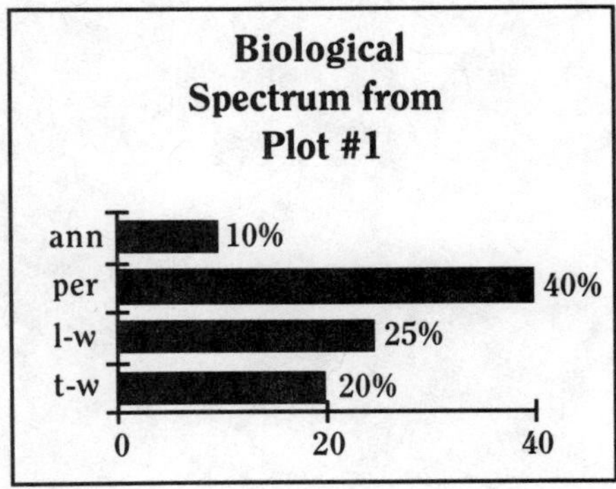

3. **Prepare for class discussion.**
When you have finished graphing your data set, compare yours to those of the rest of the class. Discuss with your group any changes you would like to make in your scheme.

4. **Present your scheme to the class.**
In addition to displaying your graphics, describe how you came to the system you did, what criteria or groupings you decided not to use, and the reasons for your decisions.

5. **All-class discussion.**
What are some differences among the groups' classification schemes? Do any of them match Raunkiaer's system? Are there ways in which the systems developed by class members are better suited than Raunkiaer's for describing your field area?

Can you combine the group systems to produce a classification of plant form that will describe all the plant forms and the importance of each in the whole study area that your class used for Exploration 1?

And a final challenge to your system: do you think this system would apply to other sites anywhere in your area? How could you test it?

EXTENSION 1
The "Standard Spectrum"

Raunkiaer called his graphs of composition by plant form a "biological spectrum." He considered that the graphs would be more meaningful if compared to a standard of some kind, so he constructed a "standard spectrum" based on the flora of the whole world. He was able to do this because the Royal Gardens at Kew, England, maintains a standard list of all plant species identified everywhere on earth, the Index Kewensis (whose first version was made possible by a bequest from Charles Darwin).

Raunkiaer took a large sample (about 1,000 species) from that Index, being careful to avoid biases in his choices. For example, some families of plants have many species, most of which belong to one life form or are concentrated in certain locations, so Raunkiaer made sure his choices were as random as possible in terms of both geography and taxonomy. He then used that sample to prepare a "standard spectrum," a kind of null hypothesis about the spectrum you might expect to find in a place. If you find that an area is very different in its spectrum from Raunkiaer's standard, you can then begin to consider possible ecological explanations. For example, a sample taken in a desert or an actively managed recreation area might deviate from the standard spectrum in striking ways.

Here is Raunkiaer's standard spectrum:

TALL WOODY	LOW WOODY	PERENNIAL HERB	ANNUAL HERB	OTHER
33%	30%	15%	16%	6%

You can use this spectrum to discuss with the class how their field site—and your region generally—relates to the rest of the world. Ask questions like the following:

How do your samples differ from the standard?

How do the other vegetation spectra differ from this standard?

How does having this standard throw light on the spectrum of a particular area?

EXTENSION 2
Site Inventory

Site inventory enables us to compare the plant community of any study site (e.g., your own) with other communities anywhere. In addition, it provides a baseline for a study of change over time on that site. Changes in the plant community (e.g., in the relative proportions of various species) can be related to changes in human use of the area, in weather from one year to another, or in the animal populations (including invertebrates) on the site. Use the **Technique: Describing and Comparing Communities**.

VARIATION WITHIN SPECIES

One feature of plants that can be bewildering is the great individual variation within and between populations of a single species. Change in size with age is a familiar notion, but the extremes of plant phenotypes under various nutrient, light, or water regimes is not. Simple laboratory experiments which grow the same species under specific, different conditions can bring this point home. The evolutionary consequences (i.e., the effects on reproductive success) can be considered if the experiments are carried on to the fruiting stage. Alternatively, wild populations can be used to make the same point.

Procedure

1. **Choose a species.**
Select some species that seem quite widespread, occur on sites that seem rather different from each other, have easily recognizable fruits, and have seeds that are not extremely small. In fall, some of the Rosaceae—even apples—may be accessible. Some legumes, such as lupine, false indigo *(Baptisia)*, and tick-trefoils *(Desmodium)*, can be worked with. Other widespread species are jewelweed *(Impatiens)*, dandelion *(Taraxacum)*, and various mustards.

2. **Find populations.**
Identify populations in different environments, ideally along a gradient of some variable, such as moisture or soil type. For example, if the plant is abundant in moist places, identify populations in wet areas, medium-wet areas, occasionally moist areas, and dry areas, or at regular increments of distance away from the wettest zone. A light gradient (transition from shade to full sun) is also interesting. And gradients of disturbance can be good to study. For instance, consider foot traffic (plants growing on a path, on its margin, 10 cm away from the deepest wear, a meter away). Another common setting is lawns or other mown places.

3. **Sampling.**
Identify within each population a sample, perhaps ten to fifty individuals, chosen randomly or at least not systematically. Take growth data for those individuals. Leaf area, height, number of flowers or fruits, and internode length can be useful. Unless the fruits or seeds are very small, you can measure fruit weight per plant and seed weight per plant. Calculate average, maximum, and minimum values, as well as the variance from the mean. All these parameters reflect plant allocation of available resources. The same characteristics can be used to measure the growth rates and patterns of growth allocation of laboratory plants.

4. **Check variation with laboratory growth results.**
Seeds collected from plants of the same species growing in different conditions can be grown in the laboratory under identical conditions and the growth of the plants compared. Are the differences in size or number of seeds produced the result of the different growing conditions alone, or are the plants in each site closely adapted to the conditions there? In the latter case, seeds from two very different sites, if grown under identical conditions, should show characteristic differences that are likely to be hereditary.

If the class carefully keeps track of its data and plant materials, this study could be continued annually by successive classes. A photographic record would be valuable.

SCIENCE BACKGROUND
Combating "Organism Ignorance"

Unfamiliarity with organisms of many kinds is a "critical barrier" that students have to overcome if they are to develop better ecological intuition. Most young people have had experience with relatively few animals and even fewer plants, and usually in more or less artificial settings.

Groups and Other Resources

One way to enhance students' learning in ecology is to exploit any knowledge anyone in the class may have along those lines. Some may have gardened, some may be birdwatchers, some may come from agricultural backgrounds, some may have wilderness experience. Observations of pets, houseplants, and the denizens of vegetable stands and grocery stores may be helpful; zoos, greenhouses, and botanical gardens are all of value as well. In short, anything you can do to enhance students' observations and contact time with specific organisms is of potential value.

You can also do this with specific assignments. For example, each student can select an area on the school grounds, a nearby park, or segment of a path to visit on a regular basis (daily if possible but at least weekly) and record their observations. Any variation on this theme is useful. It is fun and valuable if the students have some opportunity to report on the changes they observe in their sites, in an oral report to the class, on a bulletin board, or by some other display.

TAXONOMY: WHEN IS THE RIGHT TIME?

One of the bugbears of doing community ecology is species identification. Exploration 1 does not require taxonomic identification, but it may show why some deeper questions require thinking in terms of known species; this is a motivator for learning taxonomy. You probably have your own way of approaching this skill. We suggest having members of the class become experts on some segment of the flora to make the work more efficient and also encourage students to become "experts" on the biology and ecology of specific plants. (Remember in **Unit 2** that each student "becomes" an animal in **Chapter 4**, then refers back to those animals throughout the Unit.) If you are going to do much field work as a class, probably everyone should learn the dominant and characteristic species of your field area.

TREES OR NOT?

This material is written with tree-dominated systems in mind, for a couple of reasons. Forest systems are widespread on this continent, and in many urban settings the artificial landscape uses trees as the scaffolding on which to arrange the rest of the vegetation. For that reason, many tree species are widespread far beyond their natural range. Thus, species from the Northern Hardwood Forest can be found on city streets across the country.

Second, the study of succession and vegetation structure is perhaps most straightforwardly illustrated by systems that become forest, developing a structure with a canopy some meters above the ground and other layers lower down. The productivity increases as the total area of the leaves over any square meter increases.

Such processes are evident in every kind of plant community, but the scale and separation of the various elements of the canopy and understory are smaller, and they are harder to see than in the forest.

RELEVANT CONCEPTS

Succession

The concept of succession is not described in much detail in the student materials. If the students are interested, direct them to more detailed descriptions, such as that found in A Peterson Field Guide to Eastern Forests, by John Kricher and Gordon Morrison.

If there is a recent construction area nearby, some students might be interested in initiating a study of succession on the site. This kind of study can be passed on to succeeding classes; if the species are identified and mapped with some care, the work might be of professional interest. Almost any situation in which a resource becomes newly available will provide an opportunity to study some kind of succession.

Patchiness

The study of patchiness and dynamics within patches is currently of great ecological interest. The response of a plant community to the creation of a new patch, for example, by the fall of a tree, depends in subtle ways on the size of the patch (both the area opened at ground level and the area opened in the canopy) and many related variables.

Land-Use History

Some students may be interested in exploring the history of land use in your study site or some other area known to them, with reference to the vegetation structure, the presence of alien species, and so on.

Plant Forms

In conjunction with field observations, the students' comprehension of the variety of plant forms and growth would be enhanced greatly by growing plants of several kinds in the laboratory (or on the windowsill). They might grow things from several families, such as grasses, mints, gourds, sweet potatoes, or legumes. If they do this, the plants could provide a context within which students can practice calculating leaf area index and also learn other measurable plant-growth parameters.

REFERENCES

(See the references at the end of **Chapter 1** as well.)

Attenborough, David. 1995. The Private Life of Plants. Princeton, NJ: Princeton University Press.

Crawley, Michael J. (ed.) 1986. Plant Ecology. New York: Blackwell Publications.

Durrell, Lee. 1986. State of the Ark: An Atlas of Conservation in Action. New York: Doubleday.

Kricher, John, and Gordon Morrison. 1988. A Peterson Field Guide to Eastern Forests. Boston: Houghton Mifflin.

Meyers, Norman (ed.) 1984. Gaia: An Atlas of Planet Management. Garden City, NY: Anchor Books.

Vessel, Matthew F., and Herbert H. Wong. 1987. Natural History of Vacant Lots. Berkeley: University of California Press.

ENERGY ALLOCATION IN PLANTS

CHAPTER THREE

CONTENTS

INTRODUCTION

Plants, like animals, must allocate the energy that is available to them for growth, maintenance, and reproduction. Their energy use equation is different from that of animals, since they gather energy by photosynthesis rather than heterotrophy. Their sessile (stationary) nature enforces different patterns of energy use as well, such as using growth as a "foraging" technique (for sunlight) and (in some cases) the ability to self-prune to respond to limited resources. The modular nature of plants makes developmental plasticity possible throughout the plant's life. Individuals of the same species can differ markedly in physical, metabolic, and genetic ways;

even different parts of the same individual may show this kind of variation. Thus, the plant, especially a tree, can be seen as a community.

This flexibility is reflected in the possible patterns of allocation of energy and materials and in the interactions between energy trade-offs and reproduction and survival.

KEY CONCEPTS

- Like other organisms, plants have an energy budget. They take in a limited amount of energy and must allocate portions of that energy to their various vital functions.
- As with other organisms, the energy is contained in organic molecules. Because all plant organs and structural tissues are built of carbohydrates of various kinds, the equivalence between energy content and carbon content is straightforward.
- Like other organisms, plants use a proportion of their energy intake for respiration, a proportion for the addition of new tissue, and a proportion for reproduction.
- The measurement of biomass is used for the analysis of many questions in plant ecology; it can be augmented by additional studies, such as the biomass of particular organs of the plants in question (e.g., stem vs. leaf vs. root) or the comparison of plants of different species (e.g., annuals vs. perennials) or plants of the same species grown under different conditions.

MATERIALS AND PREPARATION

In Advance

The activities in this chapter require the raising of bean plants as experimental subjects. Start the plants about a month ahead of time; you will need at least five plants per student group, plus a few extra, just in case. (You can use the growing and preparation of the plants as an experimental procedure in itself.) See Exploration 1 Guide for details.

After Exploration 1, the plant specimens should be weighed (wet), then dried for use in Exploration 2.

Materials

- **Hand lenses**
- **Scales** (to 0.1 or 0.01 g)
- **Notebooks**
- **Technique: Carbonometry** and **Technique: Calorimetry**
- **Reference materials** describing the life strategies of various species, especially beans (used in Exploration 2)

SUGGESTED SEQUENCE OF SESSIONS (5–8)

Homework

Case Study Guide: What Is an Individual? introduces the idea of a plant as a population of partially integrated modules. That idea helps make sense of the plant's allocation of resources under various conditions to various organs—leaf, stem, root, fruit.

Class Session 1

Discuss the case study.

In Exploration 1: Allocation to Root and Shoot, students describe and measure individual plants to determine their allocation of energy (in biomass) to various organs.

Homework

Reading 1: Making a Living—Plant Life-History Strategies.

Class Session 2

Class discussion of Reading 1 and how plants' plasticity or flexibility is limited by their evolutionary history.

Class Session 3

In Exploration 2: Energy and Carbon Content of Plant Organs, students build on Exploration 1, using carbonometry and calorimetry to verify their predictions of the energy and carbon content of various portions of individual plants. They weigh and measure dried specimens and divide them into root, shoot, and (if present) reproductive parts.

Class Session 4

Calculate average allocation to each type of tissue and estimate from biomass the energy content in each portion.

Discuss the meaning of those averaged data (Optional Reading), and how most usefully to use them (e.g., ignore wildly different individuals?).

Class Session 5

Continue Session 4. Test estimates from that session of energy (and, optionally, carbon) content in samples.

Homework

Assign Reading 2: Costs of Reproduction.

Class Session 6

Discuss energy allocation as a zero-sum game: giving more energy to one function leaves less for other functions. Plants, like all organisms, must trade off reproduction against survival or other kinds of growth.

Class Session 7

Integration: The Plant Energy Equation. Like other organisms, plants have energy budgets, but they are somewhat different from those of animals. The students use their accumulated information to outline a plant's balanced energy use equation.

SESSION GUIDES, BY WORKSHEET

CASE STUDY GUIDE
What Is an Individual?

This Case Study raises issues of plant allocation of resources in a novel context. For many species, it is not at all easy to define an "individual." Allocation to various portions of even a genetic individual might best be explained in terms of competition between the various modules of the plant. A plant is organized quite differently from an animal!

Our view of plants is largely shaped by the "domesticated" plants we see—marigolds in pots, corn planted in rows in a garden, or bunches of individual beets in the produce section of the grocery store. When we grow plants in school or in a window box, we think of "one seed, one plant."

But from a biological point of view (and certainly from an ecological point of view) that is far from being the "normal" situation. When we look at a forest of hundreds of tree trunks or a field with millions of stalks of grass and stems of clover, we actually may be seeing just a few individuals. When we look at a potted plant on the windowsill, in many ways we actually are looking at a population of organisms that both cooperate and compete for space and that may differ from each other in shape, size, color, physiology, and even genetically.

Class Discussion

Ask students to name modular or colonial organisms, plant or others (corals, algae, slime molds, and many less well known sea invertebrates, such as bryozoans, sponges, hydrozoans, sea anemones). You might want some reference books with pictures.

What advantages might there be for modularity? If part of the whole is separated, it may establish itself as a separate organism and continue living. Conversely, if some part dies, the remainder may survive quite well.

Because modules might differ genetically, the whole may be suited to a broader range of conditions than is an single module. So if selection changes, some parts might still survive. The "offspring" might also be more genetically diverse and so able to survive under a broader range of conditions.

What are potential drawbacks to modular or colonial living? They might include competition between modules for nutrients, gases, sun, whatever. If part of the whole becomes infected or infested, the whole is at risk.

Ask students to compare such a lifestyle with that of a single organism. If a raccoon loses its paw, can it generate a new one? Or a moth a new wing? Can vertebrates reproduce by cloning? (No.) Can vertebrates separate reproduction from sex, or meiosis from sex? (No.)

Social insects (ants, termites, and some bees and wasps) have been compared to modular organisms and to superorganisms: different individuals do different "work," which together adds up to all the tasks performed by an individual cat, crane, crayfish, or cranefly. Some gather food, some protect the colony, some reproduce, some care for the young. Benefits and drawbacks are as above: the whole colony can continue if part is lost; a part might or might not be able to continue without the colony.

Note that modularity is not restricted to sessile (stationary) organisms. Some sea invertebrate colonies are mobile, and certainly individual social insects are mobile. The combination of modularity and mobility slightly alters the costs and advantages of modularity. But on the whole, modularity is a lifestyle restricted to non-vertebrates.

Overall, it, like all strategies, has costs and benefits; it is not better or worse than other strategies, just different.

EXPLORATION 1 GUIDE
Allocation to Root and Shoot

Students look at, then measure, how a plant can allocate its resources, especially the fixed carbon produced from photosynthesis.

If you start with plants raised expressly for this laboratory, build some comparison into your plantings. That is, choose seeds to provide some realistic contrast that might be expected to have an effect on the biomass of the crop. "Might be expected" is the key phrase here, because some factors seem to have little effect on biomass or affect them in unexpected ways. So if you do raise a crop for this experiment, make sure you and your students make predictions of expected results—and why you might have those expectations—before you collect your data.

For example, compare biomass with energy and carbon content of plants planted at various densities. That setup models agricultural settings in which we find that individual plant size varies inversely with density of planting, but total biomass (and therefore total energy fixed) remains relatively constant.

A few more ideas follow.

No Contrasts

Do not build in any contrasts. Use the Exploration to measure biomass and energy allocation to different plant parts, in preparation for Exploration 2 and for any experiments of the class's design.

Same Species, Different Densities

Plant the same species but at different densities. For example, plant only ryegrass or only sunflower seeds, but in one series of pots, plant the seeds at a rate of five per pot, in another series, fifteen per pot, in another, fifty per pot. It is not at all clear what to expect from this, so encourage the students to conjecture widely, as long as they can argue for their predictions.

Some plant ecologists have suggested that for monoculture (same species) stands there is a "law of constant yield." That is, within a wide range of densities, a given area of land will yield a fairly constant biomass. Plants more densely packed will each be smaller than plants in less crowded plots, but their total biomass will be about the same. This "law" has been shown in some experimental and agricultural settings, but it has not been conclusively demonstrated with wild populations.

Density differences provide excellent opportunities for looking at contrasting patterns of allocation within individuals. Will more crowding result in more stem, more root, more leaf? No change? Such work provides a basis for experiments related to intraspecific competition.

Different Species, Same Densities

Plant different species at the same densities, to compare different plant types and their tissue allocations under fixed conditions. Good, quick-germinating species to contrast include ryegrass, lettuce, radish, sunflower, bean, and pea.

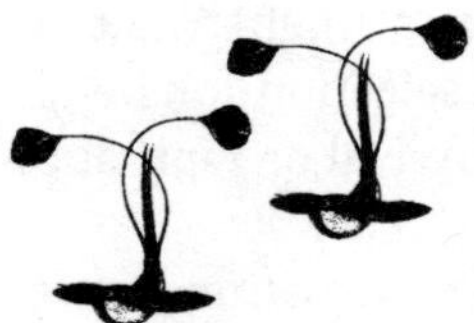

READING 1 GUIDE
Making a Living—Plant Life-History Strategies

A life-history strategy is the suite of characteristics or attributes any organism has evolved over time (its size, shape, energy source, genetic makeup, reproductive style, etc.) and how those characteristics express themselves. The characteristics and their expression might be under conflicting selective pressures. So a plant may suffer competition for light (which is potential selective pressure to be taller) but be constrained by low water availability in its habitat (another potential selective pressure).

Producing many offspring may seem evolutionarily advantageous. But perhaps the cost of producing those offspring is so high that the female uses up all her reserves or dies (remember **Unit 2**, **Chapter 7**?). Or perhaps each offspring is smaller, and itself has a lower probability of surviving. So starting with a large number of weaker offspring may not be more successful than starting with fewer, stronger offspring.

It is easy to fall into adaptationist thinking, as well. That is, not every characteristic has an advantage (or a disadvantage). Some just are. In a famous paper two evolutionary biologists (Gould and Lewontin) point out that people (researchers as well as the general student) can get carried away with the idea that everything is for the "adaptationist best." One example they use is the chin, pointing out that a chin is just the byproduct of the growth of jaws and the mouth. So despite selection, some traits just "are."

Students may be reminded of the balances they saw among traits in animals (**Unit 2**). Being either an endotherm or ectotherm is not better or worse than the other: the two are just different. And each is associated with a different set of accompanying traits (size, diet, etc.). The same applies to plants. Different species have different sets of traits, which add up to different life-history strategies.

Because reproductive success will make such individuals more numerous in a population (**Chapter 7**, Integration), traits that enhance reproductive success will, all else being equal, be selected for. But all else is rarely equal. The environment and other organisms change constantly. What was successful before may be irrelevant now. Remember the finches in **Module 1**?

EXPLORATION 2 GUIDE
Energy and Carbon Content of Plant Organs

Students' results will vary depending on whether they examine one or more species. If they study one species, have them consider the following: at the current age, into which type of tissue do the plants put most of their energy? Might that change as the plants mature and develop? Read with students or let them read about the study species and other species as dissimilar and as similar as possible. How does tissue allocation vary with plant life history? Refer them to their work in **Chapter 2** with Raunkiaer's classification system.

If only one species is studied, also consider variation among individuals. How much variation is there? What might it show (selection by humans or by nature)? Is it biologically meaningful, that is, if one plant is 10% taller than the others, does that matter to either the tall plant or the other individuals? (A farmer interested in taller grass might want to breed taller plants with each other, exerting artificial selection for height. Or a taller individual may be no more successful at survival or reproduction—the difference may be meaningless.)

If several species are studied, consider variation between species in tissue allocation. How does it fit the species' life-history strategy? You likely planted all annuals, so there may not be much difference, but again, refer to Raunkiaer. How do tulips and potatoes allocate their biomass compared to daisies and beans (below ground, above ground)? Which species are annuals and which are perennials?

Finally, sampling issues are always interesting. Do student groups differ in their techniques? Do their results differ also? Why are standardization and adequate sample sizes important?

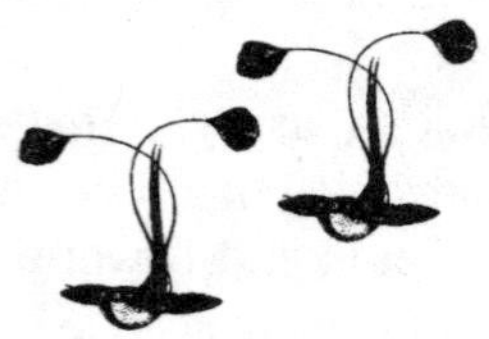

Optional READING GUIDE
Averages

Consider with students how their data represent their plants. What about individuals that vary markedly from others? Should those be included in the averages? What if they are excluded?—the sample is diminished but perhaps more representative.

Help students see that highly non-average plants (traits, whatever) actually raise interesting questions. They are not "mistakes" to be ignored or eliminated. They, too, tell us something, even if it is something other than what we expected.

OPTIONAL READING

AVERAGES

In **Module 1**, we talk a lot about "average" values for seed crackability; in other Units, we also use average values. When we are looking at data that represent many values of a biological variable, the way we handle the data may tell us a lot, but it also may hide a lot of information crucial to the biology we are interested in. It is worth spending a few minutes recalling what an "average value" does and does not tell us.

WHAT IS AN AVERAGE?

First, remember that usually when people say "average" they are referring to the **mean**. As we recall, to calculate the average, or mean, we add all the values in a dataset, and then divide that number by the number of values. For example, here is a dataset of ten annual incomes of people on a (hypothetical) city block.

1. $8,500
2. $15,500
3. $16,500
4. $16,500
5. $25,000
6. $26,000
7. $27,000
8. $35,000
9. $39,000
10. $100,000

The sum of those incomes is $309,000. The mean is $309,000 / 10 = $30,900.

Now, what does this tell us? Well, if all ten people had to divide up $309,000 so that they all had identical incomes, the even-size pieces would be $30,900. That is informative—if I tell you my town has a per capita income of $10,000, and your town has a per capita income of $20,000, you can conclude that your town has more money coming in per person than mine does. But a lot of interesting information is not shown. The next step, then, is to take the mean and use it as a point of comparison to look at the individual data, and how they relate to the mean and to each other.

POINT OF COMPARISON

Of the ten incomes, seven are less than the mean and three are more—the mean is not any of the actual values. The three higher values give the impression that most people in the sample make a lot more than is the case. To get some sense of the effect that an unusually high or low value can have, we can recalculate the mean using all but one of the extremes. For example, if we do just a mean of nine incomes, leaving aside #10, we get a mean of $209,000 / 9 = $23,222—much closer to the majority of actual values. To get some sense of this, compare the mean to the most common value—$16,500—and to the **median**, the value at which equal numbers of people are above or below. In this case, the median must lie between #5 and #6; in such cases, take the mean of the two values between which the median lies: ($25,000 + $26,000) / 2 = $25,500. The mean value for 1–9 ($23,222) is much closer to the median, or middle value ($25,500), than is the mean for 1–10 ($30,900).

Thus, the mean gives an initial feeling for the values that the variable can take, but the actual values that make up the mean can vary widely. There are many other ways of analyzing the data that may help us understand more about the situation we are actually measuring. In the case of the incomes, you can say that one person earns a lot more than all the rest; that almost all people earn below $40,000; and that a majority actually earn below the mean income. This is not a particularly wealthy group, even though the mean income seems like a solid middle-class amount.

In the same way, when we look at "average plant biomass" or height, we may see a number calculated from plants with wide-ranging biomasses or heights. It is only when we look at the actual data that we can see the likelihood of finding a plant of a particular size. The average is a good way to start a comparison of one set of seeds with another, but the analysis does not end there.

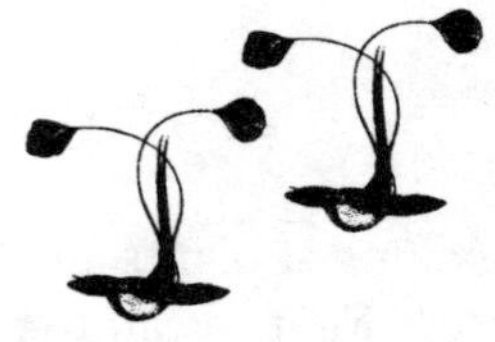

READING 2 GUIDE

Costs of Reproduction

Discuss with students the similarities and differences between plants and animals vis à vis reproduction. Reproduction is energetically costly for all organisms; it requires moisture and involves meiosis. But plants, unlike animals, lose and regrow their reproductive organs seasonally. Mobile organisms can find mates directly; plants, however, depend on flowers, bees, or flies, sharing displays, giving away energy (e.g., nectar), and other tricks to get their "sperm" and "eggs" together. If plants had feet, they might not have flowers.

INTEGRATION GUIDE

The Plant Energy Equation

Students reflect on both the plant and solar capture models they made earlier in the Unit. Now they make a flowchart that tracks the solar energy that strikes a plant over some period of time.

The energy use equation we used for animals (**Unit 2**) will not work here. Differences between plants and animals can be discussed either as preparation for or after the Integration. Such discussion may seem simple-minded, but in fact it is returning to first principles. It makes clear differences in the ecology of energy between animals and plants. This is in contrast to their deep similarities at the molecular level, which are perhaps more emphasized in basic biology classes than are ecological differences.

The students should also bear in mind that energy allocation is a zero-sum game—energy allocated to one function is unavailable to another.

The plant situation is complicated by the fact that different tissues respire at different rates. That is true in animals as well, but in plants the proportion of the whole that is made up of fast-respiring new leaves, for example, varies over the course of a season and over the life of the plant. That variation often is the result of the plant's response to the environment, to damage to tissues, or to herbivory.

The energy use equation for plants, therefore, is quite general and looks something like this:

insolation = sunlight fixed + sunlight shed
shed sunlight → transpiration + reflection
fixed sunlight → tissue + respiration
(**P**roduction + **R**espiration)
tissue → all types: structural, photosynthetic, root, reproductive

Ten percent of sunlight fixed is an average for the growing season; an annual average is more like 1–3%.

Transpiration is not the same as reflection. The transpiration stream is important functionally to the plant, providing a major element in circulation and also in heat regulation.

Each of these elements varies with plant size and species, temperature and other weather conditions, soil characteristics, and other factors.

INTEGRATION
The Plant Energy Equation

All through this Unit, you have been looking at plants and their use of energy. Now take stock of what you have seen. First, recall the energy use equation used for the animals in **Unit 2**: **I**ntake = **A**bsorption + **E**xcretion and its variant forms.

How might that equation look for plants? What happens to the energy that strikes a plant growing in a pot on your windowsill or in the middle of the rain forest?

Describe what you know about a plant's energy budget. Assume that a plant ends up fixing about 10% of the energy that strikes it over the course of a particular period of time.

You may want to make a flowchart first, describing just the various pathways that energy will take once it reaches a plant. Once you have done that, suggest what proportion of the light will follow each path.

Based on your work in this Unit so far, how would you go about testing your ideas?

REFERENCES

Gould, S. J., and R. C. Lewontin. 1979. The Spandrels of San Marco and the Panglossian Paradigm: A Critique of the Adaptationist Programme. Proceedings of the Royal Society of London, B 205, pages 581–598. Printed in Great Britain.

ABOVE-GROUND BIOMASS
MEASURING PRODUCTIVITY

CHAPTER FOUR

CONTENTS

INTRODUCTION

Energy flow at the level of ecosystem biomass, as a measure of primary productivity, integrates many consistent characteristics of a system over time. It allows us to describe an ecosystem, to compare ecosystems, and to draw generalizations about patterns of energy flow at the system level (e.g., productivity of a desert or a wheat field). In addition, as we have seen, plants respond to most environmental changes by a change in growth rate or energy allocation. Thus, any experiments on plant competition, response to environmental variables, or energy flow rates (flux) rely on biomass as a crucial outcome indicator.

Here we explore the biological side of energy capture. The class sequence allows for further discussion of energy capture in the ecosystem and an initial harvest of the plants that students are growing in the Extension. For students unable to do fieldwork, this harvest is the main activity for Exploration 2. In the field or laboratory, students confront the same concepts about plant biomass, productivity, and energy flow through a system (see also **Unit 2**).

KEY CONCEPTS

- Primary productivity is the rate at which solar energy is converted to plant tissue. It is a key descriptor of ecosystems, because all other organisms depend on it.
- The rate at which primary productivity is respired as CO_2 by the organisms at all trophic levels is also characteristic of an ecosystem, since it is a function of the interaction between the primary productivity (the rate of photosynthesis) by plants and the rate of consumption (secondary productivity) of other organisms.
- Net primary productivity (NPP) is the net rate of increase in organic matter in plants, calculated by subtracting the organic matter used in respiration from gross primary productivity (GPP).
- Biomass is the amount of dry matter that comprises living and dead organisms in a system. It represents the total available energy in the system. In terrestrial systems, plants account for the vast bulk (sometimes up to 98%). Therefore, biomass and its dynamics describe the energy interactions among and between abiotic and biotic components of a system.

MATERIALS AND PREPARATION

- **30-m tape measure**
- **5-m cloth measuring tape**, in cm
- **Meter stick**
- **Tent stake** or other markers
- **Homemade clinometer**

Safety

WARNING

Before your class goes on a field trip, determine whether any of your students has a strong allergic reaction to plants or insect bites or stings (especially bee stings). Take precautions as necessary.

WARNING

Visit the field site before the class outing. Note possible safety hazards, such as piles of broken glass, abandoned buildings or wells, cliffs, hornets' nests, and plants such as poison ivy or poison oak.

WARNING
When students do fieldwork, they should always work in pairs at least and use the buddy system.

SUGGESTED SEQUENCE OF SESSIONS (5–6)

Homework

Case Study: Plants as Prey: Why Is the World Still Green? The Case Study introduces the question of plants as prey and their mechanisms of self-defense. An important conceptual point is that "animals" do not eat "plants." Rather, an animal can make use only of some portion of some plants, and that portion can vary in its availability.

Class Session 1

Exploration 1: Old MacGregor's Farm is a thought experiment, to be done in class. It draws together many notions students have considered before about allocation, efficiency of energy use, and food chains.

Homework

Reading: How Do You Weigh a Tree? describes the rationale behind and the basic approach to the field activity in Exploration 2.

Class Sessions 2 and 3

Students estimate how much energy is available on your study site (which may be a city park or a wooded area) in Exploration 2: Above-Ground Biomass in the Field.

Class Session 4

Exploration 3: Above-Ground Biomass: The Data and the Calculations. Students calculate the volume and then, using their field data, the biomass of trees on their site. Each group uses its biomass data to predict the biomass in a hectare of similar composition. Most habitats are somewhat heterogeneous, so there should be substantial differences in their predictions. (Such differences engage the class in a consideration of sampling and serve as preparation for **Unit 4: Global Carbon**.)

Students are also encouraged to brainstorm ideas for possible follow-up studies at the field site.

Class Session 5

Integration: Forest and Savannah. After individual homework, students have a class discussion using and applying all the concepts raised in this Chapter. They examine our two model ecosystems from the point of view of primary productivity, as the fundamental process that enables all other processes.

SESSION GUIDES, BY WORKSHEET

CASE STUDY GUIDE
Plants as Prey: Why Is the World Still Green?

This Case Study focuses on plants as prey, because the obvious greenness of the world is not questioned most of the time. Why is there so little herbivory, relatively speaking? Why is animal biomass such a trivial element in most terrestrial ecosystems?

This section also raises the issue of the partitioning of resources. Competition—the "arms race" between herbivores and plant defenses– has resulted in the evolution of a vast range of specialist herbivores. Insects are the most important herbivores, and their adaptations to specific food plants or specific plant parts are a vivid illustration of the results of natural selection. The result is that, to an animal, most of the vegetation covering the landscape is not relevant as food, although it may serve other vital functions, for example, as shelter or nesting. That means the process of energy capture for most animals is complex and chancy. Thinking about this on the scale of an insect that can make use of only one species of plant (or one per life stage) shows that by partitioning the light and soil resources plants have made life complicated for other organisms.

(You may want to refer back to the **Evolution Module** and the evolutionary processes described there, which are similar. Students may or may not see the similarity at first, since this section is about insects, not finches, in the process of natural selection, but this is an important chance to point out similarities.)

If weather permits, you may want to assign an observation task to your students, either as part of a laboratory or as homework. Have them examine a few individual plants to see the insects living on them and note where the insects occur on the plant. Do they move between plants? Between individuals of the same or different species? Are they feeding? Do they stay only on leaves, or only on stems or flowers? What do they seem to be doing?

EXPLORATION 1 GUIDE
Old MacGregor's Farm

Old MacGregor's Farm uses Fermi calculations—order-of-magnitude estimates—to study implications of variations in primary productivity for a system. Help students understand that on an ecosystem scale, especially at the global level, ecological measurements of movements of nutrients or energy can never be precise. The right order of magnitude is usually the best we can hope for. (We reconsider that subject in **Unit 4**.)

At every stage of transfer, there can also be variation and inefficiencies that exceed the amounts of transfer. Thus, a transfer of 8% results from an inefficiency of about 90%, over ten times the transfer. In discussing this Exploration with the class, you may want to point out some of the assumptions that lie behind its wording.

Answers and Assumptions

How much grain does Farmer MacGregor need to raise 10 cows to a weight of 500 kg each?

$10 \times 25 \times 0.5 \times 500 = 62{,}500$ kg of grain. Note that this means an efficiency of 5,000/62,500 = 8%. Ask the students to compare that efficiency with the efficiencies of some of the ungulates in the animal cards (**Unit 2, Chapter 4**). What is a more realistic figure than 8%?

How much total grain plant growth do those 10 cows require for 1 year's growth?

625,000 kg of grain biomass. Ask the students to refer to their notes about the plants they measured. Is 10% biomass allocated to fruit realistic? Refer to the table in Science Background for some proportions of fruit biomass in woody species. In many systems, the fruits and seeds represent far less than 10% of the total plant biomass. That is so even in plants cultivated for their fruits, such as grains or legumes.

How much land is required to feed the herd for 1 year?

625,000 m^2. That is about 0.8 km^2 (ask students that have calculators to calculate that square root and consider the area covered by this planting). Another assumption here is that all the grain is completely harvested—not at all realistic!

What effect will the drought have?

$625{,}000 \times 0.8 = 500{,}000$ kg plant biomass, which means, if all else is constant, 50,000 kg of grain. Divide by (0.5×25) for 4,000 kg beef. Will that be 10 animals all 20% smaller, or 8 animals at 500 lb, or what? Some important physiology questions here translate into ecological ones. Are smaller animals less healthy? Are they less (or more) efficient at using grain? Another assumption is that even with the drought the plants still put 10% of their resources into fruit. Is that realistic? Ask the students to consider how they could design an experiment to test that assumption.

Should Farmer MacGregor invest in the SunScheme?

The SunScheme, or something like it, has been proposed at least once in the past few years. Discuss its possible implications. If we have more light, we have more heat and more growth. But will plants grow 24 hours a day at a constant rate? Can all species take the heat? If plants do increase photosynthesis, they will need more water and nutrients. If we are fertilizing them (as is usually the case for crops), will we actually benefit under SunScheme?

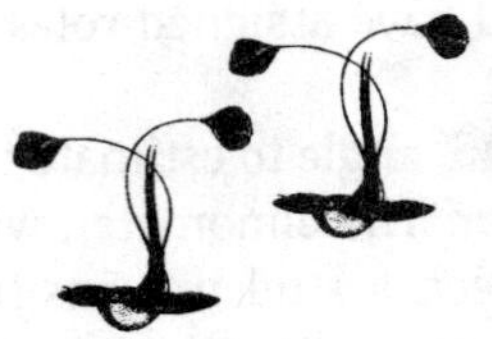

READING GUIDE
How Do You Weigh a Tree?

Discuss the Reading as background to the fieldwork of Exploration 2. The most important thing is that the measurement of biomass is a kind of probe. There is no "biomass meter," but biomass (and sometimes the relative proportions of various kinds of tissue in a plant) is the way the plant sums up its life experience. It is, therefore, a crucial "instrument" for ecological investigations and experiments.

For class discussion, you might want to use these questions and answers, as well as those in the Science Background.

What is productivity?

Productivity is the rate at which an organism increases in weight and is measured per unit area. After students have finished Reading: How Do You Weigh a Tree?, ask them to consider the possible units for productivity.

What units can we use to describe the productivity of a plant or a group of plants?

The units are weight per unit area per unit time. Have students explore the possible kinds of units that could be combined to describe the productivity of a system: grams per square centimeter per second, kilograms per hectare per year, kilograms per square meter per year, grams per square meter per day, and so on.

Consider also gross primary production (GPP) and net primary production (NPP).

What are GPP and NPP in an ecosystem?

GPP is the rate of increase in plant biomass plus the organic matter used for respiration (maintenance of the plant). It is often estimated, because respiration is difficult—if not impossible—to measure. NPP is simply GPP minus respiration. It is the net rate of increase in organic matter in plants after accounting for respiratory losses. It is also called the apparent photosynthesis or net assimilation. In practice, GPP is calculated by adding to NPP an estimate of respiration.

Note that NPP is estimated by adding all the different components of a plant or group of plants and seeing how much more they weigh today than they weighed at some previous time. Thus, to estimate NPP, we need as complete a list of parts of a plant as possible. Include shoot, root, leaf, seed, fruit, trunk, bark, and flower.

Exploration 2 Guide

Above-Ground Biomass in the Field

The term "biomass" is meaningless except by reference to a unit of area. That may not be obvious when students are working with seedlings in pots, because pots already standardize the planting area. Biomass is always measured in grams per unit area (g/cm^2, kg/m^2, etc.).

You may want to have students divide up into small groups of five to do the fieldwork. The group members should have assigned roles—recording data, taking heights, taking diameters.

Students need a way of measuring a 45° angle to estimate tree heights. Use a clinometer (Figure 1) or a protractor. The clinometer, with a plumb attached, is used to sight the angle between a student's position and the treetop. Either make clinometers of heavy cardboard with a string and washer plumbs or buy plastic models and attach the plumb.

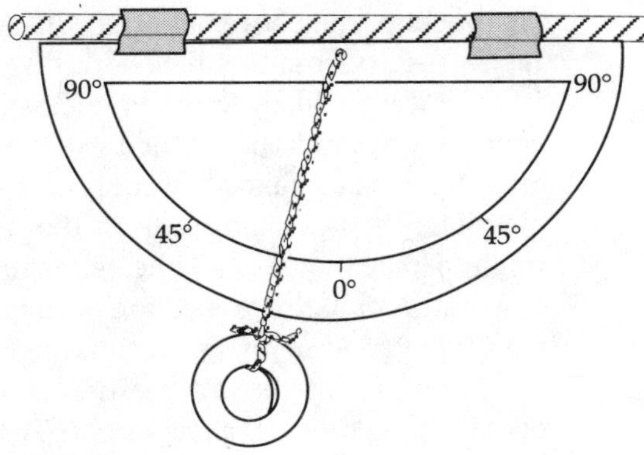

Figure 1

The illustration (Figure 1 in Exploration 2) shows students how to use themselves, the clinometer, and a measuring tape to estimate the height of any tree in their site. Using height and tree circumference, students apply the formula for a cone to the trunk of the tree, in standard forestry methodology, to calculate the tree's volume and then density (Exploration 3).

If possible, have students note the species or size classes of the dominant (most common) species in each study site. They might use something like the following data table for in-field and in-class work (Explorations 2 and 3 together).

TREE # #, species	CIRCUMFERENCE (cm)	DBH (cm)	HEIGHT (cm)	VOLUME (cm^3)	BIOMASS (g)
EXAMPLE	100.5	32.0	1,800	482,534	241,267
1.					
2.					
3.					
4.					

EXPLORATION 3 GUIDE
Above-Ground Biomass: The Data and the Calculations

Back in the classroom, each group converts its height and diameter data to volume, then to weight. Sometimes the calculations give students pause, so an example is worked through in the Exploration. Then students make a simple extrapolation. Given that they have a certain biomass estimate for their plot (100 m^2) and that a hectare is 10,000 m^2, what do they predict as the total tree biomass for 1 ha of the forest?

Presenting and Interpreting the Results

Each group presents its results. Unless the field area site is exceptionally uniform in age and composition, each group will come up with different predictions for the biomass of a hectare. What does that mean?

Is the study area uniform? Were student samples "representative"?

(This echoes the conversation in **Chapter 2**. If your study area is the same, revisit results from that fieldwork.)

Since it is likely that each plot will be somewhat different, let students consider ways to improve their estimates of the biomass of the whole study area. They might take an average of the biomass estimates of all their sample plots, then extrapolate from that to a hectare area. Alternatively, they might decide that it would be better to divide the area according to habitat type, estimating the proportion occupied, for example, by field, by forest, by parking lot, and so on, and estimating each proportion separately.

Another interesting question is what proportion of the total biomass does the biomass of trees represent? The answer varies from place to place, of course (e.g., between the Serengeti and the NHF). In posing that question, remind students of their work on plant forms and life-form spectrums.

Patchiness

An important point here is to reemphasize the patchy nature of almost all ecosystems, both in space and in time. A current area of research is whether primary productivity tends toward some equilibrium level for any area. So whether an area is covered by primary forest, a tree farm, or some other type of vegetation, the tendency over time is for the primary productivity to increase to some maximum. Indeed, some ecologists have suggested that we can define a forest's state of development by whether the rate of primary productivity is increasing (in a young forest, perhaps recovering from a hurricane, fire, or clear-cutting) or slowing (as the trees reach maturity). Although the Northern Hardwood Forest seems to behave that way, it is not clear whether other habitats follow the same pattern.

Finally, each group can write a report of its work. Encourage them to include some reflection on their data in the light of the other groups' findings.

The Exploration suggests that each group make a list of a few topics that they might like to study further. You may want to have a brainstorming session of 15 or 20 minutes about that, helping students think of observations and questions that may be of interest. You probably will need to help shape their ideas somewhat, for example, by using the **Technique: 21 Questions to Conclusions** (first used in **Unit 1**, **Chapter 2**). How you guide the discussion depends on how you hope students will use their ideas—for thought experiments, as subjects for library research or topics for research projects, or for conversations with professional ecologists.

INTEGRATION GUIDE
Forest and Savannah

The goal of these activities is to encourage the students to think about whole systems. The comparison between woodland and savannah is also a way to bring together the studies of productivity, life form, and allocation, so their biological implications for whole systems become clearer. The aim is for students to look at the two systems in depth and from various points of view. Where is the biomass? In what form is the plant biomass? How accessible to animals is the plant biomass? How does that shape the animal communities in the ecosystem?

Here you may want to refer to the Readings on the Northern Hardwood Forest and the Serengeti (**Unit 2**, **Chapters 4** and **10**) and the Case Study in this Chapter. Again, some of the plant material can be eaten by some animals. Students should consider what kinds of animals there might be in an area, and (given the plant forms) would the principal herbivores be grass eaters, leaf eaters, fruit eaters, or a mixture? Does every system have an "animal life-form spectrum" that reflects the plant spectrum?

Look back at the Whittaker chart on vegetation communities versus temperature and precipitation (Figure 7 in **Chapter 2** of this Unit). What are the determining factors in the primary productivity of a woodland versus a savannah? This is straightforward and recalls issues raised in the descriptions of the Serengeti and Northern Hardwood Forest ecosystems (**Unit 2**, **Chapter 10**, Readings 1a and 1b). The more precipitation there is, the more likely there will be a forest. Countervailing forces include a long growing season, frequent fires, and the presence of large numbers of grazing or browsing animals and of humans.

Students might use lawns as model (artificial) grasslands. What contributes to a healthy, productive green lawn? Lawnmowers graze them, homeowners water and fertilize them—what are the analogues with the Serengeti? What effect does lawnmowing have on species composition? How about fertilizer? Some comparative studies of lawns in similar locations but receiving different kinds of care might be interesting. You may find the **Technique: Describing and Comparing Communities** useful here.

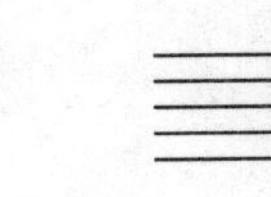

INTEGRATION
Forest and Savannah

Here are photographs of representative vegetation for two important biomes, tropical savannah (grassland with some trees and bushes) and hardwood forest (such as in New England, Michigan, or Minnesota).

Describe the biomes in terms of plant-form spectrum and other aspects of the system that you might deduce from the information in the picture. Compare it with your study site.

Consider the following questions:

Where is the plant biomass concentrated? (There may be several reservoirs.)

Consider each major kind of biomass (stems, leaves, etc.). How is each available to the rest of the ecosystem? That is, in what ways do other organisms in the ecosystem get to make use of each part?

How quickly does the biomass become available (daily, seasonally, yearly, every few years, etc.)?

EXTENSION
A Plant Efficiency Experiment

As an additional Exploration, here is a protocol to measure the efficiency of energy capture in a simple laboratory system. This design draws on Exploration 2b: Transforming Light to Electricity from **Chapter 1**. The experiment can be used as is, or you may wish to have students design the experiment themselves, based on the notion of harvesting biomass and the procedure described in that Exploration.

BACK TO PLANT PRODUCTION AND EFFICIENCY

Why is the world not covered 10 feet deep in plants? With all the incoming sunlight, why are we not up to our necks in primary productivity?

How much of the potentially available energy from the sun do plants actually capture? You can guess already that the capture rate cannot be 100%. (What evidence do you have for that supposition?)

How can you confirm your hunch? How can you measure how much sunlight is actually converted from radiant energy to chemical energy in plant tissue? Remember our work with photocells (Exploration 2b in **Chapter 1**)? For that activity, we used the total incoming light, 1,000 W/m^2 and measured how much was available in the form of electricity. In the case of light energy and photosynthesis, we want to know what proportion of the total light energy available to plants is converted into biomass, that is, into sugars and other energy and carbon-rich compounds.

An Experimental Test

To find out, let's grow plants under a known flux and use calorimetry to estimate the caloric content of the plant tissue that is grown. Because fixed carbon is the principal source of all energy for the ecosystem, knowing the rate and the efficiency of photosynthesis or carbon fixation is useful in considering energy relations between plants and between plants and animals. And combining knowledge of the efficiency of carbon fixation with information on the dynamics of solar inputs (either daily or seasonally) is useful in estimating the productivity of ecosystems.

Plant Ryegrass Seeds

Use ryegrass or any perennial lawn seed. Soak the seeds for 24 hours before planting them under standard conditions (pot size, soil type and amount, light, temperature, and water). Any pots will do—yogurt or milk containers—and clay kitty litter (the non-clumping kind) ensures that all the energy is coming from the sun (clay is free of energy and nutrients).

Let the seedlings germinate in a warm place. Once they germinate, put them under a known light source, and keep track of how much light they receive, for how long, and at what intensity.

Insolation Data: How Little Plants Get

Researchers have determined that the sun radiates about 40 cal/cm^2/h. How much energy is that per average sunny day?

40 cal/cm²/h × 12 h/day = 480 cal/cm²/day

A cup of spinach has a caloric value of approximately 20 kcal, but a square centimeter is not the most useful measure for spinach or plant growth. So let's convert that measure to square meters.

How many square centimeters are in a square meter? How many cups of spinach is that per day?

So why are we not knee deep—no, neck deep—in plant material? Why are plants not taking over?

The answer is that not all the sunlight striking an area is converted into plant tissue; plants are inefficient in terms of the total solar input versus the biomass output. How much energy is in a lump of charcoal? How much spinach or any other plant tissue is that? Think back to our calorimetry experiments. Were we able to get the exact values we expected from burning the foods? What happened to the lost energy? How could we have improved the efficiency of the calorimeter? Of all the energy that enters an ecosystem, 46% is lost as heat, 30% to reflection, 23% to evaporation. That does not leave much for plants!

In fact, only 0.8% of solar radiation is used by plants in photosynthesis, and 35% of that goes into respiration, not into the making of additional biomass. What percentage does that leave for biomass production? The standard value for total solar input is 37.41 cal/cm²/h. How many calories per square meter per hour is the actual value that plants use? Let's measure that by measuring the efficiency of our ryegrass.

CALCULATING PLANT EFFICIENCY

For the output, subtract the energy of the first ryegrass harvest from that of the second harvest.

For the input, calculate the amount of energy striking the plants between the first and second harvest:

time × surface area for half the plants × light intensity of 37.4 cal/cm²/h = light energy

Then calculate the percentage efficiency:

efficiency = (output / input) × 100

CARBON AND CALORIES

Using the same plants you have grown, after their canopy has closed, harvest half the plants (e.g., grass) from half the cups. To do that, saturate the soil and carefully remove the plants from the soil; some clay will lodge in the roots but can be removed by teasing the root mass. Be sure to retrieve all the root material.

You may chose to evaluate the carbon-calorie difference between root and shoot biomass or between whole individual plants.

You may want to test the soil for carbon and calories before and after planting, and then test the grass itself. Is there carbon or energy in the soil? Is there carbon or energy in the grass? Why?

ESTIMATES OF CARBON CONTENT

If we know the carbon content of the growing medium before the seeds are planted and after the plants are harvested, and we measure the amount in the various parts of the plants at stages in the growing cycle, we can determine the net amount of fixed carbon (carbon in a plant minus the carbon in its seed); determine the carbon uptake rate at various stages of development; and differentiate between carbon in the growing medium and the atmosphere.

USING CALORIMETRY TO ESTIMATE CALORIC CONTENT

The caloric content of the seeds and other plant parts (roots, blades, etc.) at different stages allows us to estimate the efficiency of the plant. We can determine the energy content of the different plant parts, estimate the total energy content of a cup of ryegrass seeds, and estimate the efficiency of light conversion to biomass.

Continue to care for the remaining plants and 4 to 5 days after the first harvest, harvest, weigh, and dry the remaining plants. Repeat the procedures of carbonometry and calorimetry. What are the differences? Why?

SCIENCE BACKGROUND
Plant Productivity and Biomass

What proportion of a plant's total mass does each of these parts make up: Root, shoot, woody tissue, reproductive tissue?

It might be fun for students to guess the proportion of total biomass found in each of the parts of a forested ecosystem. The proportion varies for different forest types and as any particular forest gets older. Some of the results of considering the question of changes in allocation with the age of a forest can be figured out just by thinking about how a forest develops. Students may be able to rank the proportions for stem, branches, leaves, roots, flowers, and fruits by graphically growing a forest on a piece of paper. Trees start small and most of the biomass is in leaves. As the tree grows, the stem gets bigger and bigger, as do the branches. Those are heavy components and quickly dominate. It turns out that leaf weight stabilizes in a given forest, as fruits and flowers. Root biomass may continue to expand, but will do so more slowly than the stem.

Table 1 compares the biomass distribution for trees in a young oak-pine forest, a mature hardwood forest, and an old-growth Douglas fir forest. Values are in percentages of total tree biomass.

Table 1 **Biomass Distribution (Percentages) in Three Types of Forest**

	Forest Type		
Plant Part	Young Oak-Pine	Mature Hardwood	Old-Growth Douglas Fir
Stem wood	36.1	69.3	66.6
Stem bark	8.4	6.3	8.1
Branch wood	16.9	10.3	6.1
Leaves	4.2	0.6	1.4
Fruits and flowers	0.2	0.03	N/A
Roots	34.2	13.5	17.7
Total (kg/m²)	9.7	58.5	87.0

So that students can see the differences, you may want to suggest that they represent the data graphically. This could be done in class if time permits or as additional homework. Encourage creative approaches to displaying the data.

How do you think the proportions might change during the year?

The distribution of biomass shifts during the year as some trees and shrubs develop and then drop leaves, and herbs die back to the ground. If we are considering individual plant parts, flowers and fruits are present for only short periods during the year. The point of this question is to get students thinking about the transient nature of some biomass pools and the dynamics of biomass allocation.

Does your list include the reproductive organs of a plant?

Although transient, the reproductive parts can be a significant portion of total plant biomass. Have students consider the many fruits we eat. Explain, if they do not suggest it, that many of these plants are bred by humans to produce food and therefore put much of their energy into making fruits.

What about the components that fix carbon?

Leaves and needles can be transient and can account for a significant portion oi the biomass of a plant. In trees, at least older trees, the proportion of biomass in needles or leaves is not high.

Did you consider the wood that trees add to their structure annually?

Humans rely on the accumulation of wood fiber on trees for paper, timber, and other products. After this activity, students can calculate the amount of wood that is added annually, by using the approximate age of the tree and the biomass that they will estimate.

What about the material that animals eat during the year?

Grasses, leaves, twigs, and (in some cases) whole plants are eaten by a variety of animals. This is often ignored in considerations of estimating NPP, but it can be a significant portion, as students will see in **Unit 4**. One way to estimate the amount eaten by animals is to exclude animals from an area and compare it to an area that animals had access to. The difference between the two areas provides an estimate of the amount consumed by herbivores.

If you want to spend more time on this topic, you may want to ask students to consider the "residence time" for each component, that is, how long the carbon in a tissue stays there. For example, how long does the wood that makes up the trunk of a tree stay with the trunk before it is dead wood on the forest floor or eaten away? Have students rank residence time for each component. Being right or wrong is less important than describing the life-cycle of different components. If a suggested residence time is very far off, ask for the students' reasoning. You and the students both may learn something. The list can be divided into components with a long residence time, an intermediate residence time and a short residence time. Consider the significance of the residence times for the individual, the species, other species, and the community.

For example, if a particular ecosystem is just accumulating biomass for long periods of time, what might be its impact on the carbon dioxide concentration in the atmosphere? To make it easier, pretend that the system students are examining is sealed in a container. What are the implications for photosynthesis rates if carbon is being built up in the biomass and therefore being pulled out of the atmosphere? One implication might be a lowering in the rates of photosynthesis due to a reduced availability of carbon dioxide.

Another implication of long turnover times is that carbon is locked in biomass, as are all the nutrients associated with the biomass. Although this is clearly outside the current work, it may come up in discussion and is worth pursuing.

LEAF BIOMASS

The following approach is one taken by teacher Mark Dewart to get estimates for leaf biomass. It was circulated as part of the Global Lab project in 1991.

> The Park Tudor School site in Indianapolis, Indiana USA [is] interested in working on a fall phenology study. We've been working since the end of September using an approach that we hope will determine the onset, duration and peak of the autumn leaf fall period. The method was summarized in The American Biology Teacher, Volume 51, Number 7, October 1989 on pages 432–435. We've deployed 4 garbage cans randomly in our 3 acre woods. Students bring in the leaves that have fallen into the cans in every 48 hour period. The leaves are counted, identified to species, dried, and their dry weight is determined. We will continue this until at least December 1st, or later, if there are still leaves falling.

UNIT 4

GLOBAL CARBON

GLOBAL CARBON

UNIT **4** CONTENTS

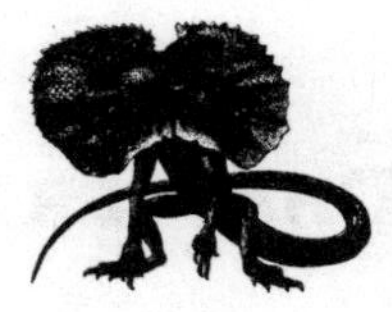

UNIT 4 OVERVIEW

GLOBAL CARBON

We use the term "global carbon" here literally to indicate the globe-wide carbon cycle and global warming, as well as metaphorically to indicate the "cosmic" nature of the full cycle. Throughout this Module, we have explored the links between carbon and energy at many levels, from bonds and molecules, from individuals, species, and populations through food chains and simple food webs to communities. In this Unit, we integrate all those levels to consider the global picture of atmospheric change, which depends on all those lower levels, including plant growth, microbial respiration, the balanced energy use equation, and your own energy use.

Recall that carbon (like other nutrients) cycles through the system as it participates in chemical transactions of various kinds. Carbon from the biosphere (by way of respiration and combustion) and from the seas and rocks mixes in the atmosphere. Some of it is absorbed into the waters of the earth, while a crucial amount is taken up by photosynthesis. But sooner or later carbon ends up as CO_2 (the most dynamic component of the cycle) in the atmosphere.

Thus, the atmosphere is a crossroads for carbon, passed around as CO_2. It is nearly impossible to monitor precisely processes at the global level, so we sample what and as we can (e.g., the makeup of air). We then build a story with those results, plus all the other data across the various levels we study.

To complete the story, we return to an individual organism's carbon budget. That allows us to close the circle from individual to global aspects of the carbon and energy cycle and to see how we humans "count" in the grand debate about the climate's future.

The Global Carbon Cycle

Chapter One

Contents

INTRODUCTION

This Unit puts the study of carbon and energy on a global stage and in the context of a current and important debate. Students start with information about global warming from the popular press and then explore some of the science behind the scenes.

How is it possible for human activity to have a worldwide, geological impact? How important are lifestyle choices to global climate change?

The Explorations build an approach to the modeling of very large systems, about which exact answers are impossible. In the course of that, they also introduce some fundamental notions about systems.

In the end, the class can return to the global warming debate armed with a deeper ecological understanding of the issues.

KEY CONCEPTS

- Among the most urgent issues facing ecology is the need to understand human influences in global changes. The global carbon cycle is at the heart of many current environmental and political issues, most obviously the nature and the extent of global warming. Clear answers are hard to get about many questions on climate change. People with the same information sometimes come to different conclusions, based on their point of view.
- Ecology is a study of systems. Organisms, food webs, communities, ecosystems, and the entire biosphere:.each can be viewed as a system.
- Systems theory can be applied to a wide variety of systems, because its concepts are useful in thinking about matter and energy flow in ecosystems, money flow in economies, and information flow in computer networks.
- Static parts of systems include pools—concentrations of things or materials in a specific form—and pathways of flow between pools.
- Dynamic aspects of systems include rates of flow along pathways and residence times in pools. In addition, material may change form as it moves from one pool to another. For example, carbon exists in different compounds in different components of the system.
- The atmospheric pool is a crossroads for the carbon (in the form of CO_2) flowing among the other pools of the global system. The carbon, in many different energy-containing compounds, is found in other large pools: in organic matter alive and dead; rocks; dissolved in water; and in ocean sediment.
- The rates of flow from one pool to another have a major effect on the climate system. Among humans, energy use for metabolic respiration varies with body size, climate, and activity level. Total energy use, however, varies largely as a result of energy expended on technological processes such as driving cars, home heating and cooling, home-appliance use, artificial lighting, and manufacturing.

MATERIALS AND PREPARATION

Safety

WARNING

To avoid puncture wounds, students must be careful not to push too hard when punching holes into cups.

Materials

- **Disposable cups** (7–15 clear plastic cups per pair of students [5 cups for building the model and at least 2 to practice making holes] per model. 9-oz cups made of PETE [#1-type plastic] work well and are recyclable. Waxed paper cups work but tend to leak.)
- **Several clear plastic straws** or approximately 2 ft of clear plastic tubing (such as from an aquarium supply shop or pet store) per student pair
- **Hole-punching implements** (thumbtacks, pushpins, or awls to start the holes and sharpened pencils to enlarge the holes to a straw's diameter)
- **Water**
- **Food coloring** (optional)
- **Flow restrictors** for experimenting with changing rates of flow in system (let students know the materials are available but let them decide how to use them):

  To restrict water flow, wrap aluminum foil over the end of a straw or roll some into a ball and ram it into a straw.

  To slow flow, use paper clips to squeeze straws from the outside. Tip: Flatten the end of a straw first and put the clip over the flattened end.
- **Graduated cylinders or measuring cups**
- **Graph paper**
- **Calculators**
- **Newspapers and news magazines from the summers of 1988 and 1992** (Time, Newsweek, U.S. News and World Report, and the science sections of newspapers like the New York Times, whose Science Section is published on Tuesdays)
- **Popular science magazines**, such as Scientific American (see especially the September 1989 special issue, "Managing the Earth"), Science News, Natural History, and Discover
- **Publications of the WorldWatch Institute** (such as their State of the World reports each year) and the **World Resources Institute** (WRI), which publishes an annual data book
- **Environmental Almanac**, put out by the publishers of the Information Please Almanac

SUGGESTED SEQUENCE OF SESSIONS (12–15)

Homework

Case Study: The Global Warming Debate: Asking the Right Questions. Divide the class into three teams and assign the Case Study in preparation for their global warming debate. That debate will engage the students with carbon-cycle science as well as the policy of global warming.

Class Sessions 1 and 2

During the first class session, teams prepare arguments from their assigned points of view on global warming. During the second session, each team gets to make its case. This can be followed by a short writing assignment for homework in which the students summarize the science issues raised.

Class Sessions 3 and 4

Exploration 1: What Is a System? and Exploration 2: Systems Everywhere. In Exploration 1, students in groups build simple physical systems to explore the basic notions of a systems model. The summary discussion in Exploration 2 suggests how the ideas used in a "model" system apply to many kinds of systems, including the global carbon–energy system.

Homework

Exploration 3: The Carbon Budget of a Small System.

Having explored a physical system and learned some basic vocabulary for systems thinking, the students engage in a thought experiment about the behavior of a sample carbon system, a small house.

Class Session 5

Use Exploration 3: The Carbon Budget of a Small System to lead the class in constructing a qualitative carbon budget of the house system.

Homework

In Exploration 4: Your Carbon Content, students consider how much carbon a person contains and how important the total human biomass is in the global carbon cycle.

Class Sessions 6–8

Exploration 5a: Global Carbon Cycle: The Atmosphere

Exploration 5b: Global Carbon Cycle: Carbon Pools

Exploration 5c: Global Carbon Cycle: Human Factors

Exploration 5d: "Truthing" Your Predictions

The class divides into three teams, each of which studies a piece of the global carbon picture. On the basis of their information, they prepare predictions of trends in global carbon concentrations for the next 20 years. Then the whole class discusses the implications of those predictions on Keeling curve data.

Homework

Reading: Human Energy Uses: Biological. What impact does one person's behavior and life have on a global cycle?

Class Session 9

Exploration 6: Human Energy Uses: Chwa and Sabrina. During this class, discuss the homework and begin to look at other kinds of energy use than those of metabolic processes. Preview the data collector portion of Exploration 7a, which is similar to that used in **Unit 2, Chapter 2.**

Homework

Exploration 7a: An Energy-Use Log. The students collect data in an activity that recalls their food and energy log from **Unit 2, Chapter 2.** Now mechanical and other energy expenditures are added to the picture.

Class Sessions 10 and 11

Exploration 7b: Calculating Your Total Energy Use for 24 Hours. The students will need one or two sessions to calculate their estimated personal energy use. (If time permits, discuss some comparisons among the various lifestyles represented in your class.)

Energy use is connected to the global carbon cycle as students see that a side effect of human use of fossil fuels is the accelerated transfer of carbon from the pool of hydrocarbons in the earth's crust to the atmospheric pool of CO_2, where it becomes an influence on the global climate.

Class Session 12

Integration. As a way to pull the whole chapter together, you may want to revisit the global warming debate, either in class or in individual writings.

SESSION GUIDES, BY WORKSHEET

CASE STUDY GUIDE

The Global Warming Debate: Asking the Right Questions

Benefits of the Debate

By preparing for and engaging in a class discussion on the global warming controversy, students remind themselves of the urgent need for a better understanding of the carbon cycle. The Case Study, assigned as homework, serves as a source of information for all points of view. The Case Study can be supplemented by other materials (as suggested in References).

This debate helps students see the connection between the carbon cycle, human activity, and the current political process. It raises questions about the kinds of information people need to make wise decisions about extremely complex issues, such as global climate change.

Background for the Debate

Discussion can rely entirely on the provided Case Study, but it is enhanced by use of other reference materials. Assign the Case Study for reading before the first session. Plan on at least one session in which the student teams develop their arguments for the debate.

You may want to supplement the reading with other materials, assigning the scouting out of such materials as homework. Some fruitful sources of information that are easy to use and that provide both some scientific background and a sense of the political and social issues are listed in References.

Logistics of the Debate

We recommend that you divide the class into three groups to speed preparation time and enrich the debate, since each group will be assigned a "point of view." Each team may find it useful to break into smaller groups to focus on particular aspects of the case. An important part of this kind of activity is bringing out what students know and feel about the issues and discussing the most effective approach. If students have been monitoring the environmental news, encourage them to bring to bear what they have collected in the previous months of the course.

The Debate

Allow one class period for the debate itself. The debate should end with a few minutes of group reflection on the strength of the arguments each side has presented. As part of the summation, ask students what questions they may have about global warming, environmental policy, and related matters.

Help students keep track of scientific as well as ethical and emotional questions that come up for them. That provides a fertile field in which to find topics for further research for interested students, or the class can revisit them during the debate in the Integration activity. You may want to ask the students to write a summary of the main points raised by all sides.

EXPLORATION 1 GUIDE
What Is a System?

The goal in this Exploration is for students to learn about the basic features of a cycling system. Start off the class with a brief discussion (10–15 min) in which students compare various systems with which they are familiar. Then student pairs build physical models to explore the basic properties of systems.

Discussion

These questions will prime students to close observation in the main activity: What is a system? What makes a system a system?

Help the students propose some predictions or tentative definitions based on class consensus. You will return to these points in the concluding analysis, so do not worry about the students' reaching clarity at this stage.

Building Model Systems

Following the introductory discussion, students start building their model systems. They will be quite focused on the practical challenges of design and construction. This is all to the good. Once prototypes are running, encourage the students to ask questions about their systems' behavior that require some measurement or systematic observation to answer. You may want to keep track of questions that are raised.

The model building has four general phases:

1. **Design with a goal in mind.**
Each group of students should have a specific design goal. Build a system in which the final container in the system (the one where most of the water ends up) fills at a rate of at least 1 liter (1,000 ml) per minute or build a system in which the final container in the system fills at a rate slower than 0.25 liter (250 ml) per minute.

2. **Measure flow rates and residence times.**
Once they have working models, students measure rates of flow along various pathways and the residence times of pools (the time needed for a pool to drain). By measuring rates of flow of water through various parts of the system, students can study the effects that changes in static properties of the system (e.g., varying the diameter of pathways and the size of pools) can have on its dynamic behavior (e.g., rates of flow and residence times).

    To measure rates of flow along various pathways and residence times of pools (the time needed for a pool to drain), students place a measuring container under the end of a pathway for the time period selected and record how much water flows into the container. Similarly, to measure residence times in pools, students measure the volume of a pool and how long it takes for each pool to empty itself. Let students decide what units to use for their measurement, but the units should take the form of volume per unit time (e.g., liters or milliliters per minute).

3. **Improve the system.**
Students probably will need to make adjustments to their system to meet their design goals. We suggest they think about how to improve their system and implement the improvements in an allotted space of time (e.g., 15 min) in the next class session.

CONSTRUCTION HINTS: Supply students with the following hints only if they are having trouble designing and building their systems. The effect of this activity will be greater if students have a good chance to explore how to build their models.

- Have the final pathway empty into a sink, where students can place a measuring cup or graduated cylinder to measure flow rates.
- Place cups in a system on multiple levels, so that gravity causes the water to flow from higher cups to lower cups.
- A simple two- or three-cup system can be held in one's hands. More complex systems should be placed on blocks or books to achieve a multilevel system.
- The lowest cup in the system should be large enough to hold all the water that gets added to the uppermost cup.

- To prevent spills, add only the amount of water that the lowest cup in the system can hold. You may want to specify the amount of water that is to be added to systems.
- Straws (flow pathways) exiting a cup should leave near the bottom, so that most of the water flowing into the cup can leave.
- Straws (flow pathways) entering a pool can come in near the top of the pool.

4. Changes are perturbations.

Changes in the students' simple model systems are analogous to perturbations in ecosystems. The rates of ecological processes may change if temperature or other environmental conditions change. In addition, the sizes of nutrient pools may change in response to environmental changes. How will changes in students' systems affect the systems?

Once they have built a system with multiple pools and pathways, the students should think of and select a couple of system changes for further study and predict in writing what effect the changes will have on their system. Then, after they have made the changes and recorded the effects, they should compare the actual effects with their original predictions.

At first, students should make only a single change at a time—even one change can drastically alter a system's functioning both "upstream" and "downstream" of the site of the change. Students should use the measuring techniques described above to quantify the effects of their changes. Later, they can experiment with making more than one change simultaneously and study the effects of such changes.

One special change that may be of interest is the use of water in a different phase than liquid in one or more pools. The easiest to work with is ice or slush, which will have a very different residence time than liquid water. This provides a good analogy with elements in various chemical compounds, such as carbon in CO_2, carbohydrates, hydrocarbons, or calcium carbonate (limestone, $CaCO_3$).

At the end of this Exploration, assign Exploration 2: Systems Everywhere for discussion in the next class.

EXPLORATION 2 GUIDE
Systems Everywhere

Students are familiar with many different kinds of systems but may not recognize them as "systems" and the many features they have in common. The purpose of this discussion is to get students to begin thinking about the features that are common to different types of systems.

The student worksheet is a semiblank version of Table 1 below. At first glance, the systems may appear to be quite different from each other. As you consider them further, however, all can be seen as a series of pools linked by pathways with something flowing through the system. Viewed from that perspective, they begin to appear quite similar.

Ask the students to fill in the blanks, either individually or in small groups, then discuss the piece as a whole group. Or you can lead a whole-

Table 1 **Sample Systems**

NAME OF SYSTEM	WHAT FLOWS IN THE SYSTEM?	POOLS	PATHWAYS
1. Water supply	Water	Storage tanks	Pipes
2. School	Students	Classes	Corridors
3. Circulatory system	Blood	Heart, spleen, lungs	Arteries, veins, capillaries
4. Economy	Money	Bank accounts	Checks
5. Digestive system	Food	Stomach, intestines	Connections between organs
6. Traffic	Cars	Garages, parking lots	Highways, streets
7.			
8.			

class discussion right away. If the students disagree on the fill-ins, have them discuss the reasons for their opinions.

Ask the students how residence time and flow rate apply to their examples. What regulates each? How can you quantify those notions? How would you measure each? You might want to consider with the class how to quantify energy in an ecosystem using this terminology. What flows and in what form? What are the units you would use to measure the flow rate or pool size?

Finally, you may want to use the material in Science Background on "open" and "closed" systems, describing the ideas to the class and asking them to apply the notions to the systems you have been discussing. Is an ecosystem an open or a closed system? What about the earth?

EXPLORATION 3 GUIDE
The Carbon Budget of a Small System

In this Exploration, students build a qualitative, graphical model of a system: a house viewed as a carbon cycle. This activity allows students to explore several crucial aspects of the global carbon cycle in a hypothetical setting that restricts the unknowns that the students will have to anticipate or work around.

This activity, with previous ones in the Unit, prepares students to consider the structure and dynamics of the global carbon cycle and emphasizes CO_2 as the major unit of exchange for the cycle.

Your task in coaching this activity is to help students imagine the pools and pathways of carbon compounds in detail. Bear in mind that this discussion prepares them to consider dynamics in the global carbon cycle. In preparation for that, you might like to review the section on cycling carbon in Science Background.

The Thought Experiment

The class can work on this thought experiment in various ways. In scenario 1, all the work is done in class; in scenario 2, students begin preparation before class (which may reduce the time needed in class).

Scenario 1

Beginning as a whole class, go over the hypothetical house and brainstorm for 15 minutes. Then divide the class into triads to work for the rest of that session and the next on their versions. The whole class then comes together to address the questions in the student sheet and to consider how to develop a composite picture.

Scenario 2

The students read Exploration 3 as homework and sketch their image of the house and its contents. In the next class session, the students work in small groups to merge their ideas and develop them in more detail. The questions on the student worksheets are a guide to help each team stay focused. After a couple of days' work, each team makes a short report to the class. The students' individual schemes then go into their notebooks.

Optional

Students may prefer to model the carbon content of their own houses. If so, suggest that the team pick one of the team members' houses and diagram its carbon system.

When they have finished their models, the teams should present their main results: estimates of relative size of the various pools of carbon, the pathways from each pool to each form of CO_2, and estimates of flow rates. Their estimates will doubtless vary widely, based on their assumptions about the sizes of the pools and flow rates; those assumptions should be noted in the class discussion. Ask the students how they might settle differences and how to improve their estimates.

During the summary discussions, ask the students questions about their understanding of ideas related to the key concepts. Can they generalize about the behavior of carbon in organic compounds (that it changes state, moves by various means at different rates, and accumulates in differing concentration in different pools and that there may be different constraints on the size of a pool or the rapidity of its turnover)?

Assessment

You may want to ask the students to summarize in writing what they have learned so far. They can respond to the questions on the student sheet, which they will be able to refer to later and also make a part of their notebook. Their answers at this stage are enriched by their own reflection and by the teamwide and classwide discussions.

EXPLORATION 4 GUIDE

Your Carbon Content

Spend some time—perhaps 15 minutes—discussing this Exploration. The main point is to be concrete about the carbon content in biomass, in preparation for the main activity in which biomass plays an important, though subordinate, role. The students might enjoy doing the Fermi calculation of total current human biomass in terms of carbon (and kilocalories, for those who enjoy arithmetic!). Assume that the average human mass is 50 kg, that dry weight is 70% of wet weight, and that carbon is about 50% of wet weight.

EXPLORATION 5A GUIDE
Global Carbon Cycle: The Atmosphere

In the previous activities, students considered some crucial ideas about the cycling of carbon. Carbon may occur in various chemical compositions and may stay in a certain form for some period of time. Some of the material may move from one concentration to another, and that transfer may accompany a change in form (from one chemical compound to another, from one state of matter to another, or both). Time is a part of the picture, as is energy, which is usually required in those chemical changes and sometimes released in the change from one chemical form to another. With this background, it is time to look at the global picture.

The four parts of this Exploration build a picture of the global cycle as a whole. Working in groups, students focus on the atmosphere, global carbon pools, or human factors data. Each team uses their data about trends in the atmospheric pool to place the human effects in perspective. Tables with relevant data are provided for each team.

If dividing your class into three teams would result in groups too large to work well together, you may want to divide each team into two, one for each subtask. This may require some negotiating at report time to reconcile differences in results.

Team 1

We have emphasized that the atmosphere is a crossroads for several elements of the carbon cycle. It is also the pool of the system whose carbon content is the easiest to measure. This first team is given measurements based on those taken over 3 years at the observation station at Mauna Loa, Hawaii. Their task is to describe what is represented in the graph and to raise some questions about it.

The measurements provided for this team cover a rather short time period, during which it is hard to see any general long-term trends. We have made this selection because the annual oscillation itself is subtle. On the other hand, there is a slight increase in the average reading from one year to the next even in this small sample. That should raise the question in the students' minds, "Is this a trend or a short-term variation?" Of course, we cannot tell for sure whether the long-term data we have gathered since the last century are anything more than a temporary variation (on the scale of geological time) or a "real" trend. We can only put together the most probable case.

The data show a periodicity with the seasons. The short explanation is that the concentration of atmospheric CO_2 drops during the growing season, as photosynthesis reaches its peak level and more carbon is stored in plant tissues. The students may remember that this takes place against a background of organismal output of CO_2, which also increases during the warmer months. That is probably why the CO_2 concentration rises early in the spring, then falls noticeably later in the summer and early fall: decomposer and plant respiration outweighs photosynthesis.

A second issue is the location of the observation station. Mauna Loa was chosen because it is isolated from mainland influences (about 3,200 km southwest of California). Fruitful questions about the reliability of the observations from such a site include:

How do the wind patterns affect it? Is there a time lag before the effects of terrestrial photosynthesis are notable there? What consequences are there from the fact that Mauna Loa is in the northern hemisphere? (The northern hemisphere has the largest land area, and the largest amount of terrestrial photosynthesis—more photosynthesis even than in all the equatorial rain forests.) Would the readings be very different if taken from an isolated island in the South Pacific (such as Easter Island)?

The team then presents its findings to the whole class. What trend do they predict for the atmospheric pool? Team 1 is likely to predict a stable, annual oscillation with no long-term trends.

EXPLORATION 5B GUIDE
Global Carbon Cycle: Carbon Pools

This team's task is to develop a representation of the global carbon cycle, including all natural processes (photosynthesis, respiration, exchanges with oceans, and geological pools). The student worksheet provides the necessary numbers; the students need to understand them to the extent that they can represent the pools and fluxes. The final task is to calculate the net effects of this version of the carbon cycle—where is carbon accumulating and in what forms? What trend do they predict for the atmospheric pool? The team will then present its findings to the whole class. This group's prediction of CO_2 trends is likely to be of a nonoscillating (flat) line with a slight trend down.

EXPLORATION 5C GUIDE
Global Carbon Cycle: Human Factors

Using graphs from the Oak Ridge (Kentucky) National Energy Laboratory, this team compiles data about CO_2 emissions from several regions of the earth. They then compute the global contribution to atmospheric carbon by human activity and present their findings to the whole class. What trend do they predict for the atmospheric pool?

The work assigned this team is not as onerous as it may appear at first. It is enough for the students to read one number from each regional graph, then total those numbers. In trying this activity, some classes have been distracted by the other information contained on the graphs—regional differences, sources of the information, and so on—information not necessary for the main Exploration.

Why, then, is this extra information here? It provides background information on regional trends and on the developments in each region that lie behind these trends. Such information may well raise important questions in the students' minds, during this work or later. (When the class moves on to the Reading and Exploration 6, this set of graphs may come in handy.)

One cannot predict what this third group might conclude from their work. They may wish to choose one of the regions as most representative of the future (Asia is a good candidate, since both India and China are likely to stay on course for the next few decades). Or they may average the trends for all regions or suggest another approach.

EXPLORATION 5D GUIDE
"Truthing" Your Predictions

After the teams have made their reports and predictions, ask the class how they might resolve the contradictions among the various teams' presentations. In the course of the discussion, propose what seems to you to be the consensus about the future trend in the levels of CO_2.

READING GUIDE
Human Energy Uses: Biological

EXPLORATION 6 GUIDE
Human Energy Uses: Chwa and Sabrina

Assign the Reading as homework. Students discover that while food-related energy uses are relatively similar, other, nonfood-related uses are wildly different. Those differences are ecologically significant.

Students compare the lifestyles of two young women of about the same size from two different cultures: the !Kung and suburban U.S. Their metabolic energy expenditures are similar, but their cultural, technological energy uses are radically different. From this qualitative comparison, the students move on to build a quantitative profile of their own energy expenditure (Exploration 7a).

Discuss the Reading with the class. First, focus on the similarities between Chwa and Sabrina's energy-use patterns, which stem from the nature of the human basal metabolic rate. You may want to review with the class that all humans need to take in enough energy to maintain their body tissues, maintain body temperature, and provide energy for activity. The Reading begins by reminding students of the idea of basal metabolic rate (BMR), energy used for basic maintenance of life. BMR is fairly constant for animals of any particular species of about the same size. Thus, it is fairly constant for same-age, same-size humans around the world. The primary point of this part of the homework assignment is that human energy expenditures for basic biological needs hardly vary.

Now, ask students to discuss how the two young women's energy-use patterns differ. The crucial element, of course, is the technological element basic to Sabrina's lifestyle. Note that Chwa does not lack technology, but it is developed in a less energy-intense process than are most of the energy uses of the developed world.

One variable that the students are asked to consider is geography. That implies climatic differences, and some important differences between Sabrina and Chwa stem from climatic contrasts. That the temperate climate does not require an energy-intensive economy can be suggested by the lives of native peoples at every latitude in North America.

EXPLORATION 7A GUIDE

An Energy-Use Log

Students explore similarities and differences in energy use among humans. This Exploration enables the students to see in concrete ways how lifestyle can have an impact even on a global scale, as with CO_2 emissions and global warming. In contrast, the amount of energy spent for purposes other than basic biological processes (where the source of energy is not food) varies widely among cultures. Nonindustrial cultures may use small amounts of energy for cooking and warmth, whereas industrial cultures use massive quantities of energy for transportation, running appliances, home heating and cooling, and manufacturing.

Students construct a personal energy-use budget similar to the one they created in **Unit 2**, **Chapter 2**. The difference is that this budget includes energy used for industrial society activities. Students compare their energy use (or the energy use of a typical American teenager described in the Reading) with energy use by a teen of the !Kung tribe in Africa. By constructing a complete energy-use budget, students get to see the effects of their own behavior on the global carbon cycle, since most technological uses of energy put large amounts of CO_2 into the atmosphere.

Start with an in-class brainstorming about students' typical uses of energy during their after-school time. The goal is for the students to leave the class with a good initial list of energy-use categories on which to base their energy-use logs.

One way to organize this activity is as follows:

1. First in small groups, then as a whole class, the students develop a set of energy uses that can be used as a data-collection form as they gather their own information. (A sample data sheet, "An Energy-Use Log," is provided, but the categories are blank—it is up to the class to decide on those.)
2. Students then keep a record of their own nonfood-related uses of energy for 24 hours, creating a new chapter for the energy budget they created earlier.

Alternatively, students can use the fictional U.S. student to imagine her food-fueled and nonfood-fueled uses of energy. Imagine what the fictional U.S. student described in the Reading would go through during the course of the day.

The Data

You will know, if you have done this Exploration yourself, that various quantities for which you collected data were not exact. The students will encounter this as well.

Some students are troubled by such imprecision. You may want to explain that this is often the case with scientific work, certainly in ecological work. While it is important to be accurate, it often is not possible to be precise, especially in systems that are dynamic and complex, such as ecosystems. Remember the Fermi calculations from **Unit 1**—that often an order-of-magnitude calculation is quite useful? While that is not true for this Exploration, it overlaps with a second important point about quantifying data or precision of any sort. It is important to keep one's perspective about numbers and to use numbers of the same general degree of preciseness. Thus, it makes no sense to time one activity to hundredths of a second (a lap in the swimming pool) while others are precise to within 5 or 10 minutes (amount of time spent moving between classes). This is an issue students likely have encountered in math and is worth coordinating a session or two with their math teacher, if possible. It is also considered in the **Technique: Introduction to Research**.

Students will need the next one or two sessions to process their data: do the addition, calculations, and conversions for energy use. The conversion of activities into kilocalories is straightforward; the student material also includes a fully worked example.

EXPLORATION 7B GUIDE

Calculating Your Total Energy Use for 24 Hours

Students calculate their nonfood energy use in kilocalories, using the charts provided. They may ask about particular things on their list that do not fit easily into the categories the class is using. You can make the judgments yourself or open them up for brief discussion by the whole group.

We expect that this process—gathering information and calculating energy values—will take at least two sessions before students are ready to draw conclusions about their energy use.

If possible, have students get copies of their family's home-energy bills. Students can get the number of kilowatt-hours used for electricity, the number of therms or cubic feet of natural gas, and gallons of heating oil delivered. The following information will guide them in converting those quantities to kilocalories.

Energy Units and Conversions

The kilowatt-hour (kWh) is used to measure electricity. One kWh is 1,000 watts of power delivered for 1 hour. (Recall that a watt is 1 joule per sec, or approximately 0.239 calorie per sec.)

$$\textbf{1 kWh} = \mathbf{8.604 \times 10^2}\ \textbf{kcal}$$

The therm is often used to measure the energy content of natural gas. One therm equals 100,000 British Thermal Units (BTUs). A BTU is the amount of heat (energy) needed to raise 1 pound of water 1°F.

$$\textbf{1 therm} = \mathbf{2.52 \times 10^4}\ \textbf{kcal}$$

DATA SHEET

Exploration7a: Your ENERGY-USE LOG for Data Collection and Analysis

PAGE 1

Name ______________________ Date ______________________

TIME	ACTIVITY	TIME SPENT	CALORIES "SPENT"

ENERGY-USE LOG

PAGE 2

Name ______________________ Date ______________________

TIME	ACTIVITY	TIME SPENT	CALORIES "SPENT"

The cubic foot is often used as a measure of natural gas. The measure is of volume, but that amount of natural gas contains 1 therm of energy. A gas bill in cubic feet can easily be converted to therms and to kcal.

Gasoline typically is measured by the gallon, another measure of volume. What is the energy content of 1 gallon of gasoline? About 31,000 kcal (that is the equivalent of a lot of jelly doughnuts in every tankfull!). To convert from gallons of gasoline to kilocalories, use this formula:

energy in 1 gallon of gasoline = 3.1×10^4 kcal

It would be useful if some students could gather data on the number of gallons of gasoline used in their family cars. Working with those energy-use data and the conversion factors provided in Table 2 (in the next subsection), students can calculate their family's total energy use in kilocalories, allowing them to compare the energy they take in as food with their nonfood energy uses.

Results

On average, U.S. citizens use 200,000 kcal of nonfood energy per person, per day; a !Kung woman burning 5 kg of wood per day uses 16,500 kcal.

Climate

In your discussions about energy use, address the importance of climate in human energy use. People living in very cold climates have a variety of options for dealing with low temperatures. All require energy; some are more effective than others. From least energy intensive (and least effective) to most intensive, the options include: eating extra food and shivering a lot, spending energy to create clothes, spending energy to build shelters, and spending energy to heat the environment (either inside a shelter or outside).

Similarly, people in very hot climates may eat less food to compensate for low costs of thermoregulation, may build shelters that are cooler than ambient temperatures, or may cool their shelters with energy-intensive air conditioning. Thus, where we live can significantly affect our energy budget—depending on what options we exercise in dealing with the climate.

DISCUSSION GUIDE
Transportation and Energy

As your students undoubtedly know, transportation of people and materials requires a great deal of energy. In fact, roughly a quarter of the nonfood energy use in the United States is used for transportation. Be sure to discuss with your class the efficiencies of different modes of transportation and have students share information about their own transportation uses.

It may prove most useful to think of transportation efficiency in terms of energy expended per passenger mile. Table 2 compares a number of common passenger vehicles in terms of their efficiencies and the quantity of energy consumed per passenger-mile. Note that the data are based on the assumption that multipassenger vehicles are filled to capacity; if they are carrying fewer passengers, the efficiency drops. You may want to create an overhead transparency of Table 2 and its companion table, Table 3, which lists freight-transportation energy requirements, to use during the discussion.

Before your students see the actual efficiencies of the various vehicles, you may want the class to attempt to rank the vehicles in terms of efficiency and estimate the relative efficiencies of the least efficient and most efficient vehicles.

When you discuss transporting freight, you may want to consider that nearly everything your students own and eat comes from quite some distance away. For example, many of their clothes probably were made in Asia or Central America, and much of their food probably was grown in another state or country. Their family cars probably were shipped several hundred miles to the dealerships, perhaps as many as 10,000 miles. To keep these students living in the style to which they have grown accustomed, a tremendous amount of energy is required. Freight is transported in four major ways: by airplane, truck, railroad, and waterways (see Table 3). With your students, rank those in order of efficiency, from most efficient to least (think in terms of energy spent per ton-mile, i.e., moving 1 ton of goods 1 mile).

Table 2

Energy Requirements for Passenger Transportation

(Romer, 1976; food energy and other fuel energies have been converted to equivalent quantities of gasoline.)

MODE OF TRANSPORTATION	MAXIMUM CAPACITY (NUMBER OF PASSENGERS)	VEHICLE MILEAGE (MILES/GAL)	PASSENGER MILEAGE (PASSENGER-MILES/GAL)	ENERGY CONSUMPTION (KCAL/PASSENGER-MILE)
Bicycle	1	1,560	1,560	20
Walking	1	470	470	66
Intercity bus	45	5	225	139
Commuter train (10 cars)	800	0.2	160	195
Subway train (10 cars)	1,000	0.15	150	208
Volkswagen sedan	4	30	120	260
Local bus	35	3	105	297
Intercity train (4 coaches)	200	0.4	80	391
Motorcycle	1	60	60	519
Automobile	4	12	48	650
747 jet plane	360	0.1	36	867
727 jet plane	90	0.4	36	867
Light plane (2 seats)	2	12	24	1,300
Executive jet plane	8	2	16	1,950
Concorde SST	110	0.12	13	2,369
Snowmobile	1	12	12	2,596
Ocean liner	2,000	0.005	10	3,125

Table 3

Energy Requirements for Freight Transportation

(Romer, 1976)

MODE OF TRANSPORTATION	MILEAGE (TON-MILES/GAL)	ENERGY CONSUMPTION (KCAL/TON-MILES)
Railroads	185	169
Waterways	182	171
Truck	44	706
Airplane	3	10,584

Class Summaries: Energy Use and CO_2 Production

By now, you and your students have spent a great deal of time (and energy) studying energy use. In this final session, you and your students can examine how their lifestyle choices can affect the global climate by way of CO_2 emissions.

How does this relate to the global carbon cycle? Of the total amount of energy used in the United States, about 85% comes from fossil fuel sources (Table 4). Even if we do not burn a great deal of gasoline, oil, or coal personally, it is likely that the local electricity utility burns a fossil fuel to generate electricity. One way or another, each of us uses a great deal of energy, and much of that energy use adds CO_2 to the atmosphere as a result of combustion.

How much CO_2 does each American produce per year as a result of our energy-use patterns? On average, each of us adds over 5 metric tons of carbon to the atmosphere annually in the form of CO_2 (the total weight of the CO_2 is about 20 metric tons, when the weight of the oxygen is included).

People in Africa produce, on average, about 5% of the amount of CO_2 that Americans do. What is more, Chwa (the !Kung tribe teenager described in the Reading), who uses no fossil fuels at all, probably produces less than 1% the amount of CO_2 as the average American teenager. Energy use definitely has an impact on the global carbon cycle.

Table 4

Sources of U.S. Energy Consumption

SOURCE	PERCENT OF TOTAL ENERGY USE
Petroleum (oil and gasoline)	40
Natural gas	23
Coal	22
Nuclear power	7
Hydroelectric power and other renewable power sources	8

(Adapted from the Environmental Almanac, World Resources Institute, 1993, Houghton Mifflin)

Background Information: Energy Use and CO_2 Production

The amount of energy used for nonbiological or technological processes by people in different parts of the world varies by as much as three orders of magnitude. Most of the nonfood uses of energy are, in one manner or another, based on combustion. Some uses are based directly on combustion (such as burning oil for home heating or gasoline for powering a car), while others are indirect (e.g., burning coal to create electricity to power a hairdryer). Because of the vast quantities of fossil fuels burned to produce the energy that industrial societies require, human energy use becomes intimately linked with the global carbon cycle: CO_2 is a major output of fossil fuel combustion.

Discussion Questions

In your classroom discussions following students' calculations of their personal energy budgets, be sure students realize that they use vastly more energy than they are able to account for at first. When they use a manufactured item, such as a stereo or an automobile, it is relatively simple to account for direct energy use. A stereo played for 2 hours uses so many kilocalories per minute, a car needs so many gallons of gasoline (which contain a known number of kilocalories per gallon), so the total energy use can be calculated. It is crucial, however, to think about a manufactured item's history when considering energy use.

The following questions are just a few you can ask about energy use by manufactured goods.

How much energy was required to build the item? To ship the item from the factory to its warehouse, to the retail store, and eventually to your home? To collect and refine the raw materials that make up the item? Was energy spent in packaging, marketing, and advertising the item? Is energy required to dispose of the item when it is no longer used?

You probably will find it useful to take a couple of concrete examples from students' energy-use logs and expand them in this manner. Even apparently innocuous activities such as eating a head of organic lettuce contain hidden energy costs: the lettuce probably was kept under refrigeration at the market, shipped from a distant farm, and required a tractor in its cultivation.

You may also want to remind your students that, like living systems, technological systems are not very efficient. Of the many kilocalories a car consumes when it is driven, only about 10–15% get converted into mechanical energy. The rest of the energy is radiated as useless heat (unless you are using your heater on a cold day or like to cook fish fillets wrapped in aluminum foil on your engine block). The following discussion describes in detail the ways in which energy is lost from an automobile engine.

Cars: Where does the energy go?

Most of the energy used by a car is lost as heat. Let's see where those losses occur by considering a 2-ton car traveling at 40 mph. We assume that the car is using the chemical energy in its gasoline at a rate of 72 kW, or 17 kcal/sec (remember, 1 W = 0.24 cal/sec; so 1 kW = 0.24 kcal/sec).

Of that energy, about 80% (around 57 kW, or 14 kcal/sec) is lost in the engine as heat (thermal energy) and unburned carbon compounds. Of the remaining 20% (more or less), about one-seventh of the energy (2.2 kW, or 0.5 kcal/sec) is used to run electrical devices, such as the fuel pump, oil pumps, and lights, while even more is lost as heat from the transmission and drive train (about 3 kW, or 0.7 kcal/sec). Thus, we are left with only around 9 kW (or 2.2 kcal/sec) to move the car's weight.

We began with an energy input of about 72 kW (17 kcal/sec), and the mechanical energy output is about 9 kW (2.2 kcal/sec), so the efficiency of our car is about 9 kW (output) for every 72 kW (input), or 12.5%. Of course, these numbers will vary somewhat depending on circumstances. If the car is lighter or has a very fuel-efficient engine, the efficiency will climb toward 15% or a little more. If the car has a very high average speed, is quite heavy, or is not tuned correctly, or the road conditions are unfavorable, the efficiency will drop toward 10%. Further, if the car stops and goes a lot, its efficiency will drop as well.

Summing Up

As the completion of this Exploration, students take all their various energy-use data and apply them to the global carbon cycle. They now can use their summary data about energy use to calculate roughly their per-capita CO_2 emission for a year. They easily should be able to calculate Chwa's per-capita emission (her biological energy use + wood burned). Ask the students to multiply their per-capita figure by the number of persons in their family and then to compare their own family's emissions with those of Chwa's family, estimated similarly.

For your own reference, the Environmental Almanac estimates approximately 22 tons (about 20,000 kg) per capita per year in the United States.

The Explorations in this chapter have given the students many pieces of the global carbon puzzle that they may not have had before. They are now ready to reconsider the global warming debate, this time from their own points of view and with a richer understanding of the issues.

INTEGRATION GUIDE
Revisiting the Global Warming Debate

This "revisit" requires the students to recall the information in the global warming debate in the Case Study and to interpret their earlier positions in light of the Explorations they have undertaken since then. It might be good to start by asking the students to state what their attitudes were when they started Exploration 1 and how their views have changed, if at all, and why.

You may prefer to keep this discussion in class short, and then assign a written report from each student. Students now should be quite aware of the interactions between policy and science, of the indeterminacy (within limits) of our ability to "know the answers" about current and future global climate change, and of the systematic connections that bind the carbon and energy budget of an individual organism to the global system. The sum of all the biotic activity, plus the abiotic dynamics of the earth system, is the global carbon cycle. A dramatic change in the behavior of one compartment of the system—the decomposers, the primary producers, the fossil carbon pool—can tip the current balance in the system, either toward more atmospheric CO_2 or toward less. The consequences are still under investigation.

INTEGRATION
Revisiting the Global Warming Debate

In the Case Study, we discussed the global warming debate from three angles. You were part of a group that argued for one of those three positions, but you may not have agreed with the position you were representing.

What was your position on the issue of global warming and what to do about it?

Has your position changed since then? Why or why not?

Do you have questions now that you did not have before? What are they?

How would you describe the relationship between the carbon and energy budget of an individual organism and the global carbon cycle?

SCIENCE BACKGROUND
Cycling Carbon

SYSTEMS

Open and Closed Systems

Systems may be either "open" or "closed." In an open system, the material flowing through the system enters the system from an outside pool (known as a source) and exits to a pool outside the system (a sink). Closed systems have neither external sources nor sinks; the material simply cycles within the system. Most systems found in nature are open, as are the model systems that students will build in class.

Nested Systems

Systems are almost always nested within larger systems. For example, we could study the traffic system of a neighborhood or the traffic system of the entire city in which that neighborhood is found. At a higher level, the traffic system of an entire state or country could be the focus of our study.

Similarly, biological systems are nested. We can study a single organ as a system, a group of linked organs, multiple individual organisms (a population), or multiple populations (a community). A biological community along with its physical environment make up an ecosystem, and a group of ecosystems can be studied as a single system. In this Unit, we are studying the sum of all the earth's ecosystems and treating them as part of a single global carbon and energy system.

ON CYCLING CARBON (for Exploration 4)

In the carbon cycle activities, we consider the various elements of the cycle with reference to the atmosphere, which is an important pool in several respects:

- It is the source from which carbon is fixed by photosynthesis.
- It is perhaps the easiest component of the global cycle to sample.
- It is the destination for all the CO_2 evolved from terrestrial systems (by metabolic respiration or combustion).
- It is the most dynamic of the major pools (on our time scale) with daily, seasonal, and annual fluctuations and (because of the nature of fluids) with much local variation.
- Atmospheric carbon plays an important role in global climate because it is a "greenhouse gas," absorbing and reradiating heat energy.
- Human activity affects the atmosphere to a large degree, both directly and indirectly, with consequences of unknown extent.

The atmosphere thus can be seen as a major crossroads for carbon pathways between several reservoirs: biomass, sea, geological formations. For that reason, we have chosen to focus on CO_2 as the state of carbon to use as the beginning and the end of the cycle.

As in the earth itself, the house that the students consider contains carbon in various compounds. You may wish to remind them that all living or previously living materials contain carbon compounds and that present and former plants may have the highest carbon content. Petroleum derivatives, especially fossil fuels, also contain large proportions of organic compounds.

Thus, the pools of carbon within the house will include living things, dead material, and carbon compounds in essentially mineral forms. The categories are straightforward enough, as shown in Table 5.

Table 5 **Household Carbon Pools**

CATEGORY	ITEMS
Living	People Pets Plants Commensal animals and parasites
Formerly living	Wood, bone, shell, etc., products Plant-fiber products, including paper Food
Other (also formerly living, but with more metamorphosis)	Fuel oil Charcoal Chalk Lime for lawns Concrete/cement in foundations (including calcium carbonate) Asphalt shingles

Each compound listed in Table 5 ends up as CO_2 by a different process, and not all of them take place in the space of the house system itself. Although the two basic processes are metabolic respiration and combustion, the "pathway" sometimes may seem more like a maze. Organic compounds in the form of food "leave" by several different routes: some stay as tissue in the inhabitants (human and nonhuman), some leave as excreta or as garbage (examples of bulk transfer out of the house system entirely). Each of those transformations or transfers happens on a different time scale. Garbage becomes CO_2 primarily by metabolic respiration by detritivores or incineration, but in landfills organic matter can last for years before decaying.

In the course of the Explorations in this Chapter, students confront the basic notions of pools, pathways, flow rates, and residence times. (You may be familiar with other terms that have slightly different connotations, such as turnover time, reservoir, and fluxes.) For each carbon-containing material, the students should estimate approximate quantities of that material and the length of time it might stay in the house and conjecture about how it will "get to" CO_2. They might rank items by size or by life span and also by the kind of transfer the substance undergoes. Thus, food probably has the shortest residence time and leaves by two routes—human ingestion or as garbage. In the latter case, some decomposition typically takes place before the garbage leaves the house, but the primary decomposition takes place elsewhere. In the case of ingestion by organisms, the students will be able then to account for the fate of the material using the energy-use equation (see **Unit 2, Chapter 2**).

The structural elements of the house probably are the largest pool and have the longest residence time. Some of the house occasionally may be replaced and thus leave (like the garbage) in bulk transfer to be burned elsewhere or perhaps to rot. Some percentage (it may be a large percentage, over time) may be consumed by insects (ants, termites) or fungi (dry rot). The majority will remain, perhaps only getting to CO_2 by way of a fire.

Living creatures, fabrics, and perhaps furniture are likely to be small or intermediate pools, with varying residence times and varying fates. Over the course of the day, the biotic pool shrinks and grows as the humans (and perhaps pets) move out and in. The biomass increases slowly over the course of the years as children and house plants grow. As a proportion of the total carbon of the house, that can be significant.

Students may want to animate the dynamics of carbon flow in a small system like this house, either using a computer program or by developing a time series of "snapshots," showing the state of each pool and the flow rates along each pathway. The models could then be used in the construction of a carbon cycle for the earth in a later activity.

REFERENCES

Gotelli, Nicholas J. 1995. A Primer of Ecology. Sunderland, MA: Sinauer Press.
A very good introduction to ecological modeling, though not to atmospheric modeling.

Primack, Richard B. 1995. A Primer of Conservation Biology. Sunderland, MA: Sinauer Press.
A concise overview of the science of biological diversity.

Wilson, E. O. 1992. The Diversity of Life. Cambridge: Harvard University Press, Belknap Press.
A moving and lucid exposition of the origins, nature, and threats to biological diversity.

WATER

MODULE THREE OVERVIEW

Water has two key roles, ecologically: it is essential to the metabolic processes of all living beings, and it is a physical medium, carrying things from place to place.

This Module considers water in both roles. It explores global patterns of water storage and cycling and their effects on habitat types and geographic distribution of those habitats. It considers how the amount of water in a habitat influences the presence, numbers, and kinds of organisms that can live there.

Water's unique physical and biochemical properties underlie its ecological characteristics. How do they differ from the properties of other substances? How do its properties contribute to water's suitability for transport, in a single cell, in a circulatory system, in rivers and watersheds, and across the globe as a whole?

The water Big Picture—water's global importance and its dual physical and biological roles—is drawn in part by integrating smaller-scale pictures (although any complex picture is more than just the sum of its parts). This Module helps students explore water at scales from the biochemical to the global, so they can develop tools and building blocks both to understand each scale independently and to integrate those blocks into an ever widening, cross-scale picture, ultimately yielding part of the Big Picture.

WATER

MODULE THREE CONTENTS

Groupings and What They Mean

Unit 1

GROUPINGS AND WHAT THEY MEAN

UNIT

CONTENTS

Unit 1 Overview

Groupings and What They Mean

This Unit helps students develop some understanding of ecology through the roles of water on this planet. When the students group the habitats in Exploration 1 of **Chapter 1**, you and they will discover ideas they have about water and ecosystems (habitats). Focusing on amounts of water in different regions and the plants that can or cannot grow there, by the end of **Chapter 1** students likely have a real sense that ecology includes nonliving (abiotic) and living (biotic) things and that it is about the relationships and interactions

- among living things
- between living and nonliving things,

as shown by the arrows below

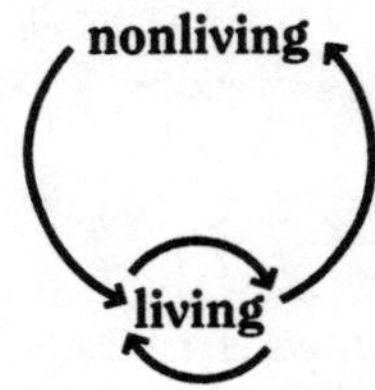

Those interactions form systems, which are both closed and dynamic. "Closed" means that (most) pieces of the system are recycled rather than used up, although they can take various forms. Thus, water is used by plants—for cooling, in photosynthesis (where it is chemically broken down to produce plant tissue and carbon dioxide), and to move stuff like nutrients around. Although water moves around, changes state, and is even broken down chemically, its component parts (elements) are preserved. The "dynamic" aspect of systems refers to that continuous movement and change of state (e.g., of water molecules).

Systems principles are by no means restricted to ecology. They are highly generalizable and can be applied to anything, from human relations of any sort to specific situations: a classroom, a factory, a family, a cultural or political group.

All the Units in this text include pedagogical as well as ecological principles or concepts. This first Unit, however, includes a few that are used throughout.

Having students group things and describe their reasons or criteria for groupings is a powerful tool. Students presented with "raw materials" must respond to those materials directly and explicitly. In doing so, they reveal much of their attitudes, conceptions, and understanding of those materials. Set up well, an Exploration that involves grouping most anything is empowering. Students discover that they do know something about the materials being grouped, whether it is that forests have trees, that some trees do and some do not lose their leaves, or that deserts have no trees at all. Forced back on their own resources, students tend to discover that they actually have resources—which they otherwise are likely to deny or at least doubt. And you may be amazed at the novelty, depth, and breadth of those resources. Your students will come up with things you have not thought of, and we hope you will delight in their abilities.

The third major idea around which this Unit is built is that of being "right" or "wrong" and making intelligent approximations. Students will group habitats in very different ways, but ways that can be equally accurate, depending on context. It is essential in doing research to keep seeing things in different ways; we hope early experience with that mode of thinking and seeing things from different perspectives will help free students from preconceptions about "right" and "wrong" and the idea that there is always one "correct" answer. The **Technique: 21 Questions to Conclusions** reinforces aspects of this type of thinking. Asking questions does not mean you are dumb, it means you are thinking (**Chapter 2**, Case Study and Excerpt). And approximating things to an order of magnitude is a useful tool, not a sloppy or inaccurate way of doing things (**Chapter 1**, Reading: Answers in the Ballpark).

Connections with Other Units

Its breadth means that this Unit connects in essence to all others. Specifically, however, it deals with topics explored in more depth in **Unit 2** of this Module. "Grouping" as a tool is used also in **Units 1**, **2**, and **3** of **Module 2** (with organisms, mammal skulls, and plant types). The **Technique: 21 Questions to Conclusions** (used in **Chapter 2**) can be used about nearly any topic throughout the whole text, indoors or out.

HABITATS—MINE IS DIFFERENT FROM YOURS

CHAPTER ONE

CONTENTS

INTRODUCTION

The work of this Chapter has three major prongs: the doing of science, students becoming more self-aware thinkers/learners, and some concepts about ecological relationships between abiotic and biotic factors. In **Module**

1: **Evolution**, students saw ecology as evolution taking place. In this Chapter, they are asked to take a different perspective, to look at ecology as systems of living and nonliving things: plants, where they live, and the physical reasons why. Certain abiotic factors determine how much plant life and which species occur in a given area. A key abiotic factor is the availability of water (other factors are temperature and light).

In the rest of this Module, we focus on the movement of water in systems such as an organism, a cell, and an ecosystem. Here, however, students think as broadly as possible about the habitats they see. What are the similarities or differences? How do the differences affect the plants and other organisms? What are the patterns in plant distribution (which directly affects the distributions of all other living things)? How do longitude and latitude influence those patterns? Where is the water?

This first Chapter of **Module 3: Water** is intended to:

- excite, interest, and empower students
- set up or illustrate concepts or principles that students will derive or encounter in the Module
- get students to raise questions about those concepts, which they will be able to answer as they progress through the Module
- be repeatable later in the Module, with students redoing the activity, building on what they have learned since their first encounter with it
- allow each student and you to assess his or her ideas about the topics
- get students (to begin) thinking about learning in a new way: by asking questions and by using tools like elaboration, making order-of-magnitude approximations, and thinking analytically

KEY CONCEPTS

- Ecology is the study of interactions between living and nonliving things and among living things.
- It is the study of systems, which are dynamic and have principles that can be generalized to most other systems.
- The physical, or abiotic, environment (climate, topography, temperature, availability of sunlight) is extremely variable across the globe, in patterns based on latitude and longitude. Plants and other organisms are more common in some parts of the world than in others partly because of those abiotic differences. The patterns of organism distributions follow patterns of abiotic factors.
- Given an open-ended assignment, students might think for themselves, see and not just look, discover they know something, and discover how to learn more.
- "Right" and "wrong" are not the only possible answers. Thoughtful "wrong" answers may have more value for students' conceptual understanding or real learning than thought-free "right" answers and answers by rote.

MATERIALS AND PREPARATION

In Advance

For Exploration 4 in **Chapter 1** of the next Unit, start collecting containers that will hold about 1 cup of soil: plastic pots, yogurt containers, cut-off milk cartons, whatever. You will need fifty if, for example, five student groups test five watering treatments of two plant species.

Also for that same Exploration, if you want students to have already-sprouted beans and corn, you must plant them yourself now and keep them warm (70°–80°F). Keep in mind, however, that doing so will markedly diminish the value of Exploration 4, since students will not be involved in designing or setting up the experimental treatments, the data analysis, or the division of labor for subsequent data collection. We strongly recommend that you do not plant the seeds now. Let that Exploration include work with students to set up and carry out the study, beginning with discussion of hypotheses and methods. Let them plant the seeds. Then in the subsequent 2 to 3 weeks, let them collect the data. Three weeks after planting the seeds, students need a few class sessions for the data analyses. The data can be analyzed pretty much at one's convenience, so it is simple to insert that work into the ongoing sequence of the Module.

Materials

- Students' **homework groupings**
- **Paper** and **writing tools**
- **White board** or **poster paper** if you plan to record and post student thoughts and questions for future reference
- **Technique: Preparing a Presentation** and **Technique: Data** (for Exploration 3)
- Photocopies of **blank world map** for amphibian distributions (Exploration 4) or **tracing paper**

SUGGESTED SEQUENCE OF SESSIONS (6–8)

Homework

Exploration 1 (Homework): Grouping Habitats. Working alone, students group some habitat photos and write brief explanations or rationales for their groupings.

Class Session 1

Discuss groupings and rationales from the homework; use the groupings to introduce the topic.

Now working in teams of three to five, students develop habitat groups using the homework as background. They note why each set has been made, its defining characteristic(s), or how the habitats are like or unlike (Exploration 1 (Class): Grouping Habitats).

Teams present their groupings and rationale to the class for general discussion.

(This can carry over into the next session, if necessary.)

Homework

In Case Study: Solving Mysteries: Everything Has Many Names, students find that adding names or roles to a thing adds to their understanding of that thing and how it fits into the world.

Class Session 2

Briefly discuss the key points of the Case Study.

Continue class discussion from Session 1. Building on student observations, pose questions about climate and plant and animal types. Note that there are no "right" and "wrong" groupings, just different groupings.

Let students, working in their original teams, find their habitats on the map (Exploration 2) (this can also be assigned as homework).

Class Session 3

Continue from Session 2, as appropriate.

Student teams compare habitats based on more detailed ecological data (Exploration 3). Each team studies two habitats, one from each list. They consider what is or is not similar about their habitats and why.

Each team then compares habitats with another team that has at least one similar habitat.

Homework

Expanding the idea that learning requires thought, students encounter the tool of order-of-magnitude approximations and how they are used (Reading 1: Answers in the Ballpark: Useful Approximations).

Class Session 4

Discuss Reading 1. Can students use this order-of-magnitude way of thinking to help them consider habitat differences?

Teams present their results of habitat comparisons and discuss key components of habitat differences (water availability, temperature, and plant productivity).

Class decides how to present data to show any trends.

Class Session 5

Continue Session 4, especially if formal reports are being presented. Then, switching modes slightly, students map amphibian distributions (Exploration 4). How do the amphibian data match their habitat distribution data? Why?

Homework

Reading 2 adds another piece to the picture of habitat differences: plant productivity where water is freely available, that is, in aquatic habitats.

Class Session 6

Discuss Reading 2, noting that the most productive habitat of all, wetlands, has unlimited water and light.

The class reflects on the work so far, including questions and predictions to be considered as the Module progresses.

For the Integration, students individually write up what they have learned about learning and about kinds of habitats and why they might be the way they are.

SESSION GUIDES, BY WORKSHEET

EXPLORATION 1 GUIDE (Homework)
Grouping Habitats

HABITAT PHOTOS

1. Desert and dry grassland (steppe)
2. Boreal forest (taiga)
3. Tropical rain forest 1
4. Tundra
5. Equatorial desert
6. Temperate hardwood forest
7. Savannah 1
8. Temperate grassland
9. Tropical grassland (savannah 2)
10. Grassy wetland (marsh)
11. Tropical evergreen rain forest
12. Tropical deciduous forest

For their homework, students worked individually on grouping the habitat pictures. Now, by way of introduction in class, have students tell you how they grouped the habitats and why. Make neutral comments on the groupings; put some on the board. The point is to let students hear each other's thoughts. Possible groupings may be ecologically sophisticated, biological rather than ecological, or based on categories like color, trees or other plants (some, many, or none), few or many species, wet or dry, some, many, or no animals, warm or cold, just to name a few. (Some of the similarities may not be detectable from photographs, and students may use many of their own assumptions about the habitats.)

How quickly you move on to the team work depends on the diversity of groupings made by individual students and the liveliness of the discussion.

EXPLORATION 1 GUIDE (Class)
Grouping Habitats

HABITAT PHOTOS

Tundra
Boreal forest (taiga)
Temperate hardwood forest
Temperate grassland
Equatorial desert
Tropical grassland (savannah 2)
Tropical deciduous forest
Tropical evergreen rain forest

Following the discussion, have students work in teams of three to five to explore further how the natural world is organized (grouped) and why. It is important that students do not feel that they are expected to know the answers to the questions they are considering here. On the contrary, a primary goal of this activity is for students to discover how much they do know and to get a baseline reading of how they currently think about the concepts involved in the Exploration. Later in this Module, after they have worked in depth with related materials and acquired more tools to help make sense of the natural world, they will revisit this Exploration and reexamine their thinking.

Getting Started and Possible Questions

Ask students to name factors they think might keep some organisms from surviving in any habitat. They likely will bring up climate (temperature, winter, snow, heat, or some other aspect); from there, other associations are easily forthcoming. Students may also have questions. Some are questions of fact (are the habitats geographically far apart?), while others are more complex and can be answered only as the Module progresses or only superficially now but with more meaning later in the Module. (Why do deserts not have trees? Why is there so much stuff in tropical forests?)

Other questions you might want to ask include these: In what ways are the habitats similar or not similar? What are the vegetation types? What physical factors are associated with each vegetation type?

Latitude and longitude, or physical location, account for the abiotic factors that affect the living things in each location. The most important factors that determine what lives where are water, temperature, and light.

Because only plants can get their energy from sunlight, locations often are categorized by the amount of plant tissue that grows there and vary widely in their plant productivity.

Since the students will raise issues that carry through the rest of this Module, you may want to set aside a section of blackboard or post some large sheets of paper on which to list and keep the questions handy for reference in the future.

Team Reports and Class Discussion: Possible Groupings

After 15 to 20 minutes, have each team put its groupings and relationships on the board. Habitats can be grouped geographically (on the same continent or within the same belt of latitude), by types of vegetation (deciduous vs. piney vs. no trees). That means that, from the point of view of geographic distribution, the second set of habitats might not be accurately grouped. It may well be, however, that the second set is grouped in a way that is ecologically valid, for instance, all deserts together. Geographic distribution makes that impossible and a "wrong" pairing, but it is correct in that it shows some ecological understanding of the habitat types.

It is, of course, important to encourage such ecological or "habitat type" thinking while also being clear that the deserts do not coexist geographically. This nicely makes the point that "right" and "wrong" can depend on context and that there are multiple ways to look at or think about something even as apparently simple as a grouping of organisms.

Save copies of the diagrams and questions to revisit later.

CASE STUDY GUIDE
Solving Mysteries: Everything Has Many Names

This Case Study considers one of three powerful tools used by ecologists (and others), that of renaming things. Substituting names and putting together information or roles are important ways of revisioning—that is, expanding one's vision—of an organism or a person. In their groupings, especially by Exploration 3, students expand their images and ideas of the habitats they are considering. This Case Study specifically articulates that tool and its value. It also uses an example of a math proof to show students they have used this tool before and to help them connect their work here with previous work. Some students may think such changing of names or roles is cheating, that no actual work has happened. But its usefulness usually overcomes such feelings. (One way you can monitor students' grasp of concepts in this Module is by the relative richness of their ideas about habitats. Do they describe a desert simply as dry? Or do they see multiple aspects: a habitat type that can be cold or hot; that has too little water to support large plants but may have plants nonetheless; that is associated with certain latitudes; that can have nutrient-rich or -poor soils?)

EXPLORATION 2 GUIDE
Mapping Habitats

Students see where various habitats occur and begin to develop distribution patterns. It is easy to see that different plants and animals live in different places. But why species live where they do and in what numbers is a central theme in ecology. Putting their habitats on the map helps students make associations between longitude and latitude and the abiotic factors (temperature, water, sunlight) they produce with animal distributions. If you have worked through **Module 2**, **Unit 2**, remind yourselves of the two habitats (the Serengeti and the Northern Hardwood Forest) and the types of life they supported. Locate them on the map.

EXPLORATION 3 GUIDE
What Makes Habitats Different?

Logistics

Depending on your class size, ask students to work in teams of two to five. There are eight habitats, four in each list. Assign each group of students one habitat from each list to read for homework. The lists are designed to provide contrast between habitat pairs with some students having a habitat in common. That makes for more stimulating discussion.

LIST 1	LIST 2
Tundras	Boreal forests (taigas)
Equatorial deserts and scrubs	Northern hardwood forests
Temperate grasslands	Tropical deciduous forests
Tropical grasslands (savannahs)	Tropical evergreen rain forests

Difference Factors

Students examine their habitat pairs in detail, especially with respect to differences or similarities. They may want to make a chart to show their data more efficiently. As they mull over those data, they likely will see a connection between water availability and plant productivity (net primary productivity) and between water availability and vegetation type.

Let a pair of teams that share one habitat discuss their findings, then have a whole class discussion. To compare all the habitats, the class must decide on some means of presenting the data in a table or a graph. (For more, see the **Technique: Preparing a Presentation** and the **Technique: Data**.)

Three major factors—water, temperature, and light—interact in determining the pattern of distribution of life on earth. Those factors determine which species of plants and other organisms and how many of them can live in a particular climate. (An additional important factor is history—which ancestor species were there. For more on this, see the Extension: Continental Drift and Evolution.)

Location

The location of an area, its latitude and longitude, determines the climate conditions to which it is subjected (rainfall, temperature, length of growing season). In general, wet habitats tend to have more organisms and more species than dry ones. The length of the growing season (i.e., the number of warm sunny days) and the average temperature also are important, although they have opposing effects as well. As temperature rises, evaporation also rises, so more water is needed. Yet, on average, the higher the average temperature, the longer the growing season.

Plant Productivity

One way of measuring the differences between habitats is net primary production (NPP). NPP is a measure of plant biomass accumulated in a habitat over a given period of time. In other words, it is all the carbon and energy the plants fixed and did not use up themselves for their own respiration. The usual units of measure of NPP are dry grams per square meter per year.

NPP increases as precipitation increases. NPP also increases as evaporation from plant leaves increases, until evaporation is too high (in deserts, for example). Plants such as cacti are found in the drier areas. Grasses predominate where not enough water is available to support forests or where rainfall is high, as in a forested area, but temperature (especially during the growing season) is higher, increasing evaporation. How much water supports a forest depends partly on temperature and partly on how fast the water evaporates.

There is a general equation for primary productivity:

$$\mathbf{GPP = NPP + R}$$

where GPP is gross primary productivity, NPP is net primary productivity, and R is autotroph or plant respiration. Gross primary productivity is all the energy and carbon fixed by autotrophs in a particular location in 1 year.

Some of the energy and carbon fixed by the autotrophs or plants is used by them for their own respiration, and therefore is not available for use by other organisms.

Conifers predominate in northern forests in part because their wood differs from that of broad-leaved trees. Their internal structure prevents the water supply from the roots from being cut off by air bubbles formed by freezing. Table 1 lists the habitats and their characteristics.

Table 1

Habitat Data

HABITAT	NPP (DRY G/M²/YR)	RAINFALL (CM/YR)	ALTITUDE (M ABOVE SEA LEVEL)	LATITUDE	AVERAGE ANNUAL TEMPERATURE (°C)	EVAPORATION FROM SOIL (G WATER/M²/DAY)	EVAPORATION FROM PLANT LEAVES (G WATER/M²/DAY)
Equatorial desert and scrubs	70	0 to 50	200 to 500	0° to 30° north and south	–5 to 30	10,000–15,000	1,380–6,900
Tundras	140	5 to 80	0 to 200	above 60° north	–6 to –15	< 2,000	207–621
Temperate grasslands	600	5 to 75	500 to 1,000	30° to 60° north	4 to 18	5,000–6,000	6,210
Boreal forests (taigas)	800	25 to 200	0 to 200	45° to 60° north	–6 to 3	4,000	1,932–2,346
Tropical grasslands (savannahs)	900	20 to 80	500 to 1,000	0° to 30° north and south	18 to 30	10,000–15,000	6,210
Tropical deciduous forests	1,600	100 to 250	200 to 1,000	0° to 30° north and south	18 to 30	5,000–6,000	1,096–1,932
Northern hardwood forests	2,000	50 to 250	0 to 500	30° to 60° north	3 to 18	5,000–6,000	1,867–5,772
Tropical rain forests	2,200	250 to 450	0 to 3,000	0° to 30° north and south	18 to 30	3,000–4,000	2,484–2,760

Possible Questions (and Answers)

Why do some places not have forests?

(Forests are in areas with higher rainfall than grasslands. Rainfall that allows a forest to grow at one average annual temperature allows only a grassland at a higher average annual temperature.)

Which habitats are most productive?

(Those with the highest NPP.)

What physical factors are associated with high NPP?

(High rainfall and high evaporation from plants, except in deserts, where high evaporation causes plants to dry out and die.)

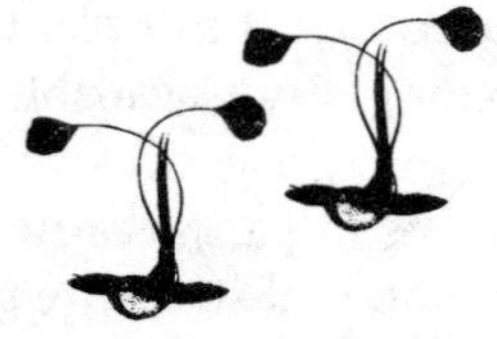

READING 1 GUIDE
Answers in the Ballpark: Useful Approximations

To keep students thinking and learning, here they encounter a useful (and sometimes unsettling) tool: order-of-magnitude approximations. They may find it unsettling because it seems so imprecise, so "unscientific." Yet it is neither. As a first approximation, it is important to get the scope or scale of a question—to find its order of magnitude. Whether considering size (length) of molecules (from 10^{-9} nanometers for water), bacteria (10^{-5} nm), or mammals (10^{1} m), it frames our thinking to know approximate size ranges. After all, molecules are influenced by things like electrostatic charges and capillarity, while mammals are subject to gravity. (For more on this, see Reading 2 in **Chapter 5** of **Module 2**, **Unit 2**.)

A first take on any problem requires some idea of its magnitude. The combination of educated guesses, facts, and common sense can be a powerful aid to framing a problem, whether about piano tuners, stars in the Milky Way, or relative habitat productivity (Exploration 3). Many fields use such rough calculations. There are, however, important caveats:

- State the assumptions made at each step.
- Remember that the numbers are rough.
- Use the numbers appropriately as approximations.
- Upgrade the numbers with direct data whenever possible.

There is also a big difference between sloppiness and a rough approximation. Sloppiness is never appropriate, but an approximation is a good starting place for problem solving.

EXPLORATION 4 GUIDE
How Are Amphibians Like Plants?

Like plants, amphibians are more common where water is plentiful (although a few specialized frogs and toads are exceptions, as described later). Amphibian skin is not waterproof. On the contrary, most amphibians get their water through their skin rather than by drinking it. And most of their "breathing," or oxygen intake and CO_2 output, is actually via dissolved gases passing through their skin.

Amphibians reproduce in or around water; their eggs have no shells, so they must be laid in spots with plenty of moisture to keep them from drying out. Some amphibians are aquatic all their lives; others hatch in water, spend part of their lives there, then undergo metamorphosis into land-dwelling adults. Even land-dwelling amphibians must stay in moist areas most of the time to keep from drying out and dying. Amphibians are cold-blooded, so they cannot keep their body temperatures much above their surroundings. Being cold-blooded also makes it impossible for them to be active during freezing weather.

As students compare the distribution of salamanders with the distribution of habitat types, they see the correlation between water availability and the numbers of salamander species. Be sure students note the number of species in each family as well as the number of families in a location.

Extreme Amphibians

Although most amphibians live in warm, moist climates, some live in very dry or very cold places. The typical amphibian requires water for all stages of its life, as do these unusual species. But "extreme amphibians" are like dry-habitat plant species. They have various specializations (adaptations) that allow them to survive even drought conditions.

The spadefoot toad lives in Arizona. It burrows into the ground down almost a meter and hides there from the heat and sun for 9 months of the year. Even during rains, spadefoot toads come out only at night. Two African frog species spend the dry season on tree limbs without drying out, but no one knows how they do that. Some frogs and salamanders that live in dry habitats form cocoons. They burrow into the ground and there make a waterproof cocoon around themselves, formed of many layers of dead skin and mucus.

Burrowing frogs and toads absorb water from the soil while they are underground. They can also store water in their bodies. Some tree-living frog species survive the hot sun by producing oils and waxes that they wipe all over their bodies to hold in the water, just as humans use creams for dry skin.

Some species of salamanders and frogs can tolerate cold temperatures and are common in North America, Europe, and Asia in areas with cold winters. These amphibians spend the winter underground and come to the surface in the spring when temperatures become warm. The common North American frogs *Hyla crucifer*, *Hyla versicolor*, and *Rana sylvatica* are among them. These frogs have survived up to 5 days at –6°C in laboratory studies. About 35% of their body fluids actually froze. The frogs survive in part by having "blood" or body fluids that include a high proportion of glycerol, a chemical that freezes at much lower temperatures than does water. The glycerol acts as an antifreeze, enabling these species to survive temperatures that would rupture them if their body fluids were more watery. (Remember that frozen water has more volume than an equal weight of liquid water.) Some insect species are active in cold times and places because they also produce glycerol.

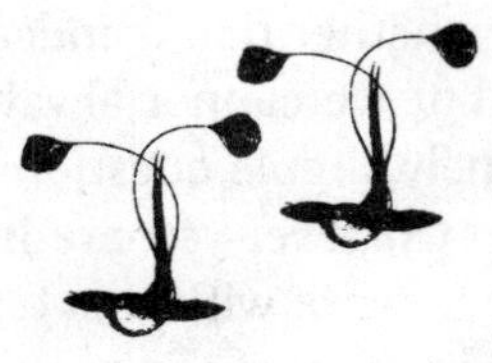

READING 2 GUIDE
Submerged Net Primary Production

Water habitats obviously differ from terrestrial ones, and since a large part of the earth's surface is covered with water, we cannot ignore them. If we look beyond precipitation at total water availability, habitats can be ordered from the most to the least moist. That scale puts oceans at one end and deserts at the other. The most productive habitats are somewhere in the middle, toward the wet end.

Nutrients

All aquatic habitats receive their nutrients and much of their water from surrounding land or bottom sediments. The NPP in an aquatic habitat depends on how many nutrients enter the habitat relative to the volume of water and how long the system is able to retain those nutrients. In other words, in an aquatic habitat there is plenty of water, but the nutrients may be less plentiful (diluted). In addition to the size of the body of water and the rate at which water flows through it, the distance of a habitat from land or the bottom (its nutrient source) is a factor in productivity.

Wetlands: The Most Productive of All

Wetlands are among the most productive habitats on earth (average NPP is 2,000 dry g/m^2/yr). They are so productive because they are not limited by water availability, and nutrients usually are plentiful. Their most obvious limitation is length of growing season.

What do wetlands have in common with the most productive terrestrial habitats? (Water is not in limited supply.) What do wetlands have in common with the most productive aquatic habitats? (Abundant nutrients, close proximity to source of nutrients.)

If you can find one, a wetland in your area makes an excellent study site.

INTEGRATION GUIDE

The Difference between Facts and Ideas

The work of this Chapter has three major prongs: the doing of science, students becoming more self-aware thinkers/learners, and some concepts about ecological relationships. You already have some measure of student progress with the first and third prongs from their work in Exploration 1 and Exploration 2. The second prong is addressed in Reading 1, the Case Study, and directly in the Integration.

Facts

The Integration directly addresses the issue of "facts" or "truth" and students' reactions. The discussion of "what is a fact?" will likely raise numerous issues: relative and absolute truth, proof, sources and their validity or accuracy, what is knowable, and how we know it. Help students develop a crude hierarchy of facts using their ideas about whether there are different kinds of facts. "The sun is shining" is an apparently simple and verifiable fact. But someone will (or you might) ask whether that is indeed the question. Technically, the sun always shines, but we cannot always see it. So what are the "facts" in this case? A genuinely simple question and answer might be, "Are you all in classroom number whatever-you-are-in?" How can the students verify that? As they continue to work with this text, they will expand their ideas about facts and truth. A key tool of analytical thinking is context: what is true under these circumstances and at this time might well not be true otherwise.

Feelings

Since the pedagogical approach of this text is somewhat unusual, you might find it interesting and helpful to follow students' self-reflection as learners and their growth as thinkers. Good science is the consequence of logical thinking, creativity, asking and answering questions, tolerating uncertainty, and the willingness to make mistakes. Some of these can be hard, and it is important for you and your students to know that. It is also important to know how students (and you!) feel about asking questions, about uncertainty, about relative truths and context-specific truth. Some people love uncertainty, some hate it, some are indifferent. Clearly it can be more difficult for someone who dislikes uncertainty to engage in open-ended work, just as it can be more difficult for someone who dislikes structure to follow detailed instructions. In our experience, however, this is much like playing an instrument, drawing, or participating in a sport. Everyone can do it, but some do it more easily and naturally than others.

Since much of the work to come will be done in small groups, you may find that mixed groups are more productive: an uncertainty tolerator with the opposite, a math hater with a number cruncher, an urban bug with a hiker nut, and so on.

You will see students' attitudes toward science and learning change over time. Ask them the same question after six weeks, after three months, and at the end of the year.

INTEGRATION
The Difference between Facts and Ideas

What is a fact? Is it what someone tells you? "No!" you probably shout, remembering things you have been told that were not true.

Well, is it something you read? No! You doubtless can also remember things you have read that did not agree with each other or with something you know. So which one is true? How can you tell? If you read things that contradict each other, it seems that one or the other but not both can be true. When is a fact not a fact?

Procedure

1. **What does a dictionary say?**
So, what is a fact? Look up a definition in one or more dictionaries. Do they make sense to you?

Do you think there are different kinds of facts? If so, give an example of each kind.

Now look up "idea." What is the difference between an "idea" and a "fact"? Do the definitions help you answer the question "What is a fact?" Write down your thoughts.

2. **Ideas, facts, and thinking.**
We have been playing a bit loosely with "facts," with "right" and "wrong" answers, and with calculations in this Chapter. Why? Because thinking, learning, and science are rarely black and white. Like most things, they include lots of gray, lots of nuance, lots of "sort ofs"—as well as facts, right and wrong answers, and highly precise calculations. But you probably have heard more about the latter things than the former ones. And although all are important, sometimes people focus on "right" and "wrong" and lose sight of the thinking, or they get too casual and lose sight of accuracy.

We especially do not want to lose sight of the thinking. Indeed, we are interested in all the above, and we have tried to design this text accordingly. In fact, we believe all are necessary for good learning (thinking) and good science. (Mostly, we hope this text will interest you in facts, ideas, and science, and how they all intersect.)

Now a question.

3. **Your feelings about facts.**
How do you feel about facts and uncertainty? What describes your feelings about "knowing" or "not knowing"? Are those feelings any different since the class discussed various groupings in Exploration 1?

Some people dislike things not being black and white, or feel uncomfortable asking questions, or just want a straight answer, please! Others love puzzles, ambiguity, answering a question with more questions. No feelings are right or wrong—they simply are different, and it is useful to know your own reactions. Knowing your feelings will help you be a more self-aware, and thus a more successful, thinker and learner. If you feel uncomfortable with puzzles and like a lot of structure, try to work with other students who have the opposite reactions. If you view Fermi calculations as a license to go wild, try to work with someone who has a more restrained attitude.

REFERENCES

Duellman, William E., and Linda Trueb. 1986. Biology of Amphibians. Baltimore: Johns Hopkins University Press.

Ricklefs, Robert E. 1976. The Economy of Nature. Portland: Chiron Press.

Rumney, George R. 1968. Climatology and the World's Climates. London: Collier-Macmillan Ltd.

Smith, Robert Leo. 1974. Ecology and Field Biology. 2nd ed. New York: Harper and Row.

Woodward, F. I. 1987. Climate and Plant Distribution. Cambridge: Cambridge University Press.

The first two books (or any basic ecology textbook) give a complete discussion of primary productivity and basic descriptions of climate types and habitats (biomes or ecosystems). The third book is a more technical description of limitations on plant distribution by climate. The fourth reference includes detailed descriptions of weather and climate in general and of the climates of seventeen different ecosystem types (habitats) plus many maps and photos. The last book on the list is a thorough treatise on all aspects of amphibian biology.

EXTENSION
Continental Drift and Evolution

Continental drift is the other major determining factor in the composition of the assemblages of organisms we find on earth today. Continental drift describes change over time in the position (latitude and longitude) of any land mass or particular location. As the continents moved, they also experienced different climates and had plant productivities and organisms suited to those climates. The existing continents are all pieces of one initial huge land mass. When any particular hunk of land broke off, its organisms were like those on the remaining land. But as time passed, the plants and animals on the now separate land masses became more and more different. For example, Australia retained many marsupial mammals, but marsupials in the Americas were displaced over evolutionary time by nonmarsupials.

It was biogeography, the geographic distribution of species, that gave both Darwin and Wallace their ideas about evolution. Modern ideas about plate tectonics have confirmed their views. Following are some references on the subject. You will find more in the fields of geology, geography, ecology, and evolution. There also are many references available under juvenile literature as well, and Duellman and Trueb's book (see References above) contains information on how the continental drift theory of evolution pertains to amphibians.

References

Colbert, Edwin Harris. 1973. Wandering Lands and Animals. New York: Dutton.

Freeman, W. H. 1976. Continents Adrift and Continents Aground: Readings from Scientific American. San Francisco: Scientific American Press.

Marvin, Ursula B. 1973. Continental Drift: The Evolution of a Concept. Washington, D.C.: Smithsonian Institution Press.

GETTING HOOKED THROUGH FIELDWORK

CHAPTER TWO

CONTENTS

INTRODUCTION

As described in the User's Guide (pg. ix), the study of ecology should include close acquaintance with various habitats and some organisms, preferably in their natural surroundings. Nothing can substitute for such direct study, familiarity, and knowledge. Here, students begin connecting their in-class study with observations of some local area(s). This work makes two major points: first, ecology "is" everywhere and can be studied everywhere and, second, asking questions is the beginning of doing science.

The Technique you use to make those two key points is dubbed "21 Questions to Conclusions." It is used widely to introduce ecology students at all levels to the process of doing science and to a field site. It is deceptively simple; its power lies in allowing students to experience the reality that science is a process no more mysterious than asking questions and making and testing predictions. It gets students to raise questions, make predictions, and design ways of testing their predictions, of collecting and analyzing data, and of drawing conclusions.

The Technique can be used as a discussion tool about the process of doing research, or, in its entirety, it can be used to design, develop, and carry out a research project (of any duration).

The full version of the Technique perfectly encapsulates the process of research, without fanfare, jargon, or complication. That means it can also be used in the classroom about various topics or repeatedly in new field sites. Part of its success is that it differs substantially from any previous experience most students have had with "doing science," so—please—try to resist changing it.

Exploration 1 (the first field trip) is designed to introduce students to whatever local habitat is available, in a double period (although it can take more time, if you have it).

Exploration 2 (which is not in the student chapter) is intended to help you set up long or longer-term research projects at the same or another field site and to involve students in more systematic data collection. Projects can be of various durations—a series of 1-hour projects; projects that can be carried out over time, 1 hour at a time (e.g., per week); or long-term monitoring of various sorts (e.g., air or water quality, changes in plant growth or regrowth, seasonal changes in an urban landscape).

KEY CONCEPTS

- Ecology is everywhere—in urban, suburban, rural, and wild areas.
- Students can experience doing science in a fresh and engaging way, via the **Technique: 21 Questions to Conclusions**. This Technique perfectly encapsulates the research process and is a powerful conceptual and enabling experience for learners of all ages.
- Asking questions is an essential step in doing science. It does not mean you are dumb—it means you are thinking.
- Students can do actual research under apparently limited circumstances inside and outside the classroom.
- Students are far more likely to pursue and carry out a project that grows out of their own questions and ideas.

MATERIALS AND PREPARATION

In Advance

- Visit the site before the class trip and become familiar with its topography and components. You may find it helpful to bring a naturalist or an ecologist of some sort—ideally, someone who can help you identify different habitats, organisms, and ecological dynamics at work. See also References.
- Read the **Technique: 21 Questions to Conclusions**. Practice it with friends, colleagues, or ecologists if you can.

Safety

WARNING

Before the field trip, visit the site and note possible safety issues, such as broken glass, abandoned buildings or wells, cliffs, hornets' nests, and plants such as poison ivy or poison oak.

WARNING

Before the field trip, determine whether any of your students has a strong allergic reaction to plants or insect bites or stings (especially bee stings). Take precautions as necessary.

WARNING

Use the buddy system. Although students do the first part of this Exploration individually, remind them to remain in sight of someone else from the group, so they neither get lost nor are ever actually alone.

Materials

- **Time:** For Exploration 1 allow an hour in the field.

Per student:

- **Exploration 1: Your Local Site: Ecology Is Everywhere**
- **Paper and a surface to write on**
- **Pencil** (best for fieldwork, since it will not "run" if it gets damp)

You need:

- **Technique: 21 Questions to Conclusions**
- **Time:** (Plan accordingly for Exploration 2 or skip it altogether if you do not expect to do more fieldwork.)

SUGGESTED SEQUENCE OF SESSIONS (3–5)

Class Session 1

The class goes to a field site, and students work individually to compile a list of 21 questions about the site and the organisms on it. If there is time, the group discusses some of the questions at the site.

Homework

Case Study: Confessions of a Terrified Science Learner

Class Session 2

Discussion of the homework, especially how asking questions affects student work.

Students continue to share their field questions in a class discussion and to add questions that arise from hearing and talking about each other's questions.

If students will be doing field-based or related research, group their general questions by topic or area of work in a class discussion and let students choose a question group to pursue in teams of two to five.

Class Session 3

Continue Session 2, if appropriate. Students begin research or prepare for research.

Homework

Read Excerpt: The Having of Wonderful Ideas.

Class Session 4

Continuing discussion of asking questions and how to do science, including the Excerpt, the Case Study, and the **Technique: 21 Questions to Conclusions**.

Integration

This worksheet can also be used to get students started on their research projects.

Class Session 5

Continue previous session, if appropriate.

SESSION GUIDES, BY WORKSHEET

EXPLORATION 1 GUIDE
Your Local Site: Ecology Is Everywhere

Your work here has two parts: facilitating the process of asking and answering questions and facilitating thinking about ecology. Whether you work in your schoolyard or go somewhere less influenced by humans, you will find much to study—ant or pigeon behavior, distribution and frequency of native and introduced weeds, intertidal organisms, whether or how similar species (bird, squirrel, mouse, plant, etc.) compete or share the habitat, how isolated organisms or populations reproduce and disperse their young, and so on.

If you feel unfamiliar with the field site, preview it with a naturalist or an ecologist to help you see things and discuss ecological concepts. Read local guides. But remember that no one knows "all" about that or any site. Indeed, part of what makes such fieldwork interesting for you as well as your students is that you will be learning with them. It is important, however, to have some ideas about what you might see there, to help students think about some of their questions.

For the Technique, see the **Technique: 21 Questions to Conclusions**.

CASE STUDY GUIDE
Confessions of a Terrified Science Learner

The Case Study continues to lay groundwork for students to think analytically. It raises issues about asking questions: why questions are often discouraged and why questions are essential for learning, especially in science.

The most important part of this Case Study, as with the Excerpt and the Technique, is actually your reaction. How do you, as a teacher, feel about student questions?

Questions Are KEY

Part of this curriculum's philosophy and approach is that questions are a key tool in thinking, learning, and especially doing science. While that may seem an obvious and laudable goal, it is not necessarily supported by the culture at large. As a teacher, you likely have encountered a parent or an authority figure who thinks that students asking questions is "lip" or disrespectful. Or that it is okay to ask questions about some things ("Is this the right answer?") but not about others ("Why do we go to church?"). It also tends to be true that a person who starts asking questions gets into the habit of asking questions, of thinking, and of analyzing things, and will also ask about topics other than those formally being studied. Not everyone is comfortable with that.

Your Feelings

So, how do you feel about student questions? Do they make you anxious because you may not know "the answer"? What if you tried the approach that you and your students are learners together? While you may have more background or information to offer, that certainly does not mean you do or should know everything. Together you and they can discover things. Part of true learning is figuring out how to ask and how to answer questions. You model half of this process—asking questions—anytime you do not know about something. So you are helping your students learn even when you cannot answer their questions, by showing them what to do with questions. You are helping them do science.

We have heard comments like the following from numerous teachers who let students ask more questions and take more of a leading role in the class.

> [About students doing "canned" lab activities] "I realized that they were just following directions. They didn't know what they were doing or why. And they didn't care. Now 50% of my labs are based on student questions. It's not much, but it's a start. And they're much more involved. They care."

"We [she and co-teachers] wish we had listened to students before. We've learned from them."

The Cat Food Analogy

As one high school principal said, "Teaching is like buying cat food: the consumer is not the shopper." Students are the learners, but they have little input to what they get to learn. When they ask questions, they become more involved, they stay involved, they work more and harder, and they come to enjoy their learning because it is self-reinforcing.

EXPLORATION 2 GUIDE

More Research—What, How Much, How Long

Ecology is a vast and complex domain about which we know very little. The list of issues, organisms, interactions, concepts that are unstudied far exceeds the list of those studied. And even what we do "know" is often only superficially or poorly known.

Two key factors contribute to our ignorance: the complexity of the natural world and the fact that many ecological processes take place in a time frame longer than that of most research studies. A master's program is just 1 or 2 years and often requires no research; a Ph.D. research project typically runs 3 to 5 years; a postdoctoral project might be 1 to 3 years. Yet biological or abiotic cycles can be far longer than any of those. How many generations of a tree species or the 17-year cicada can be encompassed in a researcher's lifetime? How many cycles of drought or high snowfall? The complexity of the natural world will begin to reveal itself as we work through this curriculum.

Short Term/Long Term

Research can be carried out on many time scales, from a few minutes to lifetimes. How you choose to work with your students might depend on external factors, like the distance to your site (behind the school vs. some miles by car), scheduling (rare vs. frequent double periods or project days), and your supervisor's attitude about the importance of research. Obviously, it depends on your interest and willingness as well.

Teachers we know have incorporated research into their classes in various ways. Some have focused on frequent short projects, inside or outside the classroom. Others have mixed short (1-hour) projects with longer (several hours a week for several weeks) projects. And a few have gone to the max. One team designed a 6-year project to be carried out by one class from their 7th through 12th grade years. Another designated 10th grade as the "ecology research year" and spent it studying many aspects of the natural world right by their (rural) school.

So consider whether you and your students are interested in a longer-term research project—from a month to a study that crosses years of students and is handed along to the next class. Maybe start small and expand as you feel comfortable.

Topics

But really, what would you do? Well, any of the questions that come out of Exploration 1 could be the starting point for a study. More broadly speaking, there is also a great need for careful natural history observation. When do the migrating birds come and go? Does it vary from year to year? Why might that be? Which native annual plants are thriving, and which are doing less well? Is it competition, invasion by nonnative species, increased average temperatures, effects of increased CO_2, or pollution? How might those effects be separated out from each other?

Start with a time frame within which you can work. Consider questions that can be studied in that time frame. Make predictions and test them by comparing different sites, different seasons, different years—or even by bringing your own predictions into the laboratory and testing them experimentally.

A Long-Term Research Site

Long-term research at a single site is rare and a valuable data source. A school is an excellent home for such a site, although different students might be involved each year. With some standardization of data collection and techniques, the site and studies can go on indefinitely.

Should you choose this route, realize that you have great latitude in what you study. Be sure to include questions that also give short-term answers and satisfaction. This term's students need to get some gratification from the work even if they cannot see, say, a full year in the life of a salamander.

Background Data

Whatever the duration of your research, you need to know things about your site, but you do not necessarily have to collect the information all yourself. A good picture of (parts of) your site can be assembled using the following: Climate data (average monthly precipitation, monthly temperatures, first and last frost); land-use data (how is the site used now? How has it been used in the past? How might that influence which organisms are or are not present?); and species inventory (which plant, animal, and other species live here now? How do they interact? What are their lifestyles and what does that tell you about the site?). Some or all such data might be available from your county extension office, newspaper, weather bureau, nature center, or conservation office.

One basic starting point

One way to begin is by cataloguing all the organisms that live on the site and build on that. In a paved schoolyard, you will find different species than in a lawn, park, or wooded area. Why? What can you learn about the site from the organism and vice versa?

Such close inspection of a site is similar to doing 21 Questions, and will likely also end you up with an armful of interesting questions.

Science Background discusses some important principles in ecology, to help you focus on possible research topics. Please see also the **Technique: Introduction to Research** (especially the first part) and the end of the **Technique: 21 Questions to Conclusions**.

INTEGRATION GUIDE

Turning Questions into Predictions

The Integration gets students to implement many steps of doing science, without calling it that. Students simply build on their interest in a particular (burning) question and end by designing a piece of research. They turn that burning question into a prediction, into a hypothesis (and alternate hypotheses), and (if they carry out the research) even some interpretation and conclusions.

For more on turning a question into a research project, see the **Technique: Introduction to Research**. It may give you fresh insights into parallels between what students are doing here and the process of doing science.

And if students actually carry out the projects they have designed with their Integration, how much the better!

INTEGRATION
Turning Questions into Predictions

After the fieldwork, we have lots of questions. Pick one that particularly interests you (or your group) and try to figure out how to go about answering it. The steps below might help you in this figuring. If any seem not to apply, skip them until later or discuss them with your group or the teacher.

Materials

- **Questions from Exploration 1**

Procedure

1. **Choosing a question.**
   My burning question from our field site is (or what I am going to find out is):

2. **Relevant background.**
   What I already know about this topic is:

3. **Expectations.**
   What I think will happen (turn out) is:

   I think this will happen because:

4. **Other possible influences.**
The following things might influence my data:

To keep track of their effects, I will:

5. **Research materials.**
The equipment I need is:

6. **Comparisons.**
If I am making some comparison, this table shows what I will change and what I will keep the same.

(Use the rest of this worksheet if you actually carry out the research you have suggested in order to answer your question. Answer these questions on a page in your notebook.)

7. **Results.**
What happened during my research or experiment?

8. **Expectations revisited.**
Is it different from what I thought would happen?

9. **What does my work mean?**
What have I found that I did not know before? Even if my work did not turn out as I expected, I learned:

SCIENCE BACKGROUND
Some Key Principles in Ecology

Ecology is a complex and multidisciplinary science. It is everywhere and includes, touches on, requires, many other topics or disciplines. Like the rest of the world, its principles are governed by the laws of thermodynamics. That means that at some levels ecology can be derived from first principles. It also includes more complex interactions, some of which can be explained by genetics, evolution, and natural selection. It includes patterns and interactions that we do not understand at all and probably others we do not even see or know about. What follows are a few broad concepts or principles about which we have some understanding.

THE LAWS OF THERMODYNAMICS

At all levels, from within organisms to global cycles, the flow of energy and matter follows the laws of thermodynamics. Matter (like carbon and nitrogen) cycles, while energy moves in one direction and is "lost." Biological systems are also inefficient at energy transfer; energy is lost (as heat) during every chemical reaction (energy transfer).

EVOLUTION BY NATURAL SELECTION AND GENETIC CONSTRAINTS

An organism has a family tree and a genetic background, which both limit a species (an ostrich cannot act like a mosquito) and provide variation among individuals so they are affected differently by their environment. Some individuals are more or less well suited to their current conditions and thus will survive more or less successfully (experience selection). (In **Module 1** we see that finches with beaks of a given size survive under one set of conditions but die under different conditions 3 years later.) Evolution represents the outcome of natural selection over time. Many studies focus on how evolution is "at work" under particular conditions.

SIZE AND SCALE IN TIME AND SPACE

For an organism, size is more or less genetically defined. It also determines which physical processes influence an organism. For example, organisms smaller than a dragonfly are affected by surface tension and air currents, not gravity; for a giraffe, the reverse is true. In terms of ecosystems, the concept of scale can be applied to many things. At what scale are we considering research? Are we studying an individual, a population, a species, many species? And over what time period might such a study need to be pursued?

Time is obviously another scale issue. Do we want to know how a thing looks right now, or at each season, or across years? How did this forest look 500 years ago? How will it look 500 years from now?

LIMITING RESOURCES

At various levels, there usually are some limiting resources. A plant might grow larger if it had more sunlight, water, nutrients, and space. A species might be more successful if it had more food, less predation, and less competition. A community might have more species if they were more specialized and thus less in competition.

UNUSED RESOURCES

It is also true that there can be resources not used by any species, which creates an apparent vacancy in a community.

INTERACTIONS

Given all the preceding factors and more, ecology focuses on interactions—within, among, and between organisms. Competition among individuals of a species and between species for water, nutrients, and space. Competition within a species for mates. Predation by species on others. Mating. Reproduction. Offspring surviving to reproduce. Dispersing those offspring. Interaction between the physical environment and organisms—how the populations of a species that live in two places can differ. Mutualism. Parasitism. We understand little about many of these interactions, and all need further study.

ECOSYSTEMS ARE DYNAMIC

Not only do interactions and interactions among interactions exist, they change with time and because of disturbances. Recently, human disturbances have become especially important, since the number of humans is so large and the land area relatively small. How do humans affect ecosystems?

ECOSYSTEMS ARE SYSTEMS

Systems principles apply to ecosystems as to other systems. Ecosystems are dynamic, have pools, flows, and reservoirs; they can be modeled and studied. What we learn about them might be applied to other systems, just as what we learn about other systems might apply to ecosystems.

EXCERPT GUIDE
"The Having of Wonderful Ideas"

This Excerpt tends to shock or excite readers, teachers as well as students. Its most striking points are that a student came up with a solution that had not occurred to the teacher (students tend to love this). And even more wonderful, the teacher listens to the student and lets him proceed—and even break a lightbulb in the process.

Students can find the idea of open-ended exploration exciting, empowering, and scary. Their reactions will help you work with them most effectively—whether that means calming fears, encouraging independence, whatever. Your own reaction is also important. Can you freely listen to your students and genuinely hear what they say? Can you make space for real exploration, not just expected answers?

REFERENCES

Begon, Michael, John L. Harper, and Colin Townsend. 1990. Ecology: Individuals, Populations, and Communities. Boston: Blackwell Scientific Publications. 943 pp.

Biological Science: An Ecological Approach. 1987. BSCS Green Version. Dubuque, Iowa: Kendall/Hunt Publishing Company. 1,024 pp.

Duckworth, Eleanor. 1987. "The Having of Wonderful Ideas" and Other Essays on Teaching and Learning. New York: Teachers College Press, Columbia University. pp. 5–7.

Martin, Paul, and Patrick Bateson. 1993. Measuring Behavior: An Introductory Guide, 2nd ed. New York: Cambridge University Press. 222 pp.

Rezendes, Paul. 1992. Tracking and the Art of Seeing: How to Read Animal Tracks and Signs. Charlotte, Vt.: Camden House Publishing. 320 pp.

Smith, Robert Leo. 1990. Ecology and Field Biology. New York: HarperCollins. 1,001 pp.

———. 1990. Student Resource Manual to Accompany Ecology and Field Biology, 4th ed. New York: HarperCollins.

Weiner, Jacob. 1995. "On the Practice of Ecology." Journal of Ecology, 83: 153–158.

Wilson, Edward O. 1992. The Diversity of Life. New York: W. W. Norton. 536 pp.

WATER: WHAT IS IT?

UNIT 2

WATER: WHAT IS IT?

UNIT 2

CONTENTS

Unit 2 Overview

Water: What Is It?

This Unit focuses on water use by all organisms. It considers the four major roles of water, at the levels of the bond, the individual, and the habitat.

The Unit considers questions such as:

- What are the four major roles of water?
- How do water's physical properties affect its importance for life?
- What chemical properties underlie those physical properties?
- How do water's properties affect its role in getting water to the top of a 100-m tree, supporting a floating needle, and dissolving life-essential molecules?
- How do plants and other organisms survive in habitats without much water?

We collect data on water use by different plant species by comparing species from habitats of various dryness. We also consider special adaptations some species (plant and animal) have to compensate for water lack or to decrease water loss (**Chapter 1**).

In **Chapter 2**, we focus on the molecular and physical properties of water—how its bonds makes it unique and give water its properties of cohesion and adhesion and the ability to dissolve most molecules.

GETTING, KEEPING, AND USING WATER

CHAPTER ONE

CONTENTS

INTRODUCTION

In **Unit 1** students saw that water limits the amount of NPP in habitats where it is in short supply. Here we consider how plants get water to their growing parts, how much they need, and what they use water for. In addition to using water to transport nutrients throughout the plant, plants actually use up water in the process of photosynthesis. Since the products of photosynthesis are what new plant material is made of, limiting water can limit plant growth (short of killing the plant). Plant species from dry habitats have various adaptations to help them conserve water.

Evapotranspiration is a key concept in the study of plants and water cycling. It refers to the process of water evaporating from the leaves of plants. As the surface of soil becomes dry, the dry layers on top form a barrier. Not much soil water moves through that barrier, so water stops evaporating from the soil. Plants' roots continue to take up soil water, and they continue to lose water through their leaves, so evaporation continues through the plants. As long as a plant has enough water, its leaves remain firm and their stomata remain all the way open. Although that allows a lot of CO_2 to enter the leaf for photosynthesis, it also allows high water loss. Evapotranspiration continues until all the capillary water in the soil is used up.

Plant biomass refers to the dry weight of a plant. The accumulation of biomass over time can be used as a measure of a plant's productivity.

KEY CONCEPTS

- Plants need water physically (as a medium to circulate nutrients) and biochemically (for photosynthesis, which is how plants acquire energy and fix carbon).
- Plant species that live in dry habitats have adaptations to conserve water, including a lower proportion of photosynthetic surface area.
- Because of water's biochemical role in photosynthesis, limiting water limits photosynthesis and the ability to grow (make new plant tissue).
- The limiting of photosynthesis applies to individual plants within a species as well as to the amount of biomass, size, and number of plant species in particular habitats.

MATERIALS AND PREPARATION

For Exploration 1

- **Celery stalks with leaves attached** (the chlorophyll-free hearts make it easy to see the food coloring)
- **Red food coloring** (1 oz per gallon of warm tap water)
- **Warm tap water** (to mix with food coloring; 0.5 to 1 liter per student group)
- **Containers** (1 per group). Paper cups, yogurt containers, milk cartons are all fine. If a group wants to test more than one hypothesis, they will need 1 container and 4 celery stalks per test.
- **Sharp knife or safety razor**

- **Experimental setups** to test predictions. Students predict factors they think affect plant uptake of water. Provide them with an array of ways to test their predictions, such as table lamps, windows (open or closed), sunny or shaded locations, radiators, fans, and large containers full of cold (iced) or hot water into which to place the smaller containers of celery and colored water.

For Exploration 2

- **Plants** from three differently wet habitats, 2 different plants per student group (e.g., cactus, fern, and a plant that likes moderate amounts of moisture like a geranium). All three plant types should have about the same amount of leaf and stem (photosynthetic) area and be in the same-size pots, with the same type of soil. Approximately equal size is OK; leaves can be snipped off for balance, but do so at least 24 hours before the classwork so the cut heals over. The setup is shown in the student text, Figures 1 and 2.
- **Felt** (enough to cut a 2-in.-wide strip, three times the length of the pot, one strip per plant; synthetic felt is fine)
- **Scissors** (1 pair per group)
- **Beakers** or any clear container into which a plant pot can fit snugly (1 per plant)
- **Plastic wrap** to keep moisture from leaving by any route except through the plant tissue.

For Exploration 3a

- **Plants:** cactus, geranium, fern (1 per group)
- **Graph paper and pencils**
- **Rulers and measuring tapes**
- **Large beaker of water** with volume marks on the side

For Exploration 3b

- **Plants** (at least 1 cactus, 1 geranium, 1 fern)
- **Clear nail polish**
- **Tweezers**
- **Microscope** (with a measuring grid or scale in the eyepiece or clear plastic rulers) or several **magnifying glasses**
- **Microscope slides**

For Exploration 4

- **Dried beans and popcorn kernels** from the supermarket (avoid corn and beans from seed companies, which are usually treated with Captan or some other poisonous fungicide)
- **Potting soil or vermiculite.** If you use vermiculite, add fertilizer with the first watering after germination. If your soil is not sterile, sterilize it by baking it 30 minutes in a 220°F oven, or by pouring boiling water over it and letting it dry on newspaper.
- **Coarse strainer and bucket** if you want to save the soil for reuse

- **Pots or used containers** (yogurt containers, cut-off milk cartons) to hold about 1 cup of soil. For example, you will need 50 containers if 5 groups test 5 watering treatments on 2 plant species, and more if you plan to make a point of large sample sizes. If you use regular flower pots, be sure to cover the hole in the bottom of each with plastic, since we are working with specified amounts of water.
- **Waterproof trays** to hold the pots (Styrofoam meat trays or trays made of corrugated cardboard and aluminum foil or plastic)

SUGGESTED SEQUENCE OF SESSIONS (6–8)

Homework

The Case Study gives an overview of water's importance for life.

Class Session 1

Students make predictions about factors that influence the speed at which water moves through plant tissue by seeing how fast dyed water moves up through celery stalks kept under different conditions (Exploration 1: How Does Water Move through Plants?). They set up and test their predictions.

While students wait for results on water uptake by their celery, they can set up the experiments in Exploration 2: Plants and Water Use: All the Same? to measure the amounts of water used by plant species from dry, wet, and moderately moist habitats. (Students will collect the data over the next few weeks, but they can start setting up now.)

Class Session 2

Class discussion of results from Exploration 1. Heat and air movement cause water to move through celery tissue more rapidly than cooler, still conditions. How do students explain these results (increased evapotranspiration)?

Students collect their first data on water use by the different plant species (Exploration 2). Do the initial differences support their expectations?

Class Session 3

In two variations in Exploration 3, students focus more closely on differences between plants from wet and dry habitats. They discover that dry-habitat plant species have a lower photosynthetic surface area and fewer stomata per unit area than do other plants.

Class Session 4

Continue Session 3, especially data analysis and class discussion of results of Explorations 3a and 3b.

Homework

Students formalize some ideas about plant volumes and their water use patterns (Reading 1: Surface Area and Volume: Plants Are Not Animals).

Class Session 5

Briefly discuss Reading 1, continuing the comparisons of plant species specialized for different habitats. Note metabolic and other differences between plants and animals.

Do students think individual plants as well as plant species are affected by the amount of available water? Exploration 4: Does Water Affect Plant Biomass? tests that hypothesis by exposing individuals of two plant species to various amounts of water (much, less, and little, water.) Discuss with the class how to design the experiment (or simply lay out a design, although the former is far more engaging to students).

Also discuss how to collect the data, division of labor, and what the data might look like. Develop a class standardized data table.

Class Sessions 6 and 7

Continue the discussion from Session 5, as necessary.

Plant the beans and corn.

Collect data from the plants in Exploration 2.

SESSION GUIDES, BY WORKSHEET

CASE STUDY GUIDE
Water's Major Roles

Why is water key to life? Its multiple roles are unique: When space explorers look for signs of life, their first question is whether water is present. If not, there is little reason to keep looking. Ask students to think of life processes that happen in the absence of water. Make a list. On examination, do any really occur without water?

EXPLORATION 1 GUIDE
How Does Water Move through Plants?

Students test their predictions about which factors influence water uptake in plants, as modeled by celery. Increased light, temperature, and wind increase the rate at which the celery will draw up water.

If student results differ from that, ask whether the celery stalks had about the same amounts of leaf area. Other possible sources of error are differences in the timing of data collection (e.g., 10 vs. 20 min) or bruising of the stalks from rough handling or an insufficiently sharp blade. Or perhaps the end of the stalk was not fully submerged when the slices were cut.

EXPLORATION 2 GUIDE
Plants and Water Use: All the Same?

Students compare water uptake through the plant tissue of species adapted to dry, moderate, and very moist habitats. They find that under constant conditions of light and temperature, plants from wet habitats (such as ferns) use much more water than plants from dry habitats (such as cacti).

Logistics

Students can gather data from the plants for anywhere from a few days to several weeks. If the room is hot or the plants are placed under a lamp, differences can appear within a few hours. The differences become more dramatic as time passes; within a week, the species from the wettest habitat likely will need its beakers replenished. After the initial differences are clear, you can end the experiment. Or you can keep it going as long as you like, noting how many times during the weeks or months each beaker needs refilling.

Reasons

Why do dry-habitat species use less water? Generally they have a lower proportion of photosynthetic surface, so they need less water biochemically. They also have adaptations to conserve water mechanically, such as fewer stomata per unit area, waxy cuticles, and furry surfaces, which give some shade. Students will discover those things themselves in Explorations 3a and 3b.

EXPLORATION 3A GUIDE
Plant Surface Area and Water Use: Photosynthesis

EXPLORATION 3B GUIDE
Plant Surface Area and Water Use: Surfaces

Dry-habitat species generally have a proportionately smaller photosynthetic area (measured by the ratio of surface area to volume) and a lower ratio of leaf area to stem than do wet-habitat species. Dry-habitat species also have photosynthetic tissue in their stems (e.g., cacti). So when the cacti, geraniums, and ferns are measured for surface area and volume, they show a pattern of increasing photosynthetic area (surface area per unit volume) along with evaporative potential or the humidity of their habitats. Graphed, that pattern would look like Figure 1.

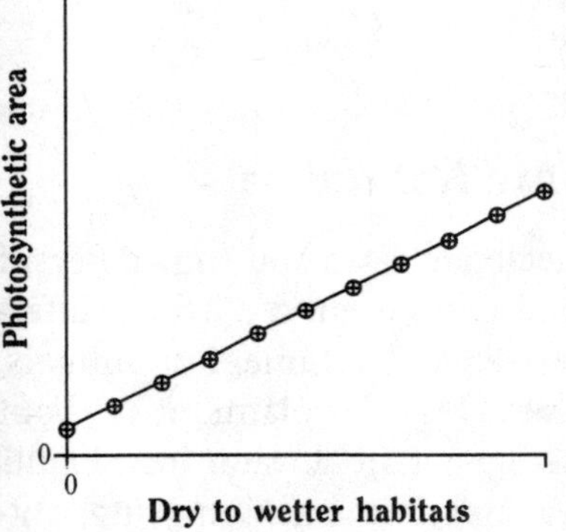

Figure 1

Stomata

Most plants have their stomata on the undersides of their leaves to cut down on loss due to evaporation. Plants from drier habitats have fewer stomata per unit of area than do plants from wet habitats. Tobacco, a medium-range species in terms of humidity requirements, has about 12,000 stomata per cm^2.

Students make impressions of leaf surfaces with clear nail polish, which they peel off with tweezers and mount on slides. If you have not looked at stomata before, start with the underside of a leaf (where most of the stomata are) and a plant species that has many stomata, such as the geranium. Students looking at fern leaves should be steered away from leaf areas where sori (spores) are located.

Sample Size and Logistics

To ensure adequate sample sizes for Exploration 3a (photosynthetic surface area), have students examine at least three plants of each type. You may want to make the group size smaller (two to three students per group) or have more than half the class working on this piece. Students might need encouragement for the surface-area or volume calculations, but the work is straightforward and the results striking.

Possible Discussion Questions

Do species from different habitats differ in their photosynthetic surface area, even though they appear to be the same size?

(Yes. And cacti and euphorbs have spines instead of leaves.)

Are there more stomata on one side of the leaves than the other? Why?

(They are mostly on the underside, where they are shaded.)

Do plant species from different habitats have different densities of stomata on their photosynthetic surfaces?

(Yes. There are fewer stomata on dry-habitat species.)

Were the stomata on each plant open or closed?

(Cacti close their stomata during the day to save water. They take in CO_2 only during the cooler night and store it to use when the sun is next shining [photosynthesis requires both sunlight and CO_2]. Other plants generally have their stomata open during the day and take in CO_2 when sunlight is present.)

Why do other species not take in CO_2 at night and store it, as do the cacti? Then they could live in more different habitats.

(It costs energy to store the CO_2, so the strategy would be a disadvantage to plants that do not live in dry habitats. And recall genetics and evolution or family history—this strategy is one that cacti happen to have evolved.)

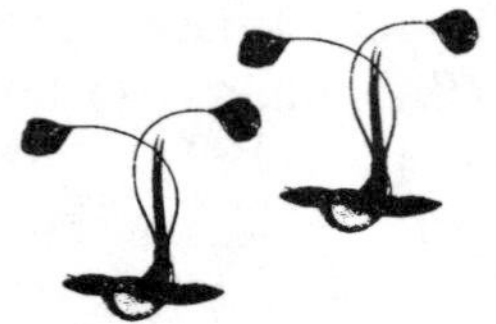

READING 1 GUIDE

Surface Area and Volume: Plants Are Not Animals

Plants and animals have different metabolic rates and thus different issues around water, thermoregulation, and getting energy. Those differences are reflected in the roles of surface area and volume. For animals, surface area is about heat and perhaps water loss; for plants, it is about energy procurement (photosynthesis) offset by potential water loss. Plants cannot regulate their interactions with the environment by moving; animals can. So plants respond by changing growth—number of stomata and surface area (proportionate and absolute)—and by using their volume (e.g., for water storage).

If you have not done so, it may be of interest to compare plant strategies and "issues" here directly with those of endotherms and ectotherms. Use **Module 2, Unit 2, Chapter 5**.

Student questions likely focus on plant/animal differences. Why are they different? What does it mean to have different metabolic rates? (Consider with students what plants and animals do and how fast.)

Comparing plants and other organisms is a rich topic. On the one hand, all have common "problems" to solve (survival, metabolism, development, growth, reproduction), and all interact with individuals of their own and other species (competition, reproduction, predation, defense, parasitism). Yet in some ways, they are profoundly different (photosynthesizers vs. nonphotosynthesizers). So they solve some of those problems in similiar ways, some in different ways. In general, plants also do things more slowly (to some researchers that is more subtle; to others, it is just boring).

EXPLORATION 4 GUIDE
Does Water Affect Plant Biomass?

Do individual plants of a species produce less tissue if they get less water? Students design several different water treatments for corn and bean seeds while keeping light and temperature constant. (Since water availability affects NPP in all the habitats we have examined, we wonder whether it also affects the biomass of individual plants in a way we can measure.)

Measuring plant tissue or biomass is a way of measuring plant growth, so students measure above-ground biomass, root biomass, total biomass, length of plant parts, and number of leaves for beans and for corn. If students measure several things, they likely will have enough data to see clear patterns even if some data are missing.

Logistics

This is a relatively sophisticated class project, requiring collaboration in setup, maintenance, and data collection. But its very sophistication likely appeals to students, and they enjoy the responsibility.

Treatments and Numbers

Discuss with students the watering treatments they want to test. We suggest using 25 ml per week as the base regimen, with the other regimens in 25-ml increments (50 ml, 75 ml, 100 ml), up to 125 or 150 ml per week per pot. We suggest watering twice a week, each time using half the amount prescribed for the regimen.

You may want to divide the water amounts more finely, say, into increments of about 12 ml. That, however, doubles the number of treatments, and thus of pots, soil, data—everything, because your treatment range should include 25 to 150 ml per week.

If your class divides into five groups, with each group testing five watering regimens on each of two plant species, you will need fifty plants (twenty-five corn and twenty-five bean), more if you subdivide the watering categories. If you can plant more pots, so much the better—it increases sample sizes and is insurance against accidental loss of plants.

All plants should be grown under the same conditions or as close as possible.

Duration

If possible, let the experiment run for 3 weeks after germination. We found differences in dry weight, number of leaves, and overall plant height by the time the plants were 2 weeks old, but only the differences between the wettest and the driest treatment were statistically significant. By 3 weeks, there should be significant differences in all or most of the treatments.

Growing Conditions

A window that receives sunlight a few hours per day is fine, and climbing beans will do well since there is more room to place strings for support. (The drawback to supermarket beans is that it is difficult to know whether they are viney or bushy plants. The pinto beans we used were climbers.) Fluorescent lights also work well as long as the pots can be placed just a few inches below them.

Beans and corn both prefer warm soil for germination. So, if your windowsill is cool and drafty and it is wintertime, do not put the containers close to the window before germination. If the classroom is very warm (around 80°F) germination will be rapid (less than a week), but you must cover the pots with plastic wrap prior to germination to keep them from drying out.

General Growth Results

Some plants in the higher water treatments will die from too much water—their roots will rot, get fungus, and so on. (Just how much water is too much depends on room temperature and humidity.) Seeds getting the least amount of water may germinate poorly or not at all. That is a result and should be noted; do not let students mistake it for "nothing" or "no data." Such results are real and useful data on the water requirements of those seeds.

Some plants may die from dehydration as the experiment progresses and they get larger. That also is a normal and important result. Some plants may be stunted from lack of water; in those, water is sufficiently scarce to be limiting, that is, to affect tissue production. Again, which treatments cause that result will vary with the conditions in your classroom. Obviously, the hotter and drier your room, the more water the plants will use.

Some treatments might give rise to disproportionately more root growth. Plants growing in dry soil often increase their root biomass in an attempt to get more water.

Corn usually survives dry conditions a little better than beans. It is a C4 plant, and is grown in hotter areas.

Save the Soil?

You can save the soil when you remove the plants from their pots and wash their roots. Use a coarse strainer and rinse the soil into a bucket. Let the soil settle to the bottom, gently pour off most of the water, then let the soil dry for reuse later.

Data Analyses

Once the plants have reached their desired age, students will need two to three class sessions to do the measuring, drying, and data analyses. Add another session if there will be group presentations.

It may simplify things to let each group analyze everyone's results from one treatment. Such pooling of data gives average values per treatment (be sure students consider Reading 2). Ask the groups to note any markedly different values and try to explain them. Data (average measures of the different plant growth variables—total biomass, root biomass, aboveground biomass, plant and root length) per treatment can be represented in various ways.

Students also can discuss and graph other results, such as number of seeds germinated, number of plants surviving to a particular age, and room temperature or days of sun.

If you want to do statistical comparisons among the results, introduce the chi-square test for number of leaves or use the t-test for biomass and plant length.

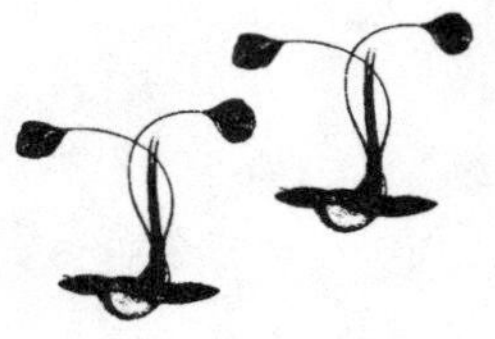

READING 2 GUIDE
Averages

Use this Reading to continue our ongoing discussion of good data and how to interpret data. Student results from Exploration 4 may vary for various reasons (as discussed above). In addition, it is important in interpreting data to consider the effects of "smoothing" it by using averages. Did such smoothing cover any markedly different individual plant responses? What might those responses mean? How could we tell?

Students discover that, while an average allows some interpretation of a data set, it can also hide meaningful differences.

For more, see the **Technique: Introduction to Research.**

INTEGRATION GUIDE
Mystery Plant

The Integration worksheet describes five types of plants. In what habitat do the students think each plant might grow. Why? Can they identify the plants, roughly?

The plant types are:

1. Cactus (leaves nondeciduous) or euphorb (leaves deciduous)
2. Temperate or boreal evergreen
3. Grass
4. Water lily
5. Deciduous tree

INTEGRATION
Mystery Plant

Where can these plants survive? Why? Using the data below and what you already know about plants, describe a habitat in which each type of plant could survive. Give your reasons. Can you also say what type of plant each is?

1. Plant type: thickish or stout, often (usually) less than 2 ft high (although some species can be 25 ft at maturity)
   - Its leaves have a very low surface-area-to-volume ratio.
   - Its leaves can be nondeciduous or deciduous.
   - Its leaves are modified into spines.
   - Its roots typically are shallow and fibrous.
   - Its stems or trunk serve as water reservoirs.
   - It reproduces irregularly. The plant itself has few predators, but birds or mammals try to get at its trunk water reservoirs.
   - Its fruits are highly prized by birds and rodents.
   - Its flowers likely are pollinated by bats.

2. Plant type: tall
   - Its branches are in whorls.
   - Its leaves are needle-shaped with very low surface-area-to-volume ratio, but they are numerous.
   - Its leaves are nondeciduous (evergreen).
   - Its roots are shallow and fibrous.
   - Its trunk acts as a reservoir for water, which can be used during dry times without damaging the plant as a whole.
   - Its predators are mostly insects or fungi, rarely mammals.
   - Its seed and fruit predators include birds and rodents.

3. Plant type: typically under 2 ft, although some species can grow to 5 or 6 ft.

- Its root system is fibrous and typically includes more biomass than does the above-ground plant itself.
- Its leaves are flat, blade-shaped, and attached at the base of the plant.
- Plant itself typically is eaten by many types of predators: mammals, insects, fungi, etc.
- It reproduces vegetatively as well as by seed.
- It is noted for rapid growth and a pronounced annual cycle.

4. Plant type: 2–3 ft

- Its photosynthetic area is broad.
- Its leaves and flowers are floating.
- Its predators include large mammals and insects.
- Its roots are submerged.
- Its stems are nonsupporting (plant cannot support its own weight).

5. Plant type: tall

- Its leaves are thin, broad, flat, and deciduous.
- Its woody perennial stems account for most of the biomass of the plant.
- Its root system is as large as its above-ground area, often with a main tap root and secondary lateral roots.
- Its fruit size and dispersal method are extremely variable.
- Its many fruit and seed predators include mammals and birds.

SCIENCE BACKGROUND
Water Use in Plants

Most plants get their water from soil. Soils usually are about 50% spaces (pore space); the rest is made of soil particles of various sizes, shapes, and materials. The amount of moisture that can be held by a particular type of soil (i.e., the moisture that does not drain away) varies, depending on the size of the soil particles. Smaller particles have smaller pores between them and can hold more water. If the soil holds more water, more water is available to plants. When the percentage of water in soil is low enough to cause plants to wilt permanently, it is said to be at its permanent wilting percentage. That percentage varies, depending on the type of soil.

Plant nutrients are inorganic. They enter the plant through its roots, and they must be dissolved in soil water to do so.

The currently accepted theory of water movement in plants (how water gets to the tops of trees) is called the cohesion tension theory. Students will see more about this subject when they reach the Chapter on the physical properties of water. What it amounts to is that water is pulled up the stem by the water evaporating from the leaves. Plant nutrients dissolved in the water also are pulled up. The products of photosynthesis, dissolved in water, are transported about the plant.

Plants use much more water than animals. Most of the water they take up through their roots (about 99%) travels through the plant and exits through the stomata (the pores in the leaves) as water vapor. The same openings (stomata) that allow CO_2 to enter the leaves allow water vapor to exit. Plants have developed certain water-conservation mechanisms, such as waxy coverings on their leaves and control over the opening and closing of stomata. Plants adapted to arid areas have developed even more water-conservation methods.

Many plants use water to remain rigid and stand upright. Even woody plants use this method to keep their leaves rigid. Wilting is the opposite condition.

Last, but certainly not least, plants use water as part of the chemistry of photosynthesis and for other physiological processes.

Reference

Raven, Peter H., Ray F. Evert, and Susan E. Eichhorn. 1992. Biology of Plants. New York: Worth Publishers.

Properties of Water and Its Suitability for Everything

Chapter Two

Contents

Introduction

Water behaves differently from many other substances with similar molecular structures. This odd behavior of water is in many ways what makes life on earth possible. Students explore the behavior of water and compare it to a few other liquids. Then they consider its molecular properties and what makes water different.

Water is a polar molecule, which means it has two ends with opposite electrical charges. The two hydrogen atoms at one end have a partial positive charge, and the oxygen atom at the other end has a partial negative charge. Because of their charged ends, water molecules are attracted to each other and to other molecules, especially other charged molecules. It is that polarity of the water molecule that gives water its unusual physical properties: making it float when frozen; giving it enough cohesiveness to "pull" itself up a very tall tree (because its molecules stick together); and giving it its affinity for other molecules, which gets it involved in and makes it essential for so many biochemical reactions.

Key Concepts

- Water's molecular structure gives it unusual physical properties such as cohesion and adhesion, high surface tension, high specific heat, and the ability to dissolve many things.
- Water is a highly charged molecule, giving it many special physical and chemical properties that are necessary for life processes.

Materials and Preparation

For Exploration 1a (for each group)

- **3 bowls**
- **250 ml each of alcohol** (at least 70%), **water, vegetable oil**
- **Toilet tissue**
- **3 sewing needles**, all the same size
- **3 sharp pencils**
- **Scissors**

For Exploration 1b

- **Pipe cleaners** (craft-use "pipe cleaners" are better than pipe-cleaning ones)
- **Bowls of water**
- **Aluminum foil**
- **Sticky tape**
- **Balance or scale** (sensitive to 0.1 g)
- **Millimeter rulers or short measuring tapes**
- **Paper**
- **Scissors**

For Exploration 2a

- Very clean **microscope slides**
- **Water**
- **Eyedroppers** (1 per group)
- **Vegetable oil**
- **Paper towels**

For Exploration 2b

- **Alcohol**, any kind but at least 70% alcohol (at room temperature)
- **Vegetable oil** (at room temperature)
- **Water** (at room temperature)
- **Table sugar** (sucrose)
- **Table salt** (NaCl)
- **50-ml beakers** (3 per group)
- **Stirring rods or long sticks or spoons**
- **Measuring teaspoons** (1 level teaspoon = 5 ml)
- **Labels or wax pencils**

For Exploration 3

- **Small bar (rectangular) magnets** (at least 8 per group)
- **Typewriter correction fluid or other marking materials**

For Optional Demonstration

- **2 glass jars** of the same size and shape, one with a lid that can be punctured
- **1 rag**, about 25 cm by 25 cm
- **2 submersible thermometers**
- **Water**

SUGGESTED SEQUENCE OF SESSIONS (5–7)

Homework

The Case Study: Insects and Antifreeze: The Moth in Winter alerts students to the molecular uniqueness of water and how that uniqueness is utilized by various animals to survive subfreezing temperatures.

Class Session 1

Discuss the Case Study briefly; be sure to ask if anyone has questions. Have any students ever made ice cream? How do you keep the water and the milk fat from separating?

Students explore the surface tension of water and two other fluids, to find that water will float a needle and other objects (Exploration 1). Discuss possible reasons for the differences in liquids.

Homework

Following on previous work, students read about various plant and animal adaptations to conserve water in Reading 1: Awesome Adaptations.

Class Session 2

Discuss Reading 1; students may have their own examples to add. Compare the solvent properties of water and other liquids in Exploration 2.

Students discover that water is a better solvent and it dissolves biologically important molecules like salt and sugar.

Class Session 3

Carry out the optional Demonstration of cooling by conductance (less effective but no water loss) versus evaporation (more effective but causes water loss).

In class or as homework, students begin Reading 2: Molecular Properties of Water.

Class Session 4

Discuss Reading 2, comparing polar and other bonds.

Class Session 5

Continue discussion from Session 4, as appropriate. Students model water cohesiveness using bar magnets (Exploration 3). Wrap up discussion on relationship among physical, molecular, and ecological properties of water.

SESSION GUIDES, BY WORKSHEET

CASE STUDY GUIDE

Insects and Antifreeze: The Moth in Winter

Glycerol is an alcohol, which looks and acts very differently from water. It is nonpolar. It also has low melting and freezing points because of its high-energy carbon-carbon and carbon-oxygen backbone. Compare it with the highly polar water molecule. (For a brief refresher on bonds, see Reading 2 and Reading 2 Guide in **Chapter 9** of **Module 2, Unit 2.**)

Ask students what differences they see between a glycerol molecule and a water molecule (Figure 1), and what those differences might mean.

$$
\begin{array}{l} H_2C-OH \\ \quad | \\ \ HC-OH \\ \quad | \\ H_2C-OH \end{array}
\qquad\qquad
\begin{array}{l} H \searrow \\ \quad 105^\circ\ O \\ H \nearrow \end{array}
$$

(a) Glycerol molecule (an alcohol). **(b) Water molecule.**

Figure 1

Ask students if anyone has made ice cream. How did they keep the water and the milk fat from separating? As the water was freezing, did it try to form crystals? Relate this to water freezing in the cells of living things.

EXPLORATION 1A, 1B GUIDE
Water Tension

What do floating needles and water striders have in common? Both demonstrate the high surface tension of water. The needles also show the absence of surface tension in alcohol and oil.

Water Tension

Students may or may not be asking why their results are so different—why needles float only on water. Start students thinking by drawing three molecules on the board: water, alcohol, and a fat (see Reading 2). Note the relative similarities between fat and alcohol and the striking differences with water. Ask students to consider those.

If anyone remembers the periodic table, which molecules are charged? Why? How might molecular charge be related to intermolecular tension? A little thinking and tension about the answers might keep student interest piqued. Or, if you want, skip ahead to Reading 2.

Water Strider Logistics

We used standard-length, furry (craft-use, not pipe-cleaning) pipe cleaners. Three twisted together at their middles weigh about 3.8 g. Our water strider made of those three pipe cleaners floated steadily on store brand aluminum foil feet that were about 3 cm by 3 cm each (3.18 cm × 3.18 cm = 10.1 cm^2 × 6 strider "feet" = 60.6 cm^2 total "foot" surface area).

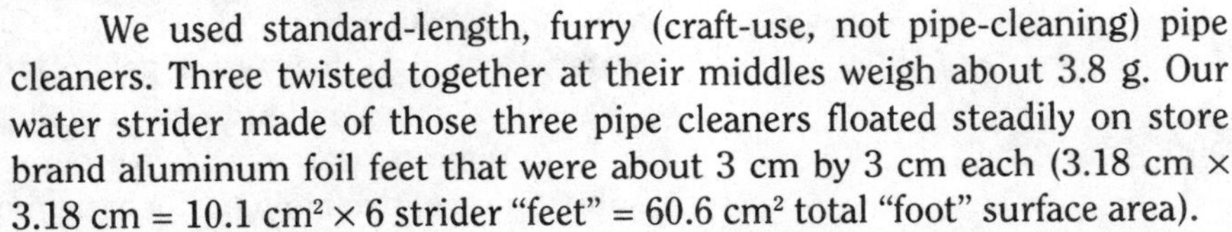

Standard 20-lb paper weighs about 0.2 g per 5-cm by 5-cm square. Squares or rectangles of different shapes and weights of paper can easily be crimped and hung over the "back" of the water strider, the intersection where the three pipe cleaners are attached to each other.

Students find a constant relationship between strider weight and foot surface area up to some maximum. We do not know if our maximum could be increased by using more substantial foil (ours was inexpensive 2-mil foil).

One property of water, surface tension, can be related directly to the physical existence and limitations of humans. Substituting their own weights, students calculate whether they can walk on water. People are often sensitive about their weight. If so, either substitute age-appropriate averages (150 lb for females, 170 lb for males) or set some figures for hypothetical people. You may want to refer students to the Reading on microworlds and macroworlds (**Chapter 5** in **Module 2**, **Unit 2**) or copy it for them.

READING 1 GUIDE
Awesome Adaptations

Students read about more adaptations for water conservation in plants and animals. Start the discussion by making a table on the board. List, or ask students to list, some organisms: those from Reading 1 (camel, dog, cactus, amphibian, *Lithops*, etc.) and others. Where do they live? How do they use or conserve water? How does that interact with thermoregulation? What are the trade-offs? (As with endotherms and ectotherms, each strategy has costs and benefits. No strategy is cost-free, and no strategy works under all conditions. This seemingly obvious idea is actually a profound aspect of ecology. This discussion is in part about "niche"—where does an organism live and how does it do so?)

If you did the work with animals in **Module 2, Unit 2**, let students consider special adaptations of their organisms. Those from the Serengeti may be more concerned with saving water during the dry heat, while those from the Northern Hardwoods may be concerned with saving water during the dry cold and with saving body heat.

Exploration 2A Guide
Water's Properties: Cohesiveness

Exploration 2B Guide
Water's Properties: As a Solvent

Students discover that water is "sticky"—it tends to stick to itself, whether between slides of glass or in drops. Remind them of a column of water. How high does water get in tall trees, and how does it get there? (Water molecules pull each other along; see Reading 2.)

Comparing water and two other solvents, students find that water dissolves more of two biologically basic molecules and more thoroughly. What implications does that have for water as a medium, that is, for water getting stuff around in plants and animals?

Ask students to list biological contexts or uses of salt and sugar (or variants thereof: glucose, carbohydrates, saline). They might include blood, food, lymph of insects, ocean water, tree sap (and maple syrup), honey, salt licks (visited by many animals, especially in hot climates), salt loss in sweat, osmoregulation of either sugar or salt, and disruptions in the balance of either (e.g., diabetes, hypertension).

Students will better understand why water is such a good solvent after the next two pieces of work.

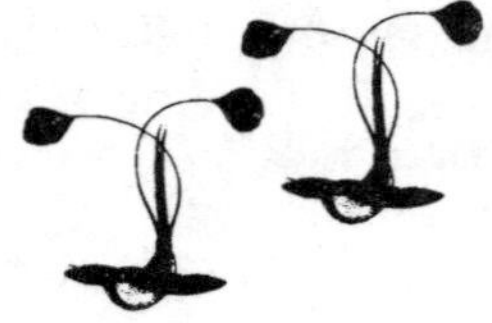

Reading 2 Guide
Molecular Properties of Water

By now students are likely curious about the behavior of water. Reading 2 explains some molecular properties that underlie those differences. (This section can be especially lively if you co-teach it with a colleague who specializes in chemistry.) Students may ask questions about "how atoms work," which can lead to a brief discussion of orbitals and shells. More likely, they will be curious about bond types—just how and why polar and nonpolar bonds actually form.

The Reading is straightforward, but it may be useful to sketch some molecules and bonds on the board, using some examples: CO_2 as a nonpolar molecule, O_2 as the perfect covalent bond, and alcohol and oil (fat) as contrasts to water.

Have students notice the shapes and the angles of bonds (Figures 1–4 in the Student Module). How do they reflect bond polarity? Is molecule size important? It depends for what. To diffuse through a membrane? Then yes, size is important. For the reactive or nonneutral part of the molecule? Perhaps not. In considering the overall property of a molecule? Likely yes.

Molecular Properties of Water

All living things use water, including those unusual nonphotosynthesizing bacteria that reduce or oxidize sulfur, nitrogen, and iron. In fact, those bacteria all live in aqueous environments or in soil (which also has water). Water is the most abundant molecule (70% by weight) in all cells, in both unicellular and multicellular organisms. All cell biochemistry has evolved based on water as a solvent. None of the molecules in cells would react with each other in the same way in a different solvent. Water is believed to have been present on the primitive earth before life evolved, and many of the chemical reactions that must have occurred to produce the first organic molecules could have occurred only in an aqueous solution.

So What Makes Water Special?

Water is a polar molecule because of the elements it includes, the type of bonding, and the shape of the molecule.

Atoms of different elements differ in their ability to attract electrons. That ability to attract electrons is referred to as electronegativity. On the periodic table of the elements, electronegativity of elements (in general) increases from right to left and from bottom to top. The most electronegative element is fluorine (4.0), followed by oxygen (3.5), nitrogen and chlorine (3.0), bromine (2.8%), iodine and carbon (2.5), hydrogen (2.1), and boron (2.0).

Bond Types

The differences between the electronegativities of any two elements predict the type of bonds that will be formed between them. At one extreme is the ionic bond, where electrons are pulled away from an atom of one element by an atom of a second element. At the other extreme is the neutral covalent bond, which forms only between two identical atoms of the same element (e.g., O_2 or N_2). Between those two extreme bond types are polar and nonpolar molecules, depending on their elements and the shapes they take in the molecules.

CO_2, for instance, is a nonpolar molecule because the atoms line up in a straight line (O=C=O) with double bonds between them. The two oxygen atoms on either side pull equally on the carbon atom's electrons, so the center of the negative charge is in the middle.

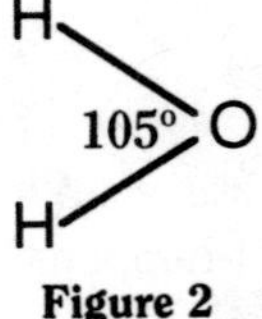

Figure 2

In water, however, the structure of the molecule is a tetrahedron (Figure 2). The oxygen atom in water still has two unbonded electrons on one side. The unbonded electrons are bulky and push the hydrogen atoms to one side.

Electronegativity

Oxygen has a much stronger electronegativity than hydrogen (3.5 vs. 2.1), so hydrogen's electrons are attracted toward the oxygen end of the molecule. That also causes the center of the negative charge to move to the oxygen end of the molecule, leaving the center of the positive charge at the hydrogen end. A molecule with different centers of positive and negative charges is called a dipole.

The energy of covalent bonds such as those between oxygen and hydrogen atoms in water is generally between 50 and 100 kcal/mole. The energy of hydrogen bonds that form between polar molecules such as water is about 5 kcal/mole.

Alcohols

Although alcohols contain –OH groups, they are not like water because they are derivatives of hydrocarbons. Hydrocarbons are chains of carbon atoms with hydrogen atoms attached. They are completely neutral and not water soluble. Adding an –OH to a hydrocarbon makes it an alcohol. (See Figure 3.) That –OH is polar, and the smaller alcohols are water soluble.

```
   H   H   H   H
   |   |   |   |
H— C — C — C — C —H
   |   |   |   |
   H   H   H   H
```

$CH_3CH_2CH_2CH_3$

(a) Butane (an alkane, hydrocarbon).

```
   H   H   H   H
   |   |   |   |
H— C — C — C — C —OH
   |   |   |   |
   H   H   H   H
```

$CH_3CH_2CH_2CH_2OH$

(b) 1-Butanol (an alcohol).

Figure 3

Alcohols do form hydrogen bonds with each other and with water. In fact, the melting and boiling points of alcohols are higher than those of hydrocarbons with the same molecular weight. The rest of the molecule, however, still has the structure of a hydrocarbon. It is neutral and cannot form hydrogen bonds. Often the rest of the molecule in alcohols is scarcely considered because the functional or reactive group is the –OH. That makes it easy to forget that the rest of the molecule is actually much larger than the functional group and so contributes greatly to the overall properties of the molecule, in this case, alcohol. In fact, the rest of the molecule is why the melting point of alcohols is very low, from –50°C to –130°C. The larger alcohols are not very soluble in water, and some have very high boiling points as well (e.g., hexanol at 157°C).

EXPLORATION 3 GUIDE
Magnets as Models of Water Molecules

Let students model the cohesive properties of water at a visible level. If you want, try to form a net with everyone's magnets. What happens? Have a class discussion summarizing connections among physical, molecular, and ecological properties of water.

Ask students to give examples of ecological or biological water use and link those users to the molecular or physical properties of water. (Osmoregulation, aquatic life, relationships between plant form and evapotranspiration; special adaptations by organisms to get around problems of heat or water loss; ice floating, which means aquatic life can continue in subfreezing habitats—the list is virtually without end.) See Denny (References) for more examples.

Optional DEMONSTRATION GUIDE
Evaporative Cooling and Conductance

Students are aware, if they have worked through **Unit 2** of **Module 2**, that animals can maintain their body temperatures actively through metabolic activity or passively through behavior. This demonstration (which is set up as an Exploration, should you prefer to use it that way) simply demonstrates an analogous situation for cooling. Evaporative cooling is more efficient but uses water; conductance is slower but conserves water.

For a demonstration, just follow the steps yourself. Discuss the questions at the end with your students.

DEMONSTRATION
Evaporative Cooling and Conductance

Evaporative cooling is faster than passive cooling by conductance. But it requires water and so can cause water stress in organisms in dry climates. Let's pretend that water is readily available and explore the relative efficiencies of the two methods of cooling.

Materials

- **2 glass jars** of the same size and shape, one with a lid that can be punctured
- **1 rag**, about 25 cm by 25 cm
- **2 submersible thermometers**
- **Water**

Procedure

1. **The two "organisms."**
For organism 1, fill one of the jars to the top with water. Then screw on the lid and insert a thermometer through a small hole in the lid. This organism can lose heat only by conduction and convection; evaporation is impossible. (Why?) But it conserves water well.
For organism 2, fill the other glass jar to the top with water. Stuff the rag into the top of the jar and let it hang out. Place a thermometer on top. This organism loses heat by conduction, convection, and evaporation, but it loses some water too.
2. **The comparison.**
Place your organisms in the sun or under a lamp and record their starting temperatures. Observe them and record their temperatures every 5 or 10 minutes throughout a class period.

3. **Another variable—moving air.**
If you have enough materials for two sets of organisms, place one set under a lamp and in front of a fan. Observe them and record their temperatures as in step 2.

4. **The data.**
At the end of class, which organism stayed cooler? Which one lost water? Explain.
How are the results affected by adding the fan?

INTEGRATION GUIDE
Your Boiling Point

Conductance of heat means simply heat moving from a hotter object or substance to a cooler one. Animals lose heat to their surroundings by conductance when the air temperature is lower than their body temperature. They absorb heat by conductance when the air temperature is higher than their body temperature. So on a hot day when air temperature is the same as body temperature, gain and loss from conductance are about equal and not much cooling can happen.

Evaporative cooling is important to large mammals such as ourselves, because we produce metabolic heat all the time. Under warm conditions, large mammals would "cook" very quickly if they had to depend on conductance alone.

Ask students to work alone to do the calculations. The intention here is to point out the limitations placed on living things by the physical and molecular properties of water.

INTEGRATION
Your Boiling Point

Now we know something about water as a cooling force. How much heat can a human take? When do we start to "cook"?

It is much more interesting to do this with your own weight, but some people are sensitive about their weight. If so, substitute someone else's or use an average weight for your age group: 150 lb for girls and 170 for boys.

Procedure

1. **Weight and metabolic rate.**
   Using your weight in kilograms (2.2 lb = 1 kg), calculate your average metabolic rate:

   $4.1 \times (\text{weight})^{0.751} =$ ______ kcal of heat per hour

2. **Raise your temperature.**
   How many kilocalories of retained heat does it take to raise your body temperature 1°C?

   $0.831 \text{ kcal} \times (\text{weight}) =$ ______ kcal of heat

3. **Lethal temperature.**
   A 6°C increase in body temperature is lethal for humans. Calculate how many kilocalories of retained heat would be lethal for you.

   6°C × ______ kcal of heat from step 2 = ______ lethal kcal of retained heat

4. **Cooking time.**
   How many hours would it take you to "cook" if you could not sweat?

   lethal kcal (from step 3) × kcal of heat per hour (from step 2) = ______ hours to "cook"

5. **Saved by sweating.**
   Sweating 1 liter, or 1,000 g, of water dissipates 300 kcal of heat. How much would you have to sweat to keep your body temperature at normal?

   kcal produced per hour (step 2) × 300 kcal per liter = ______ liters of sweat per hour to keep body temperature normal

6. **Pool your class data (no names).**
   Who will cook the fastest if they cannot sweat, big people or small people? A 2-ton elephant, a 1-ton moose, a 0.5-ton horse, a 200-lb man, or a 30-g rodent?

   Who must sweat more per kilogram of body weight, big people or small people (kg sweated per kg body weight per hour)? What about the mammals listed above?

REFERENCES

Denny, Mark. 1993. Air and Water: The Biology and Physics of Life's Media. Princeton, NJ: Princeton University Press.

Heinrich, Bernd. 1993. The Hot-Blooded Insects. Cambridge: Harvard University Press.

Water Use by Humans

Unit 3

WATER USE BY HUMANS

UNIT 3 CONTENTS

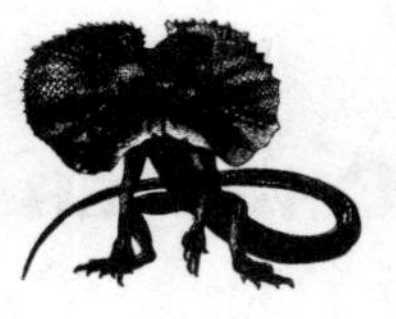

Unit 3 Overview

Water Use by Humans

Unit 3 focuses on both biological and technological water use by humans. It moves from considering the level of the individual to the level of community and watershed. Water is all connected, and its use in any one place affects it in other places. Similarly, water pollution in any place also affects pollution in other places.

The Unit considers questions like these:

- How much water does a human being actually need, biologically speaking?
- How much water is used by technology, and what effects does that have?
- How do cultural differences influence water-use patterns?
- How does habitat destruction follow from our water-use practices? What about destruction twice over—in the habitat to which water is brought and in habitats from which it is brought?
- What is pollution? Who gets to say? And who pays the consequences?

We collect data on water use by the human species, by comparing members of two different cultures. Then we consider the other ways in which those cultures use—or do not use—water and the consequences of such use. There is a difference of four orders of magnitude between developed and traditional cultures in their water use per person. Must that be so? Can we curb water appetites? How?

Chapter 1 raises some of these issues and allows students to collect comparative data. They also consider the consequences of moving water from one place to another—that it can affect both places adversely.

In **Chapter 2**, we focus on pollution as a relative concept. One person's pollution may be another person's pleasure or profit. That can make water rights a touchy issue.

Direct Use of Water by Humans

Chapter One

Contents

Introduction

The human animal has simple and small water needs. Cultures, especially technologized cultures, however, are prodigious and even rapacious users of water. Here we compare and consider the differences between the water needs of humans as animals and the unbounded water needs of cultures.

Water use by humans affects the habitats of other organisms in many ways. Just by using more water, humans often make it unavailable for other organisms. In our constant quest for more water to use for technology, we often have extensively altered huge areas of habitat. When dams and reservoirs are built, one set of habitats is destroyed and another created. By irrigating land, we remove water from streams and aquifers and cause it to evaporate and become unavailable locally much faster than it would have naturally. Irrigated farmland has replaced natural habitats in many areas. Whole watersheds have been altered and diverted for municipal water supplies, industry, and agriculture. Our demand for large quantities of water has dramatically altered large areas of the earth and endangered many habitats.

KEY CONCEPTS

- All humans need a basic and similar amount of water to stay alive.
- Different societies, however, have additional uses for water.
- Much of our technology causes us to use much more water than we would otherwise.

MATERIALS AND PREPARATION

You may find it helpful to carry out Exploration 1 yourself and see what your water uses are for a 24-hour period. (If you carried out the energy budget in **Chapter 2** of **Module 2**, **Unit 2**, this work is familiar.) Here we are studying water rather than energy use, but the reasoning and principles are much the same. You may also find some categories not listed in Table 1 and can help students estimate their water "cost."

SUGGESTED SEQUENCE OF SESSIONS (4–6)

Homework

Case Study: Human Water Uses: Biological introduces students to the idea that humans, like other species, need water to live and that all humans need about the same amount of metabolic water.

Class Session 1

Discuss the Case Study briefly; use it to introduce the topic of water use. Discuss with students how to collect data on how and how much water they use during the next 24 hours (Exploration 1). Hand out copies of Table 1 or let students make a data table in their notebooks based on it.

Class Session 2

Consider results and questions from Exploration 1. Students need time and perhaps some support with their calculations.

Homework

Reading 1: Human Water Uses: Technological compares societies on the basis of water use.

Class Session 3

Continue as necessary from Session 2. Do students vary widely in their water use? Is there any pattern by sex? How do the results help explain the differences between Chwa and Sabrina?

What do students conclude from the Reading? Emphasize how technology has led to increased water use. Consider the global effects as you begin Exploration 2.

Class Session 4

Students "scale up" their numbers, to discover something about how much water above and beyond biological necessity is being used in the United States (Exploration 2).

Class Session 5

Discuss the results from Exploration 2. How do students feel about the results? What do they think can or should be done about so much water use?

Homework

Reading 2: Habitats Destroyed by Our Water Use describes natural habitat lost to humans' greed for water or developable land.

Class Session 6

Using data from all their work in this chapter, students discuss water uses and the issues surrounding them.

SESSION GUIDES, BY WORKSHEET

CASE STUDY GUIDE
Human Water Uses: Biological

The point of the Case Study is the similarity in the biological water needs of two young women despite the marked differences in their lifestyles. How is the similarity possible? Both women are members of the same species, are the same approximate size, and thus have about the same metabolic needs (all else being equal; for instance, neither is much more active or lives in a much drier area).

If students worked through **Module 2**, **Unit 2**, they realize that species members have much in common, so humans are no exception. And if they also studied the material in **Module 2**, **Unit 4**, they know that Chwa and Sabrina are remarkably alike in their energy needs. The Case Study shows that the teenagers are just as alike in their water needs.

Students might be distracted by the lifestyle differences; those become important in the following work, as we focus on the difference between biological and other uses of water.

EXPLORATION 1 GUIDE
Your Actual Water Use

Using copies of Table 1 or their own data sheets, students work in groups to calculate and compare their water uses. Ask students to work out their own water budgets and those of the !Kung San using the worksheet. It is not necessary for students to come up with exact numbers; they will still find large differences between their own water use and Chwa's.

If it was not clear before, it probably will become clear to students now that we use water for many things that are not even done by some societies. Ask students whether their water-use habits might change if they had to carry their water to their houses in buckets from a well in the center of the neighborhood.

Are there also differences among individuals within groups? Students may be shy about discussing this, but there may be interesting patterns by sex (who washes dishes, the car, or babies in the household), activity level (athletes may shower more frequently), jobs (laundromat vs. fast food), or just personal preferences. Some people like water, others do not.

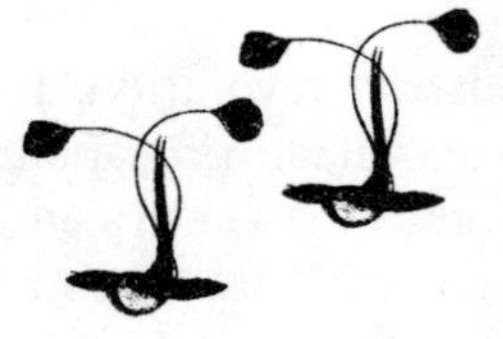

READING 1 GUIDE
Human Water Uses: Technological

Country of origin and even habitat are less important to a people's water use than how much technology they use. All humans have about the same biological needs; it is other needs that vary so widely. Agriculture is directly tied to human life, but what about golf courses or air conditioners? As for agriculture, how much is done in technologically inappropriate ways, because we work at different scales and in different ways than did the Papago Indians? (In Tucson, the average per-capita water use is 925 m^3, 925 times as much water as the traditional Papago Indians used.)

Part of the dream behind the European Economic Community is that not every culture will need to raise its own food, that agriculture can be limited to areas most suitable for it. But that raises many cultural, sociological, and diplomatic issues. What about people who have been farmers for generations? What about a country that raises no food but is wholly dependent on others for its food? One study showed that in east Africa, even though an acre of land with its wildlife could bring tourists and turn a profit more than 100% what that same acre would turn if used for agriculture, people still preferred to be independent and grow their own food.

EXPLORATION 2 GUIDE
Total Water Use

Students calculate how much water is used in their state for household and industrial technology versus simple human biological needs. They compare those numbers with the amount that would be used if everyone lived the lifestyle of the !Kung San.

Ask students to think about things that would not be available to them if less water were available for industry and agriculture. How would their lives change if water became limited and expensive?

Changes?

Many researchers think that water will be the limiting factor in the twenty-first century and that we will need to alter our lifestyles. Do students have any thoughts about, say, changing agricultural practice, diet, or even seemingly small things like using the dishwasher less often? How might dietary changes make a difference? (If we ate more grains and less beef, we would get more meals per unit water—remember Old MacGregor in **Module 2, Unit 3**?) How about eating native animals, which are adapted to their environment, rather than water-needing domestic animals, which are a holdover from colonial times and other habitats? Buffalo, kangaroo, whatever herbivore is native to a habitat is apparently well adapted—how about buffalo burgers?

Historical Perspective

Ask students what two major social revolutions have occurred in human history, both involving increased and new uses of water. The first was agriculture, shortly after which came irrigation. Much U.S. agriculture, especially in the west, depends on irrigation. Most rice cultivation worldwide is irrigation dependent, and rice is the staple grain of the world's most heavily populated countries, India and China.

The second revolution was the industrial revolution. Industry uses water in large quantities, both directly for manufacturing and indirectly for cooling and washing. In the eighteenth and nineteenth centuries, thousands of streams were dammed for water power. More recently, dams have been built for hydroelectric power, irrigation water, and drinking water. Humans have altered the courses and the water of streams all over the world for centuries, draining wetlands and creating lakes and cropland.

If students wish to pursue this topic, have them do some reading in newspapers or reference materials about water uses. We debate the issues in **Unit 4** of this Module; you may want to skip ahead.

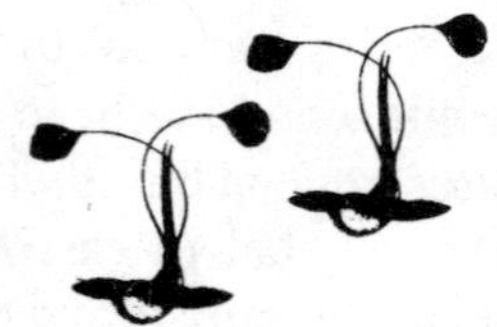

READING 2 GUIDE

Habitats Destroyed by Our Water Use

Start the discussion by asking students if there is a right or wrong position. Or, ask what is behind the two cases of habitat loss. Everyone wants food, water, some comfort in life. Yet in the Aral region, desertification and loss of habitat and life (not to mention food or comfort) are resulting from the very efforts to achieve comfort. Why? (Resources are inadequate to support the population. And continuing to use those resources in the same ways simply destroys the habitat. There need to be new solutions: getting wood and food from less dry habitats; returning the population levels to what the land can support; and altering how people get their support.)

What suggestions do students have? Can they see the pattern as worldwide and therefore requiring worldwide solutions? Populations are just outstripping their resources. If many areas do not work together to curb the population and trade or share locally abundant resources, everyone loses. Help students think globally: who has wood, water, rice, and who does not? Can it be moved around? What about using habitat-appropriate livestock. Do not raise sheep in the Aral region, but instead camels and desert rabbits. They are adapted to the habitat and far less destructive of it.

The Everglades present a different angle on the same general problem. Sugar growers and developers make their livings indirectly from the Everglades. That is, they do not harvest their food or fuel; they run businesses to earn salaries with which they buy food, fuel, and so on. But those businesses have the same effect—they destroy existing habitats and replace them with others. Is there an alternative? What can students suggest?

While a sugar plantation or building complex is a habitat, it is clearly not naturally occurring. Nor is it an ecosystem, self-maintaining in any sense of the phrase. Ask students what might be an acceptable world balance between non-natural and natural habitats. (Remember we wondered whether a city was an ecosystem, since it is not self-maintaining, e.g., no dung beetles?) How could we tell if the balance worked? What would they want to know, or on what bases might they make decisions?

These are tough questions, which we need to resolve before we destroy the planet we know and replace it with something we can only imagine, model, and think about.

INTEGRATION GUIDE
Connecting Some Pieces

Have students do some research on water use in a country or area of their choice. Try to get a mix of technologized and less developed places. Specifically, ask students to focus on conflict between different parts of the population (e.g., industry, agriculture, direct human uses, fishing). Is there enough water for humans? Is there conflict among any of those components? And is there conflict between water use and protecting property for humans or other animals?

Are there patterns? Who thinks water should be used and how? Who controls water? How is it apportioned? We pick up this topic again in **Unit 4**, so keep track of student ideas and results for reference then.

INTEGRATION
Connecting Some Pieces

Pick a country or area that interests you from the point of view of water. Perhaps Chile, with its long coastline; Ireland, with so much water vapor and shore; Wisconsin, with all its lakes; the Amazon basin; France or India, because there is so much agriculture; Portugal, because there is so much fishing; Tunisia, parts of the United Arab Emirates, or Israel, because they are so dry; east Africa, because water is so seasonal.

You actually have some good ideas about how much water there is in different parts of the world, ecologically speaking. Let's also consider the political aspects of water.

Procedure

1. **The data and questions.**
   Do some research to answer the following questions:
   What does each place think about water?
   How does it treat water?
   Who controls water?
   How is it used?
   Is there enough water for all the people?
   What about for wildlife?
2. **The write-up.**
   Summarize your findings in a page or two. Exchange your work with another member of your class, someone who chose a completely different place. Together, try to draw some conclusions about water as a resource.
   Write a paragraph, if possible together, summarizing your conclusions and add them to your original work.
   Save your work, since we return to this topic in **Unit 4**, and you may want to refer to it.

REFERENCES

Cessna, Jacobs, and Foster, eds. 1993. Water, No Longer Taken for Granted. Wylie, Texas: Information Plus, 75098-9990.
This 120-page booklet is a compilation of information about water use and current issues surrounding water use. It contains many useful tables, charts, and maps concerning water use in the United States, as well a list of resources for more information.

Misuse of Water by Humans
Water Pollution

Chapter Two

Contents

Introduction

This Chapter focuses on water pollution caused by individuals and households instead of big industrial polluters. In many heavily populated areas, such pollution is now a bigger threat to waterways and drinking water than is industrial pollution. Industrial pollution is certainly important, but students can more easily measure (and change) individual and household pollution.

Many factors determine water quality: temperature, flow rate, dissolved oxygen, microorganisms, organic chemicals, inorganic chemicals, salinity, pH, among other things. Some of these factors exist naturally, but many are a consequence of human behavior. Such consequences typically are considered pollution if they make water less suitable for use by living organisms. But there can be strong differences of opinion about which organisms. For example, Florida sugar growers see native water plants as pollutants of the cane fields; naturalists and others consider sugar fields and their runoff to be pollutants because they kill native species.

KEY CONCEPTS

- Pollution is a relative thing—oil in a car engine is fine; in drinking water, it is not.
- Relative and absolute are important concepts. They are another way of emphasizing the importance of context and are part of our ongoing discussion of facts, truth, right, and wrong.
- Anything that alters the quality of water is a pollutant.
- Any body of water can become polluted.
- Many small polluters add up to one big pollution problem.

MATERIALS AND PREPARATION

For Exploration 1

- Copies of the worksheet, 1 for each student

For Exploration 2

- **2 sheets of glass or clear plastic**, 10 in. by 20 in.
- **Sheet of 1-in.-thick Styrofoam**
- **Roll of duct tape**
- **Stones**
- **Gravel**
- **Sand**
- **Clay**
- **Soil**
- **Dye or a tube of water color** (yellow or orange is easy to see)
- **Watering can with sprinkler head**

In Advance

Set up the landscape model for Exploration 2, as shown in Figure 1.

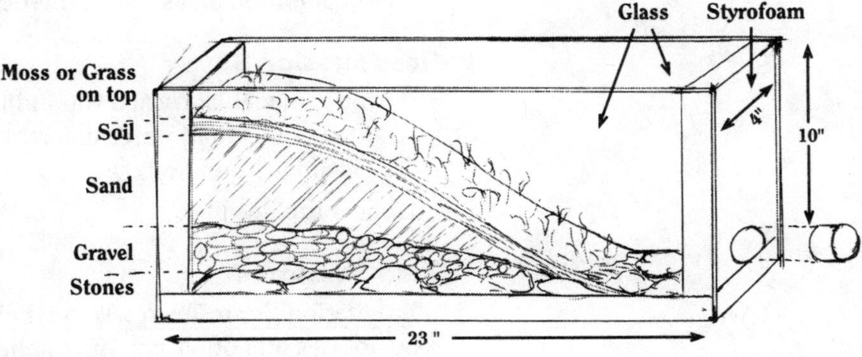

Figure 1

For a quick and simple model, or if you cannot go outside, use a large beaker or other clear plastic or glass container. Fill the container with the four soil-like materials, then let it rain, as per Exploration 2. It is not necessary to buy materials; local gravel, soil, and sand will work, as will aquarium gravel and potting soil.

For Integration

- **Names and descriptions of industries and businesses in your area** (from the yellow pages, business section of the newspaper, town hall)
- **Common occupations** of people in your area (census data)

SUGGESTED SEQUENCE OF SESSIONS (3–5)

Homework

Case Study: Pollution: What and Where Is It?

Class Session 1

Discuss homework questions briefly; use them to introduce the topic.

Working individually, students begin to consider what types of pollution are coming from their homes (Exploration 1: Water Pollution from MY Home?).

Homework

Students take home their data tables and inventory potential pollutants in their households (Exploration 1).

Class Session 2

Student groups average their household Pollution Potentials and likelihood of polluting water. The averages allow some anonymity and decrease self-consciousness; they also show how much pollution may be going on.

Homework

In Reading: Pollution Sources Large and Small, students see other examples of pollution and some of their effects.

Class Session 3

With the model landscape you built in advance, illustrate how different textures of soil hold water differently, using colored water (Exploration 2: Modeling Groundwater).

Discuss the Reading.

Class Session 4

Integration: Your Town's Water Pollution. Students gather data about businesses and other potential polluters in your area. They consider, in light of what they know, whether or how they might influence any pollution sources, even just by ceasing to buy certain products.

SESSION GUIDES, BY WORKSHEET

CASE STUDY GUIDE
Pollution: What and Where Is It?

Ask students what water pollution is. Make a chart on the board, listing whatever students name. Next to each item, write a place or situation in which the item would be inappropriate (polluting) and appropriate (nonpolluting).

Does everyone agree about when or where things are appropriate? Leaf litter in the woods or on a flower bed (as mulch) might be appropriate, but people likely rake it off a lawn. (Include non-ecological examples if discussion flags.) Some fertilizer for a potted plant is healthful; too much is toxic. Water in your basement is a pollutant; in a river it is fine. Sugar cane in the Everglades is pollution to us, but a livelihood to sugar growers; to them, native plants are pollutants.

If people disagree about whether something is a pollutant, how can they work out their differences? Are there substitutes, other technologies, or other approaches?

Discuss the homework assignment and either hand out copies of the data table for Exploration 1, or ask students to copy it into their notebooks.

EXPLORATION 1 GUIDE
Water Pollution from MY Home?

Discuss student data tables for 5 or 10 minutes—ask what surprised them most.

Remind them that the data table does not include all potential pollutants. It also leaves out nonpolluting alternatives, such as vinegar and baking soda as cleansers, water-based paints, and detergent-water solutions as insecticides.

Have students average both their Pollution Potential and their household likelihoods of polluting water. By using averages, no student's household is singled out.

The highest possible Pollution Potential in the data table is 297 if a household uses large amounts of all the chemicals and flushes them all. A score lower than 99 suggests a relatively low risk of causing pollution, since the household probably is using mostly small amounts, if any, and disposing of leftovers correctly. Between 99 and 198 probably is average. Over 198 shows a higher-than-average risk of causing water pollution. What is the average score for your class?

How many items in the data table are absolute necessities? How many are conveniences? Are there less toxic substitutes? (For example, vinegar and baking soda are excellent cleansers, quite inexpensive, and easy to manage from the water-pollution point of view.)

Let the class multiply its averages for a class total. How serious is it? Multiply the average for a few pollutants by the number of students in the whole school. How much potential pollution is that? How many households are there in the United States? Keep ramping up the numbers until you have, Fermi-style, some idea of the amount used in the United States (population 270,000,000; average household 2.7). Students can see that even if one household does not pollute much, those numbers add up across many households.

The point is not to scare anyone out of using a particular product but to make students more aware of the effects of the products they use. It is important for students to understand that they do have some direct control over some pollution.

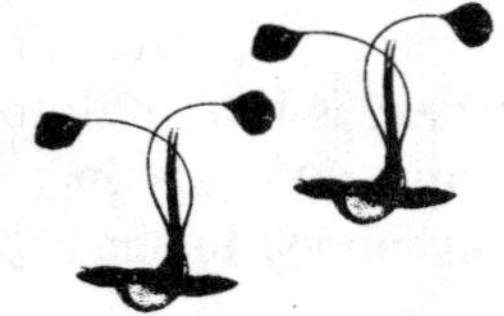

READING GUIDE
Pollution Sources Large and Small

Note again that pollution is relative: the heat generated by industries is considered a pollutant (undesirable) by them, yet simply pouring it into local water supplies is considered pollution by people interested in those habitats. Different organisms live in water of different temperatures, and changing stream flow or temperature alters it as an environment.

List sources of industrial or commercial nonpoint pollution (Exploration 2 focuses on point source and household pollution). Can students name local businesses or practices that might contribute? Can any be influenced or stopped? Such thinking can make people upset, since livelihoods, habits, and behavior are involved, so tread carefully. On the other hand, some students testing other curriculum materials found lead in their water supplies and induced their town management to alter water practice and solve the problem. The Mitchell and Stapp reference has many useful ideas for monitoring local water quality: what, how, and what to do with the information. A research project might grow out of this Reading and discussion; alternatively, students use information from this Reading for the Integration.

EXPLORATION 2 GUIDE
Modeling Groundwater

If you have a large class and only one model, you may want groups of students to take turns repeating the demonstration so everyone can see clearly.

Consider septic systems and groundwater. Why are watersheds set aside to protect drinking-water supplies? If all water is connected, what are the implications "there" of pollution "here"?

How about nutrient cycling or flow? Inorganic and organic molecules move via groundwater (as well as in water vapor). Such molecules must dissolve in water to enter the biological part of the water cycle. Carbon is more likely to be taken by plants from the air, but other elements must come via water. If the colored water models any of those, what can you conclude about residence times, likely distances traveled, pathways, and so on, between the water, its dissolved matter, and the movement of those particles back into or out of the biological cycle? How do plants get the materials? What about soil being washed into water (through flooding and leaching, via groundwater, or otherwise)?

How many students have town-supplied water? Well water? Other sources? Where does it all really come from? Can they tell? Do they know how it is being treated? For example, if they get town water, they might have noticed a faint taste of chlorine after heavy rains. That suggests treatment by the town water management to offset potential drain overflow and potential pollution from excess runoff or flooding. Is not chlorine itself a pollutant? How do people make decisions about choosing the lesser among various costs to the environment? Everyone wants clean drinking water, yet there seem so many obstacles.

If your drinking water comes from a reservoir, you might arrange a field trip to see the water and how it is treated. Or perhaps someone working for the local water supply system could talk to the class about the drinking water supply.

On a more optimistic note, it also might be a good idea for students to locate clean, unpolluted water near your community and see what has been done to protect it. You might discuss with students improvements in sanitation and sewage treatment, abatement of industrial pollution and pesticide bans, and tightening up building requirements and penalties for pollution. Such measures tend to be controversial locally since they usually require tax dollars and costs to business and industry.

INTEGRATION GUIDE

Your Town's Water Pollution

You probably can name some of the big industries in your area. Simple sources of information are the yellow pages and the business section of the newspaper. Public libraries often have references that list businesses and what they do. Your town or city hall may well have information from the last census that will tell you what occupations are most common in your area.

This Integration is not meant to be data intensive; rather, it could be the beginning of an awareness of what would have to be altered to turn off water pollution instantly and the challenges and expenses involved in treating industrial, agricultural, and household waste. Through an investigation of the occupations of students' family members, it should become clearer how many people can be adversely affected if polluting industries are forced to shut down.

REFERENCES

Mitchell, Mark K., and William B. Stapp. 1994. Field Manual for Water Quality Monitoring: An Environmental Education Program for Schools. 8th ed. Dexter, MI: Thomson-Shore.

Mitchell and Stapp is the classic for student-based water quality–monitoring projects. Full of practical information and guides on setting up and managing any scale of water testing, it also helps you plug into a network of fellow researchers and gets your data into a national pool. Fully two-thirds of the water bodies in the United States have never been tested; go forth and test that water.

Waring, Richard H., and William H. Schlesinger. 1985. Forest Ecosystems: Concepts and Management. New York: Academic Press.

This tome on forest ecology is quite accessible—it uses simple graphs and clear diagrams instead of complex mathematics to explain concepts.

GLOBAL WATER USE

UNIT 4

GLOBAL WATER USE

Unit 4 Overview

Global Water Use

What are water rights? Who has them? Do nonhumans have rights? Do some humans have more rights than others? On what basis?

All water on the globe is connected, so what someone does with water "here" affects water "there," as well as affecting all the living things dependent on that water.

The global water cycle is a key issue facing us now. We consider whether and how to address it.

We use the term "global water" literally to indicate the globe-wide water cycle (and global warming), as well as metaphorically to indicate the "cosmic" nature of the full cycle. Throughout this Module, we have explored the links between water and life at many levels, from bonds and molecules, from individuals, species, and populations through habitats and communities. In this Unit, we integrate all those levels to consider the global picture of water change, which depends on all those "lower" levels, including plant growth, water rights, pollution, water the biochemical, climate—and your own water use.

Recall that water (like other nutrients) cycles through the system as it participates in physical and chemical transactions of various kinds. Water from the seas and the ground mixes in the atmosphere. So the atmosphere is a crossroads for water passed around as vapor. It is nearly impossible to monitor precisely processes at the global level, so we sample what and as we can (e.g., turnover and movement of water, change in weather and climate, temperature) and build a story with those results, plus all our other data across the various levels we study.

To complete the story, though, we return to a habitat's water uses under a drastic but not impossible scenario of water shortage and global warming. That allows us to close the circle from individual to global aspects of the water cycle and to see how we as individuals count in the grand debate about the climate and the planet's future.

Global Water Reservoirs

Chapter One

Contents

INTRODUCTION

This Unit considers the study of water on a global level and in the context of the current, important debate on global warming, water use, and desertification. Students explore some of the issues and consider how it is possible for human activity to have a worldwide, geological impact. How important are lifestyle choices to global ecological change?

This Chapter integrates the rest of the Unit, building an approach to the modeling of very large systems, about which exact answers are impossible. In the course of that work, it also introduces some fundamental notions about systems.

In the end, the students return to their habitats from **Chapter 1** of **Unit 1**, armed with a deeper ecological understanding of the issues, and make some predictions using what they have learned.

KEY CONCEPTS

- Among the most urgent issues facing us and the field of ecology is the need to understand human influences on global changes. The global water cycle is at the heart of many current environmental and political issues, most obviously who gets how much water and how we affect the global water cycle and the rest of the planet. Clear answers are hard to come by: the magnitude of the issue makes it difficult to study. At the global level, any phenomenon is more than the sum of its parts—it shows synergy among its parts, so even if we knew all the parts, we likely still would not have clear answers.
- Ecology is a study of systems. Organisms, food webs, communities, ecosystems, the entire biosphere: each can be viewed as a system.
- Systems theory can be applied to a wide variety of systems, because its concepts are useful in thinking about matter and energy flow in ecosystems, money flow in economies, and information flow in computer networks.
- Static parts of systems include pools—concentrations of things or materials in a specific form—and pathways of flow between pools.
- Dynamic aspects of systems include rates of flow along pathways and residence times in pools. In addition, the material that is moving may change form as it moves from one pool to another. For example, water exists in three different physical forms (gas, liquid, solid) as well as biochemically in many compounds in different components of a system. When water moves between reservoirs, it usually carries chemicals and particles with it.
- The atmospheric pool is a crossroads for the water (in the form of vapor) flowing among the other pools of the global system. Water is found in solid (ice and snow) and liquid (streams and oceans) reservoirs, as well as in many different compounds in organic matter, alive and dead.
- Flow rates from one pool to another have a major effect on the climate system. Among humans, water use for metabolic respiration varies with

body size, climate, and activity level. Total water use, however, varies largely as a result of technological processes, such as home heating and cooling, home-appliance use, diet, and manufacturing (**Unit 3, Chapter 1**).

- An additional factor is overpopulation by humans. Everyone wants to eat and be comfortable, and we are outstripping the planet's ability to support us.

MATERIALS AND PREPARATION

For Exploration 2

- **Maps of weather patterns and prevailing winds** for the United States or your region
- **Regional map(s)** showing rivers, streams, and (if possible) topography (mountains, flatlands, hills). A road map will do if it shows major streams. Topographic maps are available from the U.S. Geological Survey (USGS).
- **Weather maps from local newspaper** (Ask students to save maps for several days ahead of time.)
- **TV weather reports**, especially satellite images of weather
- **Local water systems data** affecting your area

For Exploration 3 (for each group)

- **2 dishpans, basins, or large bowls,** with sides higher than those of the small bowls
- **2 small bowls**
- **Plastic wrap**
- **Ice**
- **Sticky tape**
- **Hot water** (The hotter the water, the faster the results, but you decide if your students can handle boiling water. It is not necessary.)
- **Water color or food dye** (2 colors, if possible)
- **Talcum or baby powder** (not cornstarch, which will clump and get sticky)
- **Pot holders** (if you use very hot or boiling water)

SUGGESTED SEQUENCE OF SESSIONS (8–10)

Class Session 1

Set up the scenario for a debate on water rights. Assign teams, do some in-class discussion or reading (Exploration 1), or send teams to the library for more data on their positions.

Homework

Case Study: Who Owns a River? and Team Data (Exploration 1) prepare students for a debate on water rights. If you like, ask them to do additional research in the library.

Class Session 2

Start the debate. Depending on class size, consider having some students act as jurors.

Class Session 3

Class discussion of the debate: which issues or positions seemed stronger? Why?

Homework

Students write a paragraph on their reactions to the water rights issue and the debate.

Class Session 4

Exploration 2: Where Does Your Water Come From? gives students a sense of water cycling in the atmosphere—as vapor and rain—and how the surface it crosses affects that vapor. It raises the idea of atmosphere as the crossroads of water cycling.

Homework

Students consider the three states of water; how water moves among those states; and that by such movement all water is connected.

Class Session 5

Discuss the global interconnectedness of water. Illustrate its three states (Exploration 3: Flux and Systems).

Homework

Reading 2: How to Make a Desert describes the terrible habitat loss wrought by human overpopulation and subsequent overuse of water.

Class Session 6

Discuss desertification (Reading 2); it is just a more extreme example of the water rights issues that students debated in Exploration 1. You might want to photocopy and hand out Science Background: How Latitude and Climate Interact.

Class Session 7

In Exploration 4: The Case of the Missing Ducks, student groups play detective to find that loss and degradation of wetland and coastal habitats are causing severe declines in some duck species.

Homework

Reading 3: Epilogue and Reading 4: Flyways: Where Is Home? help pull together the data from Exploration 4.

Class Session 8

Discuss Exploration 4, and Readings 3 and 4, and the factors involved in the decline of waterfowl. Do nonhumans have water rights, too?

Homework

Integration: Revisiting Your Habitat.

Class Session 9

Discuss the Integration and wrap up the Module.

SESSION GUIDES, BY WORKSHEET

CASE STUDY GUIDE
Who Owns a River?

Begin by considering any questions from the Case Study. The Reading does not answer every question about the history of water rights and the use of the Colorado River. In fact, you may want to have students do some independent research for the debate (Exploration 1).

Be sure students understand that there is a timely issue at stake here and that there are competing interests, human and ecological. The point is that a finite amount of water is available. How should it be allocated, and how would such an allocation affect natural and human systems? Most questions will come up during and after the debate.

EXPLORATION 1 GUIDE
Who Owns Water? A Debate

In this debate, students present and defend different points of view about water use and priorities. Have them refer to their work in **Unit 3, Chapter 2**, both the Integration and the Readings. They also may want to do additional research about their positions. Raise (if no one else does) the question of overpopulation. Is water the real issue? How come there are so many people needing water? What about their lifestyles? What about people who want those lifestyles?

The discussion begun here integrates the work of the rest of the Module. At the end of the debate, students can revisit their team positions and write briefly whether they might take a different position. Or raise that question repeatedly throughout the chapter; the issue recurs.

Logistics

Assign student groups or let them volunteer for the different teams. Let each team have a spokesperson but ensure that other group members also have opportunities to speak.

If you want, make this a formal debate before other classes, the PTSA, or some other group. Let students do additional research on the topic and even write up individual or group reports.

In any case, try to come up with some consensus or set of priorities with which all the teams can live. The debate might become quite heated, and no consensus may be possible. Keep reminding students to substantiate their points or when they need more data to address a question or issue. This debate is designed as a discussion, not a filibuster, and data count. The final decision on water allocation can be written up individually for homework, or one group can take the role of a jury and make a decision.

EXPLORATION 2 GUIDE
Where Does Your Water Come From?

By considering where their water comes from and goes to, students see that they and their water needs are just pieces of the whole. Physical features affect how much water your area gets and when. (If you do this during a nonrainy season or period, consider why there is no rain.)

If your area does not get water from rainfall, is groundwater the source? Is water brought in from far away? Has the town suffered from flooding or drought? Does it do so often or regularly? Why? (Latitude, location on the dry or wet side of mountains?) (Some of these issues are raised in Reading 1, and you might want to carry them along until students have read that.)

Ask students to figure out, using stream maps, how the water that runs off from their community reaches the ocean. Often, many of the storms that hit an area come from the same direction. By looking at the prevailing weather patterns, it is possible to get some idea where your rainwater was before it evaporated into the atmosphere. Information on paths of storms, prevailing winds, the jet stream, and so forth, should be available locally from the National Weather Service.

Do the water patterns affect students' lives directly? Areas can have shortages and flooding; a community that farms, fishes, or has a tourist industry can be greatly affected by changes in weather patterns.

If older folks think the weather has changed, why might that be (global warming; long-term cycles; habitat changes such as water being diverted, forests cut down, or buildings on former wetlands)? Ask students if they worry about water availability, now or for the future. Have they any suggestions?

See the Science Background for more on climate and latitude. You might want to photocopy that section and hand it out.

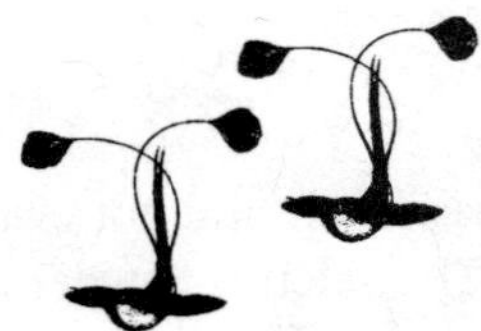

READING 1 GUIDE
Water Gets Around

Water is a finite resource, and the global water cycle is a good example of a system. Water reservoirs are mostly liquid (streams, oceans) and solid (ice caps, glaciers), but water cycles among the reservoirs as water vapor and moves around in liquid form (vapor, rain, groundwater).

Students might be surprised that all water is connected and might wonder how that can be. Have them examine a topographic map or reexam-

ine their habitat maps (**Unit 1**, **Chapter 1**) to remember that most places have some water in liquid or solid form.

Much of the planet is covered with water, plus there is groundwater, which we cannot see, and is often quite deep. Referring to Exploration 2, remind them that prevailing winds carry moisture from place to place. Water rises through evaporation, condenses to come back down as snow or rain, runs through or over land along paths of least resistance (and underground), joining larger and larger bodies of water. From those bodies, the water evaporates again, is carried up into the atmosphere, and repeats its cycle. Illustrate that cycle with them, asking for examples from their habitats (**Unit 1, Chapter 1**). Note the residence times in various reservoirs. What does that suggest about water turnover? What pools do humans affect most directly? (Water as a liquid; all water by pollution; ice by global warming.)

Where do they least expect to find water? Why? (Permafrost, in deserts, underground.) Can they think of a break in the cycle or connection? How might they test that thought?

Watersheds can be defined on many scales and often are used as a unit of study for movement of nutrients, pollutants, or the water itself. Since all water ultimately is connected, it can be difficult to set boundaries on a watershed, but researchers decide on the scale of their interest and limit accordingly.

Suggest an analogy to sap in plants and blood in animals to show that water carries around nutrients and waste (pollution) in habitats as well as in the bodies of individuals. Consider examples of what would be carried around habitats by water and how those things might affect the habitat. Wastes from human societies are carried around—sewage , chemicals of all sorts, pollutants and agricultural runoff, salts from overusing and concentrating water. Remind students that pollution is relative, and some "waste" can be nutrients to plants and algae (**Unit 3**, **Chapter 2**).

EXPLORATION 3 GUIDE
Flux and Systems

This activity illustrates water: as a closed system, how it moves between reservoirs and changes state, and that it carries matter along with it—the points of Reading 1.

Logistics

If time is short, make this a demonstration while students work on Exploration 2.

What to Expect

The food dye should stay in its small reservoir and not evaporate with the water. The rainwater should be clear. The talcum powder should rain down into the reservoirs and pollute them both. The intention is to show students how water moves among reservoirs (specifically from the atmosphere) and carries other things with it, especially airborne chemicals, dust, pollutants, and so on. These can travel long distances and then be washed out of the atmosphere by rain.

Discussion

Ask students to list or diagram the system components and principles as illustrated in the model. What, based on Reading 1, is missing from the model system? (Groundwater.) Do students have suggestions for altering the system to make it work differently or make it more realistic? (Since it actually is quite realistic, we cannot think of improvements, but perhaps they or you can.)

Have students list other systems and their components: the circulatory system, a watershed, the carbon cycle, a financial system, heat in the school building. In each case, name the pools or reservoirs, the pathways between and among them, the stuff that is cycling and its different forms, residence times in different pools, and turnover rates. Use the data on water (Reading 1) for possible residence times, proportions of stuff in various reservoirs, and so on. Or consider another system, any one for which they can look up the systems data in an introductory text. How much blood is in the heart versus the circulatory system at any time? (10% in humans.) How fast does it turn over? (With every heart stroke.) How long does any blood cell survive? (120 days.)

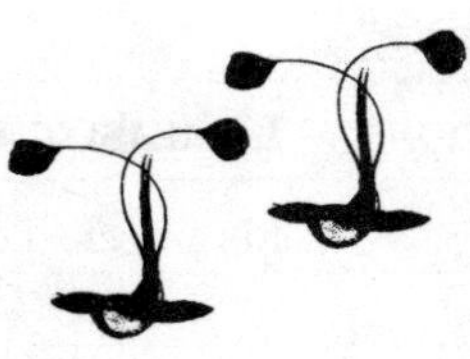

READING 2 GUIDE
How to Make a Desert

Because of overpopulation and human water needs, we are conducting a dangerous experiment on ourselves and the planet. What is that experiment?

Ask students what factors have contributed to the making of a desert where there was no desert before? How about overpopulation? We are changing the face of the planet faster than nature can adapt or even adjust, and the costs are high: social (human death from habitat loss), cultural (peoples and whole ways of life literally dying out), and ecological (irreplaceable habitat and species loss).

You might revisit students' debate decisions now. Given the new information they have about desertification, salinity and desert irrigation, and population growth, would students allocate water differently? What key issues do they see ecologically, culturally, socially? What choices or suggestions might they make now?

The unpredictability of the situation in developed and developing cultures makes social planning nearly impossible. Bilger's book on global warming (see References) may offer some helpful suggestions for discussion.

The population growth data are astonishing: around the turn of the century, the human population passed the 1 billion (1×10^9) mark and has increased since to about five times that in less than a century (currently at about 5.2×10^9). At that rate, we soon will be out of room, globally. Suggest that students make projections for the world population in another 50 years using the current rate of increase. Now how does that affect their ideas about water use?

EXPLORATION 4 GUIDE
The Case of the Missing Ducks

This exploration raises some key concepts and questions. All water is connected, so changing the habitat in one place affects water availability in other places, as well as in that habitat. It also prompts questions like, Where is "home" for a migrating species? Does a migrating species behave differently or have different roles in its two residences? (Usually yes.) Since migration is seasonal, what does that suggest about reasons for migration? Migrating organisms might cover small distances (wildebeest) or thousands of miles (birds, fishes, whales), but the issues are comparable. You likely will end up discussing this Exploration and Reading 3 together.

Logistics

Assign each student group three to five ducks from Table 1 (depending on class size and how much data you think students can handle). Make sure each group gets at least one "missing" or declining species and one with stable or increasing populations. Species overlap between groups is fine and even enlivens the discussion.

Table 1 **U.S. Duck Species**

STABLE POPULATIONS	DECLINING POPULATIONS	INCREASING POPULATIONS
Mallard	Northern pintail	Ring-necked duck
Northern shoveler	American black duck	
Green-winged teal	Bufflehead	?Green-winged teal
Greater scaup	Common goldeneye	
Lesser scaup	Canvasback	
?Redhead duck	Redhead duck	
Eastern mallard	Prairie mallard	
Gadwall		?Gadwall
?American wigeon	American wigeon	
?Ruddy duck	Ruddy duck	

Note that some species may have recently stabilized. Between the 1950s and late 1980s, there were marked habitat degradation and species loss. Some habitats subsequently were restored, and the censuses of the 1990s suggest that a few species may be responding with increased numbers.

Class Discussion

Once groups have worked through their data and clues, make a chart on the board. What is the status of each species? What factor(s) seem to contribute to its decline or increase? Be sure students give evidence for their statements. For some species, data sources or interpretations differ (hence the "?" in Table 1). (That is a good example where Fermi numbers, or order-of-magnitude calculations, are not appropriate. An order-of-magnitude difference of more or fewer black ducks is the difference between survival and extinction.) How can the class resolve those differences? (Unless they have jumped ahead to Reading 3, students are working with only their clues and data.)

Why might species migrate?

(To get to different and better conditions.)
(To escape "harsher" conditions, such as cold or drought.)

Why are some species declining?

(Habitat loss or destruction, so they cannot feed or survive at some point along their migration route. Loss of breeding grounds is especially damaging. Pollution is also a factor; foods once available at sites along the route are destroyed.)

What progress has been made? Are the missing ducks doomed? How can we prevent their extinction?

Do animals besides humans have rights, too? And who decides those rights?

Conservation Status of Dabbling Ducks: Habitat Destruction

Dabbling ducks are the most abundant and widespread group of ducks in North America. The highest densities of breeding dabblers are found on the prairies, with smaller numbers ranging north into Alaska. Early nesting species, such as mallards and pintails, have been affected by losses of upland nesting habitat on the prairies. Intensive agricultural land use on the prairies, combined with drought years that began in the 1980s, have degraded the breeding habitat. Land-use changes that have helped predator species also have affected the birds.

Specifically in the east, natural wetlands are being lost or degraded by agriculture, urbanization, industrial development, pollution, water-control projects, and certain forestry practices.

Of the ten most common species breeding in the prairies, only pintails continue to decrease. Pintail numbers declined from 5.6 million during the 1970s to 2.1 million in 1993.

The black duck population in eastern North America has been decreasing for the past 30 years. The greatest decreases have occurred in the Mississippi flyway. The eastern population of mallards has increased lately. Problems may relate to the conversion of breeding habitat to farmland and to habitat loss and degradation caused by human activity in migration areas.

Conservation Status of Diving Ducks: Habitat Degradation

The highest breeding densities of divers occur on the prairies, although ring-necked ducks and lesser scaup are widespread and the greater scaup breed mainly in the sub-Arctic. Diving ducks tend to use the deeper inland marshes, rivers, and lakes of the continent for breeding and migration and coastal bays, estuaries, and offshore waters for wintering.

With the exception of the lesser scaup, diving ducks are not as abundant as dabblers. Lesser scaup are relatively abundant compared to other divers, but still below the numbers aimed for by the North American

Waterfowl Management Plan. In the prairies, canvasbacks have stabilized, but this species and the redhead remain below population goals.

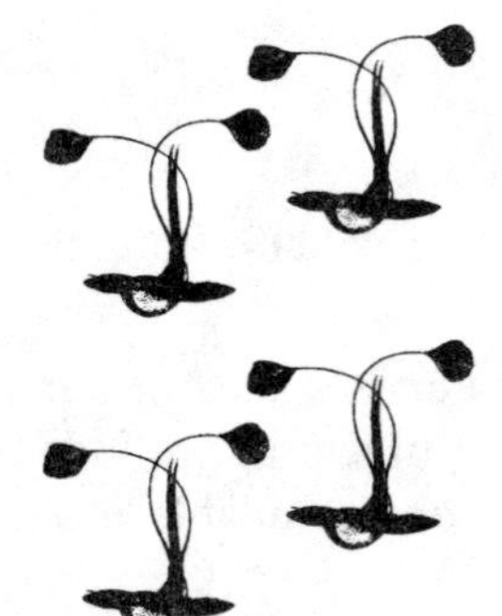

READING 3 GUIDE
Epilogue

READING 4 GUIDE
Flyways: Where Is Home?

Now armed with more information, students have a better overview of the issue and its magnitude. Two key concepts emerge. Let students describe them to you. Ask what management issues are being added to the issues already under consideration (managing migrating species). Is everything connected?

How do the ducks illustrate systems effects? (Change something here, it has an effect elsewhere. Change something this season, it has effects during other seasons. Everything is interconnected, and everything depends on water—humans, ducks, duck-food species, plants.)

Management of a migrating species is extra tough, since it requires protection and maintenance of multiple habitats along the route and at both ends. Such routes often cross political boundaries, so all parties affected need to develop common policies, yet different states or countries may have very different wants or needs. Farming has destroyed much of the U.S. prairies, replacing them with habitat not suitable for duck breeding. Similarly, wetlands are being developed. Water and watery habitats are at a premium. How do we manage them wisely?

The other concept is one we encountered elsewhere for both plants (**Module 2, Unit 3**) and animals (**Module 2, Unit 2, Chapter 10**)—the concept of multiple roles. Many organisms occupy multiple roles or niches during their lives, at different ages or developmental stages, by sex, by season. This added complexity raises important questions: when and where is an animal's niche or home? How can we manage organisms so they are protected in all their roles and throughout their lives? If any piece is lost, the species is lost.

Salmon neatly illustrate both points about migration and such roles. The young leave their "birthplace" to mature and develop hundreds of miles away. But they reproduce only in their birthplace, so if they cannot return to that same spot (e.g., because of dams, which let them go down a river but keep them from going back up), they cannot complete their life-cycle, and the species will cease to survive. (Fortunately that has been recognized, and dams have been modified to allow salmon to return upstream.)

U.S. songbirds and monarch butterflies illustrate a less clear resolution. They overwinter 7,000 miles away in South and Central America, and the forests in which they live during winter are being replaced by farmland at enormous speed and on vast scales. People want to eat and live well; songbirds need overwintering grounds or they will be wiped out. The outcome of these stories is not clear.

Other factors that may have minor additional effects on migratory birds.

- While some duck species use tree-cavity nests, forest fragmentation is probably more detrimental to neotropical landbirds that require large territories and are easily affected by nest predation.
- Global warming will cause sea levels to rise and may affect species using the coastline for feeding and those that nest in coastal areas. It probably has not contributed to population declines yet.
- Hunting for waterfowl can be a positive factor, since public interest in maintaining duck populations is widespread and includes naturalists and other conservationists, as well as hunters.
- Harvesting of ducks for food and for down used in clothing occurs mainly in the northern part of the continent in the spring and fall and is an estimated 5% of the total continental duck harvest. Again, this type of hunting is watched and probably does not contribute to major decline in numbers.
- Entanglement of waterfowl does occur in fishing nets, but it seems more common for marine mammals and sea turtles.
- Ecotourism has increased greatly recently. Birdwatching tours of wetland habitats may affect ducks and other water birds, especially during breeding season. The American Birding Association publishes a Birding Code of Ethics so trip leaders can follow good conservation practices.

INTEGRATION GUIDE
Revisiting Your Habitat

Ask students to revisit one of their initial habitats (**Unit 1**, **Chapter 1**) and consider how that habitat might look if some predicted changes in global warming and the water cycle occurred. Would their wetland still be a wetland, their desert a desert, and so on? Be sure someone studies wetlands and coastal areas, since they will change most radically. This Integration brings the Module full cycle, pulling together all the pieces on which students have worked throughout.

Predictions of Global Warming

There is some consensus among climatologists that some global warming will occur over the next century even if we reduce CO_2 emissions immediately and markedly. How much, how fast, and what those effects might be, however, are under considerable debate. Thus, there are varying and even contradictory predictions about what might happen.

Computer models have helped, but the phenomenon is so vast and the data so scant (relatively speaking) that those models are inadequate. The best we can do is make predictions for specific geographic areas of the world. Such predictions tend to use data on past climate changes and known effects of changes in temperature and humidity on existing organisms. For example, we know that evapotranspiration increases as temperatures increase. But how might that affect overall water flow or distribution? More precipitation might offset the increased evapotranspiration, or the area might simply become drier overall. If plants grew more, would their increased production of CO_2 simply fuel the cycle, or would they cut back on CO_2 intake because water supplies were limited?

Existing organisms are more or less adapted to their current environments. Change in the environment is not unnatural. The current rate at which we (humans) are changing the environment, however, is nearly unprecedented. (There have been three or five previous natural disasters of possibly comparable magnitude, depending on whom we ask.) So we can only suggest that rates of evolution naturally occur more slowly than the current rate of environmental change. That implies that many species will not survive such rapid change. Certainly there will be large-scale physical changes, including ones in temperature and water availability and distribution, and associated changes in organism species and distributions.

Student scenarios will vary depending on their initial habitats and which data they use. Wetlands almost surely will cease to exist, even if they are protected; many islands will disappear; and coastal areas will change dramatically, within the bounds of whatever efforts humans make to protect them.

SCIENCE BACKGROUND
How Latitude and Climate Interact

The earth receives more solar energy near the equator, which makes the equator hotter than the poles, and water evaporates at a higher rate in higher temperatures. As air warms, it rises, then sinks again as it cools. These are the basic elements of climate. Air heats up near the earth's surface and cools as it rises into the atmosphere; then it sinks as it becomes cooler than the air below it.

At the equator, water evaporation and heat both are high. Warm wet air rises from equatorial regions and is replaced by cooler, drier air from the north and the south. As the hot equatorial air rises and cools, the water vapor in it condenses to fall back down to earth as the high rainfall that typifies the tropical rain forests of that region.

Now that the air has lost much of its water vapor, it flows either north or south in the upper atmosphere and keeps losing water vapor. Some of this dry air sinks toward the surface again between 25 and 35 degrees north and south latitude, the latitude of deserts. There is no longer enough water vapor left in the air to produce much precipitation.

The rest of the now dry air that once rose from the equator continues to move north and south, toward the poles, cooling and sinking along the way. It finally sinks at the poles producing cold winds out of the north and south near the surface of the earth.

That scenario is a bit oversimplified. For instance, the earth turning on its axis produces the Coriolis effect. Since the earth rotates toward the east, the trade winds between 5 and 30 degrees north and south blow westward. In both the north and south at about 30 to 35 degrees and at the equator are areas of the atmosphere where different cells of air from north and south meet. Both cells either are rising (at the equator) or are sinking (at

30 to 35 degrees N and S). These areas have extremely variable wind conditions and are where sailing ships used to get stuck, or "becalmed," for weeks at a time.

The topography of the earth's surface secondarily modifies weather patterns, such as creating deserts in the rain shadows of mountains, causing Mediterranean climate in five places on the planet (only one of which is in the Mediterranean), and causing rain or snow near large bodies of water or at high altitudes.

REFERENCES

Bilger, Burkhard. 1992. Global Warming. New York: Chelsea House Publishers.
This book is part of a series called Earth at Risk. The series is described as one for young readers, but it is suitable for any nonscientist new to these topics.

Greenberg, Russell, and Jamie Reaser. 1995. Bring Back the Birds—What You Can Do to Save Threatened Species. Mechanicsburg, PA: Stackpole Books.
Materials on migratory songbirds and habitat destruction.

Kerlinger, Paul. 1995. How Birds Migrate. Mechanicsburg, PA: Stackpole Books.

Pasquier, Roger. 1977. Watching Birds: An Introduction to Ornithology. Boston: Houghton Mifflin Company.

The Potential Effects of Global Climate Change on the United States: Draft Report to Congress Executive Summary. October 1988. Washington, DC: U.S. Environmental Protection Agency, Office of Policy, Planning and Evaluation, Office of Research and Development.

The EPA Journal. Vol. 15, No. 1, January/February 1989.

The Potential Effects of Global Climate Change on the United States: Draft Report to Congress. Vol. I: Regional Studies. October 1988. Washington, DC: U.S. Environmental Protection Agency, Office of Policy, Planning and Evaluation, Office of Research and Development.

The last three references may be available in the government documents section of your public library. If not, contact the EPA office nearest you.

EXTENSIONS

THE DEBATE REVISITED

Students can revisit their debate team positions to consider whether they might take a different position now, after the work of the rest of the Chapter. Let them write briefly about how they felt initially; if that has changed; and, if so, why?

MORE WEATHER

You may be able to find a meteorologist in your area who will help you or the class with information on where your weather and rain come from. Try contacting the National Weather Service in your area or the public relations department at a local TV or radio station that has its own meteorologist.

TECHNIQUES

CONTENTS

Technique
Introduction to Research

This Technique discusses aspects of scientific reasoning and the scientific process. It aims to provide a brief overview of the elements of careful science practice and procedure, such as solid experimental design, that you will need to keep in mind if you undertake research that you intend to share, especially with scientists. Careful methods and clear reporting of your assumptions, methods, and results are the essence of scientific research.

It is important to recognize that there is a difference between doing interesting activities, even "discovery-oriented" activities, and engaging in scientific research, that will be instructive to you and of value to other researchers in the field. This Technique is more about the latter. You are likely to have a good feel for where both you and your students are along the continuum represented by those two points. Although you will learn a lot no matter where you begin, your experience may be more satisfying sooner if you try for an approximate match between your class's familiarity with science process and their first activities. True research is readily within the reach of any science class, so do not shy away from it even if you or your class has no experience with research.

Kinds of Science

Science can be descriptive or experimental, depending on what is already known about the specific topic under study. If little is known, basic data or information must be gathered: describe what you can see. For instance, one exploration in this curriculum is a field trip to describe the vegetation on your study site. Such data can be compared across sites at a given time, to gauge differences due to geographic location. They can also be compared across time at given sites, to gauge changes due to influences such as pollution or global warming. Such observations of phenomena subject to the influence of climatic or ecosystem changes can make you notice new developments or unusual events. Those observations, in turn, can serve as the basis of a thorough scientific investigation.

Alternatively, when enough descriptive data exist to suggest a cause-and-effect relationship between two phenomena or events, we can test, by carrying out experiments, whether there actually is causality or just coincidence. Do increased concentrations of carbon dioxide (CO_2) actually make plants grow faster, all else being equal? Or is the apparent relationship a coincidence? Perhaps increased CO_2 concentrations and plant growth are related, but only indirectly: CO_2 causes atmospheric heat retention (global warming), and the resulting rise in temperature may cause some plant species to grow more rapidly. Your conjectures about such relationships can be tested experimentally: you can try growing different plant species at different combinations of CO_2 concentrations and temperatures.

The investigations in this curriculum take the form of descriptive science, experimental science, or both. In this Technique, we consider both somewhat formally—not because we want to be rigid, but because some formality or standardization makes things easier to discuss and consider. For example, to talk about testing hypotheses, we need to say what we are including and excluding for consideration. So, let us examine the full chronology of a scientific study: the steps involved and how to carry them out. We explore here the design of a hypothetical research project that includes the use of some of the curriculum activities, as well as other work of your own.

THE SCIENTIFIC PROCESS

The scientific process can be thought of as having roughly three steps, each of which has three parts. Although these divisions are somewhat arbitrary, they do correspond to functional divisions and help less experienced researchers keep track of their progress through the scientific process. The "three threes" are summarized here.

Learn: Step 1

1. Observe and describe the phenomenon.
2. Ask questions and make comparisons.
3. Perform a literature search and organize an overview of the topic.

Test quantitatively: Step 2

1. Develop a tentative causal explanation: what seems to cause the phenomenon?
2. Design experiment(s) to test the tentative causal explanation.
3. Carry out the experiment(s).

Analyze and interpret: Step 3

1. Tabulate and analyze the experimental results.
2. Interpret the results narrowly and broadly.
3. Disseminate the results via publication and/or presentation.

In the remainder of this Technique we consider these steps in some depth from the perspective of science process and science reasoning. Each activity or procedure in the body of this curriculum provides some parts of or materials for the first two steps, with participating students and teachers providing the rest. The third step—analyzing and interpreting data—comes primarily from participants, since it is based on the data they collect. However, we consider major issues affecting data analysis and interpretation.

LEARNING AND BACKGROUND: STEP 1

OBSERVING, ASKING QUESTIONS, INVESTIGATING

Very often, you come to a research question because you observe something that seems out of the ordinary, or you make a connection between facts or processes that you had not connected before.

For example, let's say we realize something about our environment: that the sky is not blue and that the air smells funny.

One thing these observations have in common is that they are comparisons—which actually means we are noticing things twice. We assume on the basis of past observation that the sky is a certain color, and now we notice it no longer is that color. When we say, "The air smells funny," we have noticed (perhaps unconsciously) how air once smelled, and now we are noticing that it smells different. (In fact, "different" is more accurate than "funny," so let's use that word from now on.)

Some people are more observant, that is, they make such comparisons more readily, than others. But everyone can improve his or her observation skills, and such skills are valuable: being a good scientist requires good observation skills, both conscious and unconscious.

Being a good scientist also requires articulating those observations—both the initial, often unconscious observation and the second, conscious one. Learners may identify more clearly with this process if it is cast in the form of solving a mystery. "The air smells different" is an observation; so is "The dog did not bark while someone robbed the house." In each case, we have an expectation of what should happen: the air should smell a certain way (it previously smelled a certain way); a dog should bark if someone robs the house. These expectations or assumptions may be unconscious, at least at first. Part of being a good detective—or a good scientist—is becoming aware of such expectations and assumptions, so we can think about and build on them.

Part of this process and of observation is curiosity—wondering, asking questions. Probably in a shorter time than it takes to read the preceding paragraph, an observer would have progressed from observation to question:

Why is the sky not blue?
Why does the air smell different?
Why did the dog not bark?

Some questions—such as "Why is the sky blue?"—can be readily answered by using appropriate reference materials (asking people, reading, etc.) that is, part or all of the answer is already known. (Part of the fun of doing research is studying things that other people also are studying or know about and getting to talk with them about it. By doing research, we join a community and its conversations, which can be pretty exciting. But more about that later.) Other questions are more complicated, such as, "Why does the air smell different?" That complication can mean several things. Perhaps there is no single answer—the air smells different for several reasons. Perhaps no one knows the answer. Either no one has ever answered that question, or we have not been able to find the answer wherever we looked. Or it may be that the question is unanswerable, either absolutely (we cannot prove that we are experiencing reality rather than a vivid hallucination) or relatively (the technology is not available to understand fully the inner structure of the atom).

We can consider any of those because science is a way of investigating questions.

ASSUMPTIONS AND EXPECTATIONS

In asking these questions, we also continue to articulate assumptions or expectations. A conversation with yourself about air might go like this:

"Why should the air smell a certain way?"

Because it has smelled that way until now.

"What does it actually mean that air smells or has an odor? What is air, anyway!?"

By looking up "air" in a basic reference book, we discover that it is a colorless, odorless, tasteless mix of gases that makes up the earth's atmosphere.

"Aha!" we say. "So air should not even have an odor . . . ," and we read more.

Air is 78% nitrogen, 21% oxygen, and small amounts of argon, carbon dioxide, helium, and other gases. It also carries gases produced by combustion and respiration, particles of physical matter, water, and other things.

"So, when air has an odor, as when we smell smoke, presumably it is carrying something that imparts that odor." Such a dialogue or articulation gives us a lead, a line of reasoning to pursue, with a set of appropriate questions to ask.

"Since combustion (burning in an engine or an oven, for example) and metabolic combustion both add things to the air, are there new sources of either nearby? A new restaurant or factory, increased traffic, or a fire? Where? Or have wind patterns changed, bringing us products of combustion we have not previously received?"

Similar reasoning applies to our burglary mystery. Why do we expect that a dog will bark when someone is robbing a house? Because we assume that the robber is a stranger and the dog barks at strangers. Or because the dog barks at everyone. Each of these statements has interesting implications. Perhaps the robber was not a stranger. Or perhaps the dog was not present—either physically not present or drugged and thus unable to bark. Again, this gives us a lead. "Was the dog present? How do we know? Who sold the homeowner the dog? Could that person have been the robber? What about other people known to the dog?" And so on.

In the case of the burglary, investigation probably would involve more asking people questions and less going to the literature. But in the research likely through this curriculum, investigation probably will involve more literature search.

READING THE LITERATURE

The so-called primary literature is a major forum for scientific conversations. And, as in any conversation, these written "conversations" show that different authors or sources usually say different things. Sometimes they say radically different—even opposite—things. That presents a challenge to the reader, perhaps especially to learners making use of primary sources. First, it is important for them to remember that the fact that something is in print is no guarantee that it is true. That applies even to the scientific literature. Everyone makes mistakes, mistakes that include misprints, misquotes, misunderstanding, and misinformation. Often, differences in the scientific literature stem from disagreements—over definitions, data, what the facts are, or how to interpret those data or facts. Sometimes such differences reflect the rapidly changing state of scientific knowledge—what was previously the "truth" or state of the art is now seen quite differently, perhaps because of some discovery or a new technique that allows new discoveries. This is particularly true in the sciences, where information often can be provisional. Sometimes disagreements are resolved in a dramatic way. Famous examples in which researchers revolutionized their fields by flouting tradition and the accumulated knowledge of their age include William Harvey demonstrating the circulation of blood; Charles Darwin putting forth his theory of adaptation by natural selection; Marie Curie discovering radium; and Barbara McClintock discovering jumping genes. Often in such instances, the relevant journals and literature show strong "before" and "after" differences. After Magellan sailed around the world, few people still believed it to be flat.

Sometimes, though, the period of discussion (even animosity) in the literature can go on for years. In one case that raged for years, the so-called "nature/nurture debate," members of the two extremes attempted to ascribe all or most human behavior to, respectively, genetics or upbringing/environment. The controversy has fizzled out, since by now it is apparent that both genetics and upbringing are involved in most human behavior. Sometimes, as in the case of McClintock's jumping genes, a finding is too divergent from the current state of "knowledge" and is scarcely acknowledged or not accepted for publication. It simply is dismissed, until the weight of evidence from various sources convinces people of the truth of the initial observations. (It took about 30 years for jumping genes to be accepted in the field of genetics—then the work won McClintock a Nobel prize.)

It may seem scarcely believable that scientists can argue over "facts"; surely, either a thing is true or it is not. Fortunately—or unfortunately—theory, state of the art, context, and interpretation play a huge part in our understanding of "truth." Some things are demonstrably true: if you drop this book, it will fall to the floor. However, many (most?) phenomena are subject to context or interpretation. Let's consider how a particular "truth" has changed over time. For some 40,000 years, humans (if they thought about it at all) probably thought the sun moved around the earth. That is, they saw the sun "rise" in the east and "set" in the west, an observation consistent with the explanation that the sun rotated around a fixed earth. Several times in the past few thousand years, different peoples had the ideas and developed instruments necessary to gather data on other celestial bodies. Those data convinced the observers both that the earth is not stationary and that the earth revolves around the sun. However, it was less easy to convince other people. In a particularly well-documented example of confrontation between new and old "truths," in seventeenth-century Europe, Galileo and then-Pope Urban VIII had words over "the truth" about the motion of the earth and the stability of the sun. Those "words" ended with Galileo's being put under house arrest and excommunicated from the Roman Catholic church, so, at least for the moment, the old "truth" held sway. But by now, few people still believe what Pope Urban believed, and the new "truth" has become the truth.

In many and perhaps most such scientific disputes or debates, there is not an immediate or cataclysmic resolution. Debate may continue for long periods, with people contributing ideas and data for both perspectives. Because this curriculum includes doing original research, most of the research topics presented are not resolved. That means a survey of the literature will turn up differing perspectives.

How, then, does a reader differentiate among those perspectives? Practically, start by grouping the literature. For any topic actively under study, there are usually two or more camps or schools of thought with major differences. (There are probably also minor differences, but concentrate on the big ones, at least to begin.) What are the differences? What evidence or reasoning does each group bring in support of its ideas? Does the evidence or reasoning actually support what it claims to support? Are there underlying assumptions that influence those interpretations, but that are themselves not substantiated? Does any of the evidence contradict other evidence, either from the same or from a different camp? Are there flaws in the logic or reasoning? Overall, submit the ideas to rigorous scrutiny. See whether they meet the same criteria we use to develop our own research.

After examining the various positions, we can come to one of three conclusions. One camp seems to us more likely to be correct; one seems likely not to be correct; or there are not enough data to decide which camp is correct.

Fortunately, in each of those cases, our general response is the same, namely, to design a research project incorporating our assessments of the schools of thought. If we agree with a perspective, we build on and extend it. If we disagree, we substantiate the disagreement. This can be direct, through restudy of the things with which we disagree, or indirect, by designing a study that avoids the points of disagreement. In the third case, the case of too few data, we design research to collect more data.

There are several kinds of scientific literature (Table 1). The most scholarly, the type containing formal conversations among scientists, is the primary literature. Here, scientists report their findings directly, and the intended audience is other scientists. Articles are reviewed by other scientists for value, accuracy, logic, and scientific and statistical validity before they are published. That is not the case for secondary and tertiary literature. Those literatures tend to be based on the work of a number of people, are written for a broader, nontechnical audience, and do not routinely get reviewed by scientists. Science and Nature are two widely available primary science journals. Scientific American, The American Scientist, and Natural History are good secondary literature. For the sake of convenience, we group all others in the tertiary category, although there are differences between the Sunday New York Times Science Supplement and Prevention Magazine. But the point is that scientists "talk" to one another in the primary literature, and being part of that conversation requires reading and, ultimately, publishing in that literature.

Table 1 **Types of Scientific Literature**

TYPE	EXAMPLES	CONTENTS
Primary	Scientific journals, meeting proceedings	Direct observations and experimental findings
Secondary	Popular scientific magazines, books	Discussion and synthesis
Tertiary	Newspapers, newsweeklies, popular magazines, some books	Limited reporting and discussion

At some point, however, merely seeing and reading are not enough. The next step is to turn some of our questions into hypotheses, that is, potential or tentative causal explanations for what we have observed, and to find a way to test those explanations experimentally.

TURNING QUESTIONS INTO A RESEARCH PROJECT: STEP 2

A hypothesis is more than a question. It is a testable statement, that is, a potentially answerable question as opposed to an inherently unanswerable one. A hypothesis includes the initial question and whatever information and reasoning can plausibly answer the question. For example, "Why does the air smell different?" is a question. But "We suggest that the air smells different because the new factory upwind of us is releasing 'stuff' into the air" is a hypothesis. It includes the question, information resulting from your reading and asking about air, and some reasoning, and it is testable.

Once we have developed a hypothesis, we must examine it for underlying assumptions and also develop a null and alternate hypotheses.

KEY INGREDIENTS OF A RESEARCH STUDY

Our starting point for a research project or study is the comparison of two observations and seeking an explanation for the observations. Designing a study and experiments just means putting our observations and potential explanations into the framework typically used by scientists. Although such formalization may seem off-putting, in fact, it is very handy. By standardizing the approach to research, scientists can more readily understand each other's work. By identifying component parts of a study, such standardization helps ensure that no components get left out. It is really just a tool, as a recipe is a tool. To bake bread, the key ingredients are flour, a leavening agent, some liquid, and a source of heat. Anything else is up to the baker. In comparing recipes, an experienced breadmaker immediately looks at the key ingredients and discounts "bread" that lacks any one of them. Similarly, there are key ingredients to a scientific study, and an experienced researcher looks for them in reading someone else's work.

We have already said that our observations and potential explanations are "key ingredients," and we have formally defined a potential explanation as a hypothesis. Let us fit all our key ingredients into our scientific framework. Figure 1 shows the progression over time of a research project. It par-

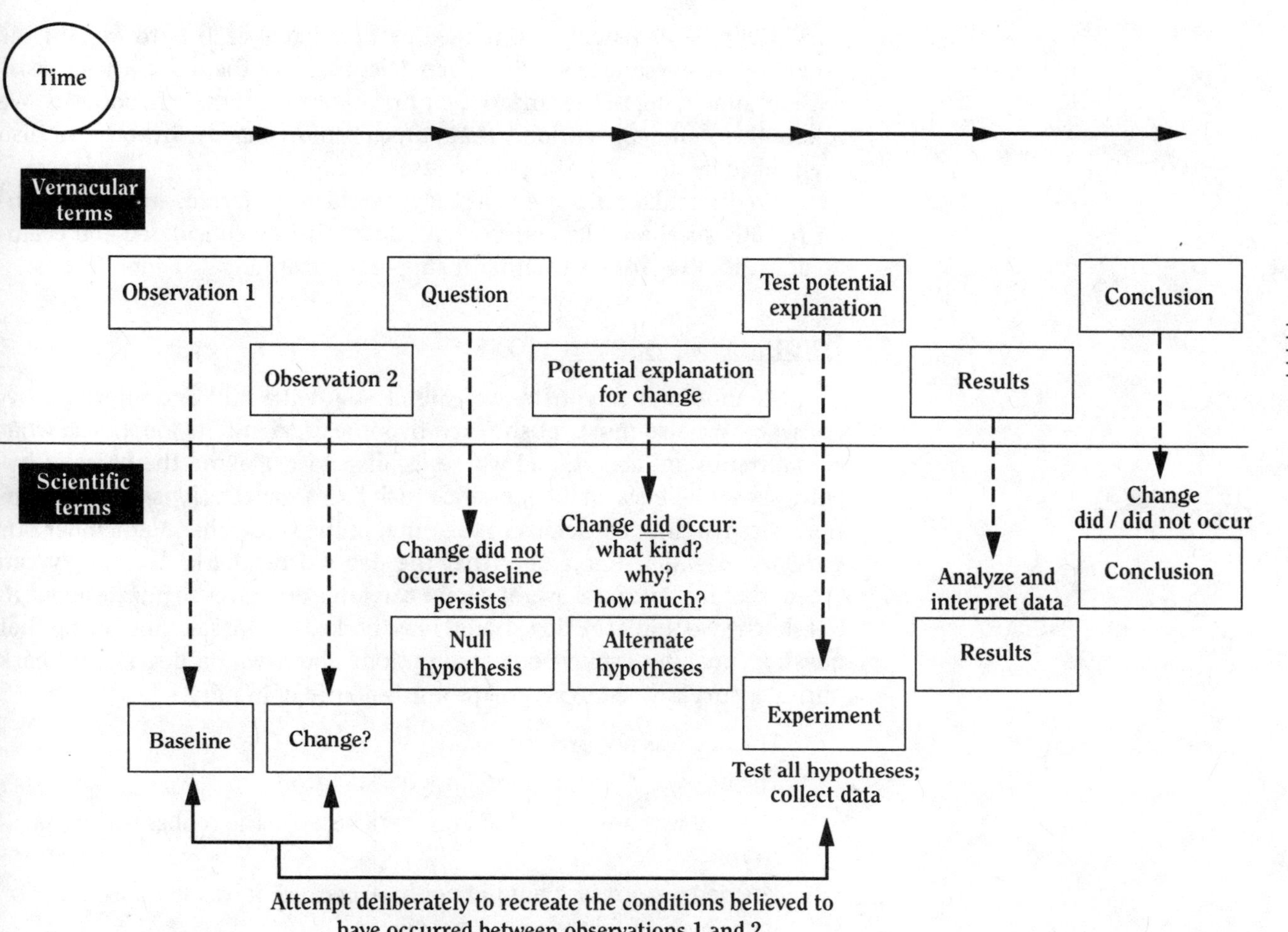

Figure 1. Research: The parallels between the vernacular and scientific descriptions of each stage or key ingredients.

allels the scientific and common (vernacular) terms for various stages and describes what happens in each stage.

NULL AND ALTERNATE HYPOTHESES

The whole process of assessing or testing for change from the baseline is research. (By "baseline," we mean the status quo, the neutral or normal situation. Sometimes, we must start by describing or defining the status quo. That can be a whole study by itself, likely of the more descriptive type.) The change from the baseline can be deliberate, as in an experiment, or unintended. Our hypotheses specify the factors that might be causing change from baseline, the direction of the change, and, perhaps, the amount of change. The null hypothesis, which is just another name for our original observation, means that there is no change from the baseline. The convention of stating a null hypothesis is one way to try to increase open-mindedness in research. It is the scientific way of saying, "innocent until proven guilty."

The other hypotheses are called alternate hypotheses. They are simply the set of possible explanations for change from the baseline, if change occurs. Hypotheses usually are ranked by how likely each is to explain the potential change under study. (When scientists use the word "hypothesis" without modifying it, they mean their first-ranked, alternate hypothesis. We follow the same convention.) Sometimes, unfortunately, hypotheses also are ranked by the preference of the researcher.

No particular outcome to a study should be preferred, and no particular hypothesis should be preferred. All data must be considered and evaluated, without regard for whether it supports the anticipated conclusions.

UNDERLYING ASSUMPTIONS

As thorough scientists, we cannot stop with null and alternate hypotheses. We also must "push" each hypothesis to find its loopholes, what actually substantiates it, and where it falls short. Making the bases of hypotheses explicit is a challenge, since such bases, expectations, and assumptions often are not conscious in the mind of the researcher. Remember our burglary example? Remember that the dog did not bark? We simply can accept that fact and pass over it. Or we can force ourselves to puzzle about it, to ask why we think the dog should have barked. As we saw, answering that question, making explicit our assumptions about why a dog should bark during a burglary, led to several promising lines of inquiry.

> The dog was not present.
>
> The dog was present but did not bark.
>
> The dog was present but did not bark because the robber was not a stranger.
>
> The dog was present but did not bark because it was unconscious, so the robber could have been a stranger.
>
> Would the dog have eaten a drug-laced tidbit from a stranger?

And so on. Each of those explicit statements can be addressed with evidence (data) of a more or less accurate nature. Based on the evidence and its reliability, some of the "statements" can be eliminated. But without the systematic listing and thinking through of each statement and what it implies, how easy it would be to miss something.

The same making explicit of assumptions, expectations, and implications is necessary in a research project.

For instance, with respect to global warming, the null hypothesis is that no systematic warming change is occurring in global temperatures owing to anthropogenic (human-based) factors. That sets up the framework within which the research and data are examined. What is the baseline with respect to global warming, that is, what are "normal" global temperatures? How have they been recorded? Why do we think that temperatures have changed? Has change been gradual or sudden? In the case of gradual change, how much change is statistically significant, that is, more than the chance variations seen in all phenomena? How much change is relevant, that is, affects biological phenomena such as plant growth or physical phenomena such as the melting of icecaps?

Having this framework within which to set global warming is useful in several ways: It clarifies our baseline and comparisons with (hypothesized) deviations from the baseline; it forces us to be explicit and precise about expectations, assumptions, and definitions; it simplifies the job of working out the logic of our explanations.

DESIGNING AN EXPERIMENT

Dissecting out the component parts of a research project makes it much easier to design an experiment. An experiment is the specific procedure by which we test hypotheses. Although it is only one stage in the research process, a true experiment cannot be carried out in the absence of the preceding stages. (That probably is why scientists often use the words "research" and "experiment" interchangeably.)

An experiment reproduces, in a controlled environment, the conditions hypothesized to be responsible for the difference between observations 1 and 2. If we have four possible explanations (alternate hypotheses) for that change, we must test each one separately. Since that is a good deal of work, it is important to rank the hypotheses by likelihood.

An Example

Global warming is beyond the scope of any laboratory experiment, although it can be modeled. Instead, let us consider a slightly more focused topic, namely, ozone. Ozone is a pungent gas with two roles in the environment. Stratospheric ozone absorbs some of the sun's ultraviolet radiation and thus helps protect the earth from its damaging effects. It is also being depleted due to release of chlorofluorocarbons into the atmosphere. However, ground level (also called atmospheric) ozone is increasing. It is produced in a series of chemical reactions involving byproducts of combustion (e.g., car exhaust) and sunlight and is noxious to various forms of life, including humans. How noxious? To which forms of life? How long does ozone stay in the atmosphere? Do combustion engines produce most of its major precursors? What is the quantitative relationship between combustion and ozone production, that is, how much exhaust yields how much ozone? Clearly, much more information is essential to understand the phenomenon and to manage it wisely.

Although there are partial answers to some of the questions we just posed, the information is spotty in many respects. And as an issue, any one of its effects is well beyond the scope of any single group of researchers. However, there also are many component parts that can be addressed fruitfully. For instance, ozone can damage plants, including crops such as corn, soybeans, wheat, and clover. In combination with acid rain, ozone may be responsible for widespread forest decline in parts of the globe subject to air pollution. But we have no systematic information on which plants are damaged, how damage relates to the amount of ozone exposure, or what effects such damage can have in a wild-plant community. So original research might involve documenting specific effects of ozone on local plants. Such data would be a real contribution to the science and understanding of ozone and its effects by helping to untangle some of those effects.

Let us proceed through the stages for designing an experiment. Let our hypothesis be that fewer individual plants belonging to five species of local annual grasses will survive to maturity in an ozone-rich than in an ozone-poor environment. Note that "ozone-poor" represents our baseline, or observation 1, and "ozone-rich," observation 2.

Controlling Variables

To ensure that we are testing only for effects of ozone, we must have a controlled environment. That means we must be certain that conditions for the two sets of plants are identical except for the factor on which the experiment is based, the amount of ozone they receive. The plants must be in same-size pots, with same-mix soil; they must be watered equally often and at the same times of day; they must receive the same amount of light, from the same compass direction, at the same time of day; they must be planted at the same time and in the same way; and the results must be noted at the same times and using standardized criteria. Without such efforts to control the environment, it would be impossible to know whether results were due to the effects of ozone or to the effect(s) of whatever else was also going on. For instance, if the ozone-rich plants were kept at a cooler temperature than the others, we could not say whether differences between the two sets of plants were due to the lower temperature or the higher ozone concentration.

Natural Experiments

We can also take advantage of "natural" experiments. For example, we might capitalize on the ozone produced on a huge highway by planting the plants requiring ozone-rich treatment under the ozone "cloud" produced by that road. (Such a cloud is not necessarily easy to find, since ozone may not be produced at the road or may drift some distance.) Using such a natural setup has the advantage that we do not need to add the ozone to the high-ozone treatment. It has the potential drawback that we can less easily control other factors. Are the low and high ozone sites sufficiently similar with respect to slope, exposure, drainage, soil, wind, other pollutants produced near the road, and so forth, that they are comparable?

Sometimes an experiment does not take into account (control for) all the relevant factors, because not all the factors are known. However, that itself can be a source of learning. It is also another reason for being objective and fair about data collection and analysis. If our results seem "wrong," that is, do not support any of our hypotheses, they may in fact point to something unexpected and even more interesting. For example, the effects of light on the pituitary gland were discovered because a scientist (Nalbandov) studying chicken reproduction developed the habit of working late in the laboratory. He would come back after dinner for another stint at his desk, which was in the same room as some of the chickens, and since it was dark, he would turn on the lights. Chickens in that room bred on a wholly unanticipated cycle, quite different from the cycle of the rest of the animals. Fortunately, he was a good observer. He realized that the difference was that the chickens kept near his desk experienced longer "days" due to the artificial light he used in the evenings. So he developed a set of experiments directly to test his new hypothesis. He was correct, and thus opened up a whole new area in physiology and reproduction. A popular expression sums up this opportunistic and highly fruitful approach to research: "If you get handed lemons, make lemonade."

By now it should be clear that the actual collecting of data is likely the simplest part of an experiment. It is the thinking through of assumptions, expectations, and hypotheses, the experimental design, controlling for all but the test variable, and considerations of sampling that require so much effort.

TESTABILITY OF HYPOTHESES

Some hypotheses cannot be tested directly. Perhaps they are too complex, asked in the wrong way, or are impossible to test, or perhaps they involve factors that it is unethical to test. Examples might be how the earth's gravitational field would vary if we put several moons into orbit around it, or testing whether human language is innate by raising children in isolation on an island to see whether they speak. Complex issues often can be investigated by the construction of models. Issues of science and research ethics tend to be of two sorts. Is the research actually science, that is, does it follow scientific methods, as we are outlining them here? Second, even if it is science by that standard, does the outcome justify the costs? Can the procedures or experiments in conscience be carried out? This latter question is more complex than the former, and the answer is likely to vary with the ethos of the time. Now there is concern among consumers about the ethics or appropriateness of using live animals to test cosmetics; 15 years ago this was a nonissue, about which consumers showed little awareness and even less concern.

An example about which most people would agree is the study in humans of brain function and its recovery. This could be studied directly as it is studied in other animals—by selectively destroying target areas in a human brain, observing the consequences, and attempting to restore normal function through systematic testing of assorted treatments. But we do not do that. Although such research would provide knowledge to benefit people who have suffered brain damage, how can we justify deliberately damaging some humans in order to help others? We cannot, and so such research proceeds indirectly, by assessing brain damage and its attempted restoration in people injured accidentally. Other, less obvious examples include the use of animals in research. Can forensic medicine justify studying the effects on live monkeys of gunshot wounds sustained from different distances? Why not assess the damage to dead animals or to sides of pork and beef and spare live animals? Deliberately to damage a live animal is a grave thing. It should be considered as part of research only when the likely benefits resulting from that damage decidedly outweigh the costs.

Examples of nonscience would include astrology, which does not proceed via scientific methods. Note that people claim various endeavors to be science, even using names like "Scientology." But just because an activity is called science, is carried out by people calling themselves scientists, or even occurs in a laboratory does not make it science.

Although we are about to consider aspects of sampling and experimental design, perhaps it is useful to recap briefly where we are in our overall scheme of "research." We have considered much of the first two sets of our "three threes," as illustrated in Table 2. By this reckoning, we are about to embark on stage 5.

Table 2

Overall Research Scheme

Step 1. Learn

1. Observe and describe.
2. Ask questions and make comparisons.
3. Perform comprehensive literature search of the topic.
   - a. Critically read the literature.
   - b. Organize an overview of the topic.

Step 2. Test quantitatively (experimental science)

4. Formulate tentative causal explanations (hypotheses) and null and alternate hypotheses.
   - a. Articulate the assumptions underlying each hypothesis.
   - b. Check that the hypotheses account for all the information available.
   - c. Check that the hypotheses are distinct.
5. Test the explanations experimentally or by modeling.
   - a. Design experiment(s), controlling for all but the test variable.
   - b. Consider sample size for statistical and scientific validity.
   - c. Consider time interval between samples for validity.
   - d. Consider method(s) of data analysis for ease of use and statistical validity.
6. Collect data.

OR

Step 2. Describe quantitatively (descriptive science)

4. Establish quantitative comparisons, formulate tentative causal explanations.
5. Carry out comparison.
   - a. Evaluate the phenomena or items being compared.
   - b. Consider sample size (as above).
   - c. Consider time interval (as above).
   - d. Consider methods of data comparison (as above).
6. Collect data.

Step 3. Analyze and interpret

7. Analyze data, that is, assess experimental results for statistical significance.
8. Organize and interpret results narrowly (quantitatively in the context of the experiment) and broadly (qualitatively in the context of the "big picture").
   - a. Assess results for scientific validity.
   - b. Compare results obtained to those expected by the null/alternate hypotheses.
   - c. Reevaluate hypotheses and reexamine their underlying assumptions.
   - d. List questions answered, unresolved questions, and new questions raised.
   - e. Draw conclusions.
9. Convey results to other people by preparing results for publication or other dissemination.

SAMPLING

When we design an experiment or any quantitative procedure, it is important to have a match among the components. For example, how does the time frame of the experiment correspond to the time frame of the phenomenon? Does the number of observations correspond to the magnitude or frequency of the phenomenon? Is the sample representative of the whole, statistically and actually?

Sample Units and Intervals

The units in which human age is expressed make a good illustration of the match between time frames. The unit used—weeks, months, or years—is roughly proportional to the age of the person being considered. Adult life span typically involves decades of years and is universally sampled and expressed in years. Counting birthdays in seconds or even weeks, at 3.2×10^6 and 52 per year, respectively, is impractical. A 20-year-old would be 6.3×10^8 seconds or 1,040 weeks old! But ages of children often are given in years plus parts of years (e.g., 5½), while for infants, months or (briefly) even days are used.

Thus, the unit of time we typically use is proportional to or representative of the total age of the person. The same reasoning applies to sampling: when taking or expressing any measure, it must be representative of the total entity being sampled.

In our discussion of age and units, however, we set ages for the individuals in our examples and worked backward toward appropriate units, that is, we considered adults, youths, and children, and what would be the most appropriate unit of age for each. In real data collection, we do not necessarily know the equivalent of "age" or whether what we are studying is an adult, a youth, or a child. But it is important to know enough about the phenomenon under study to make an intelligent guess at the equivalent of "age" or its range and thus to choose an appropriate unit of measurement. Indeed, a preliminary or descriptive study often is necessary to discover things like the "age" equivalent, so we can carry out more quantitative hypothesis testing.

Suppose we were actually sampling human age and that we wished to compare the survivorship of urban dwellers in New Haven, Connecticut, and Calcutta, India. Would we get the information we wanted simply by censusing the population of each city? Not really—what about immigration, emigration, and the birth rate? We could count individual people in some part(s) of each city and re-count them later, asking how many are there, how many have left, how many have died. But when is "later"? How much "later"?

The answer depends partly on which hypothesis is being tested or which question is being asked. Are we suggesting that there is a causal, short-term relationship between a particular month and increased mortality? For instance, does Ramadan, the month-long holy fast, increase mortality among older Muslims for whom all-day fasting is too taxing? Does mortality increase around the Christmas holidays due to drunk driving? Does intense summer heat increase infant mortality or aggression and killings among young street toughs? Alternatively, are we suggesting that longer-term causal influences are involved—nutrition, health care, social support systems? Are lifestyles in the two countries sufficiently similar (or dissimilar) that long-term mortality rates are similar (or dissimilar)? Clearly, if the question is more short-term, the interval between samples, between the "now" and "later" counts of individuals, must be shorter; if the question is about life expectancy, the interval between samples can be longer. Suppose we hypothesize that life expectancy is higher in Calcutta because the social support systems are better there—most of the social support organizations are run by religious orders and thus are ethically rather than politically motivated.

Another aspect of this between-sample interval must also be clarified. Even if we decide that life expectancy is our focus of study, we must specify whose life expectancy—that of infants, children, adults, or all ages of people as a whole? Again, scale, or the fit between sample interval and phenomenon, applies. If we are studying adult survivorship, a 6-month or yearly intersample interval is appropriate. But for infants less than 1 year old, monthly or bimonthly sampling would give more useful information and therefore be more appropriate. Let us select for study the population of children 3 years or younger. We have established that the specific topic (life expectancy), the age group or population of interest (3 years or younger), and the phenomenon (survivorship) are critical aspects of choosing the appropriate sample units and intervals. In addition to units and intervals, we will now consider sample size or number and sample significance or validity, scientific and statistical. Still other aspects to consider are reliability, sources of error, coherence, and relevance. (For an outstanding and comprehensive discussion of sampling, data collection, and experimental design, see Moore 1991.)

Sample Size and Validity

There are two issues to sample size: how representative is our sample of the population as a whole, and how large a sample do we need? To some degree, these issues are inversely related—the more representative our sample is of the whole population, the fewer items from it (up to a point) we need to measure or sample. Or the less representative our sample, the more items we need to sample. In terms of our life expectancy example, that means which children will we follow or sample and how, and how many children do we need to sample and for how long?

To answer those questions, we must refer to our original hypothesis or question and to some statistical considerations. What do we really want to know? How narrow or broad is the basic question: how much do we want to extrapolate from the answer? How broad or narrow is our study population? Does it include all the under-3-year-olds or just the one named Solh? If we ask, "What is the longevity of the single person of 3 years or younger named Solh?" we need measure only that child's life span. But an observation based on so small a "population" cannot be generalized. Since a single child is not representative of all children, data on that child is not representative, is not a valid sample, of the population of children under 3. This "sample" gives us information only about the single person we measured. If we want to know about the longevity of a population, we must define the population and choose a representative sample, just as we defined the phenomenon—age—and chose representative units.

The Study Population

Although we chose our study population as children 3 years or younger, we must be more specific about which children we will include. If our interest is in comparing social services in the two cultures, are certain children more likely to use such services? Do we wish to know survivorship among children in each culture as a function of whether they use these services? Or do we wish to know survivorship of children given that they use those services? How are we defining "use"? It may be that the services are very good once children get to them, but few children do get to them. Since we are interested in "use" in the broadest sense, let's more accurately define our population as all children under 3 or whose family socioeconomic status (income, family composition, and background) makes them likely to use public social services. Note that by focusing the question to this extent, we already have narrowed the ways in which we can extrapolate from our results. They are likely to be of limited utility in understanding longevity of same-age children from other socioeconomic backgrounds or longevity of other-age children from any background. That is not necessarily bad—it is an inevitable consequence of being precise (focused) and objective. And it has the advantage of allowing greater understanding of the specific phenomenon and the causality or causalities involved. Indeed, one reason that thorough research is relatively time-consuming is this inverse relationship between generalizability and precision. To generalize precisely requires the accumulation of a number of focused studies.

Now we can illustrate the possible relationships between a population and samples, using bull's-eyes (from Moore 1991, pp. 24f). If a sample is representative of a population, the sample can stand for the population. That means the results we obtain from sampling are not different from the results we would get if we actually measured all members of our population. (In fact, some statistical tests and concepts are evaluated by collecting data on whole populations and then comparing those data with data from samples or subsets of the same populations.) For our sample to be representative, our sampling methods must be unbiased and random, our sample must be large enough, and our target population must be clearly defined. In this illustration, the defined population is the eye of the bull's-eye, and each dot represents a sample. A sample usually is described with respect to the population it should represent and with respect to other samples of the same population and made the same way. If a group of samples differs from the population in a consistent way, those samples are biased. If a group of samples differs from the population and they also differ from each other, they are considered to be unbiased or to have low bias. Finally, if the samples in a group are like one another, whether or not they resemble the population, they are considered to show high precision or to be highly precise. The process of sampling can give four possible combinations of these properties—let's look at the properties and the outcomes in Figure 2.

The outcome in Figure 2a is that samples are highly repeatable. That is, they are very similar to one another and precise. However, they are off the target population (the center of the bull's-eye) and off in a particular direc-

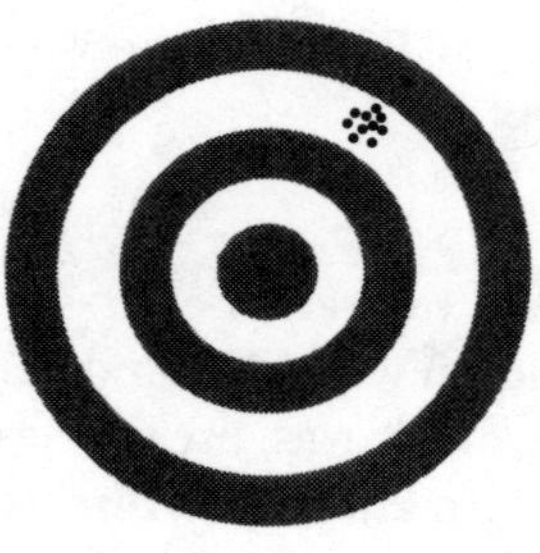

a. High bias, high precision

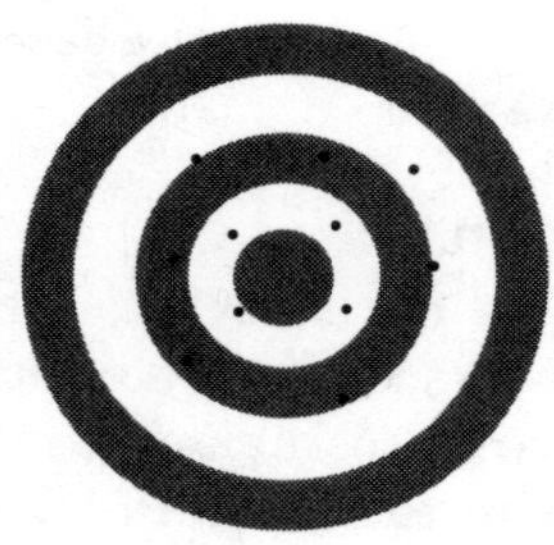

b. Low bias, low precision

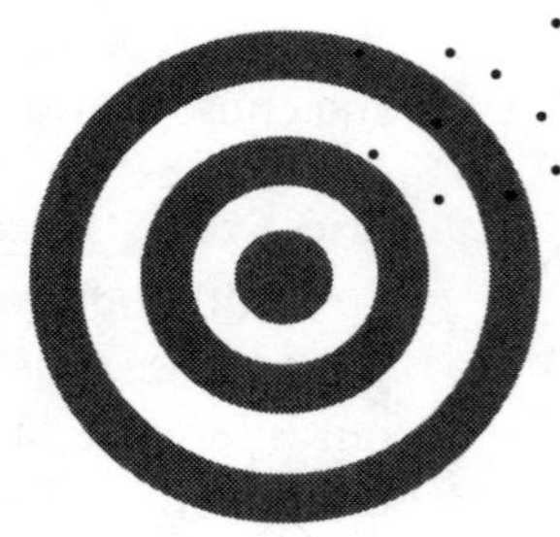

c. High bias, low precision

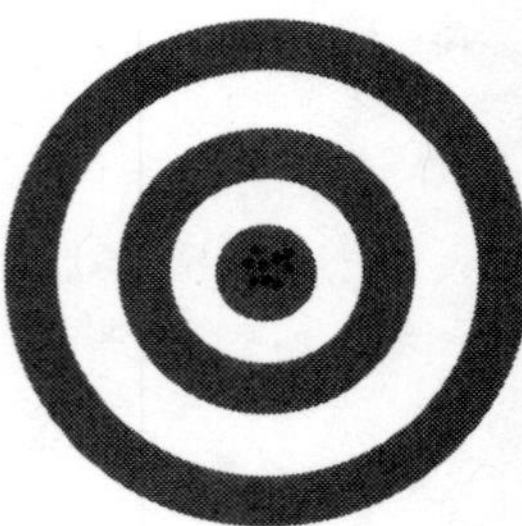

d. Low bias, high precision

Figure 2

tion or with a particular bias. That means we have a reliable (repeatable or replicable) sampling procedure, but the sample differs from the population in a consistent way.

A second possible outcome is that the samples are scattershot across the bull's-eye (Figure 2b). That means they are unbiased—they do not fall in any particular direction—but they also are not repeatable; each is rather different from the others.

Another possibility is that the samples are scattershot but in a particular direction (Figure 2c). That is, our samples are scattered so our method is not reliable or repeatable, and our samples are biased.

The ideal outcome is shown in Figure 2d. The samples are unbiased and highly precise or repeatable; they center on the population and are thus representative of it.

Validity and Bias

Now that we have accurately defined our population, we must determine how to sample it in a representative or valid way. That means we must sample wisely and be sure our sample is large enough. Suppose we want to know how many blue marbles are in a multicolored population of 200 marbles? To sample the marbles randomly, we pour them all into a bag, shake well, and, without looking, scoop out two dozen marbles. Unlike most things we are likely to sample, the marbles are approximately alike in size, shape, and weight; they differ only in color. They also do not move, and by confining them in a small area, we make our sampling even easier. Most things are not so easy to sample randomly; the evenly-shaken-marbles-in-a-bag are our ideal. How does this translate into our previous example?

People are not going to be in a single place. That means, for instance, that we cannot restrict our sampling to telephone interviews, to a single neighborhood, or to written questionnaires (unless we actually know that all our population families have telephones, live in that neighborhood, and can read). Since it is most unlikely that all three of these conditions (as well as others we have not even mentioned) are true, we must devise techniques that will sample children of all families in our population, including those who do not meet one or another of these conditions.

For a valid sample, one that is representative of its population, adequate sample size can be determined relatively easily. There are excellent guidelines for setting sample size (see Moore 1991, Sokal and Rohlf 1981).

Remember that sample size depends on the things we have considered here, on the phenomenon being studied, on which statistical tests will be used, (to some degree) on what is typical in the field involved, and sometimes on purely practical considerations (such as how rarely the phenomenon occurs). For our example, we need to consider the number of children sampled relative to all children in that class. If we sample only five children per city, although the total population of children 3 years in age or under is 20,000 in New Haven and 80,000 in Calcutta, our sample is too small to represent its class accurately for either city. Another way of saying this is that the sample is not valid or significant. (The words "significant" and "significance" have technical meaning in statistics: the assignment of a specific probability or likelihood of occurrence. Unfortunately, in the vernacular they simply mean that something is important or meaningful. It is best to avoid the word unless you are using it with reference to specific statistical probabilities.) We must increase our sample size. To how much? How many children must we sample?

Increasing the size of the sample increases how accurately it reflects the population, but only if sampling is random and unbiased and if the population is much larger than the sample. If both these conditions hold, a sample of 1,500 will give a highly precise representation of the population. However, this size sample is impractical for most of the laboratory experiments considered in this curriculum. Moreover, initial sample size also must be larger than what is ultimately desired, because things always go wrong: people move, some data are suspect (a child's birthday may be misremembered or misreported), and so on. For our survivorship example, if all conditions are met and we take into account that Things Will Go Wrong, an initial random sample of 2,000 should be adequate to give a final sample of 1,500.

Difficulties also can arise if we doubt whether the sample is representative, or if we do not sample randomly. In both cases, increasing the sample size can improve its likelihood of representativeness. Be aware of the problem, be prepared to question your results, and consult a statistics book.

Significance

Once we have collected our data, how can we tell whether our sample (and the conclusion we draw from it) is indeed valid and representative of our population? Statistics, a systematic, math-based way of getting information from data, includes various tests that were devised to answer just that question. An appropriate statistical test or tests can tell us whether our sample is on target or off, as in the outcomes we illustrated with the bull's-eyes. We mentioned that in statistics "significance" has a more precise and narrower meaning than it does in common usage. Commonly, the word means that something is important—it has a remarkably high or low frequency, size, cost, weight, whatever. Statistically, significance refers to the probability or chance that a sample differs from its population, based on whichever statistical test was used.

Different kinds of data and experiments require different statistical tests. To find which are most appropriate for a given experiment, consider the test(s) mentioned in scientific works you have read on the subject. Then use an introductory statistics book to learn more about those tests, the data you will be collecting, and how to match data to a statistical test. See also References, especially Moore 1991.

GOOD DATA: OTHER ISSUES

Whether any data we collect are sound depends on everything we have considered so far, as well as a few other things: the coherence, relevance, and reliability of the data and sources of error. Authors often discuss these issues as part of data analysis, that is, after data have been collected and as a way of interpreting the data, especially if the results are not as expected. However, by considering those issues before data collection and as part of designing our experiment, we can avoid some common pitfalls. That seems preferable to considering and understanding pitfalls when it is too late to avoid them.

Reliability and Sources of Error

Reliability has statistical and other aspects. We considered the statistical aspect in the section Validity and Bias: is a sample a true representation of the population? Other sources of error not related to sampling include Things That Go Wrong , which we also mentioned earlier, including missing data, response errors (misreporting or misremembering), processing errors (typographical and other errors such as computer bugs), effects of the sampling method, and instrument inaccuracy or failure.

Coherence

Coherence refers to whether the data hang together; relevance refers to whether data actually pertain to the subject being studied. Do data hang together logically—are appropriate comparisons being made? In the life expectancy example, are we comparing survivorship between people of different socioeconomic status? Even if we collect exactly the same kind of data, if they are from people who differ in basic ways, we will not be able to say much about influences on survivorship in the two cities, since we will be unable to distinguish between city effects and socioeconomic effects. Inappropriate comparisons can be made in the actual experimental design (as just suggested) or in the interpretation of results. Thus, someone may report temperatures from a site in the midwestern prairies over the past 80 years. The data are sound and the analyses appropriate. But say the author attempts to interpret those analyses by direct comparison with analyses of data recorded in a major urban site that had a tenfold increase in population during the same period. What insights about global warming can come from comparing two such different sites?

A frequent miscomparison is seen in some ecology literature. A phenomenon is reported for a plant or animal species, say, that a given plant species grows as well under ozone levels three times the normal concentration as at normal concentrations. The paper then lists other plant species that also tolerate ozone. From a list like that, which contains no further information about the species, we cannot tell whether it is appropriate or inappropriate to compare them. Were all the plant species raised under the same conditions: same temperature, humidity, photoperiod, and so on? Do they all use the same photosynthetic pathway? How are the plant species related—are they all in the same family or genus? What does it mean that the plants are ozone tolerant? How can we make sense of that information? How can we understand it? Without appropriate comparisons, we have information but not understanding.

Relevance

Relevance has obvious and less obvious meanings in the context of research. The first meaning includes whether the data apply to the topic. For instance, while collecting survivorship data, we may deliberately or incidentally collect data on other aspects of life in New Haven and Calcutta, such as personal habits, family ties, or uses of money. Although those data might be interesting, they cannot be used directly to test our hypothesis. They have no direct relevance to it, no matter how nicely we organize or analyze them.

However, such data can contribute in other ways to our understanding of the topic. In fact, this illustrates a more subtle aspect of relevance—having a feel for the topic and learning everything about it in order to have as complete a picture as possible in which to interpret the data. For instance, we may learn that one of our study cultures condones selective neglect and even infanticide of female infants. Clearly, that will affect the survivorship data, probably for both sexes: girls may be neglected, boys spoiled.

Once you have discussed and agreed on the specific question or hypothesis, the population being sampled and how to sample it, the unit of measurement, approximate sample interval, approximate sample size, desired generalizability of results, and which statistical tests to use, you are ready to set up and carry out experiments and collect data.

ANALYZE AND INTERPRET: STEP 3

Rather than replicate examples and discussions of actual data analysis that can be found elsewhere (see References), we will skip on briefly to consider interpretation and reporting of results.

The biggest part of interpretation is this: what do the results mean? What do they tell us about the test phenomenon? How do they increase our understanding, not just what facts do they contribute? Facts alone are uninteresting and trivial; it is the implications of those facts, the bigger picture to which they contribute. Suppose Nalbandov's chickens had bred on an idiosyncratic cycle? He could have rushed the facts into print or stopped to learn more and try to understand those facts. What did that new breeding cycle imply? How was it controlled? How could Nalbandov find out? And so on. Sometimes interpretation requires thinking about your results; sometimes it requires more research, because you do not have enough information to find a pattern or understanding.

Finally, how about reporting results? Up to this point, your role in our scientific conversation has been that of a good listener, that is, a reader. But now that you have results, you may wish to participate more actively, by sending or actually talking to scientists about your results, by attending conferences, by presenting your results at a conference, by writing up and publishing your results.

There are many ways to get your results out; we mention only a few. You may be working more or less closely with other schools, with scientists from a university, with a government organization such as the EPA, with a nongovernment organization such as the Audubon Society, or with a local body such as your local waterways management committee. How you proceed depends on the nature of your arrangement with those persons or groups. For instance, say a scientist offers you use of some equipment or space in a laboratory. In exchange, that person may expect to incorporate your data into his or her next paper, with or without formal acknowledgment of your efforts. Or, he or she may expect to publish with you as coauthor, or that you will publish independently but with acknowledgment of the support you received. Still other possibilities might be that you are adding data to an ongoing, long-term study, so your work will be included in the whole. Or you may have observations and records of some phenomenon you want to make available to others, so you publish them as such.

There are also several kinds of scientific publications, each corresponding to a type of study. From least to most sophisticated they might be ranged something like this:

- A **note** presents an observation and may raise a question. An example is reporting that baleen whales were seen ingesting sea birds as well as their target food of krill when they lunge up through and out of the ocean. Although brief, a note must include the frequency of occurrence and over what period of time; the names of the species involved; where the incident(s) were seen; and why they are of interest. This example is of interest because no one thinks of baleen whales as eating sea birds or of the seabirds, some of which stay near the whales to catch fish the whales disturb, as possibly paying a price for their proximity to the whales.
- A longer descriptive **paper** is based on more than a few observations and considers the matter it reports in more depth.
- A full-blown **test of a hypothesis** must include all the parts of a research study outlined in this chapter.
- A **theoretical paper** might have no data at all, or none of the author's collecting, but makes a point on theoretical grounds.

It is important to choose an appropriate journal for each type of study and for the topic of the study. One way to find the appropriate journal for your study is to determine where studies similar to yours have been published.

References

Bashaw, W. L. 1969. Mathematics for Statistics. New York: John Wiley & Sons.
A good refresher or reference book for basics such as exponents, logs, ratios, fractions.

Hairston, Nelson G., Sr. 1989. Ecological Experiments—Purpose, Design, and Execution. New York: Cambridge University Press.
Logistics, techniques, etc.

Huff, Darrell. 1982. Lying with Statistics. New York: W. W. Norton & Co.

A slim book which gets people thinking about precision and quantitative relationships with an approach which combines accuracy and amusing examples.

Keller, Evelyn Fox. 1985. Reflections on Gender and Science. New Haven: Yale University Press.

Chapter 8 is a more concise treatment than Kuhn of "truth" and how it grows.

Kuhn, Thomas S. 1970. The Structure of Scientific Revolutions. Chicago: University of Chicago Press.

Interesting, slightly windy discussion of some "truths" in the field of physics and how they have changed over time.

Lehner, Philip N. 1979. Handbook of Ethological Methods. New York: Garland STPM Press.

Includes logistics, techniques, technologies, and some discussion of data analysis as well.

Moore, David S. 1991. Statistics: Concepts and Controversies. 3rd ed. New York: W. H. Freeman and Co.

———. 1991. Instructor's Guide. New York: W. H. Freeman and Co.

Outstanding discussion of sampling and procedures. Less comprehensive than Sokal and Rohlf but more detailed for what it covers and directed at the intelligent non-academic reader.

Sokal, Robert R., and F. James Rohlf. 1981. Biometry. 2nd ed. New York: W. H. Freeman and Co.

This is the bible of statistical methods and reasoning. It can be overwhelming at first look, but is quite readable and an outstanding reference book.

TECHNIQUE
ANIMAL BEHAVIOR

> The general public believes that all of the common aspects of nature are already well known. Nothing could be further from the truth in the field of bird behavior. This was one of the biggest surprises to me when I started writing this book. . . . Even with the birds that have been well studied, such as the Song Sparrow, Red-Winged Blackbird and Mallard, there are still far more mysteries than answers . . . In fact, in most cases there has not been enough observation to know for sure what is individual behavior and what is the general behavior of the species.
>
> —Donald Stokes, Bird Behavior, Vol. 1

What Donald Stokes says about bird behavior is also true for all other groups of animals. Careful observation of almost any animal over time will produce interesting and perhaps significant information and insight. The key is to prepare for your observations, to record them in a useful way, to think about them, and to use them to answer questions.

Animals do a lot of their moving around in response to other animals, so it is important to do some planning before you go out to take data. This technique suggests how you can plan for any project that involves watching animal behavior. You might practice by watching a pet, a brother, a sister, a parent, a friend, or kids on the playground.

BEFORE COLLECTING DATA: OBSERVATIONS AND QUESTIONS

As with any research, before you collect data, start by deciding what you are looking for. That does not mean to ignore everything not on your list; it does mean you can choose methods and equipment that will help you take the data you need and then make additional (or simultaneous ones) observations.

List some questions about your research. You may need to start with the simplest question: does the animal occur in the study area? If so, do you know how to recognize it? Are there other animals of its type in the area that might be confused with it? For example, someone interested in sparrows needs to know how to tell one kind from another, preferably by song as well as by appearance. If the animal is hard to see because it hides most of the time, you may have to look for signs—tracks, scat, leftovers from meals, burrows or nests, and similar traces.

If you know your animal is present, you are ready to ask some ecological questions. It is not hard to come up with good questions, but some good questions are hard to collect data on! You may have such questions in mind. If not, think about the animal's lifestyle and life-cycle, and think of questions about each kind of activity or life stage. For example, suppose you want to work on an insect, and you are considering the common cricket *(Grylla humilis)*. Your question list might include any of the following.

> Interactions with other animals and with plants: do you always find the cricket in the company of another kind of animal or plant? Does it have a home territory or range?
>
> Environmental constraints: where does the cricket occur? For example, must it be near water? Does it live on its food (i.e., is the cricket a leaf eater)?
>
> Describe its life stages: early juvenile, late juvenile, reproductive adult, postreproductive.
>
> Describe its life activities: foraging, defense, courtship and reproduction, social relations.

Once you have an idea of your interest, you can think about how to go about investigating it.

BECOME FAMILIAR WITH THE ANIMAL

Start slowly. If you are not familiar with the animal, you may want some sessions in which you just observe it, take notes, and think about what you see.

How do individuals of the species differ from one another? That includes appearance (color, markings, shape, size, notches in the ears, broken tails, etc.), age (can you tell the difference among adults, babies, juveniles?), and sex (can you tell the difference between males and females?).

Does it move much? All the time? Every few minutes? Once or twice an hour? Note the weather: sunny? Cool? Very cool? Very hot? Windy?

Does the animal stay in one small area or move freely? If it stays in one area or its movements seem limited to just a few areas (out of all the possible areas it might go), does it seem to center on certain plants or features (such as rocks or holes)?

What does it do? Eat, dig, fly, clean itself, interact with others of its kind? Hide? Communicate? How do you define each of those activities?

Such exploratory observations give you a feeling for how quickly the animal moves and how far, how easy it is to see its activities, how close you can get to it, and so on. Then you can plan a more realistic and effective study (because you have some idea of when and how to observe the animal), or you might decide to study a different species, because this one is too secretive, too hard to follow, or too active when you cannot be.

"CHUNKING": KINDS OF BEHAVIORS

When you first watch an animal, it can be hard to sort out the different actions you see. As you get to know the species, you begin to identify acts, actions, or behaviors. That practice often is called "chunking," that is, breaking up a stream of information into manageable chunks. The next level is to break manageable chunks into meaningful chunks. Remember, it is essential that you see **what** the animal does. **Why** it does it is quite another question, which can be answered only by careful observation, identification, and recording of what it actually does.

The question of meaningful chunks—what is a meaningful chunk and how do you know—is itself interesting and hugely important. Much behavioral research is flawed by unclear or inappropriate chunking. Often researchers mix chunk levels, interpret or categorize behaviors or actions without enough data, or make unconscious assumptions about chunks.

EXAMPLES

Picking Up Stuff

Suppose we observe a common sparrow. A first chunk level might be a single physical act (the bird picks up something in its bill). Your understanding of that act is enriched when you see what the bird picks up (a peanut or some twigs). And you hit a third chunk level with some analysis of the act, given what was picked up. If the species is unstudied, you cannot interpret the act until you see what happens next. Does the sparrow eat the twigs? Does it eat the peanut? If either happens, you can categorize that act of picking up as food gathering. But you must not assume that picking up stuff is food gathering—you must see the bird eat what it has picked up.

What about those twigs? You might see the bird carry the materials into a tree hole, then emerge empty-beaked. Since it is unlikely that the bird is feeding a tiny horse in there, you might call the activity collecting twigs and grasses. The bird probably is building a nest, but to be very strict about it, until you actually look in the hole and see a nest, you should not make that assumption.

Movement

Let's consider another example. Say the bird sometimes spreads its wings or tail or hops about, moving from one place to another. You may not know why the bird is doing that, but clearly motion or locomotion are taking place. You may see that when the bird is around other sparrows, it spreads its tail or wings but apparently does not change location. Perhaps such motion is a kind of communication, not locomotion. Only by seeing acts over and over, and noting what acts come before and after can you understand what your sparrow is doing. Some acts happen rarely, so they are hard to chunk; sometimes you might see acts happen in a new sequence, which causes you to rethink some previous chunking you did. That is OK; that is what happens when you watch animals.

CATEGORIES

As you chunk things, you can also think about your categories: whether you have left out any, whether some actions should be separated or other actions categorized together. For example, you may decide after watching a bird species for a while that the birds communicate in several ways: by sound, by gestures and body language, by color. Mammals often use all those, plus odors. Fish do not seem to make much use of odors, and most fish seem not to use sounds, but they do use colors (including color changes) and body position to signal to other members of their species. Insects also make use of all these means of communication.

A special kind of communication also occurs between species, most often between animal prey and possible predators. The bright colors of some snakes, frogs, and butterflies advertise poison; the rattle of a rattlesnake is a warning; and some moths "flash" large spots on their wings to startle bird predators.

General categories you can expect from other experiences or work in this curriculum are reproduction (mating, and care of young), feeding, resting, grooming—what else? By what actions does your species accomplish those general categories? How much time does it spend on any activity or category compared to another species? Compared to you?

If you are interested in a particular kind of animal (fish, birds, amphibians, insects), after you have watched for a while, look at a book on the behavior of that kind of animal, to see how other observers have chunked the organism's behavior.

COLLECTING DATA

How long should you watch? What should you note? Do you have to write down everything? Fortunately, no. You sample in some way and note rare or unusual events as they occur.

A DATA TABLE

You already have in mind the chunks you have identified. You already have some question(s) or a hypothesis. Using your chunks, make a data table, perhaps with your chunks across the top (the rows) and space for time down the leftmost column.

Acts	Abbreviations	Acts	Abbreviations
Forage	Fr	Groom self	Gs
Eat	E	Groom other	Go
Fly	F	Vocalize	V
Hop	H	Enter nest hole (with or without object)	Enh
Walk	W	Leave nest hole	Lnh
Sit	S	Fight with ____	Fw ____
Collect nest material	Cnm		

It also helps to put a space at the top or the bottom for the date, location, page number, and the observer's initials (yours). You might need abbreviations to fit all your chunks across the page—something like this:

Sample Data Table

Date: ______________ **Place:** __________________________ **Observer:** ________________________

Behavior: Fr E F H W S Cnm Gs Go V Enh Lnh Fw ____

Time:

10:00
10:01
10:02
10:03

OR

10:00:00
10:00:10
10:00:20
10:00:30

Page ____ of ____

Figure 1. Sample data table.

Since you have already spent some time watching your animal, you have decided that hopping and walking are distinct actions; you want to know how many kilocalories per day the sparrow uses, and hopping is energetically more expensive.

"Fight" is another high-level category. Are you sure you can tell the difference between fighting and playing or courtship? Would you call fighting by another name if it were an interaction over food or territory (i.e., competition)? You can make some of those decisions later in the data analysis, but you need chunks to start.

If you are doing an ethogram (a complete inventory of all behaviors performed by the animal, plus the amount of time spent on each), you need to include all your chunks. If you are doing a narrower study, include only the relevant chunks.

Make sure you keep several copies of your abbreviations and their meanings!

An Example: Pumas

The following list is from an actual study of play and social behavior in three zoo-raised puma cubs.

Behaviors:
Nurse
Wrestle (name of other cub)
Approach (name of other cub or object)
Be approached (name of other cub)

Chase (name of chaser and chased)
Be chased (name of other cub)
Move away from (name of other cub)
Be moved away from (name of other cub)
Jump on (name of cub or object)
Be jumped on (name of other cub)
Jump off (name of cub or object)
Play with object (name)
Rest
Sleep
Walk

Over the 2-month study, the three puma sisters showed significant differences in the amount of time they spent doing most of the things in the list. For example, one cub (Calamity Jane) started most of the chases and wrestling and spent the most time wrestling and the most time nursing. Another cub (Saguaro) was most often chased and spent the least amount of time nursing. The third cub (Susanna) played with the toys in the cage the most. (The study was designed to test the hypothesis that play between two young animals has a predictable pattern, that is, their behaviors occur in predictable statistically significant sequences. The hypothesis was supported by the data. A walking cub is likely to approach or be approached by a second cub, to jump or be jumped on, to wrestle, and to withdraw or to be left. If the first cub withdraws, she is likely to be chased or approached, and the cycle repeats; if the first cub is left by the second, the first cub likely plays with a toy or rests.)

SAMPLES AND SAMPLE FREQUENCY

Researchers generally do not observe and record everything an animal does for a long period of time. Rather, they make detailed observations on only some behaviors or for some periods of time. Your questions will shape how much time you spend collecting data. Following are some possible ways you can plan your schedule.

Choose only certain times of day to observe or a few times throughout the day. (The pumas were most active early and later in the day, so those were good times to watch them.)

An important decision is whether to keep a continuous record of everything done by a single animal or to sample what the animal is doing, say, every 10 or 30 or 60 seconds. Sampling means to take data on a subset of all the animal's actions at some regular time intervals. (One study of lemurs showed no significant differences between data collected at 10-second intervals and those same data analyzed at 60-second intervals, i.e., using only every sixth observation. If there is no difference, how much easier on the observer to record once a minute rather than six times a minute.)

If you are observing a social animal that is part of a group (like the puma cubs), you can collect data on your animal and others, for example, by noting what your individual is doing, say, every 60 seconds, and noting what other members of the group are doing every 5 minutes. Such scanning of the whole group enriches the data on your individual animal by providing some context or background. If you are observing social interactions, you likely will get data on other group members anyway, as they interact with your animal.

Take data only when the animal is within a certain area.

Take data only when the animal is doing certain kinds of things: is near its young, is near others of the same species, is engaging in the behaviors relevant to your question.

NOTES

Make sure you write down enough information that you can make sense of the data later on without having to rely on your memory. Ideally, the notes should make sense to another researcher who was not observing with you. Both these things will be much easier if you use a data table rather than longhand notes. You will also have some longhand notes about things not on your table.

The notes should be readable. Abbreviations can be a huge help in getting a lot of information down quickly, but you have to be able to read them later! If you use abbreviations, be sure to keep copies of them and their meanings in several places.

Note questions to yourself for further exploration (to ask your teacher, to look up in a reference book, to investigate another time).

Make sketches if they make the notes clearer. Do not worry about producing "good" drawings—they should just be meaningful to someone who is watching that kind of creature.

Draw a rough map, including instructions to yourself for finding the place again. Note a couple of really distinct features that you will recognize easily.

AFTER DATA COLLECTION

As soon as you can after the data collection, read over your notes. Do not change what is written, but you may want to add things. For example, make sure all abbreviations are understandable. If you are reminded of things you noticed but did not write down, jot them in the margins or at the end of the day's notes.

Were there things that confused you or that made you want to see more? Are there new questions you want to follow up now or in the future?

Did your observation plan work? Did you have too much to do or too little? Did you need optical instruments, get cold, forget a watch? Note anything that will help you interpret the data you took and get through the next field session.

Try to use what you saw to move your research along. You may get the answer to your question on the first try. More likely, you will learn something that you hoped to see, but also things that you did not expect, cannot make sense of, never imagined. Formulate a hypothesis, make a prediction, set a new goal, revise your schedule.

After you have some or a lot of notes on the behavior you are studying, start writing your report. For suggestions about how to deal with your data and how to represent it, see the **Technique: Data** and the **Technique: Preparing a Presentation**.

IN THE FIELD: MATERIALS

Before you go out, assemble your field supplies:

Notebook, data tables
Pencils (more than one)
Small pencil sharpener (if you are not using mechanical pencils)
Optical equipment (Do you need binoculars? A hand lens?)
Camera (optional)

If you are to be out for a while, make sure you have water. If you will be out for more than a couple of hours, bring some kind of food. Unless you are going out for a short time, be prepared for the weather. Listen to the weather report and make sure you bring appropriate clothing, sunscreen, something to sit on, rain gear, sun hat, and so forth. Remember that on cool days, if you are sitting still, you will get cold, so bring extra clothing. If it is warm and sunny, you will get hot and thirsty faster than you might imagine. Even on a cloudy day, you can get sunburned, so hats and sunscreen are important.

Settle in, become part of the scene, and watch. Enjoy!

TECHNIQUE
DATA

"Data" is the plural form of "datum," a Latin word that means "what is given." In English, "data" essentially means "facts." You have been dealing with data all your lives but probably do not realize it.

WHAT ARE DATA?

Objects exist in the world, regardless of whether humans interact with them or think about them. Data, however, do not exist until humans abstract information about real objects in the world. We create data when we describe real objects.

HOW TO USE THEM

If you want to inform someone about a particular object, you can bring the object to the person (or the person to the object). Alternatively, you can abstract some information about the object and bring those abstracted data to the person. Our example of dragonfly behavior helps demonstrate some of the different forms that data can take.

DRAGONFLY BEHAVIOR: AN EXAMPLE

Imagine sitting by a secluded pond early in the morning. You are fishing, but nothing is biting, so you have plenty of time to watch the world. You notice a twig poking out of the water. Your gaze keeps returning to the twig until, a couple of hours later, you see a large, blue dragonfly land there. You are quite certain that the twig was unoccupied until then—the blue dragonfly is the first creature you have seen all morning. As you watch the insect, you are struck by its beauty. You check your watch—only to discover that you had grabbed a child's wrist thermometer from the kitchen table. It is 20°C when the dragonfly lands on the twig.

A few minutes later, a second dragonfly arrives. This one is red and noticeably smaller than the first dragonfly. It attempts to dislodge the blue dragonfly from the twig but fails. The day is warming up, and you note that the temperature is 21°C. The red dragonfly flies off, but every so often you notice it swooping through the air. Perhaps an hour after the first dragonfly's arrival, a green dragonfly flies by the twig. This one appears to be intermediate in size between the other two. Again, the newcomer attempts—and fails—to dislodge the large blue dragonfly. Glancing at your thermometer, you find that the temperature is now 25°C. Eventually, as the day gets even warmer (you still have not gotten any nibbles, but you are having a great time watching the dragonflies!), the large blue dragonfly takes off and flies into the forest beside the pond. The temperature has now reached 28°C. The small red dragonfly arrives and perches on the stick, but almost immediately the medium-size green one appears. The two insects fly around each other rapidly for a few seconds, then the red one takes off; the green dragonfly has dislodged the red one and assumed the perch.

Impressed by the dragonflies' behavior and acrobatic skills, you are overcome by the urge to discuss the experience with a friend. You gather your fishing gear and rush off—full of data. What types of data did you collect?

TYPES OF DATA

There are three major types of data: categorical (or qualitative or attribute) data, quantitative (or measurement) data, and ranked data. In the dragonfly example, you recorded each of these types of data.

CATEGORICAL DATA

Categorical (or qualitative or attribute) data are used to describe attributes that form discrete and nonoverlapping categories. When you describe a dragonfly as blue, red, or green, you are treating color as categorical data. Each dragonfly can belong to one and only one of the color categories. The categories cannot be ordered in any way or treated as quantitative information. If you were able to observe the dragonflies up close, you could also determine their sex, another example of categorical data, since an individual can be either male or female but not both.

QUANTITATIVE DATA

Quantitative (or measurement) data are measured numerically, according to a specific scale. With the thermometer, you measured the air temperature as each dragonfly arrived or departed—temperature is an example of quantitative data. With an insect net, a ruler, and quick reflexes, you could have caught the dragonflies and measured their lengths, which would have given you a second set of quantitative data.

RANKED DATA

Ranked data are ordered in some fashion, but they are not measured quantitatively. In the dragonfly example, the blue dragonfly arrived first, the red dragonfly arrived second, and the green dragonfly arrived third, so time of arrival is ranked data. (If you had had a watch with you, you could have noted the time of each insect's arrival and treated that as quantitative data.) Similarly, by noting the relative sizes of the dragonflies (large, small, and intermediate), you created a second ranking scheme. Finally, the behaviors of the dragonflies can be ranked: the large blue one was able to retain the perch despite the efforts of the red and green dragonflies. The green one, however, was able to replace the red one. Although you need to collect more data, you can see the beginnings of a ranking of ability to retain the perch: the blue dragonfly is best, the green one is second best, and the red one is last. We typically use ranked data in situations in which we cannot measure a quantity or decide not to do so (if we think that the measurements will add little to our understanding).

DISPERSION OR VARIATION AMONG DATA POINTS

When summarizing a data set that consists of multiple independent data points, most people begin by calculating the mean, or average, of the data points. When we analyze quantitative data, however, it also is crucial to calculate some measure of the dispersion, or spread, of the data. Even though it may be impractical here to explore fully the topic of dispersion in datasets, it is important that we appreciate its importance. (For more information on averages, see Exploration 2 in **Module 2, Chapter 7.**)

The simplest description of dispersion is the range, the difference between the highest and the lowest values in a data set. The two data sets listed below have the same mean and the same number of data points. However, the ranges of the two data sets are quite different, since the lengths of the blue dragonflies are much more widely dispersed than those of the red dragonflies.

	LENGTHS OF RED DRAGONFLIES (CM)	LENGTHS OF BLUE DRAGONFLIES (CM)
	2.6	2.3
	2.6	2.4
	2.6	2.5
	2.6	2.6
	2.7	2.7
	2.8	2.8
	2.8	2.9
	2.8	3.0
	2.8	3.1
Mean length	2.7 cm	2.7 cm
Range	0.2 cm	0.8 cm
Number	9	9

When we present quantitative data, we should always give some indication of how much variation exists in the data, even if we say only "Lengths of red dragonflies ranged from 2.6 to 2.8 cm, with a mean of 2.7 cm; lengths of blue dragonflies ranged from 2.3 to 3.1 cm, with a mean of 2.7 cm."

Ecologists typically use statistical measures such as standard deviations and variance to describe dispersion in a data set, but these may be too involved for your first data analyses. Scientific calculators can calculate these measures for small data sets; you may wish to explore their use.

TECHNIQUE
PREPARING A PRESENTATION

For science to be effective and useful, it must be communicated well. That is why scientists write so many articles for their fellow scientists (as well as for the general public) and hold conferences to share their findings.

As part of your doing science, you should learn how to make a good public presentation of a scientific study. Such communication skills will also be useful to you in other contexts throughout your life, so do not feel your efforts are wasted if you do not plan a career in science.

1. **Choose a good title.**
Your title should be as short as possible, but still let the audience know what you studied. A bit of humor is fine, if you are sure your topic is clear.

   Examples

   Testing the hypothesis that height is a good predictor of weight in gorillas

   Variations in daily foraging patterns: does the early bird always get the worm?

2. **Tell your listeners what you were trying to learn when you began your investigations.**
You may have been testing a hypothesis, or perhaps just exploring a certain phenomenon. Whatever the case, let your audience know what you hoped to do. If it is relevant, tell your audience about key pieces of background, such as important theories or previous research on the topic. This part of your talk is like the Introduction section of a scientific paper.

   Example

   This study began with a question: are height and weight related in gorillas? If they are related, that would be useful for field research, since it is difficult to weigh wild, live gorillas, but it is relatively easy to estimate their heights. Because data on chimpanzees and humans, the closest relatives of gorillas, show that height and weight are closely correlated, we hoped—predicted—that the same might be true for gorillas. Thus, we set out to test the specific hypothesis that height is a good predictor of weight in gorillas.

3. **Tell your listeners the relevant aspects of the methods you employed.**
You do not want to tell them every single detail of what you did—you do not have time for that. But sketch out your methodology for them. If they want the details, they can read them after you publish your paper. This part of your talk is like the Methods section of a scientific paper.

   Example

   We studied captive populations of the mountain gorilla at ten zoos in the United States. In all, we studied seventeen female gorillas and fourteen males. Each individual was measured for height with a standard tape measure and weighed on a Bauhaus 1000 Commercial Scale. The data were analyzed on an Orange IIu computer using the Datanalysister software package.

4. **Tell your listeners the results of the investigation.**
What major analyses did you perform? Typically your results will be quantitative, that is, they will involve numbers. If possible, present statistical tests to show whether your results were significant (such tests may be beyond the scope of your class, but they are useful to learn and use.

Prepare visual aids such as graphs and charts to show your results. People absorb information much better if they see patterns as well as hear them. Your visual aids can be on the blackboard, large pieces of paper, overhead projection transparencies, or slides—but they must be visible to all of your audience. Make sure text is large enough to be seen by people in the back of the room. This part of your talk is like the Results section of a scientific paper.

Example

We decided to analyze data for the two sexes separately, since it seemed that, on average, male gorillas are much heavier than females. As you can see in Graph 1, the weight of male gorillas ranged from 80 kg to 140 kg and averaged 103 kg. Male height ranged from 1.30 m to 1.63 m, with an average of 1.41 m. We found that as height increased, so did weight. There were, however, several exceptions: Gordon, from the San Diego Zoo, is very heavy for his height.

5. **Interpret your results for your audience.**
In many ways, this is the most important and most difficult part of your presentation. You need to help your audience understand what your results mean and how they can (and cannot) be used. Discuss any problems you ran into and how you might have improved the project. Also briefly mention directions in which you might follow up this research. This part of your talk is like the Discussion section of a scientific paper.

Example

In both sexes we found a close relationship between a gorilla's height and its weight. These results will enable field researchers to estimate gorilla weight from height data (which they can gather relatively easily). The relationship between height and weight is not perfect, however. Several older individuals from two zoos were heavier than younger individuals of the same height. If we pursue this research further, we will study a larger number of gorillas and pay special attention to the role of age in determining weight. We would also like to compare the feeding policies at different zoos, since they may affect gorilla weight.

6. **In all parts of your presentation be brief but clear.**
Scientific presentations at conferences are often limited to 10 or 15 minutes. These presentations frequently cover the results of many months of study and analysis, so the speakers must make every word and visual aid count. You, too, will have a limited amount of time for your presentation, so do not spend time on unessential information!

7. **Make your visual aids easy to understand.**
Your graphs, charts, and text visuals can really help your listeners absorb what you are discussing. In addition, do not be afraid to use text aids to emphasize crucial points.

Example

Taller gorillas are heavier (and older ones are too!).

TECHNIQUE
21 QUESTIONS TO CONCLUSIONS

The Technique dubbed "21 Questions to Conclusions" is widely used to introduce ecology students of all levels to the process of doing science and to a new field site. It is deceptively simple; its power lies in allowing students to experience the reality that science is a process no more mysterious than asking questions and making and testing predictions. It helps students see—not just look—and raise questions, make predictions, design ways of testing their predictions, collecting and analyze data, and drawing conclusions. This Technique can serve as a discussion tool about the process of doing research or help you actually design and develop a research project (of any duration, from an hour to a year or more).

Since it perfectly encapsulates the process of research, without fanfare, jargon, or complication, this Technique also can be used in the classroom about various topics or repeatedly in any new field site. Part of its success is that it differs substantially from any previous experience most students have had with "doing science," so if you do it in the field, try to carry it out just as described.

Teachers have used "21 Questions to Conclusions" in the classroom simply to introduce a new topic. For instance, one teacher began an introduction to marine biology by presenting students with a table full of sea organism specimens. He asked students to write ten questions about what they saw, then incorporated those questions throughout the 6 weeks of subsequent classes. (In that case, research as such was not the outcome; student interest and student-based learning were.)

Another teacher used the same approach for a chemistry class by asking students to think of questions about the chemistry of anything in the room, including a pile of items on the laboratory bench. She had included potato chips, sunflower seeds, a bicycle wheel, a can of motor oil, a piece of jewelry, and so on. Again, here the Technique was used to arouse student interest and thinking rather than to initiate research. And the student questions were used throughout as a guide and a hook to maintain that interest.

A third teacher modified the technique slightly. He began each physics section with a few examples and invited students to add their own. Together, they filled in a large chart (which was kept posted for the entire unit) with three columns, labeled "I know" "I think I know" "I want to know" about whatever came up around the examples. As he wryly noted, with a roomful of students asking questions, he got enough to include all the topics he wanted and plenty to spare. He used relevant topics as the backbone of the work and either addressed the other questions in a single class discussion or saved them for the appropriate unit.

ASKING QUESTIONS

Asking questions does not mean you are dumb; it means you are thinking. It is also a necessary first step in thinking, learning, doing research. Without questions, there can be no predictions; without predictions, there can be no experiments; without experiments, there can be no data; and without data, there can be no conclusions or results.

Asking questions can be tricky, for several reasons. People can feel exposed, that they are showing ignorance, being impertinent, talking back, or behaving inappropriately. Conversely, people do not necessarily appreciate being asked questions for those same reasons.

Even if asking or answering questions in general is OK, some topics might be off limits: religion, politics, human behavior, sex, to name a few.

Yet to do science or think about anything, it is essential to ask questions. So the more and more fully articulated questions people can ask, the better positioned they will be to get answers.

PROCEDURE

ASKING QUESTIONS: STEP 1

Before sending students off, give them only these guidelines:

- Work alone but stay in sight of at least one other class member.
- Pick a place that looks interesting. Write down the first 21 questions that occur to you as you look at the place. Do not censor yourself.
- Return to a designated spot after 30 minutes or after you have 21 questions, whichever comes first.

DISCUSSING THE QUESTIONS: STEP 2

Ideally, this is done at the field site, but it can be done inside.

Once everyone has returned, form a circle. Allow a few minutes for people to prioritize their questions. Starting with a volunteer, ask each student to share a question, a "burning question," one of great interest to that student.

After the student has posed the question, ask for thoughts or comments from everyone present. Do not ask the questioner and be sure to make eye contact with others in the circle. Encourage any attempts at comments—right now you are looking for discussion and participation, for consideration, ideas, thoughts—not answers.

Help the discussion along as best you can. That includes asking clarifying questions; inviting comparison or extrapolations; making connections with any ideas or information you or anyone in the group might offer; applying general problem-solving abilities such as logic, association, and contextualization; and asking repeatedly, "How could we find out about that?" The discussion can wander and will need redirection to the point at hand, especially how that point illustrates or embodies key principles and concepts in ecology. A professional ecologist can be especially helpful at this point.

TYPES OF QUESTIONS AND "TRIAGE": STEP 3

You can use this technique for discussion on how to develop and carry out a research project or actually to get students started on some research. Naturally, we strongly endorse the latter. In either case, this step—sorting potential research questions from others—is important.

Once each student has shared at least one burning question, make a list of everyone's three to five most interesting questions. It will be clear from the group discussion that some questions are richer than others and that there are types of questions. Some are strictly factual "what is it?" questions. Since those are rather narrow, they do not support discussion or real research. They can be answered immediately (if someone knows) or later with a field guide. Perhaps they can be turned into comparison, if comparison is available. Thus, rather than sticking with "what is it?" turn the question into something like, "Are there any of those [near the school, at another field site, in your yard], what is different/the same here and there, and what might explain that difference/similarity?"

Questions that already involve comparison are inherently rich. Describing and elaborating on the comparison support discussion—everyone likely has some observation, comment, or question to contribute—and can give rise to research.

The questions most likely to support both rich discussion and potential research are those that can be "ramped up," or expanded, such as those that emphasize interactions between organisms and their environment (the physical environment, other organisms): how X affects Y; the availability of resources of various kinds; how organisms get them. Does Y need X? Is it rare? Does anything else need X? (For some general ecological principles, see Science Background, **Unit 1, Chapter 2**, in **Modules 2** and **3**.)

Each discussion of a rich question involves a mini-version of aspects of the process of doing science. A question is focused, sharpened, clarified; predictions are made; test or experimental methods are discussed; possible outcomes might be considered. This is where both ecology and the science process are most in evidence. (The entire process of doing science necessarily includes the actual research: data collection, analysis, interpretation, and drawing conclusions.)

Thus, each question is considered by the group as a whole—the group members typically ask for clarification or offer relevant information and suggestions. You keep asking the individual and the group to consider how any question might be answered; that is, how to turn it into a set of testable predictions and what techniques might be available for testing those predictions. This emphasis also keeps expanding the questions, to show underlying and related concepts in ecology. Thus, the question "Why so many different weeds?" in an urban site leads to considerations of dispersal, succession, population size, introduced versus native species, plant requirements such as soil type and water availability, possible comparisons with other habitats, and so on.

DEVELOPING THE RESEARCH PROJECT: STEP 4

Either have students each pick one question from the list and develop it as a research project in class or for Homework or (if students will actually be doing research) have students group around one or two questions they wish to pursue. Two to five people per group is reasonable.

Let each group develop its plan: questions, predictions, how to collect data, what to do with the data, how to present their conclusions.

If actual research will take place, be sure you have any equipment students might need.

SUMMARY OF THE PROCESS

In **vernacular** and *scientific* terms, the entire process looks like this.

21Q (questions) → focus, expectations, predictions →
question → identify concepts, hypothesis, alternate hypotheses →

ways of finding out → collecting information →
experiments, techniques → collecting data →

processing and understanding the information → presenting results
data analysis and interpretation → presenting results

For more details, see the **Technique: Introduction to Research.**

SAMPLE FIELD SESSION

This session was held in an urban site in the industrial, "bad" end of town under several highway overpasses and near a river. The text inside the brackets is a comment on the process. The letters represent different students.

A: Why was there all that wood in the stream?
TEACHER: Did anyone else see that?
SEVERAL: Yes.
TEACHER: What did you notice about it?

[Notice that this neutral question is just about getting more information]

A: It wasn't lumber, it was, like, cut trees.
B: Beaver—maybe beaver did it.

[Given that the site is in downtown Albany, that seems implausible. But rather than say so, which could be taken as criticism, the teacher simply addresses the matter factually and respectfully.]

TEACHER: Could anyone see the ends of the trees—whether they were chewed or sawed?

[This is a specific form of the general question, "How could we find out about that?" Since the ends are underwater, no one can answer the question, and it is set aside temporarily as unanswerable but worth answering.]

C: Maybe the trees were swept down here from somewhere else?
D: How big are these trees?

A: I don't know? Maybe 6 or 8 feet long. And skinny.
TEACHER: Does anyone know if it has rained a lot lately?
B: Yes, it has.
F: Were the trees parallel to the stream or lying across it?
A: I think they were hung up on a bend in the shore.
D: Maybe they're garbage, and somebody just dumped them.

[At this point, the teacher summarizes what is known, what needs to be known, what can be eliminated, and what seems worth pursuing.]

TEACHER: OK, so there is a bunch—how many? a dozen?—of skinny short trees caught on a bend in the river. They could be local garbage, or they could have washed downstream in the recent rains. We don't know how they are cut because no one has seen their bases, but that would tell us for sure whether they were cut by beaver or humans. Anything else?
E: I don't think it could be beaver, because we're downtown.
TEACHER: How could we find out about that?
A: Look up whether beavers live in cities.

[And so even the beaver were directly incorporated.]

At the same urban site, students raised other particularly interesting questions. What follows are those questions, follow-up questions from the group, and discussion of the topics.

"How do these plants get their seeds around?"

- Why do you ask that question?
- What seeds or fruits can you see here?
- Do you think the plants tend to be dispersed by the same or several agents?
- How might seed-dispersal characteristics affect the species composition here?
- Are the young plants growing up the same species as the older plants on the site, or are they different?

Seeds both shape and reflect the species composition of a site and also of its surroundings. The seeds available attract some animals and not others. If the site is embedded in a very different type of habitat (say an urban woods surrounded by train tracks and residential areas), the seeds that come will be determined mostly by the species in the nearby area. That then affects the course of succession on this site, and as the vegetation changes, the composition of the fauna changes as well.

"What effect does the railroad have on this area?"

- What kinds of effects do you have in mind?
- How would you detect those effects?
- How could you measure the size of the effects?
- When you say "this area," what do you have in mind? Near the tracks, 2 meters away, 100 meters away?

The building of a railroad can cause a lot of disruption, but in most areas the site has had decades to recover from the construction. Some effects, however, linger. On the level of landscape processes, the track is a barrier, preventing some animals from crossing and also affecting plant dispersal. It can be a channel along which animal and plant "colonists" travel to the area (species that come in the wake of human activities). That tends to homogenize species composition, so that this place looks rather like other places near train tracks in the general zone of latitude and longitude. An interesting study might be to look at other areas crossed by the tracks, to see whether and how they differ. What likely was there before the tracks were put in? How has that affected what is currently there? Compare these track areas with areas some distance away from the tracks. What can you say about the effects of the railway on the basis of this comparative study?

Of course, the track will have changed the flow of water and wind (if the track bed is raised); it may have created an area of permanent shading or otherwise changed microclimates nearby. The right of way makes a long opening and an area that will be more changeable in its temperature range, its precipitation, and its winds. Further, the materials used to build the railroad bed will have introduced new materials to the area (such as lots of gravel) and so provides physical habitat different from what was there before. Runoff also can include new chemicals that leach from those trackbed materials.

"It's so noisy, how can animals live here?"

- What animal sign is there?
- What kinds of animals would you expect to find here?
- Which of them might be affected by noise?
- How noisy is it here? How do you measure noise?
- Is the noise constant or periodic? Would that affect the animal life?
- How do you determine what kinds of animals live in an area?

"How come there are so many different plant species growing here?" [in an urban area]

- How many are there, in fact?
- Is that a lot? In comparison with what?
- Is there a pattern to the diversity of growth form—that is, are there more species of trees, herbs, bushes, and grasses here?
- Are these plants native to the area, or did they come in along the tracks? Where are they native?

"How can all these insects survive?"

- How many insects are there and what kinds?
- Is the diversity evenly spread about?
- How does it match the microhabitat? Are there different insect species on the gravel bed, on the rough grass beside it, and in the tall grasses farther from the tracks?

"What effect does the litter have?" [There was a lot of broken glass and paper in some places.]

- What could it affect?
- What kinds of trash are there? How much is there, in fact?
- Is it distributed evenly, or is it concentrated in some places and not others?
- Would you expect it to have a positive or a negative effect?
- What advantages might litter have?
- What kinds of comparative or experimental studies could you design to test your conjectures about the effects of litter?

Again, having noticed the basic phenomenon—trash—what other observations can you make, to see what kinds of relationships or processes might be involved? Is there enough trash to have a detectable effect? What kinds of trash? How is the trash distributed?

Then questions might concentrate on physical and biological effects. Does it block or clog a waterway? Does it collect water? Is it mobile (e.g., paper) or stationary (bottles, barrels, mattresses). Does it kill plants below it? Prevent human access? Provide habitat? Are a lot of food scraps mixed in? Who might that feed?

"How old is that tree? Was it here before the overpasses were built?"

- How could you answer that question?
- Is there any predictable correlation between tree size and age?
- What kind of tree is it, anyway? Is it unusual (e.g., the only specimen of that species on the site)?
- Why is that an interesting question? That is, if you knew the answer, then what?

"Why aren't there any pigeons here?"

- Are there no pigeons, or just very few?
- How does the pigeon density compare with that of other nearby areas?
- Does it make sense to be surprised at pigeon scarcity?
- Is there any reason to believe that pigeons might have been present before this period of observation?
- What kinds of places do pigeons like?
- Are there places that pigeons avoid?
- Do pigeons move periodically? That is, are they likely to come here in the evenings, in the spring, or at some other time?

Thinking about pigeons is a way to think about birds, and that is a way to think about animals, and then other organisms. Many of the questions are alternative ways of exploring the pigeon's niche and ecological relationships. The idea of periodic shifts in locale relates to migration: annual or smaller scale in time or space. Why would an animal migrate? Can animals that do not migrate on a seasonal basis migrate under other conditions?

Does a bird that occurs in two or more different locales be said to have two niches? Or one complex niche that includes disjunct sites? What might be the evolutionary consequences of that?

EPILOGUE: DRAWING THE SCIENCE LESSONS

With all the other things going on in a field discussion like this, it is sometimes hard to bear in mind that the ultimate goal of this technique is to help participants take steps to learn more science, not just to design a research project or to awaken and discipline the participants' curiosity.

You as facilitator are a juggler. You need to think, as the burning questions are shared, about what principles are likely to be relevant to the question. At first, you will not want actually to label them as such, but after the conversation has gone on for a while, it helps to do so. If you have the principles in mind, you can help shape the discussion through the questions and suggestions you offer, and you will recognize when a participant has raised a more fruitful line of conversation.

As facilitator, you are responsible for making the best use of the resources in the group, so the questions are discussed respectfully and not superficially.

HAVING AN ECOLOGIST ALONG

It may also happen that a conversation gets to the point where some specific technical expertise would be productive. A participant might be interested in comparing the bird communities in the woods along a pond and on the hill above the pond. You might not be sure about how to go about describing bird communities or how to compare two communities, whereas an ecologist can suggest approaches. If you had trouble putting your finger on the important science idea behind a burning question, you could ask the ecologist, "If we were doing a literature search about this, what kinds of things should we look for?"

In preparation for such using this technique in the field, you might find it helpful to review in your mind or with colleagues some of the primary principles of ecology you likely will encounter during the field experience. If you can include an ecologist in this work, so much the better.

TECHNIQUE
CALORIMETRY AND CARBONOMETRY

INTRODUCTION

The basic method for both calorimetry—determining heat (energy) content—and carbonometry—determining carbon content—is to (1) dry and weigh the sample, (2) burn the sample in an atmosphere with sufficient oxygen, and (3) measure the carbon dioxide or heat that evolves. Please recognize that the process of oxidation by combustion is different from digestion as carried out by organisms (which occurs largely by way of enzymatic and chemical oxidation)—we are using combustion merely as a way to measure carbon and energy contents.

Safety

WARNING

You will be working with burning matches, burning samples, and perhaps a Nichrome wire–battery ignition system that gets very hot.

DO NOT PERFORM THIS TECHNIQUE IN AN OXYGEN-ENRICHED ATMOSPHERE.

DO NOT ALLOW THE TWO NICHROME WIRES OR ALLIGATOR CLIPS TO TOUCH EACH OTHER.

DO NOT TOUCH ANY BURNING, HEATED, OR RECENTLY BURNING ITEMS WITH BARE FINGERS OR ANYTHING BUT APPROPRIATE TOOLS.

WEAR SAFETY GOGGLES DURING THE PROCEDURE.

SAMPLES THAT CAN BE ANALYZED

The techniques described here can be used to analyze samples that represent the three major food sources: protein, carbohydrate, fat. Natural samples such as wood and leaves can also be analyzed, with some limitations. Table 1 lists properties of some materials relevant to their combustion.

Table 1

Properties of Some Materials Relevant to Their Combustion

MAJOR FOOD MOLECULES	EXAMPLE	% CARBON BY WEIGHT	O_2 REQUIRED TO OXIDIZE 1 G (LITERS)	CO_2 PRODUCED IN OXIDIZING 1 G (LITERS)	HEAT RELEASED IN OXIDIZING 1 G (KCAL)
Protein	Gelatin	50–70	0.96	0.77	4.0–4.4
Carbohydrate	Sugar (dextrose), starch (cornstarch), cellulose (wood, paper)	40–50	0.75–0.83	0.75–0.83	3.7–4.2
Fat	Paraffin (candle wax), peanut, olive, corn oil	80	2.0	1.4	9.0–9.5

Source: Medical Physiology, 13th ed. (Vernon B. Mountcastle, ed.)

NOTE: We use the term "calorie" to mean the heat required to raise the temperature of 1 g of water by 1°C (at 15°C); 1 kcal = 1,000 calories. The standard international (SI) unit for heat is the joule, and 1 calorie is equivalent to 4.184 joules. Dietary literature and food labels often use the term "Calorie" (with uppercase "C") when, in fact, "kilocalorie" is meant.

SAMPLE PREPARATION FOR BOTH CALORIMETRY AND CARBONOMETRY

If the sample contains a significant amount of water, dry the sample to constant weight in a 100°C oven.

Use a sample size of 0.5–1.0 g. That amount is easy to weigh and will yield enough carbon and energy to be measured easily. Larger samples would consume too much oxygen when burned in the carbonometer.

Measure the mass of the dry sample to 0.01 g using an analytical balance (e.g., Ohaus Dial-omatic triple-beam balance with 0.01-g vernier). Compare the initial mass of the sample with its mass after combustion to determine the mass burned.

THE TECHNIQUE OF CALORIMETRY

Materials

- **One calorimetry apparatus** per group (3–5) of students (if possible), as described in Table 2 and shown in Figure 1.
- **One Nichrome wire–battery ignition system** per group (if possible), as described in Table 3.

Table 2 **Calorimetry Apparatus Components**

ITEM	DESCRIPTION	WHERE WE OBTAINED IT
Calorimeter	Empty 12-oz soda can	Recycle bin
Thermometer	±0.1°C electronic thermometer	Lab supply catalog
Mounting for calorimeter	Ring stand and clamp	Chemistry lab
Mounting for sample	Cork and bent paper clip	
Nichrome wire–battery ignition system	See Table 3	We assembled it (Fig. 3)

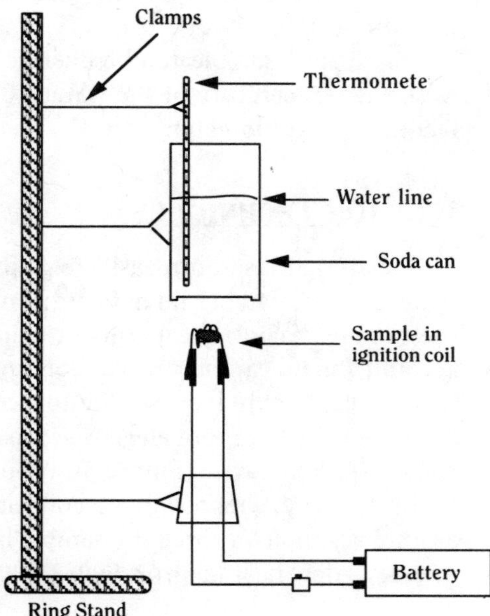

Figure 1. Calorimetry apparatus.

Table 3 **Nichrome Wire–Battery Ignition System**

ITEM	DESCRIPTION	WHERE WE OBTAINED IT
Ignition coil	12- to 15-cm coil of 22-gauge Nichrome wire	Edmund Scientific; cost approx. $20 per roll
Wire	12-gauge household electrical wire	Hardware store
Alligator clips		Hardware or electronics store
Battery	7.2 V, 1.2 amp hour NiCad battery pack	Radio Shack P/N 23-230; cost approx. $15
Recharger	NiCad battery recharger (120 V AC @ 10 amp in, 7.2 V DC @ 0.4 amp out)	Radio Shack P/N 23-231A, cost approx. $10

Procedure

The technique is taken from Markow (1992). The sample is burned beneath a soda can containing 200 ml of water (see Figure 1). For most effective heat transfer, the sample should be burned 1–2 cm below the bottom of the can.

The sample can be ignited using a match or the Nichrome coil. To take into account the heat contributed by the match or the Nichrome, do a control experiment using the ignition method alone (without a sample).

The initial and final temperatures of the water are measured with a ±0.1°C immersion thermometer to determine the quantity of heat transferred from the burning sample to the water. Be aware that the temperature of the water may not be uniform—we found that the water at the top of the can was up to 1°C warmer than that at the bottom. Stir the water to eliminate this as a source of error.

A typical sample might liberate 2,000 calories. This is sufficient to raise the temperature of the water 10°C—easy to measure using a typical laboratory thermometer.

IGNITION TECHNIQUES

Materials that burn easily (e.g., paper, wood, peanuts) can be lit with a match. Paper matches do not contribute much carbon or heat compared to the sample. A control experiment using the match alone will allow you to account for its carbon or heat content. The sample can be mounted on a wire (or paper clip) loop stuck into a cork or rubber stopper (Figure 2).

A somewhat more elegant approach is to ignite the sample with a hot coil of Nichrome wire (Figure 3). We use a 12- to 15-cm length of 22-gauge Nichrome wire, wrapped into a coil with 3–10 turns. Wrap the wire directly around a sample or force the sample between the coils. Heat the coil to an orange-yellow heat (approx. 900–1,100°C) using a NiCad battery pack (nor-

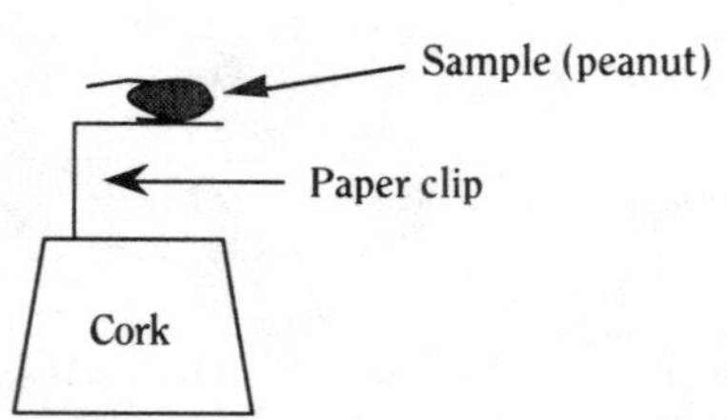

Figure 2. Mounting of sample for ignition with matches.

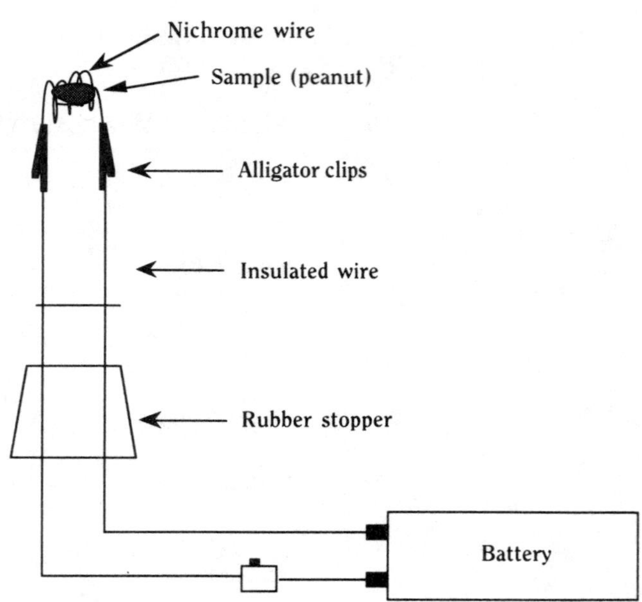

Figure 3. Mounting of sample for ignition with Nichrome coil.

mally used to power radio-controlled toy cars). Samples that are easy to ignite will burst into flame in 5–10 seconds and then continue to burn on their own. **Turn off the coil once the sample is burning.**

Less flammable samples (e.g., green leaves) will burn better if the coil is left hot until the sample is completely burned. Heating the coil draws approximately 8 amps from the battery, with about a 4 V drop across the coil, so it consumes about (8 amps × 4 volts) = 32 watts = 32 joules/second = 8 calories/second. If we estimate 1 minute per burn, the coil will produce about 500 calories (assuming all the electrical energy consumed by the coil is released as heat). This is a significant fraction of the heat generated by combusting the sample and will need to be taken into account for calorimetry experiments.

Since the battery can deliver 1.2 amp hours before needing a recharge, it will need to be recharged after about (1.2 amp/hour) / (8 amps × 1 hour/60 minutes) = 10 minutes of use. The battery can be recharged fully in 4–5 hours using an AC recharger.

Samples that do not liquefy or fall apart when they burn can be ignited and burned within the coil, using the coil itself to support the sample. For example, we burn plant material (e.g., both green and dry leaves) in this manner. For messier samples (e.g., sugar), we use a ceramic crucible for containing the sample and the residue that remains after burning.

Oils, fats, and waxes can be burned with a wick (although the combustion of the wick must be taken into account).

RESULTS FROM CALORIMETRY EXPERIMENTS

Example: Burning a Peanut with a Match

A roasted salted peanut (with the salt wiped off with a damp towel) was burned 1.5 cm below the bottom of the soda can. Two paper matches were used to ignite the peanut, which burned for about 1 minute. Room temperature was about 25°C.

The water in the soda can changed temperature as follows: (final temperature) – (initial temperature) = 41.6 – 22.5°C = 19.1°C.

The amount of peanut consumed is also calculated "before" and "after": (initial peanut weight) – (final peanut weight) = 0.97 g – 0.10 g = 0.87 g, which means that by weight 90% of the peanut was burned.

Example: Data Calculation

The energy released in terms of kilocalories is calculated using both temperature and weight data. Remember, it takes 1 calorie of energy to raise the temperature of 1 g of water by 1°C. And 1 g of water equals 1 ml. Since our calorimeter (the soda can) contains 200 g of water, each increase of 1°C requires an input of 200 calories. In this experiment, the temperature rose 19.1°C, so the amount of energy that was taken up by the calorimeter is 19.1 × 200 calories = 3,800 calories (3.8 kcal).

The two matches together weigh 0.11 g, and about 0.03 g (2.7%) of their mass burned. Assuming that the matches are cardboard (cellulose), their caloric value is 4 kcal/g. Thus, the match burning contributed 4,000 cal/g × 0.03 g = 120 cal.

Total calories of the sample, therefore, are 3,800 cal – 120 cal, which is a 3% difference. So the total energy from the peanut itself is about 3,680, or, rounding up, 3,700 cal.

How much energy is in a gram of the sample? In the end, only 0.87 g of the peanut was burned. How many calories are there per gram of peanut? With a little algebra, we find that the heat released per unit mass = 3,700 cal / 0.87 g = 4,252.9 cal/g, or 4.2 kcal/g.

Example: Burning a Peanut with the Nichrome Wire–Battery Ignition

Used the same setup, this time with the wire coil. Turned on the coil for 10 seconds to ignite the peanut, which burned on its own for about 1 minute.

The water in the soda can changed temperature as follows: (final temperature) – (initial temperature) = 36.0—26.5°C = 9.5°C.

The amount of peanut consumed is also calculated "before" and "after": (initial peanut weight) – (final peanut weight) = 0.48 g – 0.04 g = 0.44 g. By weight, 92% of the peanut was burned.

The Nichrome coil contributed about (8 cal/sec) × (10 sec) = 80 cal to the heat measured.

Heat released = (1 cal g^{-1} $°C^{-1}$) × (200 g water) × (9.5°C) = 1,900 cal.

Heat released per unit mass = 1,900 cal / 0.44 g = 4,300 cal/g = 4.3 kcal/g.

This result is about 71% of that expected for peanuts. The Nichrome coil probably contributed about 80 cal, or 4%, of the heat measured (80 cal / 1,900). So results are similar to those obtained when matches were used to ignite the sample.

Evaluating the Results

The results are about 72% of the expected caloric value of peanuts, based on the 6.0 kcal/g listed on the peanut wrapper and the USDA Handbook, which estimates that roasted peanuts contain 5.9 kcal/g. Markow's paper suggests and our experience confirms that efficiencies of 70–90% are readily obtainable with this technique.

THE TECHNIQUE OF CARBONOMETRY

Materials

- **One carbonometry apparatus** per group of students (if possible), as described in Table 4 and shown in Figure 4.

Table 4 **Carbonometry Apparatus Components**

ITEM	DESCRIPTION	WHERE WE OBTAINED IT
Plastic container	Inverted, empty, 6-gallon plastic water jug	Costs probably \$10–\$15 if you have to buy one
Stopper	Rubber stopper (No. 8)	Lab supply catalog
CO_2 detector tube	Dräger CO_2 diffusion tube	Dräger 500/a-D carbon dioxide diffusion tube P/N 8101381; cost approx. \$40 per pack of 10. We ordered from BGI Inc., 58 Guinan St., Waltham, MA 02154, Tel. 617-891-9380.

Procedure

Set up the sample in the inverted container so the sample is approximately 20 cm above the neck of the jug, to encourage free air flow to the burning sample. The sample should be mounted on the rubber stopper so you can seal the sample in the container. (See Figure 4.)

If you are using a match to light the sample, you will ignite the sample and then lower the container over the burning sample. If you are using the Nichrome coil, seal the container before you ignite the sample.

Place a tray of ice cubes on the top of the container during the burning to prevent the top of the jug from becoming too warm and to encourage convection in the jug.

The container is large enough to contain excess oxygen (O_2) for the combustion of at least 1 g of material. The jug contains 6 gallons, or 22.7 liters, of air, of which 21%, or 4.8 liters, is O_2. Burning 1 g of fat will consume approximately 2 liters of O_2, about 40% of the available oxygen.

In our experiments so far, the burning of 0.3–0.5 g of material has taken 1–2 minutes for fast-burning materials, such as paper, and as long as 8 minutes for slower-burning materials, such as candles.

Once burning has ceased, open the container briefly to insert a Dräger CO_2 diffusion tube, then reseal it. We have also used a Dräger tube to test for CO as an indicator of incomplete combustion. Opening the container undoubtedly results in some loss of the combustion gases and is probably a small but significant source of error. We have not found a practical way to avoid opening the container to insert the Dräger tube.

If your container is clear, you can watch the color change progress as the CO_2 diffuses through the length of the Dräger tube. We have found that a 15- or 30-minute exposure is usually sufficient to react nearly half of the Dräger CO_2 tube. Dräger tubes can be read to about one significant figure (an uncertainty of about 10–20% per reading). Typical readings correspond to 1–3% CO_2. (That compares to 700–900 ppm, or 0.07–0.09%, for ambient indoor CO_2 levels, a low enough level that we ignore the CO_2 present in the container before burning.)

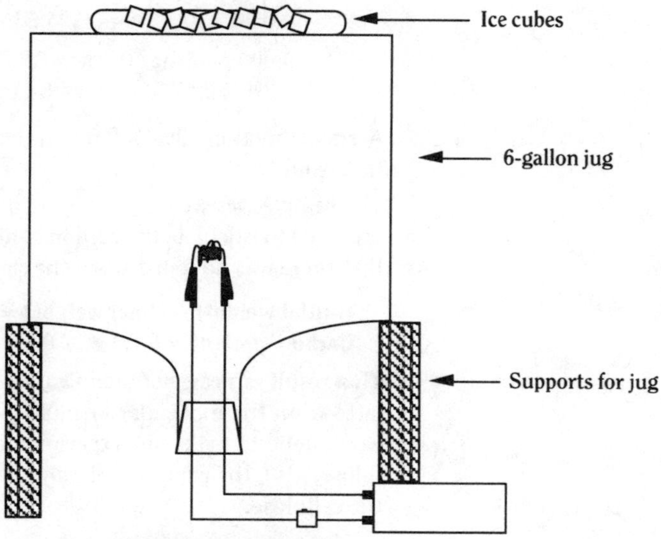

Figure 4. Carbonometry apparatus.

To clean out the carbonometer jug between runs, flush it (e.g., with water or room air) to remove the combustion gases.

RESULTS FROM CARBONOMETRY EXPERIMENTS

Example: Burning a Candle

We burned a birthday candle for approximately 8 minutes. Approximately 5 cm of the candle length was burned. (Note: gC is an abbreviation for grams of carbon.)

- 15-minute Dräger tube readings

  CO 25 ppm-hr / 0.25 hr = 100 ppm = 0.01%
  0.01% × 22.7 liters / (24.5 l/mole @ 25°C) × 12 gC/mole = 0.001 gC

  CO_2 7,000 ppm-hr / 0.25 hr = 28,000 ppm = 2.8%
  2.8% × 22.7 liters / (24.5 l/mole @ 25°C) × 12 gC/mole = 0.31 gC

- 30-minute Dräger tube readings

  CO 40 ppm-hr / 0.5hr = 80 ppm = 0.008%
  0.008% × 22.7 liters / (24.5 l/mole @ 25°C) × 12 gC/mole = 0.001 gC

  CO_2 12,000 ppm-hr / 0.5 hr = 24,000 ppm = 2.4%
  2.4% × 22.7 liters / (24.5 l/mole @ 25°C) × 12 gC/mole = 0.27 gC

Less than 1% of the carbon released was in the form of carbon monoxide.

The sample was weighed after burning. The weight difference after burning was used to calculate the carbon content per gram of dry weight (we assumed that there was no moisture in the candle).

(initial candle weight) – (final candle weight) = 1.04 g – 0.69 g = 0.35 g
Carbon content = 0.27 to 0.31 gC / 0.35 g = 77% to 89% carbon

This result agrees well with the values of 80–82% taken from the literature and calculated from the molecular formula for wax.

Example: Burning a Paper Towel

We burned a piece of paper towel for approximately 1 minute.

- 30-minute Dräger tube readings

  CO 250 ppm-hr / 0.5hr = 500 ppm = 0.05%
  0.05% × 22.7 liters / (24.5 l/mole @ 25°C) × 12 gC/mole = 0.006 gC

  CO_2 9,000 ppm-hr / 0.5 hr = 18,000 ppm = 1.8%
  1.8% × 22.7 liters / (24.5 l/mole @ 25°C) × 12 gC/mole = 0.20 gC

A small fraction (3%) of the carbon released was in the form of carbon monoxide.

The sample was weighed after burning. The weight difference after burning was used to calculate the carbon content per gram of dry weight (we assumed that there was no moisture in the sample).

(initial weight) – (final weight) = 0.61 g
Carbon content = 0.20 gC / 0.61 g = 33% carbon

This result is near, but significantly different from, the value of 44% calculated from the molecular formula for cellulose. Any moisture in the sample would tend to make our experimental result less than that predicted for cellulose. Also, the paper towel may contain binders and finishes, in addition to the cellulose.

Table 5 translates CO_2 diffusion results into grams of carbon.

Table 5 **Translation of CO_2 Diffusion Results into Grams of Carbon (gC)**

TUBE EXPOSED FOR 15 MINUTES

5-Gallon Jug CO_2 ppm-hr	gC	6-Gallon Jug CO_2 ppm-hr	gC
500	0.02	500	0.02
1,000	0.04	1,000	0.04
2,000	0.07	2,000	0.09
3,000	0.11	3,000	0.13
4,000	0.15	4,000	0.18
5,000	0.19	5,000	0.22
7,000	0.26	7,000	0.31
10,000	0.37	10,000	0.44
15,000	0.56	15,000	0.67
20,000	0.74	20,000	0.89

TUBE EXPOSED FOR 20 MINUTES

5-Gallon Jug CO_2 ppm-hr	gC	6-Gallon Jug CO_2 ppm-hr	gC
500	0.01	500	0.02
1,000	0.03	1,000	0.03
2,000	0.06	2,000	0.07
3,000	0.08	3,000	0.10
4,000	0.11	4,000	0.13
5,000	0.14	5,000	0.17
7,000	0.20	7,000	0.24
10,000	0.28	10,000	0.34
15,000	0.42	15,000	0.51
20,000	0.56	20,000	0.67

TUBE EXPOSED FOR 30 MINUTES

5-Gallon Jug CO_2 ppm-hr	gC	6-Gallon Jug CO_2 ppm-hr	gC
500	0.01	500	0.01
1,000	0.02	1,000	0.02
2,000	0.04	2,000	0.04
3,000	0.06	3,000	0.07
4,000	0.07	4,000	0.09
5,000	0.09	5,000	0.11
7,000	0.13	7,000	0.16
10,000	0.19	10,000	0.22
15,000	0.28	15,000	0.33
20,000	0.37	20,000	0.44

(CONTINUED)

TUBE EXPOSED FOR 60 MINUTES

5-Gallon Jug CO_2 ppm-hr	gC	6-Gallon Jug CO_2 ppm-hr	gC
500	0.00	500	0.01
1,000	0.01	1,000	0.01
2,000	0.02	2,000	0.02
3,000	0.03	3,000	0.03
4,000	0.04	4,000	0.04
5,000	0.05	5,000	0.06
7,000	0.06	7,000	0.08
10,000	0.09	10,000	0.11
15,000	0.14	15,000	0.17
20,000	0.19	20,000	0.22

TECHNIQUE
DESCRIBING AND COMPARING COMMUNITIES

This Technique presents some ways to describe and analyze communities or local associations of species. Community ecology is a complicated and controversial discipline, but it is a fascinating way to see ecological interactions at a more accessible scale than an ecosystem. We focus on ways to describe and analyze biological diversity. Who lives where, how many of them, and how many we might reasonably expect.

Two fundamental activities are necessary for describing communities: identifying what is there and counting. Everything else is based on those two tasks. They can be pretty challenging, however, and even counting can be harder than you might think!

Communities come in many sizes, and while the term implies an identifiable entity, it can be used flexibly (some might say "loosely").

For example, we can speak of a "stream bank community," meaning the characteristic vegetation along the stream bank in a particular location. We might then speak of the "birds of the stream bank community." On the other hand we can speak of the "bird community of the oak-hickory forest" or the "amphibian community." The common theme is frequent, perhaps predictable, associations of species—plant, animal, or both. In what follows, we discuss basic indexes for community description. Bear in mind, though, that the ways of taking data on plant species in a community are different from ways of censusing insect or reptile diversity. Such practical matters of natural history will shape the studies you might do.

The measures we address are richness, diversity, and similarity.

SPECIES RICHNESS

The basic information we need about a community is how many species are present (in the study area).

Establish the area within which you will collect data. As you travel through the area, note any species you encounter. If the study area is very large, you may wish to sample it rather than try to visit and catalog every square meter.

If you have comparable information from elsewhere, a simple species list can be revealing, since species live in characteristic habitats, have associations with other species, and tolerances and intolerances of various kinds. Further, your list may raise interesting questions when compared with the species list of a comparable or contrasting plot of the same size. If on one hectare of forest in Ecuador, you find as many tree species as are found in all of North America (as is quite possible), you have reason to suspect that the ecosystems differ in some important respects. Just what causes such differences is, of course, a matter of great interest and intense study.

If you are interested in describing diversity, the simple list of species is only a starting point. To carry your description further, keep track of the number of individuals of each species. For very numerous or very mobile species, such as grasses or gnats, you may need to settle for estimates or standardized sampling techniques (number of individuals along a transect or in some manageable, small unit of area).

Example

See Figures 1 and 2. Each figure represents a plot with a small number of plant species present. Take a census of each plot. Name the species or merely label them somehow.

1. How many species are present on each plot?
2. How many individuals of each species are present on each plot?

Are the communities similar or different?

Arrange the species lists in descending order of number of individuals. What is the total number of individuals?

Your species lists for the two communities might be the same, but the numbers of individuals of each species are quite different. Assuming that each species has other species associated with it (e.g., animals that eat its fruit or leaves or use it for shelter), that may mean that the animal (including microbial) elements of the community are quite different. It may also suggest that the soil, moisture, or other physical characteristics of the site are quite different. To differentiate among those factors or to decide whether the communities are similar, more data are needed.

DIVERSITY

Now we consider not only how many species are on a site but how many individuals of each species are present.

First, we need the following raw data:

- the species list
- the number of individuals of each species encountered
- the total number of individuals of all species

Once we have this information, there are several ways to calculate diversity. Usually, various bits of information are combined to yield a single number, an index, that sums up the diversity information for a study site. Like the species list, we can compare the index with indexes from other sites. We focus on one common index, the Shannon-Weaver (also known as the Shannon-Wiener) diversity index, often represented by H' for short.

Figures 1 through 6 show some imaginary plant communities that we will census and compare. Note that these sample plots are all of the same size. You will learn best if you do the counting and calculating yourself. All the calculations can be done with pencil, paper, and a calculator for doing logarithms, although a spreadsheet makes things easier. At the end of this Technique is a sample spreadsheet for the examples.

The calculation uses the number of individuals of each species present in the sample (e.g., species 1), the number of individuals of all species, the ratio of those two numbers, and the logarithm of the ratio. (It is customary to use the natural log, ln, or $\log_{10}$.)

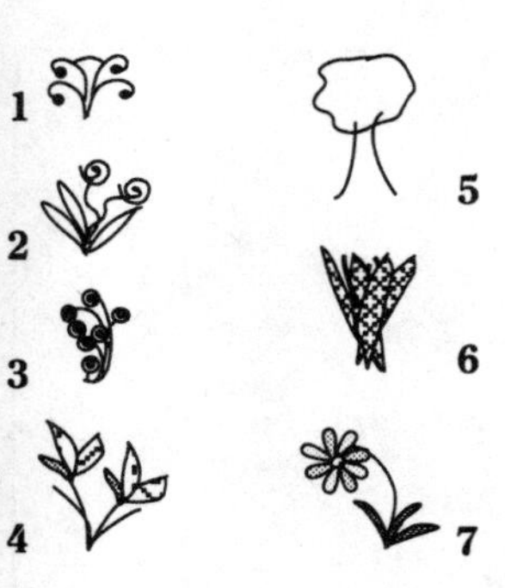

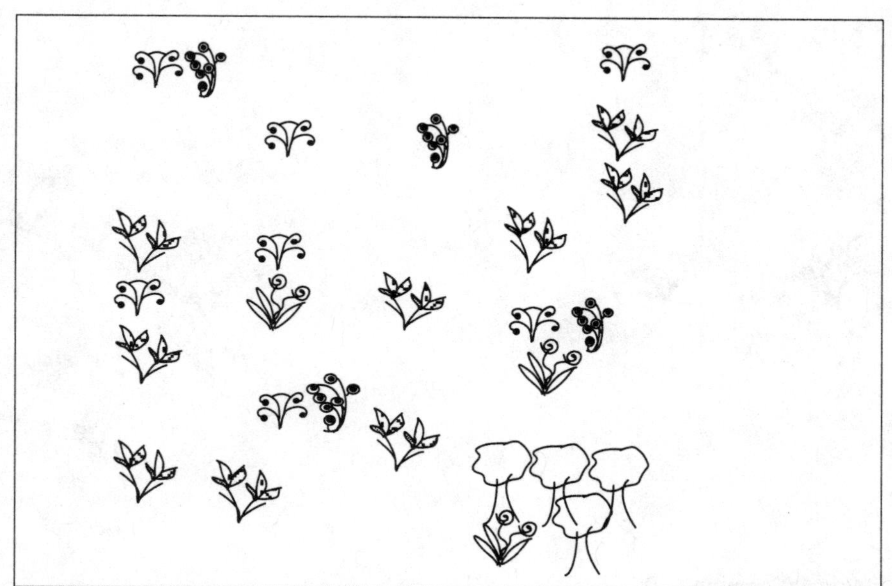

Figure 1. Community A

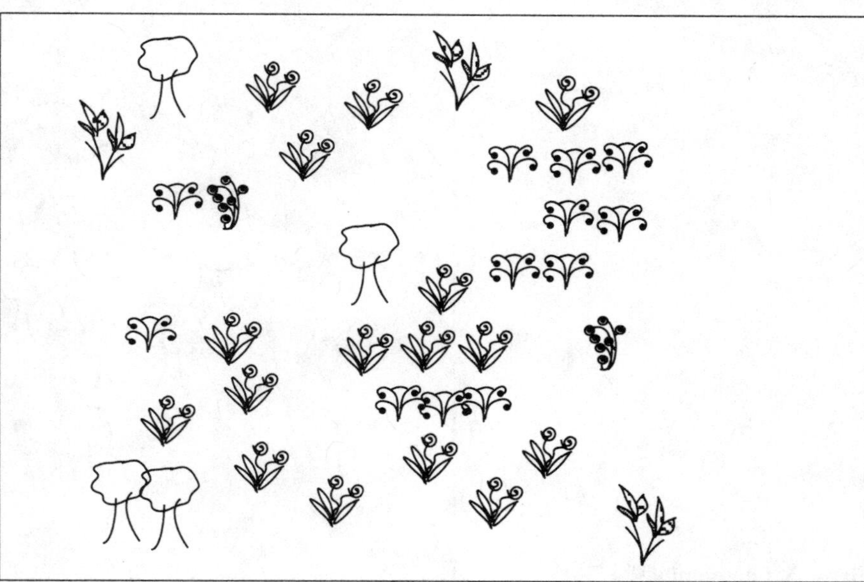

Figure 2. Community B

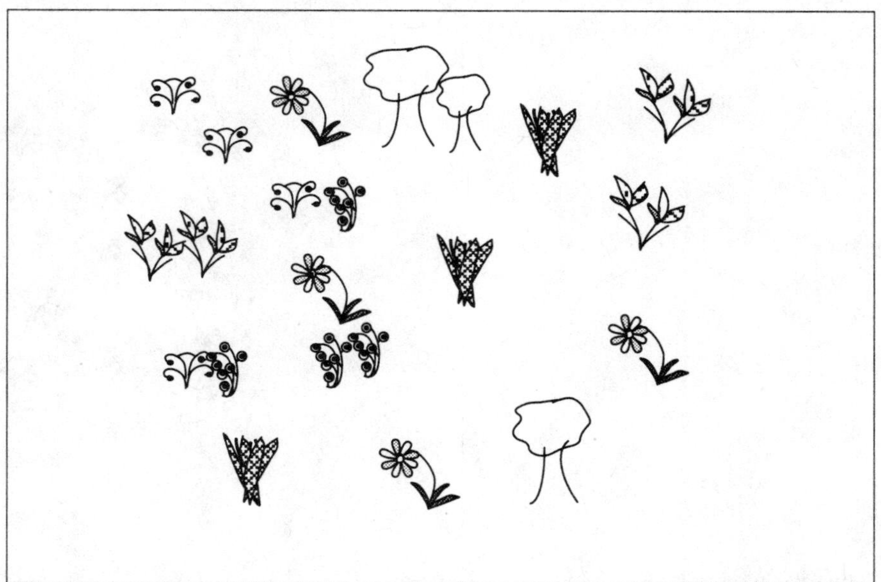

Figure 3. Community C

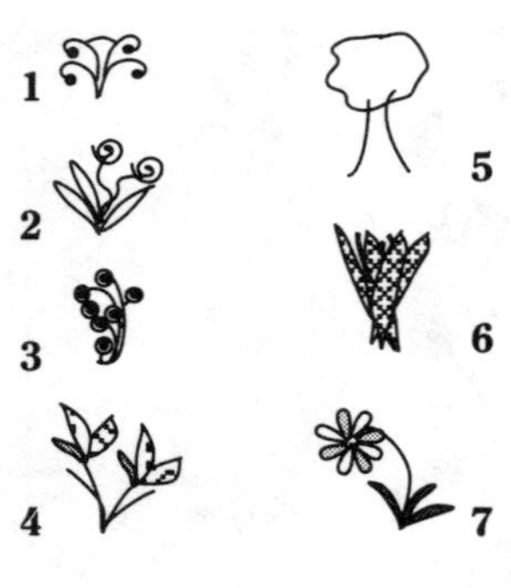

Figure 4. Community D

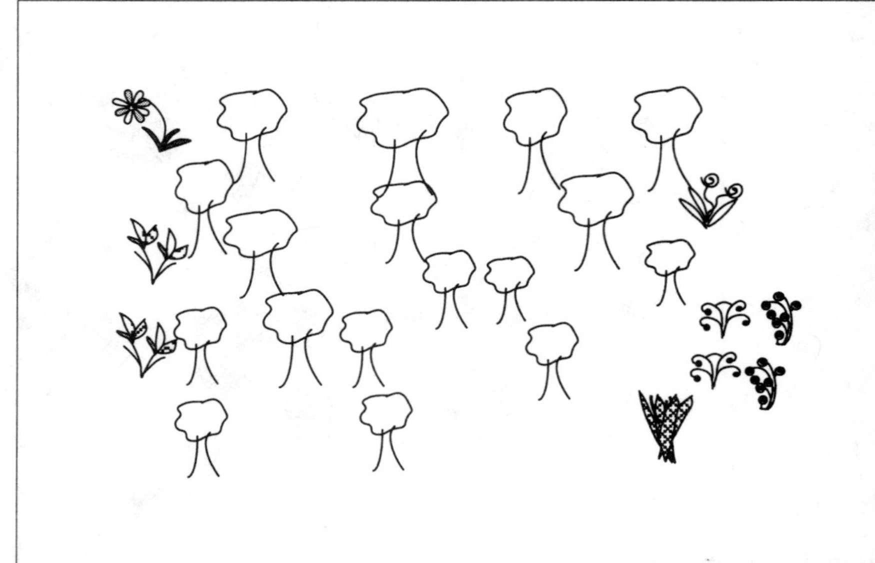

Figure 5. Community E

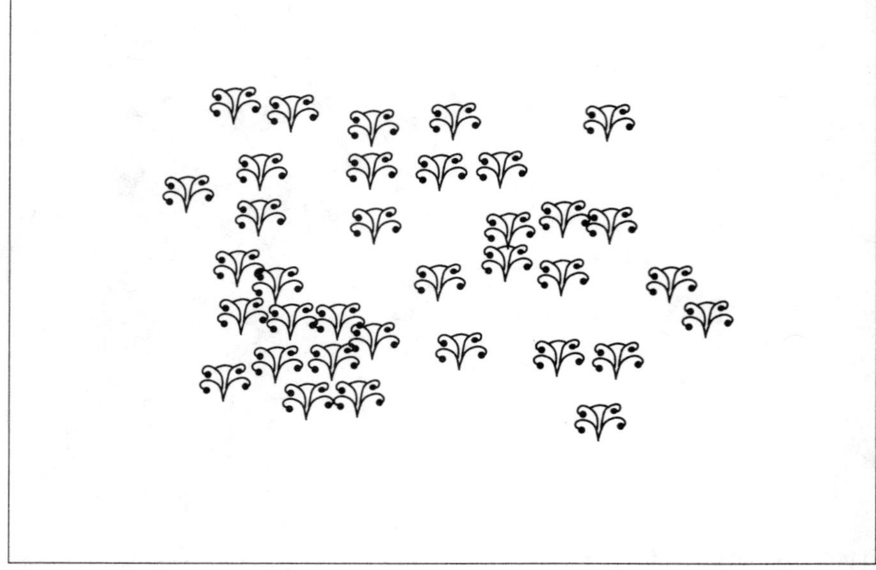

Figure 6. Community F

Thus, for each species:

1. Divide the number of individuals of species 1 by the number of individuals of all species.
2. Find the log of that number.
3. Now multiply the number calculated for step 1 by the log calculated in step 2.
4. Repeat steps 1–3 for each species represented, then add all the results.
5. Multiply the total from step 4 by –1.

In formal terms, the Shannon-Weaver index is:

$$H' = -\Sigma p_i(\ln p_i)$$

or

$$H' = -\Sigma p_i(\log p_i)$$

where p_i is the proportion of each species i in the total sample of individuals.

Use the communities in Figures 1–6 and compare two or more species i. For help with the method, see the worked out example at the end of this Technique.

SIMILARITY

Even though a whole region is identified as belonging to a general biome type (e.g., "Northern Hardwood Forest"), within such a region are many types of ecosystems, with many types of communities. Sometimes it is easy to tell that there is little or no similarity. For example, we do not expect the lichen community on oak trees in New Hampshire to have much in common with the stream-bottom invertebrate community in the same region.

It is not always so easy to tell how different or similar two communities are, even using species lists, a diversity index, and information on which species tend to associate with which other species.

One simple step beyond comparing two communities on the basis of their diversity indexes is to compare their composition directly. Again, various indexes are used for this kind of comparison, but the simplest and most widespread is Jacard's index of similarity.

To calculate the similarity of two communities, X and Y, we need to know the following:

- which species are in X and how many species there are (let's call that number X)
- which species are in Y and how many species there are (let's call that number Y)
- how many species are in common, that is, how many species occur in both X and Y (let's call that number c)

Then we can calculate the Jacard's index as follows:

$$\frac{X + Y - c}{X + Y}$$

Example

Using the formula for Jacard's index, calculate the similarity between community A (Figure 1) and itself. The result shows you the index value you get for two identical communities.

Then compare the community A with some of the other communities in Figures 2–6, to see how the results differ. The communities shown here are very simple ones, but the process is the same. Compare your results with those shown in Table 2.

Once you find out that there are some differences, the next level of questions start, for example, what difference do the differences make? Why are there such differences?

Table 1 **Community Data from Schematic Communities in Figures 1–6**

Community A

SPECIES	n	i/N equals p_i	$\ln p_i$	$p_i \times \ln p_i$
1	7	0.26	–1.35	–0.35
2	3	0.11	–2.20	–0.24
3	4	0.15	–1.91	–0.28
4	9	0.33	–1.10	–0.37
5	4	0.15	–1.91	–0.28
Total individuals	27 = N			
		Shannon-Weaver		–1.53

Community B

SPECIES	n	i/N	$\ln p_i$	$p_i \times \ln p_i$
1	12	0.32	–1.13	–0.37
2	16	0.43	–0.84	–0.36
3	2	0.05	–2.92	–0.16
4	3	0.08	–2.51	–0.20
5	4	0.11	–2.22	–0.24
Total individuals	37 = N			
		Shannon-Weaver		–1.33

Community C

SPECIES	n	i/N	$\ln p_i$	$p_i \times \ln p_i$
1	4	0.18	–1.70	–0.31
3	4	0.18	–1.70	–0.31
4	4	0.18	–1.70	–0.31
5	3	0.14	–1.99	–0.27
6	3	0.14	–1.99	–0.27
7	4	0.18	–1.70	–0.31
Total individuals	22 = N			
		Shannon-Weaver		–1.78

Species called i, with i = 1 through however many species are in the community.

n = number of individuals counted for each species i

N = total individuals of all species

i/N = proportion of all species made up by individuals of species i (that is the same as p_i)

p_i = proportion of all species made up by individuals of species i

ln = log normal

CONTINUED

Community D

SPECIES	n	i/N	lnp_i	$p_i \times \ln p_i$
4	15	0.79	–0.24	–0.19
7	4	0.21	–1.56	–0.33
Total individuals	19 = N			
		Shannon-Weaver		–0.51

Community E

SPECIES	n	i/N	lnp_i	$p_i \times \ln p_i$
1	2	0.08	–2.56	–0.20
2	1	0.04	–3.26	–0.13
3	2	0.08	–2.56	–0.20
4	2	0.08	–2.56	–0.20
5	17	0.65	–0.42	–0.28
6	1	0.04	–3.26	–0.13
7	1	0.04	–3.26	–0.13
Total individuals	26 = N			
		Shannon-Weaver		–1.25

Community F

SPECIES	n	i/N	lnp_i	$p_i \times \ln p_i$
1	35	1.00	0.00	0.00
Total individuals	35 = N			
		Shannon-Weaver		0.00

Hypothetical Community G

SPECIES	n	i/N	lnp_i	$p_i \times \ln p_i$
1	2	0.10	–2.30	–0.23
2	2	0.10	–2.30	–0.23
3	2	0.10	–2.30	–0.23
4	2	0.10	–2.30	–0.23
5	2	0.10	–2.30	–0.23
6	2	0.10	–2.30	–0.23
7	2	0.10	–2.30	–0.23
8	2	0.10	–2.30	–0.23
9	2	0.10	–2.30	–0.23
10	2	0.10	–2.30	–0.23
Total individuals	20 = N			
		Shannon-Weaver		–2.30

Table 2 **Coefficient of Similarity (Jacard's Index) for Several Pairs of Communities in Figures 1–6**

	Compared with Community					
Community	**A**	**B**	**C**	**D**	**E**	**F**
A	1	1.00	0.57	0.17	0.714	0.2
B	1	1.00	0.57	0.17	0.714	
C	1	0.57	1.00	0.30	0.54	

Acknowledgments and credits (*continued* from p. iv)

Module 2, Unit 2, Chapter 2
Pg. 111: From Robert Henry Peters (1983: Fig. 6.6[A]). *The Ecological Implications of Body Size*. Cambridge, UK: Cambridge University Press. Reprinted with the permission of Cambridge University Press.

Module 2, Unit 2, Chapter 5
Excerpt: Stephen Jay Gould. "This View of Life: Size and Shape" *Natural History* 83(1): 20–26. With permission from *Natural History*, January, 1974. Copyright the American Museum of Natural History 1974.

Module 2, Unit 3, Chapter 2
Pg. 287: From Christen Raunkiaer (1934: Fig. 7). *The Life Forms of Plants and Statistical Plant Geography: Being the Collected Papers of C. Raunkiaer*. Oxford, UK: Clarendon Press, by permission of Oxford University Press.

Technique: Introduction to Research
Fig. 2: From: STATISTICS: CONCEPTS AND CONTROVERSIES 2/E by David S. Moore © 1985 by W. H. Freeman and Company. Used with permission. (Fig. 1-2)

INDEX